I. C. S.
REFERENCE LIBRARY

A SERIES OF TEXTBOOKS PREPARED FOR THE STUDENTS OF THE
INTERNATIONAL CORRESPONDENCE SCHOOLS AND CONTAINING
IN PERMANENT FORM THE INSTRUCTION PAPERS,
EXAMINATION QUESTIONS, AND KEYS USED
IN THEIR VARIOUS COURSES

ARITHMETIC
ELEMENTS OF ALGEBRA
LOGARITHMS
GEOMETRY AND TRIGONOMETRY

9741C

SCRANTON
INTERNATIONAL TEXTBOOK COMPANY
40

PRINTED IN THE UNITED STATES.

20315

ARITHMETIC.

(SECTION 1.)

DEFINITIONS.

1. Arithmetic is the art of reckoning, or the study of numbers.

2. A **unit** is *one*, or a single thing, as *one*, *one* boy, *one* horse, *one* dozen.

3. A **number** is a unit or a collection of units, as *one*, *three* apples, *five* boys.

4. The **unit of a number** is one of the collection of units which constitutes the number. Thus, the unit of *twelve* is *one*, of *twenty* dollars is *one* dollar.

5. A **concrete number** is a number applied to some particular kind of object or quantity, as three *horses*, five *dollars*, ten *pounds*.

6. An **abstract number** is a number that is not applied to any object or quantity, as *three, five, ten.*

7. Like numbers are numbers which express units of the *same kind*, as six *days* and ten *days*, two *feet* and five *feet*.

8. Unlike numbers are numbers which express units of *different kinds*, as ten *months* and eight *miles*, seven *dollars* and five *feet*.

NOTATION AND NUMERATION.

9. Numbers are expressed in three ways: (1) by words; (2) by figures; (3) by letters.

10. Notation is the art of expressing numbers by figures or letters.

11. Numeration is the art of reading the numbers which have been expressed by figures or letters.

12. The **Arabic notation** is the method of expressing numbers by figures. This method employs ten different **figures** to represent numbers, viz. :

Figures	0	1	2	3	4	5	6	7	8	9
Names	*naught, cipher, or zero*	*one*	*two*	*three*	*four*	*five*	*six*	*seven*	*eight*	*nine*

The first character (0) is called **naught, cipher,** or **zero,** and when standing alone has no value.

The other nine figures are called **digits,** and each has a value of its own.

Any whole number is called an **integer.**

13. As there are only ten *figures* used in expressing numbers, each figure must have a different *value* at different times.

14. The value of a figure depends upon its *position* in relation to others.

15. Figures have **simple** values and **local,** or **relative,** values.

16. The **simple** value of a figure is the value it expresses when standing alone.

17. The **local,** or **relative,** value of a figure is the *increased* value it expresses by having other figures placed on its right.

For instance, if we see the figure 6 standing alone, thus   6
we consider it as *six units*, or simply **six.**

Place another 6 to the *left* of it; thus   66
The original figure is still *six units*, but the second figure is *ten times* 6, or 6 **tens.**

If a third 6 be now placed still one place further to the *left*, it is increased in value *ten times* more, thus making it 6 **hundreds**   666

A fourth 6 would be 6 **thousands**   6666

A fifth 6 would be 6 **tens of thousands,** or **sixty thousands**   66666

A sixth 6 would be 6 **hundreds of thousands** .   666666

A seventh 6 would be 6 **millions**   6666666

The entire line of seven figures is read *six millions six hundred sixty-six thousands six hundred sixty-six.*

18. The **increased value** of each of these figures is its *local*, or *relative*, value. Each figure is *ten times* greater in value than the one immediately on its *right*.

19. The **cipher** (0) has no value in itself, but it is useful in determining the place of other figures. To represent the number *four hundred five*, two digits only are necessary, one to represent *four hundred*, and the other to represent *five units;* but if these two digits are placed together, as 45, the 4 (being in the second place) will mean 4 *tens*. To mean 4 *hundreds*, the 4 should have two figures on its right, and a *cipher* is therefore inserted in the place usually given to *tens*, to show that the number is composed of *hundreds* and *units* only, and that there are no *tens*. *Four hundred five* is therefore expressed as 405. If the number were *four thousand five*, two ciphers would be inserted; thus, 4005. If it were *four hundred fifty*, it would have the *cipher* at the right-hand side to show that there were no *units*, and only *hundreds and tens;* thus, 450. *Four thousand fifty* would be expressed 4050, the first cipher indicating that there are no units and the second that there are no hundreds.

20. In *reading* numbers that have been represented by figures, it is usual to *point off* the number into groups of three figures each, beginning with the right-hand, or **units,** column, a comma (,) being used to point off these groups.

Billions.			Millions.			Thousands.			Units.		
Hundreds of Billions.	Tens of Billions.	Billions.	Hundreds of Millions.	Tens of Millions.	Millions.	Hundreds of Thousands.	Tens of Thousands.	Thousands.	Hundreds of Units.	Tens of Units.	Units.
4	3	2	, 1	9	8	, 7	6	5	, 4	3	2

In *pointing off* these figures, begin at the right-hand figure and count—*units, tens, hundreds;* the next group of three figures is *thousands;* therefore, we insert a comma (,) before beginning with them. Beginning at the figure 5, we say *thousands, tens of thousands, hundreds of thousands,* and insert another comma. We next read *millions, tens of millions, hundreds of millions* (insert another comma), *billions, tens of billions, hundreds of billions.*

The entire line of figures would be read: *four hundred thirty-two billions one hundred ninety-eight millions seven hundred sixty-five thousands four hundred thirty-two.* When we thus *read* a line of figures it is called **numeration,** and if the **numeration** be changed back to *figures,* it is called **notation.**

For instance, the writing of the following figures,

$$72,584,623,$$

would be the **notation,** and the **numeration** would be *seventy-two millions five hundred eighty-four thousands six hundred twenty-three.*

21. Note.—It is customary to leave the *s* off the words millions, thousands, etc., in cases like the above, both in speaking and writing; hence, the above would usually be expressed seventy-two million five hundred eighty-four thousand six hundred twenty-three.

22. The four fundamental processes of arithmetic are **addition, subtraction, multiplication,** and **division.** They are called fundamental processes because all operations in arithmetic are based upon them.

ADDITION.

23. **Addition** is the *process of finding* the *sum of two or more numbers.* The sign of addition is $+$. It is read *plus,* and means *more.* Thus, $5 + 6$ is read *5 plus 6,* and means that 5 and 6 are to be added.

24. The sign of equality is $=$. It is read *equals* or *is equal to.* Thus, $5 + 6 = 11$ may be read *5 plus 6 equals 11.*

25. *Like* numbers can be added, but *unlike* numbers cannot be added. Thus, 6 dollars can be added to 7 dollars, and the sum will be 13 dollars; but 6 dollars cannot be added to 7 feet.

26. The following table gives the sum of any two numbers from 1 to 12:

1 and 1 is 2	2 and 1 is 3	3 and 1 is 4	4 and 1 is 5
1 and 2 is 3	2 and 2 is 4	3 and 2 is 5	4 and 2 is 6
1 and 3 is 4	2 and 3 is 5	3 and 3 is 6	4 and 3 is 7
1 and 4 is 5	2 and 4 is 6	3 and 4 is 7	4 and 4 is 8
1 and 5 is 6	2 and 5 is 7	3 and 5 is 8	4 and 5 is 9
1 and 6 is 7	2 and 6 is 8	3 and 6 is 9	4 and 6 is 10
1 and 7 is 8	2 and 7 is 9	3 and 7 is 10	4 and 7 is 11
1 and 8 is 9	2 and 8 is 10	3 and 8 is 11	4 and 8 is 12
1 and 9 is 10	2 and 9 is 11	3 and 9 is 12	4 and 9 is 13
1 and 10 is 11	2 and 10 is 12	3 and 10 is 13	4 and 10 is 14
1 and 11 is 12	2 and 11 is 13	3 and 11 is 14	4 and 11 is 15
1 and 12 is 13	2 and 12 is 14	3 and 12 is 15	4 and 12 is 16
5 and 1 is 6	6 and 1 is 7	7 and 1 is 8	8 and 1 is 9
5 and 2 is 7	6 and 2 is 8	7 and 2 is 9	8 and 2 is 10
5 and 3 is 8	6 and 3 is 9	7 and 3 is 10	8 and 3 is 11
5 and 4 is 9	6 and 4 is 10	7 and 4 is 11	8 and 4 is 12
5 and 5 is 10	6 and 5 is 11	7 and 5 is 12	8 and 5 is 13
5 and 6 is 11	6 and 6 is 12	7 and 6 is 13	8 and 6 is 14
5 and 7 is 12	6 and 7 is 13	7 and 7 is 14	8 and 7 is 15
5 and 8 is 13	6 and 8 is 14	7 and 8 is 15	8 and 8 is 16
5 and 9 is 14	6 and 9 is 15	7 and 9 is 16	8 and 9 is 17
5 and 10 is 15	6 and 10 is 16	7 and 10 is 17	8 and 10 is 18
5 and 11 is 16	6 and 11 is 17	7 and 11 is 18	8 and 11 is 19
5 and 12 is 17	6 and 12 is 18	7 and 12 is 19	8 and 12 is 20
9 and 1 is 10	10 and 1 is 11	11 and 1 is 12	12 and 1 is 13
9 and 2 is 11	10 and 2 is 12	11 and 2 is 13	12 and 2 is 14
9 and 3 is 12	10 and 3 is 13	11 and 3 is 14	12 and 3 is 15
9 and 4 is 13	10 and 4 is 14	11 and 4 is 15	12 and 4 is 16
9 and 5 is 14	10 and 5 is 15	11 and 5 is 16	12 and 5 is 17
9 and 6 is 15	10 and 6 is 16	11 and 6 is 17	12 and 6 is 18
9 and 7 is 16	10 and 7 is 17	11 and 7 is 18	12 and 7 is 19
9 and 8 is 17	10 and 8 is 18	11 and 8 is 19	12 and 8 is 20
9 and 9 is 18	10 and 9 is 19	11 and 9 is 20	12 and 9 is 21
9 and 10 is 19	10 and 10 is 20	11 and 10 is 21	12 and 10 is 22
9 and 11 is 20	10 and 11 is 21	11 and 11 is 22	12 and 11 is 23
9 and 12 is 21	10 and 12 is 22	11 and 12 is 23	12 and 12 is 24

This table should be carefully committed to memory. Since 0 has no value, the sum of any number and 0 is the number itself; thus 17 and 0 is 17.

27. For addition, place the numbers to be added directly under each other, taking care to place *units* under *units*, *tens* under *tens*, *hundreds* under *hundreds*, and so on.

When the numbers are thus written, the *right-hand figure of one number is placed directly under the right-hand figure of the one above it*, thus bringing units under units, tens under tens, etc. Proceed as in the following examples:

28. EXAMPLE.—What is the sum of 131, 222, 21, 2, and 413?

SOLUTION.—

```
              1 3 1
              2 2 2
                2 1
                  2
              4 1 3
        sum   7 8 9   Ans.
```

EXPLANATION. — After placing the numbers in proper order, begin at the bottom of the right-hand, or units, column, and add, mentally repeating the different sums. Thus, three and two are five and one are six and two are eight and one are nine, the sum of the numbers in units column. Place the 9 directly beneath as the first, or units, figure in the sum.

The sum of the numbers in the next, or tens, column equals 8 tens, which is the second, or tens, figure in the sum.

The sum of the numbers in the next, or hundreds, column equals 7 hundreds, which is the third, or hundreds, figure in the sum.

The sum, or answer, is 789.

29. EXAMPLE.—What is the sum of 425, 36, 9,215, 4, and 907?

SOLUTION.—

```
              4 2 5
                3 6
            9 2 1 5
                  4
              9 0 7
              ───────
                2 7
                6 0
            1 5 0 0
            9 0 0 0
        sum 1 0 5 8 7   Ans.
```

EXPLANATION.—The sum of the numbers in the first, or

units, column is seven and four are eleven and five are sixteen and six are twenty-two and five are twenty-seven, or
27 units; i. e., two tens and seven units. Write 27 as
shown. The sum of the numbers in the second, or tens,
column is six tens, or 60. Write 60 underneath 27, as
shown. The sum of the numbers in the third, or hundreds,
column is 15 hundreds, or 1,500. Write 1,500 under the two
preceding results as shown. There is only one number in
the fourth, or thousands, column, 9, which represents 9,000.
Write 9,000 under the three preceding results. Adding
these four results, the sum is 10,587, which is the sum of
425, 36, 9,215, 4, and 907.

NOTE.—It frequently happens when adding a long column of figures, that the sum of two numbers, one of which does not occur in the
addition table, is required. Thus, in the first column above, the sum
of 16 and 6 was required. We know from the table that $6 + 6 = 12$;
hence, the first figure of the sum is 2. Now, the sum of any number
less than 20 and of any number less than 10 must be less than 30, since
$20 + 10 = 30$; therefore, the sum is 22. Consequently, in cases of this
kind, add the first figure of the larger number to the smaller number,
and if the result is greater than 9, increase the second figure of the larger
number by 1. Thus, $44 + 7 = ?$ $4 + 7 = 11$; hence, $44 + 7 = 51$.

30. The addition may also be performed as follows:

$$
\begin{array}{r}
4\,2\,5 \\
3\,6 \\
9\,2\,1\,5 \\
4 \\
9\,0\,7 \\
\hline
sum \quad 1\,0\,5\,8\,7 \quad \text{Ans.}
\end{array}
$$

EXPLANATION.—The sum of the numbers in units column
is 27 units, or 2 tens and 7 units. Write the 7 units as the
first, or right-hand, figure in the sum. Reserve the two
tens and add them to the figures in tens column. The sum
of the figures in the tens column, plus the 2 tens reserved
and carried from the units column, is 8, which is written
down as the second figure in the sum. There is nothing to
carry to the next column, because 8 is less than 10. The
sum of the numbers in the next column is 15 hundreds, or
1 thousand and 5 hundreds. Write down the 5 as the third,
or hundreds, figure in the sum and carry the 1 to the next

column. $1 + 9 = 10$, which is written down at the left of the other figures.

The second method saves space and figures, but the first is to be preferred when adding a long column.

31. EXAMPLE.—Add the numbers in the column below:

SOLUTION.—

```
          8 9 0
          8 2
          9 0
          3 9 3
          2 8 1
          8 0
          7 7 0
          8 3
          4 9 2
          8 0
          3 8 3
          8 4
          1 9 1
     sum  3 8 9 9  Ans.
```

EXPLANATION.—The sum of the digits in the first column equals 19 units, or 1 ten and 9 units. Write down the 9 and carry 1 to the next column. The sum of the digits in the second column +1 is 109 tens, or 10 hundreds and 9 tens. Write down the 9 and carry the 10 to the next column. The sum of the digits in this column plus the 10 reserved is 38.

The entire sum is 3,899.

32. Rule.—I. *Begin at the right, add each column separately. and write the sum, if it be only one figure, under the column added.*

II. *If the sum of any column consists of two or more figures, put the right-hand figure of the sum under that column and add the remaining figure or figures to the next column.*

33. Proof.—*To prove addition, add each column from top to bottom. If you obtain the same result as by adding from bottom to top, the work is probably correct.*

EXAMPLES FOR PRACTICE.

34. Find the sum of:

(a)	$104 + 203 + 613 + 214.$	(a)	**1,134.**
(b)	$1,875 + 3,143 + 5,826 + 10,832.$	(b)	**21,676.**
(c)	$4,865 + 2,145 + 8,173 + 40,084.$	(c)	**55,267.**
(d)	$14,204 + 8,173 + 1,065 + 10,042.$	(d)	**33,484.**
(e)	$10,832 + 4,145 + 3,133 + 5,872.$	(e)	**23,982.**
(f)	$214 + 1,231 + 141 + 5,000.$	(f)	**6,586.**
(g)	$123 + 104 + 425 + 126 + 327.$	(g)	**1,105.**
(h)	$6,354 + 2,145 + 2,042 + 1,111 + 3,333.$	(h)	**14,985.**

Ans.

SUBTRACTION.

35. In arithmetic, **subtraction** is the process of finding how much greater one number is than another.

The greater of the two numbers is called the **minuend.**

The smaller of the two numbers is called the **subtrahend.**

The number left after subtracting the subtrahend from the minuend is called the **difference,** or **remainder.**

36. The sign of subtraction is —. It is read *minus*, and means *less.* Thus, $12 - 7$ is read *12 minus 7*, and means that 7 is to be taken from 12.

37. EXAMPLE.—From 7,568 take 3,425.

SOLUTION.—
$$\begin{array}{lr} minuend & 7\ 5\ 6\ 8 \\ subtrahend & 3\ 4\ 2\ 5 \\ \hline remainder & 4\ 1\ 4\ 3 \end{array} \text{ Ans.}$$

EXPLANATION.—Begin at the right-hand, or units, column and subtract in succession each figure in the subtrahend from the one directly above it in the minuend, and write the remainders below the line. The result is the entire remainder.

38. When there are more figures in the minuend than in the subtrahend, and when some figures in the minuend are *less* than the figures directly under them in the subtrahend, proceed as in the following example:

EXAMPLE.—From 8,453 take 844.

SOLUTION.—
$$\begin{array}{lr} minuend & 8\ 4\ 5\ 3 \\ subtrahend & 8\ 4\ 4 \\ \hline remainder & 7\ 6\ 0\ 9 \end{array} \text{ Ans.}$$

EXPLANATION.—Begin at the right-hand, or units, column to subtract. We cannot take 4 from 3, and must, therefore, borrow 1 from 5 in tens column and annex it to the 3 in units column. The 1 ten = 10 units, which added to the 3 in units column = 13 units. 4 from 13 = 9, the first, or units, figure in the remainder.

Since we borrowed 1 from the 5, only 4 remains; 4 from 4 = 0, the second, or tens, figure. We cannot take 8 from 4, and must, therefore, borrow 1 from 8 in thousands column. Since 1 thousand = 10 hundreds, 10 hundreds + 4 hundreds = 14 hundreds, and 8 from 14 = 6, the third, or hundreds, figure in the remainder.

Since we borrowed 1 from 8, only 7 remains, from which there is nothing to subtract; therefore, 7 is the next figure in the remainder, or answer.

The operation of borrowing is performed by mentally placing 1 before the figure following the one from which it is borrowed. In the above example the 1 borrowed from 5 is placed before 3, making it 13, from which we subtract 4. The 1 borrowed from 8 is placed before 4, making 14, from which 8 is taken.

39. EXAMPLE.—Find the difference between 10,000 and 8,763.

SOLUTION.—
$$
\begin{array}{rl}
minuend & 1\,0\,0\,0\,0 \\
subtrahend & 8\,7\,6\,3 \\
\hline
remainder & 1\,2\,3\,7 \ \ \text{Ans.}
\end{array}
$$

EXPLANATION.—In the above example we borrow 1 from the second column and place it before 0, making 10; 3 from 10 = 7. In the same way we borrow 1 and place it before the next cipher, making 10; but as we have borrowed 1 from this column and have taken it to the units column, only 9 remains from which to subtract 6; 6 from 9 = 3. For the same reason we subtract 7 from 9 and 8 from 9 for the next two figures, and obtain a total remainder of 1,237.

40. Rule.—*Place the subtrahend (or smaller number) under the minuend (or larger number), in the same manner as for addition, and proceed as in Arts.* **37, 38,** *and* **39.**

41. Proof.—*To prove an example in subtraction, add the subtrahend and the remainder. The sum should equal the minuend. If it does not, a mistake has been made, and the work should be done over.*

Proof of the above example:

$$
\begin{array}{rr}
subtrahend & 8\ 7\ 6\ 3 \\
remainder & 1\ 2\ 3\ 7 \\
\hline
minuend & 1\ 0\ 0\ 0\ 0
\end{array}
$$

EXAMPLES FOR PRACTICE.

42. From:

(*a*)	94,278 take 62,574.	
(*b*)	53,714 take 25,824.	
(*c*)	71,832 take 58,109.	
(*d*)	20,804 take 10,408.	
(*e*)	310,465 take 102,141.	Ans.
(*f*)	(81,043 + 1,041) take 14,831.	
(*g*)	(20,482 + 18,216) take 21,214.	
(*h*)	(2,040 + 1,213 + 542) take 3,791.	

Ans.
(*a*) 31,704.
(*b*) 27,890.
(*c*) 13,723.
(*d*) 10,396.
(*e*) 208,324.
(*f*) 67,253.
(*g*) 17,484.
(*h*) 4.

MULTIPLICATION.

43. To **multiply** a number is to *add* it to itself a certain number of times.

44. Multiplication is the process of multiplying one number by another.

The number thus added to itself, or the number to be multiplied, is called the **multiplicand.**

The number which shows how many times the *multiplicand* is to be taken, or the number by which we *multiply*, is called the **multiplier.**

The result obtained by multiplying is called the **product.**

45. The sign of multiplication is ×. It is read *times* or *multiplied by.* Thus, 9 × 6 is read *9 times 6*, or *9 multiplied by 6.*

46. It matters not in what order the numbers to be multiplied together are placed. Thus, 6 × 9 is the same as 9 × 6.

47. In the following table, the product of any two numbers (neither of which exceeds 12) may be found:

1 times 1 is 1	2 times 1 is 2	3 times 1 is 3
1 times 2 is 2	2 times 2 is 4	3 times 2 is 6
1 times 3 is 3	2 times 3 is 6	3 times 3 is 9
1 times 4 is 4	2 times 4 is 8	3 times 4 is 12
1 times 5 is 5	2 times 5 is 10	3 times 5 is 15
1 times 6 is 6	2 times 6 is 12	3 times 6 is 18
1 times 7 is 7	2 times 7 is 14	3 times 7 is 21
1 times 8 is 8	2 times 8 is 16	3 times 8 is 24
1 times 9 is 9	2 times 9 is 18	3 times 9 is 27
1 times 10 is 10	2 times 10 is 20	3 times 10 is 30
1 times 11 is 11	2 times 11 is 22	3 times 11 is 33
1 times 12 is 12	2 times 12 is 24	3 times 12 is 36
4 times 1 is 4	5 times 1 is 5	6 times 1 is 6
4 times 2 is 8	5 times 2 is 10	6 times 2 is 12
4 times 3 is 12	5 times 3 is 15	6 times 3 is 18
4 times 4 is 16	5 times 4 is 20	6 times 4 is 24
4 times 5 is 20	5 times 5 is 25	6 times 5 is 30
4 times 6 is 24	5 times 6 is 30	6 times 6 is 36
4 times 7 is 28	5 times 7 is 35	6 times 7 is 42
4 times 8 is 32	5 times 8 is 40	6 times 8 is 48
4 times 9 is 36	5 times 9 is 45	6 times 9 is 54
4 times 10 is 40	5 times 10 is 50	6 times 10 is 60
4 times 11 is 44	5 times 11 is 55	6 times 11 is 66
4 times 12 is 48	5 times 12 is 60	6 times 12 is 72
7 times 1 is 7	8 times 1 is 8	9 times 1 is 9
7 times 2 is 14	8 times 2 is 16	9 times 2 is 18
7 times 3 is 21	8 times 3 is 24	9 times 3 is 27
7 times 4 is 28	8 times 4 is 32	9 times 4 is 36
7 times 5 is 35	8 times 5 is 40	9 times 5 is 45
7 times 6 is 42	8 times 6 is 48	9 times 6 is 54
7 times 7 is 49	8 times 7 is 56	9 times 7 is 63
7 times 8 is 56	8 times 8 is 64	9 times 8 is 72
7 times 9 is 63	8 times 9 is 72	9 times 9 is 81
7 times 10 is 70	8 times 10 is 80	9 times 10 is 90
7 times 11 is 77	8 times 11 is 88	9 times 11 is 99
7 times 12 is 84	8 times 12 is 96	9 times 12 is 108
10 times 1 is 10	11 times 1 is 11	12 times 1 is 12
10 times 2 is 20	11 times 2 is 22	12 times 2 is 24
10 times 3 is 30	11 times 3 is 33	12 times 3 is 36
10 times 4 is 40	11 times 4 is 44	12 times 4 is 48
10 times 5 is 50	11 times 5 is 55	12 times 5 is 60
10 times 6 is 60	11 times 6 is 66	12 times 6 is 72
10 times 7 is 70	11 times 7 is 77	12 times 7 is 84
10 times 8 is 80	11 times 8 is 88	12 times 8 is 96
10 times 9 is 90	11 times 9 is 99	12 times 9 is 108
10 times 10 is 100	11 times 10 is 110	12 times 10 is 120
10 times 11 is 110	11 times 11 is 121	12 times 11 is 132
10 times 12 is 120	11 times 12 is 132	12 times 12 is 144

This table should be carefully committed to memory.

Since 0 has no value, the product of 0 and any number is 0.

48. **To multiply a number by one figure only:**

EXAMPLE.—Multiply 425 by 5.

SOLUTION.—

multiplicand	4 2 5
multiplier	5
product	2 1 2 5 Ans.

EXPLANATION.—For convenience, the multiplier is generally written under the right-hand figure of the multiplicand. On looking in the multiplication table, we see that 5×5 are 25. Multiplying the first figure at the right of the multiplicand, or 5, by the multiplier, 5, it is seen that 5 times 5 units are 25 units, or 2 tens and 5 units. Write the 5 units in units place in the product, and reserve the 2 tens to add to the product of tens. Looking in the multiplication table again, we see that 5×2 are 10. Multiplying the second figure of the multiplicand by the multiplier, 5, we see that 5 times 2 tens are 10 tens, and 10 tens plus the 2 tens reserved are 12 tens, or 1 hundred plus 2 tens. Write the 2 tens in tens place, and reserve the 1 hundred to add to the product of hundreds. Again, we see by the multiplication table that 5×4 are 20. Multiplying the third, or last, figure of the multiplicand by the multiplier, 5, we see that 5 times 4 hundreds are 20 hundreds, and 20 hundreds plus the 1 hundred reserved are 21 hundreds, or 2 thousands and 1 hundred, which we write in thousands and hundreds places, respectively.

Hence, the product is 2,125.

This result is the same as adding 425 five times. Thus,

$$
\begin{array}{r}
4\ 2\ 5 \\
4\ 2\ 5 \\
4\ 2\ 5 \\
4\ 2\ 5 \\
4\ 2\ 5 \\
\hline
sum \quad 2\ 1\ 2\ 5 \quad \text{Ans.}
\end{array}
$$

EXAMPLES FOR PRACTICE.

49. Find the product of:

(a)	$61,483 \times 6.$			(a)	368,898.
(b)	$12,375 \times 5.$	Ans.		(b)	61,875.
(c)	$10,426 \times 7.$			(c)	72,982.
(d)	$10,835 \times 3.$			(d)	32,505.

(e) 98,376 × 4.
(f) 10,873 × 8.
(g) 71,543 × 9.
(h) 218,734 × 2.

Ans. {
(e) 393,504.
(f) 86,984.
(g) 643,887.
(h) 437,468.
}

50. To multiply a number by two or more figures:

EXAMPLE.—Multiply 475 by 234.

SOLUTION.—   *multiplicand*   4 7 5
                   multiplier   2 3 4
                            ――――――――
                                   1 9 0 0
                                   1 4 2 5
                                   9 5 0
                            ――――――――
            product 1 1 1 1 5 0 Ans.

EXPLANATION.—For convenience, the multiplier is generally written under the multiplicand, placing units under units, tens under tens, etc.

We cannot multiply by 234 at one operation; we must, therefore, multiply by the *parts* and then *add* the **partial products.**

The parts by which we are to multiply are 4 units, 3 tens, and 2 hundreds. 4 times 475 = 1,900, the *first partial product;* 3 times 475 = 1,425, the *second partial product,* the right-hand figure of which is written directly under the figure multiplied by, or 3; 2 times 475 = 950, the *third partial product,* the right-hand figure of which is written directly under the figure multiplied by, or 2.

The sum of these three partial products is 111,150, which is the *entire product.*

51. Rule.—I. *Write the multiplier under the multiplicand, so that units are under units, tens under tens, etc.*

II. *Begin at the right and multiply each figure of the multiplicand by each successive figure of the multiplier, placing the right-hand figure of each partial product directly under the figure used as a multiplier.*

III. *The sum of the partial products will equal the required product.*

52. **Proof.**—*Review the work carefully, or multiply the multiplier by the multiplicand; if the results agree, the work is correct.*

53. When there is a *cipher* in the *multiplier*, multiply by it the same as with the other figures.   Thus,

(*a*)	(*b*)	(*c*)	(*d*)
0	2	1 5	7 0 8
× 0	× 0	× 0	× 0
0 Ans.	0 Ans.	0 0 Ans.	0 0 0 Ans.

(*e*)	(*f*)	(*g*)
3 1 1 4	4 0 0 8	3 1 2 6 4
2 0 3	3 0 5	1 0 0 2
9 3 4 2	2 0 0 4 0	6 2 5 2 8
0 0 0 0	0 0 0 0	0 0 0 0 0
6 2 2 8	1 2 0 2 4	0 0 0 0 0
6 3 2 1 4 2 Ans.	1 2 2 2 4 4 0 Ans.	3 1 2 6 4
		3 1 3 2 6 5 2 8 Ans.

When multiplying by a number containing a cipher, the work may be shortened by writing the first cipher of the partial product, then multiplying by the next figure of the multiplier and writing the partial product alongside of the cipher.   Thus, examples (*e*) and (*g*) above might have been solved in the following manner:

3 1 1 4	3 1 2 6 4
2 0 3	1 0 0 2
9 3 4 2	6 2 5 2 8
6 2 2 8 0	3 1 2 6 4 0 0
6 3 2 1 4 2 Ans.	3 1 3 2 6 5 2 8 Ans.

EXAMPLES FOR PRACTICE.

54. Find the product of:

(*a*)	3,842 × 26.	
(*b*)	3,716 × 45.	
(*c*)	1,817 × 124.	
(*d*)	675 × 38.	
(*e*)	1,875 × 33.	
(*f*)	4,836 × 47.	
(*g*)	5,682 × 543.	
(*h*)	3,257 × 246.	

Ans.
(*a*)	99,892.
(*b*)	167,220.
(*c*)	225,308.
(*d*)	25,650.
(*e*)	61,875.
(*f*)	227,292.
(*g*)	3,085,326.
(*h*)	801,222.

(*i*)	2,875 × 302.		(*i*)	868,250.
(*j*)	17,819 × 1,004.		(*j*)	17,890,276.
(*k*)	38,674 × 205.		(*k*)	7,928,170.
(*l*)	18,304 × 100.	Ans.	(*l*)	1,830,400.
(*m*)	7,834 × 10.		(*m*)	78,340
(*n*)	87,543 × 1,000.		(*n*)	87,543,000.
(*o*)	48,763 × 100.		(*o*)	4,876,300.

DIVISION.

55. **Division** is the process of finding how many times one number is contained in another of the same kind.

The number to be *divided* is called the **dividend.**

The number by which we *divide* is called the **divisor.**

The number which *shows* how many times the *divisor is contained in the dividend* is called the **quotient.**

56. The sign of division is ÷. It is read *divided by.* 54 ÷ 9 is read *54 divided by 9.* Another way to write 54 divided by 9 is $\frac{54}{9}$. Thus, $54 \div 9 = 6$, or $\frac{54}{9} = 6$.

In both of these cases, 54 is the *dividend* and 9 is the *divisor.*

Division is the reverse of multiplication.

57. **To divide when the divisor consists of but one figure,** proceed as in the following example:

EXAMPLE.—What is the quotient of 875 ÷ 7 ?

SOLUTION.—
$$\begin{array}{r} \text{\textit{divisor} \quad \textit{dividend} \quad \textit{quotient}} \\ 7\,)\,8\,7\,5\,(\,1\,2\,5 \quad \text{Ans.} \\ \underline{7} \\ 1\,7 \\ \underline{1\,4} \\ 3\,5 \\ \underline{3\,5} \\ \textit{remainder} \quad 0 \end{array}$$

EXPLANATION.— 7 is contained in 8 hundreds, 1 hundred times. Place the 1 as the first, or left-hand, figure of the quotient. Multiply the divisor, 7, by the 1 hundred of the quotient, and place the product, 7 hundreds, under the 8 hundreds in the dividend, and subtract. Beside the remainder, 1, bring down the next, or tens, figure of the dividend, in this case 7, making 17 tens; 7 is contained in 17, 2 times. Write the 2 as the second figure of the quotient. Multiply the divisor, 7, by the 2 in the quotient, and subtract the product from 17. Beside the remainder, 3, bring down the units figure of the dividend, making 35 units. 7 is contained in 35, 5 times, which is placed in the quotient. Multiplying the divisor by the last figure of the quotient, 5 times 7 = 35, which subtracted from 35, under which it is placed, leaves 0. Therefore, the quotient is 125. This method is called **long division.**

58. In **short division,** only the divisor, dividend, and quotient are written, the operations being performed mentally.

$$\begin{array}{r} \textit{dividend} \\ \textit{divisor } 7 \;) \, 8^1 7^3 5 \\ \textit{quotient} \quad 1 \; 2 \; 5 \;\; \text{Ans.} \end{array}$$

The mental operation is as follows: 7 is contained in 8, once and 1 remainder; imagine 1 to be placed before 7, making 17; 7 is contained in 17, 2 times and 3 over; imagine 3 to be placed before 5, making 35; 7 is contained in 35, 5 times. These partial quotients, placed in order as they are found, make the entire quotient 125.

59. If the divisor consists of *two or more* figures, proceed as in the following example:

EXAMPLE.—Divide 2,702,826 by 63.

$$\begin{array}{l} \quad\quad \textit{divisor} \quad \textit{dividend} \quad\quad \textit{quotient} \\ \text{SOLUTION.—} \quad 6\,3\,)\,2\,7\,0\,2\,8\,2\,6\,(\,4\,2\,9\,0\,2 \;\; \text{Ans.} \\ \quad\quad\quad\quad\quad 2\,5\,2 \\ \quad\quad\quad\quad\quad \overline{1\,8\,2} \\ \quad\quad\quad\quad\quad 1\,2\,6 \\ \quad\quad\quad\quad\quad\quad \overline{5\,6\,8} \\ \quad\quad\quad\quad\quad\quad 5\,6\,7 \\ \quad\quad\quad\quad\quad\quad\quad \overline{1\,2\,6} \\ \quad\quad\quad\quad\quad\quad\quad 1\,2\,6 \end{array}$$

EXPLANATION.—As 63 is not contained in the first two figures, 27, we must use the first three figures, 270. Now, by trial we must find how many times 63 is contained in 270. 6 is contained in the first two figures of 270, 4 times. Place the 4 as the first, or left-hand, figure in the quotient. Multiply the divisor, 63, by 4, and subtract the product, 252, from 270. The remainder is 18, beside which we write the next figure of the dividend, 2, making 182. Now, 6 is contained in the first two figures of 182, 3 times, but on multiplying 63 by 3, we see that the product, 189, is too great, so we try 2 as the second figure of the quotient. Multiplying the divisor, 63, by 2 and subtracting the product, 126, from 182, the remainder is 56, beside which we bring down the next figure of the dividend, making 568. 6 is contained in 56 about 9 times. Multiply the divisor, 63, by 9 and subtract the product, 567, from 568. The remainder is 1, and bringing down the next figure of the dividend, 2, gives 12. As 12 is smaller than 63, we write 0 in the quotient and bring down the next figure, 6, making 126. 63 is contained in 126, 2 times, without a remainder. Therefore, 42,902 is the quotient.

60. Rule.—I. *Write the divisor at the left of the dividend, with a line between them.*

II. *Find how many times the divisor is contained in the lowest number of the left-hand figures of the dividend that will contain it, and write the result at the right of the dividend, with a line between, for the first figure of the quotient.*

III. *Multiply the divisor by this quotient; write the product under the partial dividend used, and subtract, annexing to the remainder the next figure of the dividend. Divide as before, and thus continue until all the figures of the dividend have been used*

IV. *If any partial dividend will not contain the divisor, write a cipher in the quotient, annex the next figure of the dividend, and proceed as before.*

V. *If there be at last a remainder, write it after the quotient, with the divisor underneath.*

61. **Proof.**—*Multiply the quotient by the divisor and add the remainder, if there be any, to the product.* *The result will be the dividend.* Thus,

divisor *dividend* *quotient*

6 3) 4 2 3 5 (6 7$\frac{14}{63}$ Ans.

3 7 8
—————
4 5 5
4 4 1

	remainder	1 4
PROOF.—	*quotient*	6 7
	divisor	6 3
		2 0 1
		4 0 2
		4 2 2 1
	remainder	1 4
	dividend	4 2 3 5

EXAMPLES FOR PRACTICE.

62. Divide the following:

(a)	126,498 by 58.		(a)	2,181.
(b)	3,207,594 by 767.		(b)	4,182.
(c)	11,408,202 by 234.		(c)	48,753.
(d)	2,100,315 by 581.	Ans.	(d)	3,615.
(e)	969,936 by 4,008.		(e)	242.
(f)	7,481,888 by 1,021.		(f)	7,328.
(g)	1,525,915 by 5,003.		(g)	305.
(h)	1,646,301 by 381.		(h)	4,321.

CANCELATION.

63. **Cancelation** is the process of shortening operations in division by casting out equal factors from both dividend and divisor.

64. The **factors** of a number are those numbers, which, when multiplied together, *produce the given number.* Thus, 5 and 3 are the factors of 15, since $5 \times 3 = 15$. Likewise, 8 and 7 are the factors of 56, since $8 \times 7 = 56$.

65. A **prime number** is one which cannot be divided by any number except itself and 1. Thus, 2, 3, 11, 29, etc. are prime numbers.

66. A **prime factor** is any factor that is a prime number.

Any number that is not a prime is called a **composite** number, and may be produced by multiplying together its prime factors. Thus, 60 is a composite number, and is equal to the product of its prime factors, $2 \times 2 \times 3 \times 5$.

67. *Canceling equal factors from both dividend and divisor does not change the quotient.*

The canceling of a factor in *both* dividend and divisor is the same as *dividing them both by the same number*, and this, evidently, *does not change the quotient*.

Write the numbers forming the dividend above a horizontal line, and those forming the divisor below it; then cancel the equal factors.

68. EXAMPLE.—Divide $4 \times 45 \times 60$ by 9×24.

SOLUTION.—Placing the dividend over the divisor, and canceling,

$$\frac{4 \times \overset{5}{\cancel{45}} \times \overset{10}{\cancel{60}}}{\underset{1}{\underset{\cancel{6}}{9 \times \cancel{24}}}} = \frac{50}{1} = 50. \quad \text{Ans.}$$

EXPLANATION.—The 4 in the dividend and the 24 in the divisor are both divisible by 4, since 4 divided by 4 equals 1, and 24 divided by 4 equals 6. Cross off the 4 and write the 1 over it; also, cross off the 24 and write the 6 under it. Thus,

$$\frac{\overset{1}{\cancel{4}} \times 45 \times 60}{\underset{6}{9 \times \cancel{24}}} =$$

60 in the dividend and 6 in the divisor are divisible by 6, since 60 divided by 6 equals 10, and 6 divided by 6 equals 1. Cross off the 60 and write 10 over it; also, cross off the 6 and write 1 under it. Thus,

$$\frac{\overset{1}{\cancel{4}} \times 45 \times \overset{10}{\cancel{60}}}{\underset{1}{\underset{\cancel{6}}{9 \times \cancel{24}}}} =$$

Again, 45 in the dividend and 9 in the divisor are divisible by 9, since 45 divided by 9 equals 5, and 9 divided by 9 equals 1. Cross off the 45 and write the 5 over it; also, cross off the 9 and write the 1 under it. Thus,

$$\frac{\overset{1}{4}\times\overset{5}{\cancel{45}}\times\overset{10}{\cancel{60}}}{\underset{1}{\cancel{9}}\times\underset{\underset{1}{\cancel{6}}}{\cancel{24}}} =$$

Since there are no two remaining numbers (one in the dividend and one in the divisor) divisible by any number except 1, without a remainder, it is impossible to cancel further.

Multiply all the uncanceled numbers in the dividend together and divide their product by the product of all the uncanceled numbers in the divisor. The result will be the quotient. The product of all the uncanceled numbers in the dividend equals $5\times1\times10 = 50$; the product of all the uncanceled numbers in the divisor equals $1\times1 = 1$.

$$\text{Hence,} \quad \frac{\overset{1}{4}\times\overset{5}{\cancel{45}}\times\overset{10}{\cancel{60}}}{\underset{1}{\cancel{9}}\times\underset{\underset{1}{\cancel{6}}}{\cancel{24}}} = \frac{1\times5\times10}{1\times1} = 50. \quad \text{Ans.}$$

69. Rule.—I. *Cancel the common factors from both the dividend and the divisor.*

II. *Then divide the product of the remaining factors of the dividend by the product of the remaining factors of the divisor, and the result will be the quotient.*

———

EXAMPLES FOR PRACTICE.

70. Divide:

(a)	$14\times18\times16\times40$ by $7\times8\times6\times5\times3$.	(a) 32.
(b)	$3\times65\times50\times100\times60$ by $30\times60\times13\times10$.	(b) 250.
(c)	$8\times4\times3\times9\times11$ by $11\times9\times4\times3\times8$.	(c) 1.
(d)	$164\times321\times6\times7\times4$ by $82\times321\times7$.	(d) 48.
(e)	$50\times100\times200\times72$ by $1,000\times144\times100$.	(e) 5.
(f)	$48\times63\times55\times49$ by $7\times21\times11\times48$.	(f) 105.
(g)	$110\times150\times84\times32$ by $11\times15\times100\times64$.	(g) 42.
(h)	$115\times120\times400\times1,000$ by $23\times1,000\times60\times800$.	(h) 5.

Ans.

ARITHMETIC.

(SECTION 2.)

FRACTIONS.

Remark.—The general term *fractions* embraces both common fractions and decimal fractions. In the older treatises on arithmetic, what are now called common fractions were termed vulgar fractions, but both terms have the same meaning. At the present time it is quite customary to omit the word fraction in speaking or writing the expression decimal fraction and to omit the word common when referring to a common fraction. As the result of this practice, the meaning of the word fraction has become restricted, it being used to designate common fractions only, while the decimal is used to designate the entire term, decimal fraction.

The subjects of fractions and decimals are among the most useful and important treated in arithmetic. As it is impossible in every-day transactions to deal in whole numbers only, it follows that it is very nearly, if not quite, as necessary to have a good knowledge of how to add, subtract, multiply, and divide fractions and decimals as how to perform the same operations on whole numbers. It is natural and easy to pay a quarter of a dollar for an eighth of a pound of some article, but as a rule calculations involving fractions are not nearly as simple as in this instance. The rules governing the operations of addition, subtraction, multiplication, and division of fractions apparently bear little resemblance to the corresponding rules for whole numbers and decimals; hence, fractions appears to be a difficult subject for many. A thorough understanding of the preliminary definitions will assist the student very materially in studying this somewhat difficult subject, and he is therefore advised to pay particular attention to the first two or three pages of this section.

DEFINITIONS.

71. A **fraction** is a *part of a unit. One-half, one-third, two-fifths* are fractions.

72. *Two* numbers are required to express a fraction; one is called the **numerator,** and the other, the **denominator.**

73. The numerator is placed above the denominator, with a line between them, as $\frac{2}{3}$. Here, 3 is the denominator, and shows into how many *equal parts* the *unit*, or *one*, is divided. The numerator, 2, shows how many of these equal parts are taken or considered. The denominator also indicates the names of the parts.

$\frac{1}{2}$ is read one-half.

$\frac{3}{4}$ is read three-fourths.

$\frac{3}{8}$ is read three-eighths.

$\frac{5}{16}$ is read five-sixteenths.

$\frac{29}{47}$ is read twenty-nine forty-sevenths.

74. In the expression "$\frac{3}{4}$ of an apple," the *denominator*, 4, shows that the apple is to be (or has been) cut into 4 *equal parts*, and the *numerator*, 3, shows that *three of these parts*, or *fourths*, are taken or considered.

If each of the *parts*, or *fourths*, of the apple were cut into *two equal pieces*, there would then be twice as many pieces as before, or $4 \times 2 = 8$ pieces in all, one of these pieces would be called one-eighth, and would be expressed in figures as $\frac{1}{8}$. Three of these pieces would be called three-eighths, and written $\frac{3}{8}$. The words three-fourths, three-eighths, five-sixteenths, etc. are abbreviations of three one-fourths, three one-eighths, five one-sixteenths, etc. It is evident that the larger the *denominator*, the greater is the number of parts into which anything is divided; consequently, the parts themselves are smaller, and the value of the fraction is less for the same number of parts taken. In other words, $\frac{7}{9}$, for example, is smaller than $\frac{7}{8}$, because if an object be divided into 9 parts, the parts are smaller than if the same object had been divided into 8 parts; and, since $\frac{1}{9}$ is smaller than $\frac{1}{8}$, it is clear that 7 one-ninths is a smaller amount than 7 one-eighths. Hence, also, $\frac{3}{8}$ is less than $\frac{3}{4}$.

75. The **value** of a fraction is the numerator divided by the denominator, as $\frac{4}{2} = 2$, $\frac{6}{2} = 3$.

76. The line between the numerator and the denominator means *divided by*, or $\div$.

$\frac{3}{4}$ is equivalent to $3 \div 4$.
$\frac{5}{8}$ is equivalent to $5 \div 8$.

77. The numerator and the denominator of a fraction are called the **terms** of a fraction.

78. The *value* of a fraction whose numerator and denominator are equal is 1.

$\frac{4}{4}$, or four-fourths $= 1$.
$\frac{8}{8}$, or eight-eighths $= 1$.
$\frac{64}{64}$, or sixty-four sixty-fourths $= 1$.

79. A **proper fraction** is a fraction whose numerator is *less* than its denominator. Its value is *less* than 1, as $\frac{3}{4}$, $\frac{5}{8}$, $\frac{1}{16}$.

80. An **improper fraction** is a fraction whose numerator *equals* or is *greater* than the denominator. Its value is 1 or *more than* 1, as $\frac{4}{4}$, $\frac{9}{8}$, $\frac{42}{32}$.

81. A **mixed number** is a whole number and a fraction united. $4\frac{2}{3}$ is a mixed number, and is equivalent to $4 + \frac{2}{3}$. It is read *four and two-thirds*.

REDUCTION OF FRACTIONS.

82. **Reduction of fractions** is the process of changing their form without changing their *value*.

83. *A fraction is reduced to higher terms by multiplying both terms of the fraction by the same number.* Thus, $\frac{3}{4}$ is reduced to $\frac{6}{8}$ by multiplying both terms by 2.

$$\frac{3 \times 2}{4 \times 2} = \frac{6}{8}.$$

The value is not changed, since $\frac{3}{4} = \frac{6}{8}$. For, suppose that an object, say an apple, is divided into 8 equal parts. If these parts be arranged into 4 piles, each containing 2 parts, it is evident each pile will be composed of the same amount of the entire apple as would have been the case had the apple been originally cut into 4 equal parts. Now, if one of these piles (containing 2 parts) be removed, there will be 3 piles left, each containing 2 equal parts, or 6 equal parts in all, i. e., six-eighths. But, since one pile, or one-quarter, was removed, there are three-quarters left. Hence, $\frac{3}{4} = \frac{6}{8}$. The same course of reasoning may be applied to any similar case. Therefore, multiplying both terms of a fraction by the same number does not alter its value.

84. To reduce a fraction to an equal fraction having a given denominator :

EXAMPLE.—Reduce $\frac{7}{8}$ to an equal fraction having 96 for a denominator.

SOLUTION.—Both the numerator and the denominator must be multiplied by the same number in order not to change the value of the fraction. The denominator must be multiplied by some number which will, in this case, make the product 96; this number is evidently $96 \div 8 = 12$, since $8 \times 12 = 96$. Hence, $\dfrac{7 \times 12}{8 \times 12} = \dfrac{84}{96}$. Ans.

85. Rule.—*Divide the given denominator by the denominator of the given fraction, and multiply both terms of the fraction by the result.*

EXAMPLE.—Reduce $\frac{3}{4}$ to 100ths.

SOLUTION.— $100 \div 4 = 25$; hence, $\dfrac{3 \times 25}{4 \times 25} = \dfrac{75}{100}$. Ans.

86. *A fraction is reduced to lower terms by dividing both terms by the same number.* Thus, $\frac{8}{10}$ is reduced to $\frac{4}{5}$ by dividing both terms by 2.

$$\frac{8 \div 2}{10 \div 2} = \frac{4}{5}.$$

That $\frac{8}{10} = \frac{4}{5}$ is readily seen from the explanation given in Art. **83**; for, multiplying both terms of the fraction $\frac{4}{5}$ by 2, $\frac{4 \times 2}{5 \times 2} = \frac{8}{10}$, and, if $\frac{4}{5} = \frac{8}{10}$, $\frac{8}{10}$ must equal $\frac{4}{5}$. Hence, dividing both terms of a fraction by the same number does **not** alter its value.

87. A fraction is reduced to its *lowest terms* when its numerator and denominator cannot both be divided by the *same* number without a remainder; for example, $\frac{3}{4}$, $\frac{2}{3}$, $\frac{11}{24}$, $\frac{8}{15}$.

EXAMPLES FOR PRACTICE.

88. Reduce the following:

(a) $\frac{7}{16}$ to 128ths.

(b) $\frac{24}{132}$ to its lowest terms.

(c) $\frac{64}{1000}$ to its lowest terms.　　　Ans. $\begin{cases}\end{cases}$

(d) $\frac{5}{7}$ to 49ths.

(e) $\frac{13}{16}$ to 10,000ths.

(a) $\frac{56}{128}$.

(b) $\frac{2}{11}$.

(c) $\frac{8}{125}$.

(d) $\frac{35}{49}$.

(e) $\frac{8125}{10000}$.

---

89. **To reduce a whole number or a mixed number to an improper fraction:**

EXAMPLE.—How many fourths in 5?

SOLUTION.—Since there are 4 fourths in 1 ($\frac{4}{4} = 1$), in 5 there will be 5×4 fourths, or 20 fourths; i. e., $5 \times \frac{4}{4} = \frac{20}{4}$. Ans.

EXAMPLE.—Reduce $8\frac{3}{4}$ to an improper fraction.

SOLUTION.— $8 \times \frac{4}{4} = \frac{32}{4}$. $\frac{32}{4} + \frac{3}{4} = \frac{35}{4}$. Ans.

---

90. **Rule.**—*Multiply the whole number by the denominator of the fraction, add the numerator to the product and place the denominator under the result. If it is desired to reduce a whole number to a fraction, multiply the whole number by the denominator of the given fraction, and write the result over the denominator.*

EXAMPLES FOR PRACTICE.

91. Reduce to improper fractions:

(a) $4\frac{1}{8}$.

(b) $5\frac{1}{9}$.

(c) $10\frac{2}{10}$.

(d) $37\frac{3}{4}$.　　　　　Ans. $\begin{cases}\end{cases}$

(e) $50\frac{4}{5}$.

(f) Reduce 7 to a fraction whose denominator is 16.

(a) $\frac{33}{8}$.

(b) $\frac{46}{9}$.

(c) $\frac{102}{10}$.

(d) $\frac{151}{4}$.

(e) $\frac{254}{5}$.

(f) $\frac{112}{16}$.

---

92. **To reduce an improper fraction to a whole or a mixed number:**

EXAMPLE.—Reduce $\frac{21}{4}$ to a mixed number.

SOLUTION.— 4 is contained in 21, 5 times and 1 remaining (see Art. **75**); as this is also divided by 4, its value is $\frac{1}{4}$. Therefore, $5 + \frac{1}{4}$, or $5\frac{1}{4}$, is the number. Ans.

93. Rule.—*Divide the numerator by the denominator, the quotient will be the whole number; the remainder, if there be any, will be the numerator of the fractional part of which the denominator is the same as the denominator of the improper fraction.*

EXAMPLES FOR PRACTICE.

94. Reduce to whole or mixed numbers:

(a)	$\frac{145}{6}$.		(a)	$24\frac{1}{6}$.
(b)	$\frac{185}{3}$.		(b)	$61\frac{2}{3}$.
(c)	$\frac{701}{6}$.	Ans.	(c)	$116\frac{5}{6}$.
(d)	$\frac{149}{3}$.		(d)	$49\frac{2}{3}$.
(e)	$\frac{76}{19}$.		(e)	4.
(f)	$\frac{125}{25}$.		(f)	5.

95. A common denominator of two or more fractions is a number which will contain (i. e., which may be divided by) the denominator of each of the given fractions without a remainder. The **least common denominator** is the least number that will contain each denominator of the given fractions without a remainder.

96. To find the least common denominator:

EXAMPLE.—Find the least common denominator of $\frac{1}{4}$, $\frac{1}{3}$, $\frac{1}{9}$, and $\frac{1}{16}$.

SOLUTION.—We first place the denominators in a row, separated by commas.

```
2 ) 4,  3,  9, 16
2 ) 2,  3,  9,  8
3 ) 1,  3,  9,  4
3 ) 1,  1,  3,  4
4 ) 1,  1,  1,  4
    1,  1,  1,  1
```

$2 \times 2 \times 3 \times 3 \times 4 = 144$, the least common denominator. Ans.

EXPLANATION.—Divide each of them by some prime number which will divide at least two of them without a remainder (if possible), bringing down those denominators to the row below which will not contain the divisor without a remainder. Dividing each of the numbers by 2, the second row becomes 2, 3, 9, 8, since 2 will not divide 3 and 9 without a remainder. Dividing again by 2, the result is 1, 3, 9, 4. Dividing the third row by 3, the result, is 1, 1,

3, 4. So continue until the last row contains only 1's. The product of all the divisors, or $2 \times 2 \times 3 \times 3 \times 4 = 144$, is the least common denominator.

97. EXAMPLE.—Find the least common denominator of $\frac{4}{9}, \frac{5}{12}, \frac{7}{18}$.

SOLUTION.—

$$
\begin{array}{r}
3\,)\,9,\ 12,\ 18 \\ \hline
3\,)\,3,\ \ 4,\ \ 6 \\ \hline
2\,)\,1,\ \ 4,\ \ 2 \\ \hline
2\,)\,1,\ \ 2,\ \ 1 \\ \hline
1,\ \ 1,\ \ 1
\end{array}
$$

$$3 \times 3 \times 2 \times 2 = 36. \quad \text{Ans.}$$

98. To reduce two or more fractions to fractions having a common denominator:

EXAMPLE.—Reduce $\frac{2}{3}, \frac{3}{4}$, and $\frac{1}{2}$ to fractions having a common denominator.

SOLUTION.—The common denominator is a number which will contain 3, 4, and 2. The least common denominator is 12, because it is the smallest number which can be divided by 3, 4, and 2 without a remainder.

$$\frac{2}{3} = \frac{8}{12}, \quad \frac{3}{4} = \frac{9}{12}, \quad \frac{1}{2} = \frac{6}{12}.$$

Reducing $\frac{2}{3}$ (see Art. **84**), 3 is contained in 12, 4 times. By multiplying both numerator and denominator of $\frac{2}{3}$ by 4, we find

$$\frac{2 \times 4}{3 \times 4} = \frac{8}{12}. \quad \text{In the same way we find } \frac{3}{4} = \frac{9}{12} \text{ and } \frac{1}{2} = \frac{6}{12}.$$

99. Rule.—*Divide the common denominator by the denominator of the given fraction, and multiply both terms of the fraction by the quotient.*

EXAMPLES FOR PRACTICE.

100. Reduce to fractions having a common denominator:

(a) $\frac{3}{4}, \frac{5}{8}, \frac{7}{8}$.

(b) $\frac{3}{16}, \frac{3}{4}, \frac{7}{32}$.

(c) $\frac{7}{8}, \frac{7}{88}, \frac{10}{11}$.

(d) $\frac{3}{5}, \frac{5}{8}, \frac{11}{40}$.

(e) $\frac{4}{10}, \frac{6}{40}, \frac{9}{20}$.

(f) $\frac{7}{15}, \frac{17}{30}, \frac{21}{30}$.

Ans.

(a) $\frac{6}{8}, \frac{5}{8}, \frac{7}{8}$.

(b) $\frac{6}{32}, \frac{24}{32}, \frac{7}{32}$.

(c) $\frac{77}{88}, \frac{7}{88}, \frac{80}{88}$.

(d) $\frac{24}{40}, \frac{25}{40}, \frac{11}{40}$.

(e) $\frac{16}{40}, \frac{6}{40}, \frac{18}{40}$.

(f) $\frac{14}{30}, \frac{17}{30}, \frac{21}{30}$.

ADDITION OF FRACTIONS.

101. *Fractions cannot be added unless they have a common denominator.* We cannot add $\frac{3}{4}$ to $\frac{7}{8}$ as they now stand, since the denominators represent parts of different sizes. Fourths cannot be added to eighths.

Suppose we divide an apple into 4 equal parts, and then divide 2 of these parts into 2 equal parts. It is evident that we shall have 2 one-fourths and 4 one-eighths. Now, if we add these parts, the result is $2+4=6$ something. But what is this something? It is not fourths, for 6 fourths are $1\frac{1}{2}$, and we had only 1 apple to begin with; neither is it eighths, for 6 eighths are $\frac{3}{4}$, which is less than 1 apple. By reducing the quarters to eighths, we have $\frac{2}{4}=\frac{4}{8}$, and adding the other 4 eighths, $4+4=8$ eighths. This result is correct, since $\frac{8}{8}=1$. Or we can, in this case, reduce the eighths to quarters. Thus, $\frac{4}{8}=\frac{2}{4}$; whence, adding, $2+2=4$ quarters, a correct result, since $\frac{4}{4}=1$.

Before adding, fractions should be reduced to a common denominator, preferably the *least* common denominator.

102. EXAMPLE.—Find the sum of $\frac{1}{2}$, $\frac{3}{4}$, and $\frac{5}{8}$.

SOLUTION.—The *least common denominator*, or the *least number* which will contain all the denominators, is 8.

$$\tfrac{1}{2}=\tfrac{4}{8}, \quad \tfrac{3}{4}=\tfrac{6}{8}, \quad \text{and} \quad \tfrac{5}{8}=\tfrac{5}{8}.$$

EXPLANATION.—As the denominator tells or indicates the *names* of the parts, the numerators only are added, to obtain the total number of *parts* indicated by the denominator. Thus, 4 one-eighths plus 6 one-eighths plus 5 one-eighths =

$$\tfrac{4}{8}+\tfrac{6}{8}+\tfrac{5}{8}=\frac{4+6+5}{8}=\frac{15}{8}=1\tfrac{7}{8}. \quad \text{Ans.}$$

103. EXAMPLE.—What is the sum of $12\frac{3}{4}$, $14\frac{5}{8}$, and $7\frac{5}{16}$?

SOLUTION.—The least common denominator in this case is **16.**

$$12\tfrac{3}{4}=12\tfrac{12}{16}$$
$$14\tfrac{5}{8}=14\tfrac{10}{16}$$
$$7\tfrac{5}{16}=\ \ 7\tfrac{5}{16}$$
$$sum \quad 33+\tfrac{27}{16}=33+1\tfrac{11}{16}=34\tfrac{11}{16}. \quad \text{Ans.}$$

The sum of the fractions $=\frac{27}{16}$ or $1\frac{11}{16}$, which added to the sum of the whole numbers $=34\frac{11}{16}$.

EXAMPLE.—What is the sum of 17, $13\frac{3}{16}$, $\frac{9}{32}$, and $3\frac{1}{4}$?

SOLUTION.—The least common denominator is 32. $13\frac{3}{16}=13\frac{6}{32}$, $3\frac{1}{4}=3\frac{8}{32}$.

$$17$$
$$13\tfrac{6}{32}$$
$$\tfrac{9}{32}$$
$$3\tfrac{8}{32}$$
$$sum \quad 33\tfrac{23}{32}. \quad \text{Ans.}$$

104. Rule.—I. *Reduce the given fractions to fractions having the least common denominator, and write the sum of the numerators over the common denominator.*

II. *When there are mixed numbers and whole numbers, add the fractions first, and if their sum is an improper fraction, reduce it to a mixed number and add the whole number with the other whole numbers.*

EXAMPLES FOR PRACTICE.

105.   Find the sum of:

(a)	$\frac{4}{6}, \frac{7}{24}, \frac{5}{8}.$	(a) $1\frac{7}{12}.$
(b)	$\frac{2}{3}, \frac{5}{15}, \frac{24}{45}.$	(b) $1\frac{8}{15}.$
(c)	$\frac{1}{2}, \frac{3}{8}, \frac{5}{16}.$	(c) $1\frac{3}{16}.$
(d)	$\frac{5}{6}, \frac{11}{72}, \frac{13}{18}.$	(d) $1\frac{51}{72}.$
(e)	$\frac{10}{11}, \frac{6}{33}, \frac{23}{66}.$	(e) $1\frac{29}{66}.$
(f)	$\frac{23}{45}, \frac{11}{15}, \frac{14}{45}.$	(f) $1\frac{5}{9}.$
(g)	$\frac{4}{11}, \frac{7}{22}, \frac{14}{22}.$	(g) $1\frac{7}{22}.$
(h)	$\frac{3}{7}, \frac{14}{49}, \frac{2}{7}.$	(h) $1.$

Ans.

SUBTRACTION OF FRACTIONS.

106. *Fractions cannot be subtracted without first reducing them to a common denominator.* This can be shown in the same manner as in the case of addition of fractions.

Example.—Subtract $\frac{3}{8}$ from $\frac{13}{16}$.

Solution.—The common denominator is 16.

$$\frac{3}{8} = \frac{6}{16}. \quad \frac{13}{16} - \frac{6}{16} = \frac{13-6}{16} = \frac{7}{16}. \text{ Ans.}$$

107. Example.—From 7 take $\frac{5}{8}$.

Solution.— $1 = \frac{8}{8}$; therefore, since $7 = 6 + 1$, $7 = 6 + \frac{8}{8} = 6\frac{8}{8}$, or $6\frac{8}{8} - \frac{5}{8} = 6\frac{3}{8}$. Ans.

108. Example.—What is the difference between $17\frac{9}{16}$ and $9\frac{15}{32}$?

Solution.—The common denominator of the fractions is 32. $17\frac{6}{16}$ = $17\frac{18}{32}$.

minuend	$17\frac{18}{32}$
subtrahend	$9\frac{15}{32}$
difference	$8\frac{3}{32}.$ Ans.

109. EXAMPLE.—From $9\frac{1}{4}$ take $4\frac{7}{16}$.

SOLUTION.—The common denominator of the fractions is 16. $9\frac{1}{4}$
$= 9\frac{4}{16}$.

$$
\begin{array}{lcc}
minuend & 9\frac{4}{16} \text{ or } 8\frac{20}{16} \\
subtrahend & 4\frac{7}{16} & 4\frac{7}{16} \\
\hline
difference & 4\frac{13}{16} & 4\frac{13}{16}. \text{ Ans.}
\end{array}
$$

EXPLANATION.—As the fraction in the subtrahend is greater than the fraction in the minuend, it cannot be subtracted; therefore, *borrow* 1, or $\frac{16}{16}$, from the 9 in the minuend and add it to the $\frac{4}{16}$; $\frac{4}{16} + \frac{16}{16} = \frac{20}{16}$. $\frac{7}{16}$ from $\frac{20}{16} = \frac{13}{16}$. Since 1 was borrowed from 9, 8 remains; 4 from $8 = 4$; $4 + \frac{13}{16} = 4\frac{13}{16}$.

110. EXAMPLE.—From 9 take $8\frac{3}{16}$.

SOLUTION.—
$$
\begin{array}{lcc}
minuend & 9 \text{ or } 8\frac{16}{16} \\
subtrahend & 8\frac{3}{16} & 8\frac{3}{16} \\
\hline
difference & \frac{13}{16} & \frac{13}{16}. \text{ Ans.}
\end{array}
$$

EXPLANATION.—As there is no fraction in the minuend from which to take the fraction in the subtrahend, borrow 1, or $\frac{16}{16}$, from 9. $\frac{3}{16}$ from $\frac{16}{16} = \frac{13}{16}$. Since 1 was borrowed from 9, only 8 is left. 8 from $8 = 0$.

111. Rule.—I. *Reduce the fractions to fractions having a common denominator. Subtract one numerator from the other and place the remainder over the common denominator.*

II. *When there are mixed numbers, subtract the fractions and whole numbers separately, and place the remainders side by side.*

III. *When the fraction in the subtrahend is greater than the fraction in the minuend, borrow 1 from the whole number in the minuend and add it to the fraction in the minuend, from which subtract the fraction in the subtrahend.*

IV. *When the minuend is a whole number, borrow 1; reduce it to a fraction whose denominator is the same as the denominator of the fraction in the subtrahend, and place it over that fraction for subtraction.*

EXAMPLES FOR PRACTICE.

112.   Subtract:

(a) $\frac{10}{24}$ from $\frac{11}{12}$.

(b) $\frac{7}{14}$ from $\frac{17}{28}$.

(c) $\frac{4}{30}$ from $\frac{5}{10}$.

(d) $\frac{15}{35}$ from $\frac{45}{70}$.

(e) $\frac{15}{16}$ from $\frac{57}{48}$.

(f) $13\frac{1}{4}$ from $30\frac{1}{2}$.

(g) $12\frac{1}{8}$ from 27.

(h) $5\frac{1}{4}$ from 30.

Ans. $\Bigg\{$

(a) $\frac{1}{2}$.

(b) $\frac{3}{28}$.

(c) $\frac{11}{30}$.

(d) $\frac{3}{14}$.

(e) $\frac{1}{4}$.

(f) $17\frac{1}{4}$.

(g) $14\frac{7}{8}$.

(h) $24\frac{3}{4}$.

MULTIPLICATION OF FRACTIONS.

113.   *In multiplication of fractions it is not necessary to reduce the fractions to fractions having a common denominator.*

114.   *Multiplying the numerator or dividing the denominator multiplies the fraction.*

EXAMPLE.—Multiply $\frac{3}{4}$ by 4.

SOLUTION.— $\frac{3}{4} \times 4 = \frac{3 \times 4}{4} = \frac{12}{4} = 3.$ Ans.

Or, $\frac{3}{4} \times 4 = \frac{3}{4 \div 4} = \frac{3}{1} = 3.$ Ans.

The word "of," when placed between two fractions, or between a fraction and a whole number, means the same as ×, or times. Thus,

$$\frac{3}{4} \text{ of } 4 = \frac{3}{4} \times 4 = 3.$$
$$\frac{1}{8} \text{ of } \frac{5}{16} = \frac{1}{8} \times \frac{5}{16} = \frac{5}{128}.$$

EXAMPLE.—Multiply $\frac{3}{8}$ by 2.

SOLUTION.— $2 \times \frac{3}{8} = \frac{3 \times 2}{8} = \frac{6}{8} = \frac{3}{4}.$ Ans.

Or, $2 \times \frac{3}{8} = \frac{3}{8 \div 2} = \frac{3}{4}.$ Ans.

115.   EXAMPLE.—What is the product of $\frac{4}{16}$ and $\frac{7}{8}$?

SOLUTION.— $\frac{4}{16} \times \frac{7}{8} = \frac{4 \times 7}{16 \times 8} = \frac{28}{128} = \frac{7}{32}.$ Ans.

Or, by cancelation, $\dfrac{\overset{}{4} \times 7}{\underset{4}{16} \times 8} = \dfrac{7}{4 \times 8} = \dfrac{7}{32}.$ Ans.

116.   EXAMPLE.—What is $\frac{4}{8}$ of $\frac{3}{4}$ of $\frac{16}{32}$?

SOLUTION.— $\dfrac{4 \times 3 \times \overset{}{16}}{8 \times 4 \times \underset{2}{32}} = \dfrac{3}{8 \times 2} = \dfrac{3}{16}.$ Ans.

117. Example.—What is the product of $9\frac{3}{4}$ and $5\frac{5}{8}$?

Solution.— $9\frac{3}{4} = \frac{39}{4}$; $5\frac{5}{8} = \frac{45}{8}$.

$$\frac{39}{4} \times \frac{45}{8} = \frac{39 \times 45}{4 \times 8} = \frac{1755}{32} = 54\frac{27}{32}. \quad \text{Ans.}$$

118. Example.—Multiply $15\frac{7}{8}$ by 3.

Solution.— $15\frac{7}{8}$ $15\frac{7}{8}$

$\underline{3}$ or $\underline{3}$

$47\frac{5}{8}$ $45 + \frac{21}{8} = 45 + 2\frac{5}{8} = 47\frac{5}{8}.$ Ans.

119. Rule.—I. *Divide the product of the numerators by the product of the denominators. All factors common to the numerators and denominators should first be cast out by cancelation.*

II. *To multiply one mixed number by another, reduce them both to improper fractions.*

III. *To multiply a mixed number by a whole number, first multiply the fractional part by the multiplier, and if the product is an improper fraction, reduce it to a mixed number and add the whole-number part to the product of the multiplier and the whole number.*

EXAMPLES FOR PRACTICE.

120. Find the product of:

(a)	$7 \times \frac{3}{19}$.	(a) $1\frac{2}{19}$.
(b)	$14 \times \frac{5}{16}$.	(b) $4\frac{3}{8}$.
(c)	$\frac{21}{32} \times \frac{5}{14}$.	(c) $\frac{15}{64}$.
(d)	$\frac{16}{27} \times 4$.	(d) $2\frac{10}{27}$.
(e)	$\frac{19}{18} \times 7$.	(e) $7\frac{7}{18}$.
(f)	$17\frac{18}{21} \times 7$.	(f) 125.
(g)	$\frac{105}{224} \times 32$.	(g) 15.
(h)	$\frac{15}{28} \times 14$.	(h) $7\frac{1}{2}$.

Ans.

DIVISION OF FRACTIONS.

121. *In division of fractions it is not necessary to reduce the fractions to fractions having a common denominator.*

122. *Dividing the numerator or multiplying the denominator divides the fraction.*

Example.—Divide $\frac{6}{8}$ by 3.

Solution.—When *dividing the numerator*, we have

$$\frac{6}{8} \div 3 = \frac{6 \div 3}{8} = \frac{2}{8} = \frac{1}{4}. \quad \text{Ans.}$$

When *multiplying the denominator*, we have

$$\tfrac{6}{8} \div 3 = \frac{6}{8 \times 3} = \tfrac{6}{24} = \tfrac{1}{4}. \quad \text{Ans.}$$

EXAMPLE.—Divide $\tfrac{3}{16}$ by 2.

SOLUTION.— $\tfrac{3}{16} \div 2 = \dfrac{3}{16 \times 2} = \tfrac{3}{32}.$ Ans.

EXAMPLE.—Divide $\tfrac{14}{32}$ by 7.

SOLUTION.— $\tfrac{14}{32} \div 7 = \dfrac{14 \div 7}{32} = \tfrac{2}{32} = \tfrac{1}{16}.$ Ans.

123. To **invert** a fraction is to *turn it upside down;* that is, make the numerator and denominator *change places* Invert $\tfrac{3}{4}$ and it becomes $\tfrac{4}{3}$.

124. EXAMPLE.—Divide $\tfrac{9}{16}$ by $\tfrac{3}{16}$.

SOLUTION.—1. The fraction $\tfrac{3}{16}$ is contained in $\tfrac{9}{16}$, 3 times, for the denominators are the same, and one numerator is contained in the other 3 times. 2. If we now invert the divisor, $\tfrac{3}{16}$, and multiply, the solution is

$$\frac{9}{16} \times \frac{16}{3} = \frac{\overset{3}{\cancel{9}} \times \cancel{16}}{\cancel{16} \times \cancel{3}} = 3. \quad \text{Ans.}$$

This brings the same quotient as in the first case.

125. EXAMPLE.—Divide $\tfrac{3}{8}$ by $\tfrac{1}{4}$.

SOLUTION.—We cannot divide $\tfrac{3}{8}$ by $\tfrac{1}{4}$, as in the first case above, for the denominators are not the same; therefore, we must solve as in the second case.

$$\tfrac{3}{8} \div \tfrac{1}{4} = \tfrac{3}{8} \times \tfrac{4}{1} = \frac{3 \times \cancel{4}}{\underset{2}{\cancel{8}} \times 1} = \frac{3}{2} \text{ or } 1\tfrac{1}{2}. \quad \text{Ans.}$$

126. EXAMPLE.—Divide 5 by $\tfrac{10}{16}$.

SOLUTION.— $\tfrac{10}{16}$ inverted becomes $\tfrac{16}{10}$.

$$5 \times \frac{16}{10} = \frac{\cancel{5} \times \overset{8}{\cancel{16}}}{\underset{2}{\cancel{10}}} = 8. \quad \text{Ans.}$$

127. EXAMPLE.—How many times is $3\tfrac{3}{4}$ contained in $7\tfrac{7}{16}$?

SOLUTION.— $3\tfrac{3}{4} = \tfrac{15}{4}$; $7\tfrac{7}{16} = \tfrac{119}{16}$.
$\tfrac{15}{4}$ inverted equals $\tfrac{4}{15}$.

$$\frac{119}{16} \times \frac{4}{15} = \frac{119 \times \cancel{4}}{\underset{4}{\cancel{16}} \times 15} = \frac{119}{60} = 1\tfrac{59}{60}. \quad \text{Ans.}$$

128. **Rule.**—*Invert the divisor and proceed as in multiplication.*

129. We have learned that a line placed between two numbers indicates that the number above the line is to be divided by the number below it. Thus, $\frac{18}{3}$ shows that 18 is to be divided by 3. This is also true if a fraction or a fractional expression be placed above or below a line.

$\dfrac{9}{\frac{3}{8}}$ means that 9 is to be divided by $\frac{3}{8}$; $\dfrac{3\times 7}{\dfrac{8+4}{16}}$ means that

3×7 is to be divided by the value of $\dfrac{8+4}{16}$.

$\dfrac{\frac{1}{4}}{\frac{3}{8}}$ is the same as $\frac{1}{4}\div\frac{3}{8}$.

It will be noticed that there is a heavy line between the 9 and the $\frac{3}{8}$. This is necessary, since otherwise there would be nothing to show as to whether 9 was to be divided by $\frac{3}{8}$, or $\frac{9}{8}$ was to be divided by 8. Whenever a heavy line is used, as shown here, it indicates that *all above the line is to be divided by all below it.*

EXAMPLES FOR PRACTICE.

130.   Divide:

(a)	15 by $6\frac{3}{5}$.		(a)	$2\frac{3}{11}$.
(b)	30 by $\frac{6}{8}$.		(b)	40.
(c)	172 by $\frac{4}{5}$.		(c)	215.
(d)	$\frac{14}{18}$ by $1\frac{7}{16}$.	Ans.	(d)	$\frac{112}{207}$.
(e)	$\frac{108}{6}$ by $14\frac{2}{3}$.		(e)	$1\frac{5}{11}$.
(f)	$\frac{142}{27}$ by $17\frac{1}{5}$.		(f)	$\frac{71}{231}$.
(g)	$\frac{14}{13}$ by $\frac{145}{72}$.		(g)	$\frac{56}{145}$.
(h)	$\frac{128}{13}$ by $72\frac{1}{3}$.		(h)	$\frac{64}{651}$.

----

131. Whenever an expression like one of the three following ones is obtained, it may always be simplified by transposing the denominator from *above* to *below* the line, or from *below* to *above*, as the case may be, taking care, however, to indicate that the denominator when so transferred is a multiplier.

1. $\dfrac{\frac{3}{4}}{9}=\dfrac{3}{9\times 4}=\frac{3}{36}=\frac{1}{12}$; for, regarding the fraction above the heavy line as the numerator of a fraction whose denominator is 9, $\dfrac{\frac{3}{4}\times 4}{9\times 4}=\dfrac{3}{9\times 4}$, as before.

2. $\dfrac{9}{\frac{3}{4}} = \dfrac{9 \times 4}{3} = 12$. The proof is the same as in the first case.

3. $\dfrac{\frac{5}{9}}{\frac{3}{4}} = \dfrac{5 \times 4}{3 \times 9} = \frac{20}{27}$. For, regarding $\frac{5}{9}$ as the numerator of a fraction whose denominator is $\frac{3}{4}$, $\dfrac{\frac{5}{9} \times 9}{\frac{3}{4} \times 9} = \dfrac{5}{\frac{3 \times 9}{4}}$; and

$\dfrac{\frac{5}{3 \times 9} \times 4}{\frac{3 \times 9}{4} \times 4} = \dfrac{5 \times 4}{3 \times 9} = \frac{20}{27}$, as above.

This principle may be used to great advantage in cases like $\dfrac{\frac{1}{4} \times 310 \times \frac{27}{12} \times 72}{40 \times 4\frac{1}{2} \times 5\frac{1}{6}}$. Reducing the mixed numbers to fractions, the expression becomes $\dfrac{\frac{1}{4} \times 310 \times \frac{27}{12} \times 72}{40 \times \frac{9}{2} \times \frac{31}{6}}$. Now transferring the denominators of the fractions and canceling,

$$\dfrac{1 \times 310 \times 27 \times 72 \times 2 \times 6}{40 \times 9 \times 31 \times 4 \times 12} = \dfrac{1 \times \cancel{310} \times \cancel{27} \times \cancel{72} \times \cancel{2} \times \cancel{6}}{\cancel{40} \times \cancel{9} \times \cancel{31} \times \cancel{4} \times \cancel{12}}$$

$$= \dfrac{27}{2} = 13\tfrac{1}{2}.$$

Greater exactness in results can usually be obtained by using this principle than by reducing the fractions to decimals. The principle, however, should not be employed if a sign of addition or subtraction occurs either above or below the dividing line.

ARITHMETIC.

(SECTION 3.)

DECIMALS.

Remark.—A knowledge of decimals is of the utmost importance to all who are required to make calculations of any kind. The subject is easy to learn, and for this reason the student is somewhat inclined to study it too hastily, the result being that he afterwards has trouble that might have been entirely avoided had he given the text the proper attention in the beginning. Decimals are much easier to use than common fractions, which they replace; at the same time it is frequently more expedient to use common fractions in certain operations, and, hence, they cannot be wholly dispensed with. Particular attention should be paid to the rules for multiplication and division—especially to the locating of the decimal point—and to the operations of changing a common fraction to a decimal and vice versa.

132. Decimals are *tenth* fractions; that is, the parts of a unit are expressed on the scale of ten, as *tenths, hundredths, thousandths*, etc.

133. The *denominator*, which is always ten or a multiple of ten, as 10, 100, 1,000, etc., is not expressed, as it would be in common fractions, by writing it under the *numerator* with a line between them, as $\frac{3}{10}$, $\frac{3}{100}$, $\frac{3}{1000}$, but is expressed by placing a *period* (.), which is called a **decimal point,** to the *left* of the *figures of the numerator*, so as to indicate that the number on the right is the numerator of a fraction whose denominator is 10, 100, 1,000, etc.

134. The *reading* of a decimal number depends upon the number of decimal places in it, or the number of figures to the right of the decimal point.

> One decimal place expresses *tenths.*
> Two decimal places express *hundredths.*
> Three decimal places express *thousandths.*
> Four decimal places express *ten-thousandths.*
> Five decimal places express *hundred-thousandths.*
> Six decimal places express *millionths.*

Thus:

$$.3 \quad = \quad \tfrac{3}{10} \quad = \text{3 tenths.}$$
$$.03 \quad = \quad \tfrac{3}{100} \quad = \text{3 hundredths.}$$
$$.003 \quad = \quad \tfrac{3}{1000} \quad = \text{3 thousandths.}$$
$$.0003 \quad = \quad \tfrac{3}{10000} \quad = \text{3 ten-thousandths.}$$
$$.00003 \quad = \quad \tfrac{3}{100000} \quad = \text{3 hundred-thousandths.}$$
$$.000003 \quad = \quad \tfrac{3}{1000000} \quad = \text{3 millionths.}$$

We see in the above that the *number of decimal places in a decimal equals the number of ciphers to the right of the figure 1 in the denominator of its equivalent fraction.* This fact kept in mind will be of much assistance in reading and writing decimals.

Whatever may be written to the *left* of a decimal point is a whole number. The *decimal point merely separates the fraction on the right from the whole number on the left.*

When a whole number and decimal are written together, the expression is a *mixed number.* Thus, 8.12 and 17.25 are mixed numbers.

The relation of decimals and whole numbers to each other is clearly shown by the following table:

hundreds of millions.	tens of millions.	millions.	hundreds of thousands.	tens of thousands.	thousands.	hundreds.	tens.	units.	decimal point.	tenths.	hundredths.	thousandths.	ten-thousandths.	hundred-thousandths.	millionths.	ten-millionths.	hundred-millionths.
9	8	7	6	5	4	3	2	1	.	2	3	4	5	6	7	8	9

The figures to the *left* of the decimal point represent *whole numbers;* those to the *right* are *decimals.*

In both the decimals and whole numbers, the *units* place is made the *starting point* of notation and numeration. Both whole numbers and decimals *decrease* on the scale of ten to the *right*, and both *increase* on the scale of ten to the *left*. The *first* figure to the *left* of units is *tens*, and the *first* figure to the *right* of units is *tenths.* The *second* figure to the *left* of units is *hundreds*, and the *second* figure to the *right* is *hundredths.* The *third* figure to the *left* is *thousands*, and the *third* to the *right* is *thousandths*, and so on; the *whole* numbers on the *left* and the *decimals* on the *right.* The figures equally distant from units place correspond in name, the *decimals* having the ending *ths*, to distinguish them from *whole* numbers. The following is the numeration of the number in the above table: nine hundred eighty-seven million, six hundred fifty-four thousand, three hundred twenty-one and twenty-three million, four hundred fifty-six thousand, seven hundred eighty-nine hundred-millionths.

The decimals increase to the *left*, on the scale of *ten*, the same as whole numbers; for, if you begin at the 4 in thousandths place in the above table, the next figure to the left is *hundredths*, which is ten times as great, and the next *tenths*, or ten times the *hundredths*, and so on through both decimals and whole numbers.

135. *Annexing, or taking away, a cipher at the right of a decimal, does not affect its value.*

.5 is $\frac{5}{10}$; .50 is $\frac{50}{100}$, but $\frac{5}{10} = \frac{50}{100}$; therefore, .5 = .50.

136. *Inserting a cipher between a decimal and the decimal point, divides the decimal by 10.*

$$.5 = \frac{5}{10}; \quad \frac{5}{10} \div 10 = \frac{5}{100} = .05.$$

137. *Taking away a cipher from the left of a decimal, multiplies the decimal by 10.*

$$.05 = \frac{5}{100}; \quad \frac{5}{100} \times 10 = \frac{5}{10} = .5.$$

138. In some cases it is convenient to express a mixed decimal fraction in the form of a common (improper) fraction. To do so it is only necessary to write the entire number, omitting the decimal point, as the numerator of the fraction, and the denominator of the decimal part as the denominator of the fraction. Thus, $127.483 = \frac{127483}{1000}$; for, $127.483 = 127\frac{483}{1000} = \frac{127000 + 483}{1000} = \frac{127483}{1000}$.

ADDITION OF DECIMALS.

139. Addition of decimals is similar in all respects to addition of whole numbers—units are placed under units, tens under tens, etc.; this, of course, brings the decimal points in line, directly under one another. Hence, in placing the numbers to be added, it is only necessary to take care that the *decimal points are in line*. In adding whole numbers, the right-hand figures are always in line; but in adding decimals, the right-hand figures will not be in line unless each decimal contains the same number of figures.

whole numbers	*decimals*	*mixed numbers*
3 4 2	.3 4 2	3 4 2.0 3 2
4 2 3 4	.4 2 3 4	4 2 3 4.5
2 6	.2 6	2 6.6 7 8 2
3	.0 3	3.0 6
sum 4 6 0 5 Ans.	*sum* 1.0 5 5 4 Ans.	*sum* 4 6 0 6.2 7 0 2 Ans.

140. EXAMPLE.—What is the sum of 242, .36, 118.725, 1.005, 6, and 100.1?

SOLUTION.—
$$
\begin{array}{r}
2\,4\,2. \\
.3\,6 \\
1\,1\,8.7\,2\,5 \\
1.0\,0\,5 \\
6. \\
1\,0\,0.1 \\
\hline
sum \quad 4\,6\,8.1\,9\,0 \quad \text{Ans.}
\end{array}
$$

141. Rule.—*Place the numbers to be added so that the decimal points will be directly under each other. Add as in whole numbers, and place the decimal point in the sum directly under the decimal points above.*

EXAMPLES FOR PRACTICE.

142. Find the sum of:

(a) .2143, .105, 2.3042, and 1.1417.	(a) 3.7652.
(b) 783.5, 21.473, .2101, and .7816.	(b) 805.9647.
(c) 21.781, 138.72, 41.8738, .72, and 1.413.	(c) 204.5078.
(d) .3724, 104.15, 21.417, and 100.042.	(d) 225.9814.
(e) 200.172, 14.105, 12.1465, .705, and 7.2.	(e) 234.3285.
(f) 1,427.16, .244, .32, .032, and 10.0041.	(f) 1,437.7601.
(g) 2,473.1, 41.65, .7243, 104.067, and 21.073.	(g) 2,640.6143.
(h) 4,107.2, .00375, 21.716, 410.072, and .0345.	(h) 4,539.02625.

Ans.

SUBTRACTION OF DECIMALS.

143. As in subtraction of whole numbers, units are placed under units, tens under tens, etc., bringing the decimal points under each other, as in addition of decimals.

EXAMPLE.—Subtract .132 from .3063.

SOLUTION.—
$$
\begin{array}{r}
minuend \quad .3\,0\,6\,3 \\
subtrahend \quad .1\,3\,2 \\
\hline
difference \quad .1\,7\,4\,3 \quad \text{Ans.}
\end{array}
$$

144. EXAMPLE.—What is the difference between 7.895 and .725?

SOLUTION.—
$$
\begin{array}{r}
minuend \quad 7.8\,9\,5 \\
subtrahend \quad .7\,2\,5 \\
\hline
difference \quad 7.1\,7\,0 \text{ or } 7.1\,7. \quad \text{Ans.}
\end{array}
$$

145. EXAMPLE.—Subtract .625 from 11.

SOLUTION.—

minuend   1 1.0 0 0
subtrahend   .6 2 5
difference   1 0.3 7 5 Ans.

146. Rule.—*Place the subtrahend under the minuend, so that the decimal points will be directly under each other. Subtract as in whole numbers, and place the decimal point in the remainder directly under the decimal points above.*

When the figures in the decimal part of the subtrahend extend beyond those in the minuend, place ciphers in the minuend above them and subtract as before.

EXAMPLES FOR PRACTICE.

147. From:

(a)	407.385 take 235.0004.		(a)	172.3846.
(b)	22.718 take 1.7042.		(b)	21.0138.
(c)	1,368.17 take 13.6817.		(c)	1,354.4883.
(d)	70.00017 take 7.000017.	Ans.	(d)	63.000153.
(e)	630.630 take .6304.		(e)	629.9996.
(f)	421.73 take 217.162.		(f)	204.568.
(g)	1.000014 take .00001.		(g)	1.000004.
(h)	.783652 take .542314.		(h)	.241338.

MULTIPLICATION OF DECIMALS.

148. In multiplication of decimals we do not place the decimal points directly under each other as in addition and subtraction. We pay no attention for the time being to the decimal points. Place the multiplier under the multiplicand, so that the *right-hand* figure of the one is under the *right-hand* figure of the other, and proceed exactly as in multiplication of whole numbers. After multiplying, *count the number of decimal places in both multiplicand and multiplier, and point off the same number in the product.*

EXAMPLE.—Multiply .825 by 13.

SOLUTION.—

multiplicand   .8 2 5
multiplier   1 3

2 4 7 5
8 2 5

product 1 0.7 2 5 Ans.

In this example there are 3 decimal places in the multiplicand and none in the multiplier; therefore, 3 decimal places are pointed off in the product.

149. EXAMPLE.—What is the product of 426 and the decimal .005 ?

SOLUTION.—
$$\begin{array}{rr} \textit{multiplicand} & 4\ 2\ 6 \\ \textit{multiplier} & .0\ 0\ 5 \\ \hline \textit{product} & 2.1\ 3\ 0 \text{ or } 2.13. \quad \text{Ans.} \end{array}$$

In this example there are 3 decimal places in the multiplier and none in the multiplicand; therefore, 3 decimal places are pointed off in the product.

150. It is not necessary to multiply by the ciphers on the *left* of a decimal; they merely determine the *number of decimal places*. Ciphers to the *right* of a decimal should be omitted, as they only make more figures to deal with, and do not change the value.

151. EXAMPLE.—Multiply 1.205 by 1.15.

SOLUTION.—
$$\begin{array}{rr} \textit{multiplicand} & 1.2\ 0\ 5 \\ \textit{multiplier} & 1.1\ 5 \\ \hline & 6\ 0\ 2\ 5 \\ & 1\ 2\ 0\ 5 \\ & 1\ 2\ 0\ 5 \\ \hline \textit{product} & 1.3\ 8\ 5\ 7\ 5 \quad \text{Ans.} \end{array}$$

In this example there are 3 decimal places in the multiplicand and 2 in the multiplier; therefore, $3+2$, or 5, decimal places must be pointed off in the product.

152. EXAMPLE.—Multiply .232 by .001.

SOLUTION.—
$$\begin{array}{rr} \textit{multiplicand} & .2\ 3\ 2 \\ \textit{multiplier} & .0\ 0\ 1 \\ \hline \textit{product} & .0\ 0\ 0\ 2\ 3\ 2 \quad \text{Ans.} \end{array}$$

In this example we multiply the multiplicand by the digit in the multiplier, which gives 232 for the product; but since there are 3 decimal places each in the multiplier and multiplicand, we must prefix 3 ciphers to the 232 to make $3+3$, or 6, decimal places in the product.

153. Rule.—*Place the multiplier under the multiplicand, disregarding the position of the decimal points. Multiply* *as in whole numbers, and in the product point off as many decimal places as there are decimal places in both multiplier and multiplicand, prefixing ciphers if necessary.*

EXAMPLES FOR PRACTICE.

154. Find the product of:

(a)	.000492 × 4.1418.		(a)	.0020377656.
(b)	4,003.2 × 1.2.		(b)	4,803.84.
(c)	78.6531 × 1.03.		(c)	81.012693.
(d)	.3685 × .042.	Ans.	(d)	.015477.
(e)	178,352 × .01.		(e)	1,783.52.
(f)	.00045 × .0045.		(f)	.000002025.
(g)	.714 × .00002.		(g)	.00001428.
(h)	.00004 × .008.		(h)	.00000032.

DIVISION OF DECIMALS.

155. In division of decimals we pay no attention to the decimal point until after the division has been performed. The *number of decimal places in the dividend must equal (or be made to equal by annexing ciphers) the number of decimal places in the divisor.* Divide exactly as in whole numbers. *Subtract the number of decimal places in the divisor from the number of decimal places in the dividend, and point off as many decimal places in the quotient as there are units in the remainder thus found.*

EXAMPLE.—Divide .625 by 25.

$$
\begin{array}{r}
\textit{divisor}\ \textit{dividend}\ \textit{quotient} \\
25\,)\,.6\,2\,5\,(\,.0\,2\,5\ \ \text{Ans.} \\
\underline{5\,0} \\
1\,2\,5 \\
\underline{1\,2\,5} \\
\textit{remainder}\quad 0
\end{array}
$$

In this example there are no decimal places in the divisor, and three decimal places in the dividend; therefore, there are 3 minus 0, or 3, decimal places in the quotient. One cipher has to be prefixed to the 25 to make the three decimal places.

156. Example.—Divide 6.035 by .05.

SOLUTION.—

divisor dividend quotient

.0 5) 6.0 3 5 (1 2 0.7 Ans.

```
      5
     ───
     1 0
     1 0
     ───
         3 5
         3 5
         ───
remainder   0
```

In this example we divide by 5, as if the cipher were not before it. There is one more decimal place in the dividend than in the divisor; therefore, one decimal place is pointed off in the quotient.

157. Example.—Divide .125 by .005.

SOLUTION.—

divisor dividend quotient

.0 0 5) .1 2 5 (2 5 Ans.

```
       1 0
       ───
         2 5
         2 5
         ───
remainder   0
```

In this example there are the same number of decimal places in the dividend as in the divisor; therefore, the quotient has no decimal places, and is a whole number.

158. Example.—Divide 326 by .25.

SOLUTION.—

divisor dividend quotient

.2 5) 3 2 6.0 0 (1 3 0 4 Ans.

```
      2 5
      ───
        7 6
        7 5
        ───
          1 0 0
          1 0 0
          ─────
remainder     0
```

In this problem two ciphers were annexed to the dividend, to make the number of decimal places equal to the number in the divisor. The quotient is a whole number.

159. EXAMPLE.—Divide .0025 by 1.25.

divisor   dividend   quotient

SOLUTION.—   1.25).00250(.002 Ans.
                   250
remainder   0

EXPLANATION.—In this example we are to divide .0025 by 1.25. Consider the dividend as a whole number, i. e., as 25 (disregarding the two ciphers at its left, for the present); also, consider the divisor as a whole number, i. e., as 125. It is clearly evident that the dividend, 25, will not contain the divisor, 125; we must, therefore, annex one cipher to the 25, thus making the dividend 250. 125 is contained twice in 250, so we place the figure 2 in the quotient. In pointing off the decimal places in the quotient, it must be remembered that there were only four decimal places in the dividend; but one cipher was annexed, thereby making $4+1$, or 5, decimal places. Since there are five decimal places in the dividend and two decimal places in the divisor, we must point off $5-2$, or 3, decimal places in the quotient. In order to point off three decimal places, two ciphers must be prefixed to the figure 2, thereby making .002 the quotient. It is not necessary to consider the ciphers at the left of a decimal when dividing, except when determining the position of the decimal point in the quotient.

160. Rule.—I. *Place the divisor to the left of the dividend, and proceed as in division of whole numbers; in the quotient, point off as many decimal places as the number of decimal places in the dividend exceed those in the divisor, prefixing ciphers to the quotient, if necessary.*

II. *If in dividing one number by another there be a remainder, the remainder can be placed over the divisor, as a fractional part of the quotient, but it is generally better to annex ciphers to the remainder, and continue dividing until there are 3 or 4 decimal places in the quotient, and then if there still be a remainder, terminate the quotient by the plus sign (+), which shows that it can be carried further.*

161.   EXAMPLE.—What is the quotient of 199 divided by 15?

divisor dividend quotient

SOLUTION.— $15) 199 (13 + \frac{4}{15}$ Ans.

$$
\begin{array}{r}
15 \\ \hline
49 \\
45 \\ \hline
\end{array}
$$

remainder 4

Or, $15) 199.000 (13.266 +$ Ans.

$$
\begin{array}{r}
15 \\ \hline
49 \\
45 \\ \hline
40 \\
30 \\ \hline
100 \\
90 \\ \hline
100 \\
90 \\ \hline
\end{array}
$$

remainder 1 0

$$13\tfrac{4}{15} = 13.266 +$$
$$\tfrac{4}{15} = .266 +$$

162. It frequently happens, as in the above example, that the division will never terminate. In such cases, decide to how many decimal places the division is to be carried, and carry the work one place further. If the last figure of the quotient thus obtained is 5 or a greater number, increase the preceding figure by 1, and write after it the minus sign (—), thus indicating that the quotient is not quite as large as indicated; if the figure thus obtained is less than 5, write the plus sign (+) after the quotient, thus indicating that the number is slightly greater than as indicated. In the last example, had it been desired to obtain the answer correct to four decimal places, the work would have been carried to five places, obtaining 13.26666, and the answer would have been given as 13.2667 —. This remark applies to any other calculation involving decimals, when it is desired to omit some of the figures in the decimal. Thus, if it was desired to retain three decimal places in the number .2471253, it would be expressed as .247 +; if it was desired to retain five decimal places, it would be expressed as .24713 —. Both the + and — signs are frequently omitted; they are

40—5

seldom used outside of arithmetic, except in exact calculations, when it is desired to call particular attention to the
fact that the result obtained is not *quite* exact.

EXAMPLES FOR PRACTICE.

163. Divide:

(*a*)	101.6688 by 2.36.	(*a*)	43.08.
(*b*)	187.12264 by 123.107.	(*b*)	1.52.
(*c*)	.08 by .008.	(*c*)	10.
(*d*)	.0003 by 3.75.	(*d*)	.00008.
(*e*)	.0144 by .024.	Ans. (*e*)	.6.
(*f*)	.00375 by 1.25.	(*f*)	.003.
(*g*)	.004 by 400.	(*g*)	.00001.
(*h*)	.4 by .008.	(*h*)	50.

REDUCTION OF DECIMALS.

TO REDUCE A FRACTION TO A DECIMAL.

164. EXAMPLE.— $\frac{3}{4}$ equals what decimal ?

SOLUTION.—
$$4\,)\,3.0\,0$$
$$\overline{\quad.7\,5\quad}\ \text{or}\ \tfrac{3}{4}=.75.\ \ \text{Ans.}$$

EXAMPLE.—What decimal is equivalent to $\frac{7}{8}$?

SOLUTION.—
$$8\,)\,7.0\,0\,0\,(.8\,7\,5$$
$$\underline{6\,4}$$
$$\overline{\quad6\,0}$$
$$\underline{\quad5\,6}\quad\text{or}\ \tfrac{7}{8}=.875.\ \ \text{Ans.}$$
$$\overline{\quad\quad4\,0}$$
$$\underline{\quad\quad4\,0}$$
$$\overline{\quad\quad\ \ 0}$$

165. Rule.—*Annex ciphers to the numerator and divide
by the denominator. Point off as many decimal places in the
quotient as there are ciphers annexed.*

EXAMPLES FOR PRACTICE.

166. Reduce the following common fractions to decimals:

(*a*)	$\frac{15}{32}$.	(*a*)	.46875.
(*b*)	$\frac{7}{8}$.	(*b*)	.875.
(*c*)	$\frac{21}{32}$.	(*c*)	.65625.
(*d*)	$\frac{51}{64}$.	(*d*)	.796875.
(*e*)	$\frac{4}{25}$.	Ans. (*e*)	.16.
(*f*)	$\frac{5}{8}$.	(*f*)	.625.
(*g*)	$\frac{10}{200}$.	(*g*)	.05.
(*h*)	$\frac{4}{1000}$.	(*h*)	.004.

167. To reduce inches to decimal parts of a foot:

EXAMPLE.—What decimal part of a foot is 9 inches ?

SOLUTION.—Since there are 12 inches in one foot, 1 inch is $\frac{1}{12}$ of a foot, and 9 inches is $9 \times \frac{1}{12}$, or $\frac{9}{12}$ of a foot. This reduced to a decimal by the above rule shows what decimal part of a foot 9 inches is.

$$
\begin{array}{r}
1\,2\,)\,9.0\,0\,(\,.7\,5 \text{ of a foot. Ans.} \\
8\,4 \\
\hline
6\,0 \\
6\,0 \\
\hline
0
\end{array}
$$

168. Rule.—I. *To reduce inches to a decimal part of a foot, divide the number of inches by 12.*

II. *Should the resulting decimal be an unending one, and it is desired to terminate the division at some point, say the fourth decimal place, carry the division one place further, and if the fifth figure is 5 or greater increase the fourth figure by 1, omitting the signs $+$ and $-$.*

EXAMPLES FOR PRACTICE.

169. Reduce to the decimal part of a foot:

(a)	3 in.		(a)	.25 ft.
(b)	4½ in.		(b)	.375 ft.
(c)	5 in.	Ans. {	(c)	.4167 ft.
(d)	6⅝ in.		(d)	.5521 ft.
(e)	11 in.		(e)	.9167 ft.

TO REDUCE A DECIMAL TO A FRACTION.

170. EXAMPLE.—Reduce .125 to a fraction.

SOLUTION.— $.125 = \frac{125}{1000} = \frac{5}{40} = \frac{1}{8}$. Ans.

EXAMPLE.—Reduce .875 to a fraction.

SOLUTION.— $.875 = \frac{875}{1000} = \frac{35}{40} = \frac{7}{8}$. Ans.

171. Rule.—*Under the figures of the decimal, place 1 with as many ciphers at its right as there are decimal places in the decimal, and reduce the resulting fraction to its lowest terms by dividing both numerator and denominator by the same number.*

172. Reduce the following to common fractions:

(a)	.125.		(a)	$\frac{1}{8}$.
(b)	.625.		(b)	$\frac{5}{8}$.
(c)	.3125.		(c)	$\frac{5}{16}$.
(d)	.04.	Ans.	(d)	$\frac{1}{25}$.
(e)	.06.		(e)	$\frac{3}{50}$.
(f)	.75.		(f)	$\frac{3}{4}$.
(g)	.15625.		(g)	$\frac{5}{32}$.
(h)	.875.		(h)	$\frac{7}{8}$.

173. To express a decimal approximatively as a fraction having a given denominator:

174. EXAMPLE.—Express .5827 in 64ths.

SOLUTION.— $.5827 \times \frac{64}{64} = \dfrac{37.2928}{64}$, say $\frac{37}{64}$.

Hence, $.5827 = \frac{37}{64}$, nearly.　Ans.

EXAMPLE.— Express .3917 in 12ths.

SOLUTION.— $.3917 \times \frac{12}{12} = \dfrac{4.7004}{12}$, say $\frac{5}{12}$.

Hence, $.3917 = \frac{5}{12}$, nearly.　Ans.

175. Rule.—*Reduce 1 to a fraction having the given denominator. Multiply the given decimal by the fraction so obtained, and the result will be the fraction required.*

176. Express:

(a)	.625 in 8ths.		(a)	$\frac{5}{8}$.
(b)	.3125 in 16ths.		(b)	$\frac{5}{16}$.
(c)	.15625 in 32ds.	Ans.	(c)	$\frac{5}{32}$.
(d)	.77 in 64ths.		(d)	$\frac{49}{64}$.
(e)	.81 in 48ths.		(e)	$\frac{39}{48}$.
(f)	.923 in 96ths.		(f)	$\frac{89}{96}$.

177. The sign for dollars is $. It is read *dollars*. $25 is read *25 dollars*.

Since there are 100 cents in a dollar, 1 cent is 1 one-hundredth of a dollar; the first two figures of a decimal part of a dollar represent *cents*. Since a mill is $\frac{1}{10}$ of a cent, or $\frac{1}{1000}$ of a dollar, the third figure represents *mills*.

Thus, $25.16 is read *twenty-five dollars and sixteen cents;* $25.168 is read *twenty-five dollars sixteen cents and eight mills*.

SYMBOLS OF AGGREGATION.

178. The **vinculum** ——, **parenthesis** ( ), **brackets** [ ], and **brace** { } are called **symbols of aggregation,** and are used to include numbers which are to be considered together; thus, $13 \times \overline{8-3}$, or $13 \times (8-3)$, shows that 3 is to be taken from 8 before multiplying by 13.

$$13 \times (8-3) = 13 \times 5 = 65.$$
$$13 \times \overline{8-3} = 13 \times 5 = 65.$$

When the vinculum or parenthesis is not used, we have
$$13 \times 8 - 3 = 104 - 3 = 101.$$

179. In any series of numbers connected by the signs $+$, $-$, $\times$, and $\div$, the operations indicated by the signs must be performed in order from left to right, *except* that no addition or subtraction may be performed if a sign of multiplication or division *follows* the number on the *right* of a sign of addition or subtraction until the indicated multiplication or division has been performed. In all cases the sign of multiplication takes the precedence, the reason being that when two or more numbers or expressions are connected by the sign of multiplication the numbers thus connected are regarded as factors of the product indicated, and not as separate numbers.

EXAMPLE.—What is the value of $4 \times 24 - 8 + 17$?

SOLUTION.—Performing the operations in order from left to right, $4 \times 24 = 96$; $96 - 8 = 88$; $88 + 17 = 105$. Ans.

180. EXAMPLE.—What is the value of the following expression: $1,296 \div 12 + 160 - 22 \times 3\frac{1}{2} = ?$

SOLUTION.— $1,296 \div 12 = 108$; $108 + 160 = 268$; here we cannot subtract 22 from 268 because the sign of multiplication follows 22; hence, multiplying 22 by $3\frac{1}{2}$, we get 77, and $268 - 77 = 191$. Ans.

Had the above expression been written $1,296 \div 12 + 160 - 22 \times 3\frac{1}{2} \div 7 + 25$, it would have been necessary to have divided $22 \times 3\frac{1}{2}$ by 7 before subtracting, and the final result would have been $22 \times 3\frac{1}{2} = 77$; $77 \div 7 = 11$; $268 - 11 = 257$; $257 + 25 = 282$. Ans. In other words, it is necessary to perform all the indicated multiplication or division included between the signs $+$ and $-$, or $-$ and $+$, before adding or subtracting. Also, had the expression been written $1,296 \div 12 + 160 - 24\frac{1}{2} \div 7 \times 3\frac{1}{2} + 25$, it would have been necessary to have multiplied $3\frac{1}{2}$ by 7 before dividing $24\frac{1}{2}$, since the sign of multiplication takes the precedence, and the final result would have been $3\frac{1}{2} \times 7 = 24\frac{1}{2}$; $24\frac{1}{2} \div 24\frac{1}{2} = 1$; $268 - 1 = 267$; $267 + 25 = 292$. Ans.

It likewise follows that if a succession of multiplication and division signs occur, the indicated operations must not be performed in order, from left to right—the multiplication must be performed first. Thus, $24 \times 3 \div 4 \times 2 \div 9 \times 5 = \frac{1}{5}$. Ans. In order to obtain the same result that would be obtained by performing the indicated operations in order, from left to right, symbols of aggregation must be used. Thus, by using two vinculums the last expression becomes $24 \times \overline{3 \div 4} \times \overline{2 \div 9} \times 5 = 20$, the same result that would be obtained by performing the indicated operations in order, from left to right.

EXAMPLES FOR PRACTICE.

181. Find the values of the following expressions:

(a)	$(8 + 5 - 1) \div 4$.		(a)	3.
(b)	$5 \times 24 - 32$.		(b)	88.
(c)	$5 \times 24 \div 15$.		(c)	8.
(d)	$144 - 5 \times 24$.		(d)	24.
(e)	$(1,691 - 540 + 559) \div 3 \times 57$.	Ans.	(e)	10.
(f)	$2,080 + 120 - 80 \times 4 - 1,670$.		(f)	210.
(g)	$\overline{(90 + 60 \div 25)} \times 5 - 29$.		(g)	1.
(h)	$\overline{90 + 60} \div 25 \times 5$.		(h)	1.2.

ARITHMETIC.

(SECTION 4.)

PERCENTAGE.

1. **Percentage** is the process of calculating by *hundredths*.

2. The *term* **per cent.** is an abbreviation of the Latin words *per centum*, which mean *by the hundred*. A certain per cent. of a number is the number of hundredths of that number which is indicated by the number of units in the per cent. Thus, 6 per cent. of 125 is $125 \times \frac{6}{100} = 7.5$; 25 per cent. of 80 is $80 \times \frac{25}{100} = 20$; 43 per cent. of 432 pounds is $432 \times \frac{43}{100} = 185.76$ pounds.

3. The **sign** of per cent. is %, and is read *per cent.* Thus, 6% is read *six per cent.;* $12\frac{1}{2}$% is read *twelve and one-half per cent.*, etc.

When expressing the per cent. of a number to use in calculations, it is customary to express it decimally instead of fractionally. Thus, instead of expressing 6%, 25%, and 43% as $\frac{6}{100}$, $\frac{25}{100}$, and $\frac{43}{100}$, it is usual to express them as .06, .25, and .43.

The following table will show how any per cent. can be expressed either as a decimal or as a fraction:

Per Cent.	Decimal.	Fraction.	Per Cent.	Decimal.	Fraction.
1%.........	.01	$\frac{1}{100}$	150%........	1.50	$\frac{150}{100}$ or $1\frac{1}{2}$
2%.........	.02	$\frac{2}{100}$ or $\frac{1}{50}$	500%........	5.00	$\frac{500}{100}$ or 5
5%.........	.05	$\frac{5}{100}$ or $\frac{1}{20}$	$\frac{1}{4}$%........	.0025	$\frac{1}{100}$ or $\frac{1}{400}$
10%.........	.10	$\frac{10}{100}$ or $\frac{1}{10}$	$\frac{1}{2}$%........	.005	$\frac{1}{100}$ or $\frac{1}{200}$
25%.........	.25	$\frac{25}{100}$ or $\frac{1}{4}$	$1\frac{1}{2}$%........	.015	$\frac{1\frac{1}{2}}{100}$ or $\frac{3}{200}$
50%.........	.50	$\frac{50}{100}$ or $\frac{1}{2}$	$8\frac{1}{3}$%........	$.08\frac{1}{3}$	$\frac{8\frac{1}{3}}{100}$ or $\frac{1}{12}$
75%.........	.75	$\frac{75}{100}$ or $\frac{3}{4}$	$12\frac{1}{2}$%........	.125	$\frac{12\frac{1}{2}}{100}$ or $\frac{1}{8}$
100%.........	1.00	$\frac{100}{100}$ or 1	$16\frac{2}{3}$%........	$.16\frac{2}{3}$	$\frac{16\frac{2}{3}}{100}$ or $\frac{1}{6}$
125%.........	1.25	$\frac{125}{100}$ or $1\frac{1}{4}$	$62\frac{1}{2}$%........	.625	$\frac{62\frac{1}{2}}{100}$ or $\frac{5}{8}$

4. The names of the different elements used in percentage are: the *base*, the *rate per cent.*, the *percentage*, the *amount*, and the *difference*.

5. The **base** is the number on which the per cent. is computed.

6. The **rate** is the number of hundredths of the base to be taken.

7. The **percentage** is the part, or number of *hundredths*, of the base indicated by the rate; or, the percentage is the result obtained by multiplying the base by the rate.

Thus, when it is stated that 7% of $25 is $1.75, $25 is the base, 7% is the rate, and $1.75 is the percentage.

8. The **amount** is the sum of the base and percentage.

9. The **difference** is the remainder obtained by subtracting the percentage from the base.

Thus, if a man has $180, and he earns 6% more, he will have altogether $180 + $180 × .06, or $180 + $10.80 = $190.80. Here $180 is the base; 6%, the rate; $10.80, the percentage; and $190.80, the *amount*.

Again, if an engine of 125 horsepower uses 16% of it in overcoming friction and other resistances, the amount left for obtaining useful work is 125 − 125 × .16 = 125 − 20 = 105 horsepower. Here 125 is the base; 16%, the rate; 20, the percentage; and 105, the *difference*.

10. From the foregoing it is evident that to find the percentage, the base must be multiplied by the rate. Hence, the following

Rule.—*To find the percentage, multiply the base by the rate expressed decimally.*

EXAMPLE.—Out of a lot of 300 bushels of apples 76% were sold. How many bushels were sold?

SOLUTION.— 76%, the rate, expressed decimally, is .76; the base is 300; hence, the number of bushels sold, or the percentage, is, by the above rule,

$$300 \times .76 = 228 \text{ bushels. Ans.}$$

Expressing the rule as a

Formula, *percentage = base × rate.*

11. When the percentage and rate are given, the base may be found by dividing the percentage by the rate. For, suppose that 12 is 6%, or $\frac{6}{100}$, of some number; then 1%, or $\frac{1}{100}$, of the number, is $12 \div 6$, or 2. Consequently, if $2 = 1\%$, or $\frac{1}{100}$, 100%, or $\frac{100}{100} = 2 \times 100 = 200$. But, since the same result may be arrived at by dividing 12 by .06, for $12 \div .06 = 200$, it follows that:

Rule.—*When the percentage and rate are given, to find the base, divide the percentage by the rate expressed decimally.*

Formula, base = percentage ÷ rate.

EXAMPLE.—Bought a certain number of bushels of apples and sold 76% of them. If I sold 228 bushels, how many bushels did I buy?

SOLUTION.—Here 228 is the percentage, and 76%, or .76, is the rate; hence, applying the rule,

$228 \div .76 = 300$ bushels. Ans.

12. When the base and percentage are given, to find the rate, the rate may be found, expressed decimally, by dividing the percentage by the base. For, suppose that it is desired to find what per cent. 12 is of 200. 1% of 200 is $200 \times .01 = 2$. Now, if 1% is 2, 12 is evidently as many per cent. as the number of times that 2 is contained in 12, or $12 \div 2 = 6\%$. But the same result may be obtained by dividing 12, the percentage, by 200, the base, since $12 \div 200 = .06 = 6\%$. Hence,

Rule.—*When the percentage and base are given, to find the rate, divide the percentage by the base, and the result will be the rate expressed decimally.*

Formula, rate = percentage ÷ base.

EXAMPLE.—Bought 300 bushels of apples and sold 228 bushels. What per cent. of the total number of bushels was sold?

SOLUTION.—Here 300 is the base and 228 is the percentage; hence, applying rule,   rate $= 228 \div 300 = .76 = 76\%$. Ans.

EXAMPLE.—What per cent. of 875 is 25?

SOLUTION.—Here 875 is the base, and 25 is the percentage; hence, applying rule, $25 \div 875 = .02\frac{6}{7} = 2\frac{6}{7}\%$. Ans.

PROOF.— $875 \times .02\frac{6}{7} = 25$.

13. What per cent. of:

(a)	360 is 90 ?		(a)	25%.
(b)	900 is 360 ?		(b)	40%.
(c)	125 is 25 ?		(c)	20%.
(d)	150 is 750 ?	Ans.	(d)	500%.
(e)	280 is 112 ?		(e)	40%.
(f)	400 is 200 ?		(f)	50%.
(g)	47 is 94 ?		(g)	200%.
(h)	500 is 250 ?		(h)	50%.

14. The amount may be found, when the base and rate are given, by multiplying the base by 1 plus the rate, expressed decimally. For, suppose that it is desired to find the amount when 200 is the base and 6% is the rate. The percentage is $200 \times .06 = 12$, and, according to definition, Art. **8,** the amount is $200 + 12 = 212$. But, the same result may be obtained by multiplying 200 by $1 + .06$, or 1.06, since $200 \times 1.06 = 212$. Hence,

Rule.—*When the base and rate are given, to find the amount, multiply the base by 1 plus the rate expressed decimally.*

Formula, *amount* $= base \times (1 + rate)$.

EXAMPLE.—If a man earned $725 in a year, and the next year 10% more, how much did he earn the second year?

SOLUTION.—Here 725 is the base and 10% is the rate, and the amount is required. Hence, applying the rule,

$$725 \times 1.10 = \$797.50. \text{ Ans.}$$

15. When the base and rate are given, the difference may be found by multiplying the base by 1 minus the rate expressed decimally. For, suppose that it is desired to find the difference when the base is 200 and the rate is 6%. The percentage is $200 \times .06 = 12$; and, according to definition, Art. **9,** the difference $= 200 - 12 = 188$. But, the same result may be obtained by multiplying 200 by $1 - .06$, or .94, since $200 \times .94 = 188$. Hence,

Rule.—*When the base and rate are given, to find the difference, multiply the base by 1 minus the rate expressed decimally.*

Formula, *difference* $= base \times (1 - rate)$.

EXAMPLE.—Bought 300 bushels of apples and sold all but 24% of them. How many bushels were sold?

SOLUTION.—Here 300 is the base, 24% is the rate, and it is desired to find the difference. Hence, applying the rule,

$$300 \times (1 - .24) = 228 \text{ bushels. Ans.}$$

16. When the amount and rate are given, the base may be found by dividing the amount by 1 plus the rate. For, suppose that it is known that 212 equals some number increased by 6% of itself. Then, it is evident that 212 equals 106% of the number (base) that it is desired to find. Consequently, if $212 = 106\%$, $1\% = \frac{212}{106} \doteq 2$, and $100\% = 2 \times 100 = 200 =$ the base. But the same result may be obtained by dividing 212 by $1 + .06$, or 1.06, since $212 \div 1.06 = 200$. Hence,

Rule.—*When the amount and rate are given, to find the base, divide the amount by 1 plus the rate expressed decimally.*

Formula, *base* = *amount* ÷ (1 + *rate*).

EXAMPLE.—The theoretical discharge of a certain pump when running at a piston speed of 100 feet per minute is 278,910 gallons per day of 10 hours. Owing to leakage and other defects, this value is 25% greater than the actual discharge. What is the actual discharge?

SOLUTION.—Here 278,910 equals the actual discharge (base) increased by 25% of itself. Consequently, 278,910 is the amount, and 25% is the rate. Applying rule,

actual discharge = $278,910 \div 1.25 = 223,128$ gallons. Ans.

17. When the difference and rate are given, the base may be found by dividing the difference by 1 minus the rate. For, suppose that 188 equals some number less 6% of itself. Then, 188 evidently equals $100 - 6 = 94\%$ of some number. Consequently, if $188 = 94\%$, $1\% = 188 \div 94 = 2$, and $100\% = 2 \times 100 = 200$. But the same result may be obtained by dividing 188 by $1 - .06$, or $.94$, since $188 \div .94 = 200$. Hence,

Rule.—*When the difference and rate are given, to find the base, divide the difference by 1 minus the rate expressed decimally.*

Formula, *base* = *difference* ÷ (1 − *rate*).

EXAMPLE.—Bought a certain number of bushels of apples and sold 76% of them. If there were 72 bushels left unsold, how many bushels did I buy?

SOLUTION.—Here 72 is the difference and 76% is the rate. Applying rule,
$$72 \div (1 - .76) = 300 \text{ bushels. Ans.}$$

EXAMPLE.—The theoretical number of foot-pounds of work per minute required to operate a boiler feed-pump is 127,344. If 30% of the total number actually required be allowed for friction, leakage, etc., how many foot-pounds are actually required to work the pump?

SOLUTION.—Here the number actually required is the base; hence, 127,344 is the difference, and 30% is the rate. Applying the rule,
$$127,344 \div (1 - .30) = 181,920 \text{ foot-pounds. Ans.}$$

18. EXAMPLE.—A certain chimney gives a draft of 2.76 inches of water. By increasing the height 20 feet, the draft was increased to 3 inches of water. What was the gain per cent.?

SOLUTION.—Here it is evident that 3 inches is the amount, and that 2.76 inches is the base. Consequently, $3 - 2.76 = .24$ inch is the percentage, and it is required to find the rate. Hence, applying the rule given in Art. **12,**
$$\text{gain per cent.} = .24 \div 2.76 = .087 = 8.7\%. \text{ Ans.}$$

19. EXAMPLE.—A certain chimney gave a draft of 3 inches of water. After an economizer had been put in, the draft was reduced to 1.2 inches of water. What was the loss per cent.?

SOLUTION.—Here it is evident that 1.2 inches is the difference (since it equals 3 inches diminished by a certain per cent. loss of itself), and 3 inches is the base. Consequently, $3 - 1.2 = 1.8$ inches is the percentage. Hence, applying the rule given in Art. **12,**
$$\text{loss per cent.} = 1.8 \div 3 = .60 = 60\%. \text{ Ans.}$$

20. To find the gain or loss per cent. :

Rule.—*Find the difference between the initial and the final value; divide this difference by the initial value.*

EXAMPLE.—If a man buys a house for $1,860, and some time afterwards builds a barn for 25% of the cost of the house, does he gain or lose, and how much per cent., if he sells both house and barn for $2,100?

SOLUTION.—The cost of the barn was $1,860 $\times$ .25 = $465; consequently, the initial value, or total cost, was $1,860 + $465 = $2,325. Since he sold them for $2,100 he lost $2,325 - $2,100 = $225. Hence, applying rule,
$$225 \div 2,325 = .0968 = 9.68\% \text{ loss. Ans.}$$

EXAMPLES FOR PRACTICE.

21. Solve the following :

(a)   What is $12\frac{1}{2}\%$ of \$900 ?

(b)   What is $\frac{4}{5}\%$ of 627 ?

(c)   What is $33\frac{1}{3}\%$ of 54 ?

(d)   101 is $68\frac{3}{4}\%$ of what number ?

(e)   784 is $83\frac{1}{3}\%$ of what number ?

(f)   What % of 960 is 160 ?

(g)   What % of \$3,606 is \$450$\frac{3}{4}$?

(h)   What % of 280 is 112 ?

Ans.
(a) \$112.50.
(b) 5.016.
(c) 18.
(d) $146\frac{10}{11}$.
(e) 940.8.
(f) $16\frac{2}{3}\%$.
(g) $12\frac{1}{2}\%$.
(h) 40%.

1. A steam plant consumed an average of 3,640 pounds of coal per day. The engineer made certain alterations which resulted in a saving of 250 pounds per day. What was the per cent. of coal saved ?
Ans. 7%, nearly.

2. If the speed of an engine running at 126 revolutions per minute should be increased $6\frac{1}{2}\%$, how many revolutions per minute would it then make ?
Ans. 134.19 rev.

3. The list price of a lot of silk goods is \$1,400, of some laces \$1,150, and of some calico \$340. If 25% discount was allowed on the silk, 22% on the laces, and $12\frac{1}{2}\%$ on the calico, what was the actual cost of the purchase ?
Ans. \$2,244.50.

4. If I loan a man \$1,100, and this is $18\frac{1}{2}\%$ of the amount that I have on interest, how much money have I on interest ?
Ans. \$5,945.95.

5. A test showed that an engine developed 190.4 horsepower, 15% of which was consumed in friction. How much power was available for use ?
Ans. 161.84 H. P.

6. By adding a condenser to a steam engine, the power was increased 14% and the consumption of coal per horsepower per hour was decreased 20%. If the engine could originally develop 50 horsepower, and required $3\frac{1}{2}$ pounds of coal per horsepower per hour, what would be the total weight of coal used in an hour, with the condenser, assuming the engine to run full power ?
Ans. 159.6 pounds.

DENOMINATE NUMBERS.

22. A **denominate number** is a concrete number, and may be either simple or compound; as, 8 quarts; 5 feet; 10 inches, etc.

23. A **simple denominate number** consists of units of but one denomination; as, 16 cents; 10 hours; 5 dollars, etc.

24. A **compound denominate number** consists of units of two or more denominations of a similar kind; as, 3 yards, 2 feet, 1 inch; 34 square feet, 57 square inches.

25. In **whole numbers** and in **decimals** the law of increase and decrease is on the scale of 10, but in **compound** or **denominate numbers** the scale varies.

26. A **measure** is a *standard unit*, established by *law* or *custom*, by which quantity of any kind is measured. The standard unit of **dry measure** is the Winchester bushel; of **weight,** the pound; of **liquid measure,** the gallon, etc.

27. Measures are of six kinds:

1. Extension.	4. Time.
2. Weight.	5. Angles.
3. Capacity.	6. Money or value.

MEASURES OF EXTENSION.

28. **Measures of extension** are used in measuring lengths, distances, surfaces, and solids.

LINEAR MEASURE.

TABLE.
Abbreviation.

12 inches (in.) = 1 foot . . ft.	in.	ft.	yd.	rd.	fur.	mi.
3 feet . . . = 1 yard . yd.	36 =	3	= 1			
5.5 yards . . = 1 rod . . rd.	198 =	16½	= 5.5	= 1		
40 rods . . . = 1 furlong fur.	7,920 =	660	= 220	= 40	= 1	
8 furlongs . = 1 mile . mi.	63,360 =	5,280	= 1,760	= 320	= 8	= 1

SURVEYOR'S LINEAR MEASURE.

TABLE.

7.92 inches	= 1 link . . . . . li.
25 links	= 1 rod . . . . . rd.
4 rods } 100 links }	= 1 chain . . . . ch.
80 chains	= 1 mile . . . . . mi.

mi.		ch.		rd.		li.		in.
1	=	80	=	320	=	8,000	=	63,360

29. The linear unit, generally used by surveyors, is **Gunter's chain,** which is equal to 4 rods, or 66 feet.

30. An **engineer's chain,** used by civil engineers, is 100 feet long, and consists of 100 links. In computations, the links are written as so many hundredths of a chain.

SQUARE MEASURE.

TABLE.

144	square inches (sq. in.) . . . =	1 square foot . . . . sq. ft.
9	square feet . . . . =	1 square yard . . . . sq. yd.
30¼	square yards . . . . . . =	1 square rod . . . . sq. rd.
160	square rods . . . . =	1 acre . . . . A.
640	acres . . . . =	1 square mile . . . . sq. mi.

sq. mi.   A.   sq. rd.   sq. yd.   sq. ft.   sq. in.

1 = 640 = 102,400 = 3,097,600 = 27,878,400 = 4,014,489,600

SURVEYOR'S SQUARE MEASURE.

TABLE.

625	square links (sq. li.) . . . . =	1 square rod . . . . sq. rd.
16	square rods . . . . =	1 square chain . . . sq. ch.
10	square chains . . . . . . =	1 acre . . . . A.
640	acres . . . . =	1 square mile . . . . sq. mi.
36	square miles (6 mi. square) . . =	1 township . . . . . . Tp.

sq. mi.   A.   sq. ch.   sq. rd.   sq. li.

1 = 640 = 6,400 = 102,400 = 64,000,000

CUBIC MEASURE.

TABLE.

1,728	cubic inches (cu. in.) . . . =	1 cubic foot . . . . cu. ft.
27	cubic feet . . . . =	1 cubic yard . . . . cu. yd.
128	cubic feet . . . . =	1 cord . . . . cd.
24¾	cubic feet . . . . =	1 perch . . . . P.

cu. yd.   cu. ft.   cu. in.

1 = 27 = 46,656

MEASURES OF WEIGHT.
AVOIRDUPOIS WEIGHT.

TABLE.

16	ounces (oz.) . . . . =	1 pound . . . . lb.
100	pounds . . . . =	1 hundredweight . . . cwt.
20	cwt., or 2,000 lb. . . . . =	1 ton . . . . T.

T.   cwt.   lb.   oz.

1 = 20 = 2,000 = 32,000

31. The ounce is divided into halves, quarters, etc. Avoirdupois weight is used for weighing coarse and heavy articles. One avoirdupois pound contains 7,000 grains.

LONG TON TABLE.

16 ounces . . . . = 1 pound . . . . lb.
112 pounds . . . . = 1 hundredweight . . . cwt.
20 cwt., or 2,240 lb. . . . . . = 1 ton . . . . T.

32. In all the calculations throughout this and the following sections, 2,000 pounds will be considered 1 ton, unless the long ton (2,240 pounds) is especially mentioned.

TROY WEIGHT.

TABLE.

24 grains (gr.) . . . . = 1 pennyweight . . . . pwt.
20 pennyweights . . . . = 1 ounce . . . . oz.
12 ounces . . . . = 1 pound . . . . lb.

lb.	oz.	pwt.	gr.
1 =	12 =	240 =	5,760

33. Troy weight is used in weighing gold and silverware, jewels, etc. It is used by jewelers.

MEASURES OF CAPACITY.

LIQUID MEASURE.

TABLE.

4 gills (gi.) . . . . = 1 pint . . . . pt.
2 pints . . . . = 1 quart . . . . qt.
4 quarts . . . . = 1 gallon . . . . gal.
31½ gallons . . . . = 1 barrel . . . . bbl.
2 barrels, or 63 gallons . . . . = 1 hogshead . . . . . hhd.

hhd.	bbl.	gal.	qt.	pt.	gi.
1 =	2 =	63 =	252 =	504 =	2,016

DRY MEASURE.

TABLE.

2 pints (pt.). . . . . = 1 quart . . . . qt.
8 quarts . . . . = 1 peck . . . . pk.
4 pecks . . . . = 1 bushel . . . . bu.

bu.	pk.	qt.	pt.
1 =	4 =	32 =	64

MEASURE OF TIME.

TABLE.

60 seconds (sec.)	= 1 minute	min.
60 minutes	= 1 hour	hr.
24 hours	= 1 day	da.
7 days.	= 1 week	wk.
365 days } 12 months }	= 1 common year	yr.
366 days	= 1 leap year.	
100 years	= 1 century.	

NOTE.—It is customary to consider one month as 30 days.

MEASURE OF ANGLES OR ARCS.

TABLE.

60 seconds (″)	= 1 minute	′
60 minutes	= 1 degree	°
90 degrees	= 1 right angle or quadrant	∟.
360 degrees	= 1 circle	cir.

1 cir. $= 360° = 21,600' = 1,296,000''$

MEASURE OF MONEY.

UNITED STATES MONEY.

TABLE.

10 mills (m.)	= 1 cent	ct.
10 cents	= 1 dime	d.
10 dimes	= 1 dollar	$.
10 dollars	= 1 eagle	E.

E.	$	d.	ct.	m.
1	= 10	= 100	= 1,000	= 10,000

MISCELLANEOUS TABLE.

12 things are 1 dozen.	1 meter is nearly 39.37 inches.
12 dozen are 1 gross.	1 hand is 4 inches.
12 gross are 1 great gross.	1 palm is 3 inches.
2 things are 1 pair.	1 span is 9 inches.
20 things are 1 score.	24 sheets are 1 quire.
1 league is 3 miles.	20 quires, or 480 sheets, are 1 ream.
1 fathom is 6 feet.	1 bushel contains 2,150.4 cubic in.

1 U. S. standard gallon (also called a wine gallon) contains 231 cubic in.
1 U. S. standard gallon of water weighs 8.355 pounds, nearly.
1 cubic foot of water contains 7.481 U. S. standard gallons, nearly.
1 British imperial gallon weighs 10 pounds.

It will be of great advantage to the student to carefully memorize all the above tables.

40—6

REDUCTION OF DENOMINATE NUMBERS.

34. **Reduction** of denominate numbers is the process of changing their denomination without changing their value. They may be changed from a higher to a lower denomination, or from a lower to a higher—either is reduction. As

$$2 \text{ hours} = 120 \text{ minutes.}$$
$$32 \text{ ounces} = 2 \text{ pounds.}$$

35. **Principle.**—Denominate numbers are changed to lower denominations by *multiplying*, and to higher denominations by *dividing*.

To reduce denominate numbers to lower denominations :

36. EXAMPLE.—Reduce 5 yd. 2 ft. 7 in. to inches.

SOLUTION.—

yd.	ft.	in.
5	2	7

```
            yd.      ft.      in.
             5        2        7
             3
           ————
           1 5 ft.
             2 ft.
           ————
           1 7 ft.
           1 2
           ————
           3 4
         1 7
         ————
         2 0 4 in.
             7 in.
         ————
         2 1 1 inches.   Ans.
```

EXPLANATION.—Since there are 3 feet in 1 yard, in 5 yards there are 5×3 or 15 feet, and 15 feet plus 2 feet = 17 feet. There are 12 inches in a foot; therefore, $12 \times 17 = 204$ inches, and 204 inches plus 7 inches = 211 inches = number of inches in 5 yards 2 feet and 7 inches.

37. EXAMPLE.—Reduce 6 hours to seconds.

SOLUTION.—

```
             6      hours.
           6 0
         ————
         3 6 0      minutes.
             6 0
         ————
       2 1 6 0 0    seconds.   Ans.
```

EXPLANATION.—As there are 60 minutes in 1 hour, in 6 hours there are 6×60, or 360, minutes; as there are no minutes to add, we multiply 360 minutes by 60, to get the number of seconds.

38. In order to avoid mistakes, if any denomination be omitted, represent it by a cipher. Thus, before reducing 3 rods 6 inches to inches, insert a cipher for yards and a cipher for feet, as

rd.	yd.	ft.	in.
3	0	0	6

39. Rule.—*Multiply the number representing the highest denomination by the number of units in the next lower required to make one of the higher denomination, and to the product add the number of given units of that lower denomination. Proceed in this manner until the number is reduced to the required denomination.*

EXAMPLES FOR PRACTICE.

40. Reduce:

(a) 4 rd. 2 yd. 2 ft. to ft.
(b) 4 bu. 3 pk. 2 qt. to qt.
(c) 13 rd. 5 yd. 2 ft. to ft.
(d) 5 mi. 100 rd. 10 ft. to ft.
(e) 8 lb. 4 oz. 6 pwt. to gr.
(f) 52 hhd. 24 gal. 1 pt. to pt.
(g) 5 cir. 16° 20′ to minutes.
(h) 14 bu. to qt.

Ans.
(a) 74 ft.
(b) 154 qt.
(c) 231.5 ft.
(d) 28,060 ft.
(e) 48,144 gr.
(f) 26,401 pt.
(g) 108,980′.
(h) 448 qt.

To reduce lower to higher denominations:

41. EXAMPLE.—Reduce 211 inches to higher denominations.

SOLUTION.—

$$12) 2\,1\,1 \text{ in.}$$
$$\overline{ 3) 1\,7 \text{ ft.} + 7 \text{ in.}}$$
$$\overline{ 5 \text{ yd.} + 2 \text{ ft.}} \text{ Ans.}$$

EXPLANATION.—There are 12 inches in 1 foot; therefore, 211 divided by 12 = 17 feet and 7 inches over. There are 3 feet in 1 yard; therefore, 17 feet divided by 3 = 5 yards and 2 feet over. The last quotient and the two remainders constitute the answer, 5 yards 2 feet 7 inches.

42. EXAMPLE.—Reduce 15,735 grains Troy weight to higher denominations.

SOLUTION.—

$$
\begin{array}{r}
24\,)\,1\,5\,7\,3\,5 \text{ gr.}\;(\,6\,5\,5 \text{ pwt.}\\
\underline{1\,4\,4}\\
1\,3\,3\\
\underline{1\,2\,0}\\
1\,3\,5\\
\underline{1\,2\,0}\\
1\,5 \text{ gr.}
\end{array}
$$

$$
\begin{array}{r}
2\,0\,)\,6\,5\,5 \text{ pwt.}\;(\,3\,2 \text{ oz.}\\
\underline{6\,0}\\
5\,5\\
\underline{4\,0}\\
1\,5 \text{ pwt.}
\end{array}
$$

$$
\begin{array}{r}
1\,2\,)\,3\,2 \text{ oz.}\;(\,2 \text{ lb.}\\
\underline{2\,4}\\
8 \text{ oz.}
\end{array}
$$

EXPLANATION.—There are 24 grains in 1 pennyweight, and in 15,735 grains there are as many pennyweights as 24 is contained in 15,735, or 655 pennyweights and 15 grains remaining. There are 20 pennyweights in 1 ounce, and in 655 pennyweights there are 32 ounces and 15 pennyweights remaining. There are 12 ounces in 1 pound, and in 32 ounces there are 2 pounds and 8 ounces remaining. The last quotient and the three remainders constitute the answer, 2 pounds 8 ounces 15 pennyweights 15 grains.

The above problem is worked out by long division, because the numbers are too large to solve easily by short division. The student may use either method.

43. **Rule.**—*Divide the number representing the denomination given by the number of units of this denomination required to make one unit of the next higher denomination. The remainder will be of the same denomination, but the quotient will be of the next higher. Divide this quotient by the number of units of its denomination required to make one unit of the next higher. Continue until the highest* *denomination is reached, or until there is not enough of a denomination left to make one of the next higher. The last quotient and the remainders constitute the required result.*

EXAMPLES FOR PRACTICE.

44.   Reduce to units of higher denominations:

(*a*) 7,460 sq. in.;   (*b*) 7,580 sq. yd.;   (*c*) 148,760 cu. in.;   (*d*) 7,896 cu. ft. to cd.;   (*e*) 17,651″;   (*f*) 1,120 cu. ft. to cd.;   (*g*) 8,000 gi.;   (*h*) 36,450 lb.

Ans.
- (*a*)   5 sq. yd. 6 sq. ft. 116 sq. in.
- (*b*)   1 A. 90 sq. rd. 17 sq. yd. 4 sq. ft. 72 sq. in.
- (*c*)   3 cu. yd. 5 cu. ft. 152 cu. in.
- (*d*)   61 cd. 88 cu. ft.
- (*e*)   4° 54′ 11″.
- (*f*)   8 cd. 96 cu. ft.
- (*g*)   3 hhd. 61 gal.
- (*h*)   18 T. 4 cwt. 50 lb.

ADDITION OF DENOMINATE NUMBERS.

45.   EXAMPLE.—Find the sum of 3 cwt. 46 lb. 12 oz.;   8 cwt. 12 lb. 13 oz.; 12 cwt. 50 lb. 13 oz.; 27 lb. 4 oz.

SOLUTION.—

T.	cwt.	lb.	oz.
0	3	46	12
0	8	12	13
0	12	50	13
0	0	27	4
1	4	37	10 Ans.

EXPLANATION.—Begin to add at the right-hand column: $4 + 13 + 13 + 12 = 42$ ounces; as 16 ounces make 1 pound, 42 ounces $\div 16 = 2$ and a remainder of 10 ounces, or 2 pounds and 10 ounces. Place 10 ounces under ounce column and add 2 pounds to the next or pound column. Then, $2 + 27 + 50 + 12 + 46 = 137$ pounds; as 100 pounds make a hundredweight, $137 \div 100 = 1$ hundredweight and a remainder of 37 pounds. Place the 37 under the pounds column, and add 1 hundredweight to the next or hundredweight column. Next, $1 + 12 + 8 + 3 = 24$ hundredweight.

20 hundredweight make a ton; therefore $24 \div 20 = 1$ ton and 4 hundredweight remaining.   Hence, the sum is 1 ton 4 hundredweight 37 pounds 10 ounces.   Ans.

46.   EXAMPLE.—What is the sum of 2 rd. 3 yd. 2 ft. 5 in.; 6 rd. 1 ft. 10 in.; 17 rd. 11 in.; 4 yd. 1 ft.?

SOLUTION.—	rd.	yd.	ft.	in.
	2	3	2	5
	6	0	1	10
	17	0	0	11
	0	4	1	0
	26	$3\frac{1}{2}$	0	2
or	26	3	1	8 Ans.

EXPLANATION.—The sum of the numbers in the first column = 26 inches, or 2 feet and 2 inches remaining.   The sum of the numbers in the next column, plus 2 feet = 6 feet, or 2 yards and 0 feet remaining.   The sum of the next column plus 2 yards = 9 yards, or $9 \div 5\frac{1}{2} = 1$ rod and $3\frac{1}{2}$ yards remaining.   The sum of the next column plus 1 rod = 26 rods.   To avoid fractions in the sum, the $\frac{1}{2}$ yard is reduced to 1 foot and 6 inches, which added to 26 rods 3 yards 0 feet and 2 inches = 26 rods 3 yards 1 foot 8 inches.   Ans.

47.   EXAMPLE.—What is the sum of 47 ft. and 3 rd. 2 yd. 2 ft. 10 in.?

SOLUTION.—When 47 ft. is reduced it equals 2 rd. 4 yd. 2 ft. which can be added to 3 rd. 2 yd. 2 ft. 10 in.   Thus,

	rd.	yd.	ft.	in.
	3	2	2	10
	2	4	2	0
	6	$1\frac{1}{2}$	1	10
or	6	2	0	4 Ans.

48.   **Rule.**—*Place the numbers so that like denominations are under each other.   Begin at the right-hand column, and add.   Divide the sum by the number of units of this denomination required to make one unit of the next higher.   Place the remainder under the column added, and carry the quotient to the next column.   Continue in this manner until the highest denomination given is reached.*

EXAMPLES FOR PRACTICE.

49. What is the sum of:

(*a*) 25 lb. 7 oz. 15 pwt. 23 gr.; 17 lb. 16 pwt.; 15 lb. 4 oz. 12 pwt.; 18 lb. 16 gr.; 10 lb. 2 oz. 11 pwt. 16 gr.?

(*b*) 9 mi. 13 rd. 4 yd. 2 ft.; 16 rd. 5 yd. 1 ft. 5 in.; 16 mi. 2 rd. 3 in.; 14 rd. 1 yd. 9 in.?

(*c*) 3 cwt. 46 lb. 12 oz.; 12 cwt. 9½ lb.; 2¼ cwt. 21⅝ lb.?

(*d*) 10 yr. 8 mo. 5 wk. 3 da.; 42 yr. 6 mo. 7 da.; 7 yr. 5 mo. 18 wk. 4 da.; 17 yr. 17 da.?

(*e*) 17 T. 11 cwt. 49 lb. 14 oz.; 16 T. 47 lb. 13 oz.; 20 T. 13 cwt. 14 lb. 6 oz.; 11 T. 4 cwt. 16 lb. 12 oz.?

(*f*) 14 sq. yd. 8 sq. ft. 19 sq. in.; 105 sq. yd. 16 sq. ft. 240 sq. in.; 42 sq. yd. 28 sq. ft. 165 sq. in.?

Ans.
(*a*) 86 lb. 3 oz. 16 pwt. 7 gr.
(*b*) 25 mi. 47 rd. 1 ft. 5 in.
(*c*) 18 cwt. 2 lb. 14 oz.
(*d*) 78 yr. 1 mo. 3 wk. 3 da.
(*e*) 65 T. 9 cwt. 28 lb. 13 oz.
(*f*) 167 sq. yd. 136 sq. in.

SUBTRACTION OF DENOMINATE NUMBERS.

50. EXAMPLE.—From 21 rd. 2 yd. 2 ft. 6½ in. take 9 rd. 4 yd. 10¼ in.

SOLUTION.—

rd.	yd.	ft.	in.
21	2	2	6½
9	4	0	10¼
11	3½	1	8¼ Ans.

EXPLANATION.—Since 10¼ inches cannot be taken from 6½ inches, we must borrow 1 foot or 12 inches from the 2 feet in the next column and add it to the 6½. 6½ + 12 = 18½. 18½ inches − 10¼ inches = 8¼ inches. Then, 0 from the 1 remaining foot = 1 foot. 4 yards cannot be taken from 2 yards; therefore, we borrow 1 rod, or 5½ yards, from 21 rods and add it to 2. 2 + 5½ = 7½; 7½ − 4 = 3½ yards. 9 rods from 20 rods = 11 rods. Hence, the remainder is 11 rods 3½ yards 1 foot 8¼ inches. Ans.

To avoid fractions as much as possible, we reduce the ½ yard to inches, obtaining 18 inches; this added to 8¼ inches gives 26¼ inches, which equals 2 feet 2¼ inches. Then, 2 feet + 1 foot = 3 feet = 1 yard, and 3 yards + 1 yard = 4 yards. Hence, the above answer becomes 11 rods 4 yards 0 feet 2¼ inches.

51. EXAMPLE.—What is the difference between 3 rd. 2 yd. 2 ft. 10 in. and 47 ft. ?

SOLUTION.— 47 ft. = 2 rd. 4 yd. 2 ft.

rd.	yd.	ft.	in.
3	2	2	10
2	4	2	0
0	3½	0	10
or	3	2	4 Ans.

To find (approximately) the interval of time between two dates :

52. EXAMPLE.—How many years, months, days, and hours between 4 o'clock P. M. of June 16, 1868, and 10 o'clock A. M., September 29, 1891?

SOLUTION.—

yr.	mo.	da.	hr.
1891	8	28	10
1868	5	15	16
23	3	12	18 Ans.

EXPLANATION.—Counting 24 hours in 1 day, 4 o'clock P. M. is the 16th hour from the beginning of the day, or midnight. On September 29, 8 months and 28 days have elapsed, and on June 16, 5 months and 15 days. After placing the earlier date under the later date, subtract as in the previous problems. Count 30 days as 1 month.

53. Rule.—*Place the smaller quantity under the larger quantity, with like denominations under each other. Beginning at the right, subtract successively the number in the subtrahend in each denomination from the one above, and place the differences underneath. If the number in the minuend of any denomination is less than the number under it in the subtrahend, one must be borrowed from the minuend of the next higher denomination, reduced, and added to it.*

EXAMPLES FOR PRACTICE.

54. From :

(*a*)   125 lb. 8 oz. 14 pwt. 18 gr. take 96 lb. 9 oz. 10 pwt. 4 gr.

(*b*)   126 hhd. 27 gal. take 104 hhd. 14 gal. 1 qt. 1 pt.

(*c*)   65 T. 14 cwt. 64 lb. 10 oz. take 16 T. 11 cwt. 14 oz.

(*d*)   148 sq. yd. 16 sq. ft. 142 sq. in. take 132 sq. yd. 136 sq. in.

(e)   100 bu. take 28 bu. 2 pk. 5 qt. 1 pt.
(f)   14 mi. 34 rd. 16 yd. 13 ft. 11 in. take 3 mi. 27 rd. 11 yd. 4 ft. 10 in.

Ans.

(a)   28 lb. 11 oz. 4 pwt. 14 gr.
(b)   22 hhd. 12 gal. 2 qt. 1 pt.
(c)   49 T. 3 cwt. 63 lb. 12 oz.
(d)   16 sq. yd. 16 sq. ft. 6 sq. in.
(e)   71 bu. 1 pk. 2 qt. 1 pt.
(f)   11 mi. 7 rd. 5 yd. 9 ft. 1 in.

MULTIPLICATION OF DENOMINATE NUMBERS.

55.   EXAMPLE.—Multiply 7 lb. 5 oz. 13 pwt. 15 gr. by 12.

SOLUTION.—

lb.	oz.	pwt.	gr.
7	5	13	15
			12
89	8	3	12	Ans.

EXPLANATION.—   15 grains × 12 = 180 grains.   180 ÷ 24 = 7 pennyweights and 12 grains remaining.   Place the 12 in the grain column and carry the 7 pennyweights to the next.   Now, 13 × 12 + 7 = 163 pennyweights; 163 ÷ 20 = 8 ounces and 3 pennyweights remaining.   Then, 5 × 12 + 8 = 68 ounces; 68 ÷ 12 = 5 pounds and 8 ounces remaining. Then, 7 × 12 + 5 = 89 pounds.   The entire product is 89 pounds 8 ounces 3 pennyweights 12 grains.   Ans.

56. Rule.—*Multiply the number representing each denomination by the multiplier and reduce each product to the next higher denomination, writing the remainders under each denomination, and carry the quotient to the next, as in Addition of Denominate Numbers.*

57.   In multiplication and division of denominate numbers, it is sometimes easier to reduce the number to the lowest denomination given before multiplying or dividing, especially if the multiplier or divisor is a decimal.   Thus, in the example of Art. **55,** had the multiplier been 1.2, the easiest way to multiply would have been to reduce the number to grains; then, multiply by 1.2, and reduce the product to higher denominations.   For example, 7 lb. 5 oz. 13 pwt. 15 gr. = 43,047 gr.   43,047 × 1.2 = 51,656.4 gr. = 8 lb. 11 oz. 12 pwt. 8.4 gr.   Also, 43,047 × 12 = 516,564 gr. = 89 lb. 8 oz. 3 pwt. 12 gr., as above.   Either method may be used.

EXAMPLES FOR PRACTICE.

58. Multiply:

(*a*) 15 cwt. 90 lb. by 5; (*b*) 12 yr. 10 mo. 4 wk. 3 da. by 14; (*c*) 11 mi. 145 rd. by 20; (*d*) 12 gal. 4 pt. by 9; (*e*) 8 cd. 76 cu. ft. by 15; (*f*) 4 hhd. 3 gal. 1 qt. 1 pt. by 12.

Ans. $\begin{cases} (a) & 79 \text{ cwt. 50 lb.} \\ (b) & 180 \text{ yr. 11 mo. 2 wk.} \\ (c) & 229 \text{ mi. 20 rd.} \\ (d) & 112 \text{ gal. 2 qt.} \\ (e) & 128 \text{ cd. 116 cu. ft.} \\ (f) & 48 \text{ hhd. 40 gal. 2 qt.} \end{cases}$

DIVISION OF DENOMINATE NUMBERS.

59. EXAMPLE.—Divide 48 lb. 11 oz. 6 pwt. by 8.

SOLUTION.—

	lb.	oz.	pwt.	gr.
8)	48	11	6	0
	6 lb.	1 oz.	8 pwt.	6 gr. Ans.

EXPLANATION.—After placing the quantities as above, proceed as follows: 8 is contained in 48 six times without a remainder. 8 is contained in 11 ounces once, with 3 ounces remaining. $3 \times 20 = 60$; $60 + 6 = 66$ pennyweights; 66 pennyweights $\div 8 = 8$ pennyweights and 2 remaining; 2×24 grains $= 48$ grains; 48 grains $\div 8 = 6$ grains. Therefore, the entire quotient is 6 pounds 1 ounce 8 pennyweights 6 grains. Ans.

EXAMPLE.—A silversmith melted up 2 lb. 8 oz. 10 pwt. of silver, which he made into 6 spoons; what was the weight of each spoon?

SOLUTION.—

	lb.	oz.	pwt.
6)	2	8	10
	5 oz.	8 pwt.	8 gr. Ans.

EXPLANATION.—Since we cannot divide 2 pounds by 6, we reduce it to ounces. 2 pounds = 24 ounces, and 24 ounces + 8 ounces = 32 ounces; 32 ounces $\div 6 = 5$ ounces and 2 ounces over. 2 ounces = 40 pennyweights; 40 pennyweights + 10 pennyweights = 50 pennyweights, and 50 pennyweights $\div 6 = 8$ pennyweights and 2 pennyweights over. 2 pennyweights = 48 grains, and 48 grains $\div 6 = 8$ grains. Hence, each spoon contains 5 ounces 8 pennyweights 8 grains. Ans.

60. EXAMPLE.—Divide 820 rd. 4 yd. 2 ft. by 112.

                   rd. yd. ft. rd. yd. ft. in.

SOLUTION.—   112) 8 2 0 4 2 (7 1 2 5.143 **Ans.**

              7 8 4

               3 6 rd. rem.

               5.5

              1 8 0

           1 8 0

           1 9 8.0 yd.

               4

        112) 2 0 2 yd. (1 yd.

           1 1 2

            9 0 yd. rem.

             3

           2 7 0 ft.

             2 ft.

        112) 2 7 2 ft. (2 ft.

           2 2 4

            4 8 ft. rem.

            1 2

            9 6

          4 8

        112) 5 7 6 in. (5.1 4 2 8+ in. or 5.143 in.

           5 6 0

            1 6 0

            1 1 2

             4 8 0

             4 4 8

              3 2 0

              2 2 4

               9 6 0

               8 9 6

                6 4

EXPLANATION.—The first quotient is 7 rods with 36 rods remaining. $5.5 \times 36 = 198$ yards; 198 yards + 4 yards = 202 yards; 202 yards ÷ 112 = 1 yard and 90 yards remaining. $90 \times 3 = 270$ feet; 270 feet + 2 feet = 272 feet; 272 feet ÷ 112 = 2 feet, and 48 feet remaining; $48 \times 12 = 576$ inches; 576 inches ÷ 112 = 5.143 inches, nearly. Ans.

The preceding example is solved by long division, because

the numbers are too large to deal with mentally. Instead of expressing the last result as a decimal, it might have been expressed as a common fraction. Thus, $576 \div 112 = 5\frac{16}{112} = 5\frac{1}{7}$ inches. The chief advantage of using a common fraction is that if the quotient be multiplied by the divisor, the result will always be the same as the original dividend.

61. Rule.—*Find how many times the divisor is contained in the first or highest denomination of the dividend. Reduce the remainder (if any) to the next lower denomination, and add to it the number in the given dividend expressing that denomination. Divide this new dividend by the divisor. The quotient will be the next denomination in the quotient required. Continue in this manner until the lowest denomination is reached. The successive quotients will constitute the entire quotient.*

EXAMPLES FOR PRACTICE.

62. Divide:

(*a*) 376 mi. 276 rd. by 22; (*b*) 1,137 bu. 3 pk. 4 qt. 1 pt. by 10; (*c*) 84 cwt. 48 lb. 49 oz. by 16; (*d*) 78 sq. yd. 18 sq. ft. 41 sq. in. by 18; (*e*) 148 mi. 64 rd. 24 yd. by 12; (*f*) 100 T. 16 cwt. 18 lb. 11 oz. by 15; (*g*) 36 lb. 18 oz. 18 pwt. 14 gr. by 8; (*h*) 112 mi. 48 rd. by 100.

Ans.
- (*a*) 17 mi. $41\frac{7}{11}$ rd.
- (*b*) 113 bu. 3 pk. 1 qt. $\frac{1}{2}$ pt.
- (*c*) 5 cwt. 28 lb. $3\frac{1}{16}$ oz.
- (*d*) 4 sq. yd. 4 sq. ft. $2\frac{5}{18}$ sq. in.
- (*e*) 12 mi. 112 rd. 2 yd.
- (*f*) 6 T. 14 cwt. 41 lb. $3\frac{14}{15}$ oz.
- (*g*) 4 lb. 8 oz. 7 pwt. $7\frac{3}{4}$ gr.
- (*h*) 1 mi. $38\frac{22}{25}$ rd.

ARITHMETIC
(SECTION 5)

INVOLUTION

63. If a product consists of equal factors, it is called a **power** of one of those equal factors, and one of the equal factors is called a **root** of the product. The power and the root are named according to the number of equal factors in the product. Thus, 3×3, or 9, is the *second power*, or **square,** of 3; $3 \times 3 \times 3$, or 27, is the *third power*, or **cube,** of 3; $3 \times 3 \times 3 \times 3$, or 81, is the **fourth power** of 3. Also, 3 is the **second root,** or **square root,** of 9; 3 is the **third root,** or **cube root,** of 27; 3 is the **fourth root** of 81.

64. For the sake of brevity,

3×3 is written 3^2, and read **three square,**
or *three exponent two;*
$3 \times 3 \times 3$ is written 3^3, and read **three cube,**
or *three exponent three;*
$3 \times 3 \times 3 \times 3$ is written 3^4, and read **three fourth,**
or *three exponent four;*

and so on.

A number written above and to the right of another number, to show how often the latter number is used as a factor, is called an **exponent.** Thus, in 3^{12}, the number ^{12} is the exponent, and shows that 3 is to be used as a factor twelve times; so that 3^{12} is a contraction for

$$3 \times 3 \times 3 \times 3 \times 3 \times 3 \times 3 \times 3 \times 3 \times 3 \times 3 \times 3$$

In an expression like 3^5, the exponent ^{5} shows how often 3 is used as a factor. Hence, if the exponent of a number is unity, the number is used once as a factor; thus, $3^1 = 3$, $4^1 = 4$, $5^1 = 5$.

65. If the side of a square contains 5 inches, the area of the square contains 5×5, or 5^2, square inches. If the edge of a cube contains 5 inches, the volume of the cube contains $5 \times 5 \times 5$, or 5^3, cubic inches. It is for this reason that 5^2 and 5^3 are called the square and cube of 5, respectively.

66. **To find any power of a number:**

EXAMPLE 1.—What is the third power, or cube, of 35?

SOLUTION.—

$$35 \times 35 \times 35$$

or

```
          3 5
          3 5
        -------
        1 7 5
      1 0 5
      ---------
      1 2 2 5
          3 5
      ---------
      6 1 2 5
    3 6 7 5
    -----------
```

$cube = 4\,2\,8\,7\,5$ Ans.

EXAMPLE 2.—What is the fourth power of 15?

SOLUTION.—

$$15 \times 15 \times 15 \times 15$$

or

```
          1 5
          1 5
        -------
          7 5
        1 5
        -------
        2 2 5
          1 5
        ---------
      1 1 2 5
      2 2 5
      -----------
      3 3 7 5
          1 5
      -----------
    1 6 8 7 5
    3 3 7 5
    -------------
```

$fourth\ power = 5\,0\,6\,2\,5$ Ans.

EXAMPLE 3.— 1.2^3 = what?

SOLUTION.— $1.2 \times 1.2 \times 1.2$

$$\begin{array}{r} \text{or} \quad 1.2 \\ 1.2 \\ \hline 1.4\,4 \\ 1.2 \\ \hline 2\,8\,8 \\ 1\,4\,4 \\ \hline cube = 1.7\,2\,8 \quad \text{Ans.} \end{array}$$

EXAMPLE 4.—What is the third power, or cube, of $\frac{3}{8}$?

SOLUTION.— $\left(\dfrac{3}{8}\right)^3 = \dfrac{3^3}{8^3} = \dfrac{3}{8} \times \dfrac{3}{8} \times \dfrac{3}{8} = \dfrac{3 \times 3 \times 3}{8 \times 8 \times 8} = \dfrac{27}{512}.$ Ans.

67.   **Rule.—I.**   *To raise a whole number or a decimal to any power, use it as a factor as many times as there are units in the exponent.*

II.   *To raise a fraction to any power, raise both the numerator and denominator to the power indicated by the exponent.*

EXAMPLES FOR PRACTICE

Raise the following to the powers indicated:

(a) 85^2		(a) 7,225
(b) $\left(\frac{12}{13}\right)^2$		(b) $\frac{144}{169}$
(c) 6.5^2		(c) 42.25
(d) 14^4		(d) 38,416
(e) $\left(\frac{3}{4}\right)^3$	Ans.	(e) $\frac{27}{64}$
(f) $\left(\frac{5}{6}\right)^3$		(f) $\frac{125}{216}$
(g) $\left(\frac{7}{2}\right)^3$		(g) $\frac{343}{8}$
(h) 1.4^6		(h) 5.37824

EVOLUTION

DEFINITIONS AND GENERAL REMARKS

68. **Evolution** is the reverse of involution. It is the process of finding the root of a number that is considered as a power.

69. The **square root** of a number is that number which, when used twice as a factor, produces the number.

Thus, 2 is the square root of 4, since 2×2 (or 2^2) $= 4$.

70. The **cube root** of a number is that number which, when used three times as a factor, produces the number.

Thus, 3 is the cube root of 27, since $3 \times 3 \times 3$ (or 3^3) $= 27$.

71. The **fourth root** of a number is that number which, when used four times as a factor, produces the number.

Thus, 9 is the fourth root of 6,561, since $9 \times 9 \times 9 \times 9$ (or 9^4) $= 6,561$.

72. The **fifth root** of a number is that number which, when used five times as a factor, produces the number.

Thus, 7 is the fifth root of 16,807, since $7 \times 7 \times 7 \times 7 \times 7$ (or 7^5) $= 16,807$.

73. The process of finding squares and cubes and square roots and cube roots are very frequently employed in connection with the solution of problems pertaining to mensuration and engineering. The process of raising a number to some power, the exponent of the number being integral (*integral* is the adjective for integer; i. e., an integral number is one that does not contain a fraction or decimal) is very simple; but the reverse process, that of finding the roots, is very long and laborious, for which reason tables are generally employed. The tables so used are of two kinds—those giving the roots directly and logarithms. While the roots of numbers can be found without the aid of a table, it is not customary to do this except in the case of square root, which is comparatively easy. At the same time it is well to know some general method of finding the roots of numbers, as it might be necessary to find a root when a table was not at hand. For purposes of this Course, a knowledge of how to use a table is all that is necessary.

74. Some idea of the importance of the processes of involution and evolution may be obtained from the following:

In finding the area of a square or a circle, it is necessary to square the length of a certain line; conversely, in finding the side of a square or the diameter of a circle that will have a given area it is necessary to find the square root. In finding the volume of a cube or a sphere it is necessary to cube the length of a certain line; conversely, in finding the length of one of the edges of a cube or the diameter of a sphere that will have a given volume, it is necessary to find the cube root. There are many other cases where it is required to extract square root and cube root, but enough has been stated so far to show the importance of the processes.

75. Cube root is not required as often as square root, and fourth and fifth roots are required but seldom, the fifth root being required oftener than the fourth root. Roots higher than the fifth are practically never required. As examples, it may be stated that the fourth root is required in finding the diameter of a revolving shaft that is to transmit a given power. The fifth root is required in finding the diameter of a pipe that will discharge a given amount of a fluid in a given time; in certain problems pertaining to mine ventilation, etc., etc.

76. Having shown the necessity of some means of finding the roots of numbers, the manner of using the table given in this connection and following the Examination Questions will now be explained. But before studying the explanations, certain definitions and properties of numbers must be carefully considered.

40—7

77. The **radical sign** √, when placed before a number, indicates that some root of that number is to be found. The vinculum is almost always used in connection with the radical sign, as shown in Art. **78.**

78. The **index** of the root is a *small figure* placed *over* and to the *left* of the *radical sign*, to show what root is to be found.

Thus, $\sqrt[3]{100}$ denotes the *square root* of 100,

$\qquad\sqrt[3]{125}$ denotes the *cube root* of 125,

$\qquad\sqrt[4]{256}$ denotes the *fourth root* of 256,

$\qquad\sqrt[5]{243}$ denotes the *fifth root* of 243, and so on.

79. When the square root is to be extracted, the index is generally omitted. Thus, $\sqrt{100}$ indicates the square root of 100. Also, $\sqrt{225}$ indicates the square root of 225.

80. In any number, the figures beginning with the first digit* at the left and ending with the last digit at the right, are called the **significant figures** of the number. Thus, the number 405,800 has the four significant figures 4, 0, 5, 8; and the number .000090067 has the five significant figures 9, 0, 0, 6, and 7.

81. The part of a number consisting of its significant figures is called the **significant part** of the number. Thus, in the number 28,070, the significant part is 2807; in the number .00812, the significant part is 812; and in the number 170.3, the significant part is 1703.

82. In speaking of the significant figures or of the significant part of a number, we consider the figures, in their proper order, from the first digit at the left to the last digit at the right, but we pay no attention to the position of the decimal point. Hence, *all numbers that differ only in the position of the decimal point have the same significant part.* For example, .002103, 21.03, 21,030, and 210,300 have the same significant figures, 2, 1, 0, and 3, and the same significant part 2103.

---

*A cipher is not a digit.

The **integral part** of a number is the part to the left of the decimal point or to the left of the fraction when the number consists of a whole number and a fraction.

83. The student will find the following principles of value, both in connection with the extraction of roots and in other arithmetical calculations:

a. In general, if any two numbers are multiplied together, no matter how many significant figures they contain, the first five significant figures of the product will be the same as the first five significant figures of the product obtained by multiplying the same two numbers when limited to five significant figures.

For example, the product of 4,562,357 and 6,421,849 is 29,298,767,738,093; limiting the numbers to five significant figures, the product of 45,624 and 64,218 is 2,929,882,032; and the value of both these products to five significant figures is 29,299. In other words, if only five significant figures are required in the product, it is not necessary to use more than five significant figures in the multiplier and multiplicand, the remaining figures, if any, being replaced by ciphers, and the fifth figures being increased by 1 if the sixth figure is 5 or a larger digit. In some cases, however, the fifth figure may be one unit too large or one unit too small; hence, if it is necessary that the fifth figure be absolutely exact, it is better to limit the multiplier and multiplicand to six figures instead of five.

For example, $4,562,347 \times 6,421,849 = 29,298,703,519,603$, or 29,299,000,000,000 to five significant figures; $4,562,300 \times 6,421,800 = 29,298,178,140,000 = 29,298,000,000,000$ to five significant figures, the fifth figure being 1 less than it should be; but $4,562,350 \times 6,421,850 = 29,298,727,347,500 = 29,299,000,000,000$ to five significant figures.

b. If the divisor and dividend are limited to six significant figures, the quotient will always be correct to five (usually to six) significant figures, regardless of how many significant figures there may have been in the dividend and divisor.

For example, $6,421,849 \div 4,562,357 = 1.407572+ = 1.4076$ to five significant figures; also, $642,185 \div 456,236 = 1.407571+ = 1.4076$ to five significant figures.

c. If the number whose root is to be extracted be limited to six significant figures, the root will be correct to five (usually to six) significant figures.

84. These principles may all be summed up in the following general statement: *In any series of arithmetical operations—addition, subtraction, multiplication, division, involution, and evolution—if it be desired to have the final result limited to a certain number of significant figures, it is unnecessary to use more significant figures in any of the numbers operated on than the desired number in the result plus 1.* For example, if only four significant figures are desired in the final result, all the numbers used in the various operations may be limited to $4 + 1 = 5$ significant figures, the fifth figure being increased by 1 in all cases if the sixth figure is 5 or a greater digit.

From the foregoing, it follows that a table that will give five significant figures of the root correctly will be sufficiently extensive for all practical purposes. Such a table is here given, following the Examination Questions, and its use will now be explained, beginning with square root and then continuing with cube, fourth, and fifth roots.

85. The smallest number that can be written with one figure is 1, and the largest is 9. Their corresponding squares are 1 and 81, respectively. The smallest number that can be written with two figures is 10, and the largest is 99. Their corresponding squares are 100 and 9,801, respectively. Arrange the following numbers and their squares thus:

$$1^2 = 1 \qquad\qquad 9^2 = 81$$
$$10^2 = 100 \qquad\qquad 99^2 = 9,801$$
$$100^2 = 10,000 \qquad\qquad 999^2 = 998,001$$
$$1,000^2 = 1,000,000 \qquad 9,999^2 = 99,980,001$$

It is seen that the square of a number containing one figure is written with one or two figures; the square of a number containing two figures is written with three or four figures. Or, the square of a number is always written with twice as many figures as the given number, or twice as many less one.

86. In order to find the square root of a number, the first step is to point off the number into periods, or groups, of two figures each, beginning at the right if the number is integral, and at the decimal point if the number is decimal. The number of periods will be equal to the number of figures in the root if the number is a perfect square.

If the last period on the right of a decimal number contains but one figure, annex a cipher to complete the period.

Thus, the square root of 83,740,801 must contain four figures, since, pointing off the periods, we get 83′74′08′01, or four periods; consequently, there must be four figures in the root. In like manner, the square root of 50,625 must contain three figures, since there are (5′06′25) three periods. The extreme left-hand period may contain either one or two figures, according to the size of the number squared.

87. The square of any number wholly decimal always contains twice as many figures as the number squared. For example, $.1^2 = .01$, $.13^2 = .0169$, $.751^2 = .564001$, etc.

The square of a number partly decimal contains twice as many decimal places as there are decimal places in the number. For example, $12.35^2 = 152.5225$.

88. It will also be noticed that the square of a decimal is always less than the decimal. Hence, the square root of a number wholly decimal is greater than the number itself. If it be required to find the square root of a decimal, and the decimal has not an even number of figures in it, annex a cipher. The best way to point off a decimal is to begin at the decimal point, and, going toward the *right*, point off the decimal into periods of two figures each. Then, if the last period contains but one figure, annex a cipher to complete the period.

If the decimal point of a number is moved one or more places to the right (or left), the decimal point in the square will be moved twice as many places to the right (or left), thus:

$$3.567^2 = 12′.72′34′89$$
$$356.7^2 = 12′72′34′.89$$
$$.3567^2 = .12′72′34′89$$

It will be observed that these squares differ only in the position of the decimal point, and when divided into periods, the corresponding group in each square contains the same figures.

Later it will be shown that numbers containing like periods have like figures in their roots.

89. There are comparatively few numbers that can be separated into exactly equal factors; these numbers are called **perfect powers,** and the factors are called *rational factors.* Numbers that cannot be separated into exactly equal factors are called **imperfect powers,** and the factors are called *irrational factors.* In the numbers from 1 to 1,000, inclusive, there are only 48 perfect powers, not counting 1, and of these only 30 are perfect squares and 9 perfect cubes. These perfect powers are as follows: perfect squares, 4, 9, 16, 25, 36, 49, 64, 81, 100, 121, 144, 169, 196, 225, 256, 289, 324, 361, 400, 441, 484, 529, 576, 625, 676, 729, 784, 841, 900, 961; perfect cubes, 8, 27, 64, 125, 216, 343, 512, 729, 1000; perfect fourth powers, 16, 81, 256, 625; perfect fifth powers, 32, 243; perfect sixth powers, 64, 729; perfect seventh power, 128. Of these numbers it will be noticed, that two of the perfect cubes, 64 and 729, the four perfect fourth powers, and the two perfect sixth powers are duplicated among the squares and cubes; hence, there are only 40 different numbers between 1 and 1000 that are perfect powers.

90. The root of any number that cannot be divided into as many equal factors as there are units in the index of the root contains an interminable decimal. For example, the number 20 lies between 16 ($= 4^2$) and 25 ($= 5^2$); hence, the square root of 20, or $\sqrt{20}$, is greater than 4 and less than 5, and is therefore equal to 4 plus an interminable decimal. In other words, no matter to how many figures the square root of 20 may be calculated, the root will never be found exactly.

91. Although the root of an imperfect power cannot be found exactly, as close an approximation may be obtained as is desired. In practice, five significant figures are all that are likely to be required, and four are generally sufficient. In the following examples, all roots will be calculated to five figures, unless the given number is a perfect power whose root contains less than five figures.

SQUARE ROOT

92. The first step in finding the square root is to point off the number into periods of two figures each as previously described. The second step is to move the decimal point until it falls between the first (left-hand) period containing a digit and the next period to the right; in other words, the first step is to make the first period the integral part of the number, if not already so. Call the result the **altered number.**

The second step is to search the table in the columns headed n^2 and find two consecutive numbers, one less and the other greater than the altered number. Opposite the smaller of the two numbers in the column headed n, will be found the first three figures of the square root. All the numbers in the columns headed n are printed in heavy-face type, and it will be noticed that there are two such columns on each page.

The third step is to find two more figures of the root and the fourth step is to locate the decimal point in the root; these two steps can be best illustrated by examples.

EXAMPLE 1.—What is the square root of 31,416?

SOLUTION.—Pointing off into periods, the result is 3′14′16. Moving the decimal point so that the first period becomes the integral part of the number, the altered number is 3.1416. Searching the table in the columns headed n^2, 3.1416 is found to lie between 3.1329 and 3.1684, on page 1. The number in the column headed n opposite 3.1329 is 1.77. The first three figures of the root are therefore 177. Find the difference between the two numbers between which the given number falls (call this the **first difference**), and the difference between the smaller number and the given number (call this the **second difference**); divide the second difference by the first difference, carrying the quotient to three decimal places and increasing the second figure by 1 if the third is 5 or a greater digit. The two figures of the quotient thus determined will be the fourth and fifth figures of the root. In the present example, dropping decimal points in the remainders, 3.1684 − 3.1329 = 355, the first difference; 3.1416 − 3.1329 = 87, the second difference; 87 ÷ 355 = .245+, or .25. Hence, the first five figures of the root are 17,725. The decimal point is located in all cases by reference to the original number, after pointing off into periods.

There will be as many figures in the root preceding the decimal point as there are periods preceding the decimal point in the given number; if the number is entirely decimal, the root is entirely decimal, and there will be as many ciphers following the decimal point in the root as there are complete cipher periods following the decimal point in the given number.

Applying this principle, there are three periods preceding the decimal point in the given number; hence, there are three figures preceding the decimal point in the root, and $\sqrt{31,416} = 177.25$. Ans.

The operations may be arranged thus:

$$1.7\,8^2 = 3.1\,6\,8\,4 \qquad \text{altered number} = 3.1\,4\,1\,6$$
$$1.7\,7^2 = 3.1\,3\,2\,9 \qquad\qquad 1.7\,7^2 = 3.1\,3\,2\,9$$
$$\textit{first difference} = \overline{3\,5\,5} \qquad \textit{second difference} = \overline{8\,7}$$

$$3\,5\,5\,)\,8\,7.0\,0\,0\,(\;.2\,4\,5,\text{ or }.2\,5$$
$$7\,1\,0$$
$$\overline{1\,6\,0\,0}$$
$$1\,4\,2\,0$$
$$\overline{1\,8\,0\,0}$$
$$1\,7\,7\,5$$

First five significant figures of the root (the fifth figure being corrected) are 17725.

Locating decimal point, $\sqrt{31,416} = 177.25$. Ans.

NOTE.—Had the given number been 314.16, 3.1416, .031416, .00031416, etc. the significant figures of the root would have been the same as in the preceding case, since the altered number would have been 3.1416 in each instance; the decimal point would have been differently located, however. Thus, pointing off into periods, the given numbers are respectively 3'14'.16, 3'.14'16, .03'14'16, and .00'03'14'16, and the corresponding square roots are 17.725, 1.7725, .17725, and .017725.

Read very carefully Art. 96.

EXAMPLE 2.—What is the square root of .0031416?

SOLUTION.—Pointing off into periods, the result is .00'31'41'60; moving the decimal point, the altered number is 0031.4160 or 31.4160. Referring to the table in the columns headed n^2, 31.4160 is found to lie between 31.3600, opposite 5.60 and 31.4721, opposite 5.61, on page 5. The first three figures of the root are therefore 560. The first difference is 31.4721 − 31.3600 = 1121; the second difference is 31.4160 − 31.3600 = 560; 560 ÷ 1121 = .499+, or .50. Therefore, the first five figures of the root are 56050. Since there is one complete cipher period immediately following the decimal point in the given number, there is one cipher following the decimal point in the root, and $\sqrt{.0031416}$ = .056050, or .05605. Ans.

EXAMPLE 3.—What is the square root of 7,500?

SOLUTION.—Pointing off into periods, the result is 75′00. Moving the decimal point, the altered number is 75.00 or 75. Referring to the table, in the columns headed n^2, 75 is found to lie between 74.9956 and 75.1689, on page 8. The first difference is 75.1689 − 74.9956 = 1733; the second difference is 75 − 74.9956 = 44; 44 ÷ 1733 = .025+, or .03. The first three figures of the square root are 866, and the first five are 86603; there are two figures in the integral part of the root; hence, $\sqrt{7,500}$ = 86.603. Ans.

EXAMPLE 4.—What is the square root of 49,074,561,800?

SOLUTION.—Pointing off into periods, the result is 4′90′74′56′18′00. Moving the decimal point, the altered number is 4.90745618. Referring to the table in the columns headed n^2, the altered number is found to lie between 4.8841 and 4.9284, on page 2. It is not necessary or advisable to retain more figures in the altered number than there are in the two numbers of the table between which it falls, in this case five figures; hence, throw off all figures after the fifth, increasing the fifth figure by 1 if the sixth is 5 or a greater digit. Doing so the altered number becomes 4.9075. The first difference is 4.9284 − 4.8841 = 443; the second difference is 4.9075 − 4.8841 = 234; 234 ÷ 443 = .528+, or .53. The number opposite 4.8841 in the column headed n is 2.21; hence, the first five figures of the root are 22153. Since there are six periods on the left of the decimal point in the given number, there are six figures in the integral part of the root; as only five figures were determined, write a cipher for the sixth figure, obtaining 221,530. Therefore, to five significant figures, $\sqrt{49,074,561,800}$ = 221,530. Ans.

EXAMPLES FOR PRACTICE

Find the square root of:

(a)	5.			(a)	2.2361
(b)	.005.			(b)	.070711
(c)	149,263.			(c)	386.35
(d)	792.06.	Ans.		(d)	28.144
(e)	88.527.			(e)	9.4089
(f)	1,000.			(f)	31.623

CUBE ROOT

93. An examination of the table will show that the columns headed n contain all the numbers between 1.00 and 9.99, inclusive, that is, all numbers that can be expressed by three figures, disregarding the decimal point. The columns headed n^2 contain the squares of all the numbers in the columns headed n. The columns headed n^3, n^4, and n^5 contain, respectively, the first six figures of the cubes and the fourth and fifth powers of the numbers in the columns headed n. The preceding explanation for square root will suffice for the cube, fourth, and fifth roots, the only difference being in the first step—that of pointing off into periods. For cube root each period (except the first) must contain *three* figures. The process is the same; that is, begin at the decimal point and point off to the left and to the right periods of three figures each. If the right-hand period is not complete, annex ciphers until it contains three figures. Then proceed exactly as before, using the columns headed n^3, and locate the decimal point by means of the principle given in the explanation to example 1, Art. **92.**

EXAMPLE 1.—The cube root of .0000062417 is what?

SOLUTION.—Pointing off into periods of three figures each, the result is .000′006′241′700. Moving the decimal point until it immediately follows the first period that contains a digit the altered number is 6.241700 or 6.24170, using but six figures, to correspond with the six figures of the table. Referring to the table, and looking in the columns headed n^3, the altered number is found to lie between 6.22950 and 6.33163, on page 1. The first difference is 6.33163 − 6.22950 = 10213; the second difference is 6.24170 − 6.22950 = 1220; 1220 ÷ 10213 = .119+, or .12. The number opposite 6.22950 in the column headed n is 1.84; hence, the first five significant figures of the cube root are 18412. Since there is one complete cipher period following the decimal point, there will be one cipher following the decimal point in the root; therefore, $\sqrt[3]{.0000062417}$ = .018412. Ans.

Read very carefully Art. ′96

EXAMPLE 2.—The cube root of 50,932,676 is what?

SOLUTION.—Pointing off into periods of three figures each, the result is 50′932′676. Moving the decimal point, the altered number is

50.932676. Reducing to six figures and increasing the sixth figure by 1, since the seventh figure is 7, the altered number becomes 50.9327. Referring to the table in the columns headed n^3, 50.9327 is found to lie between 50.6530 and 51.0648, on page 3, the first three figures of the root being 370. The first difference is $51.0648 - 50.6530 = 4118$; the second difference is $50.9327 - 50.6530 = 2797$; $2797 \div 4118 = .679+$, or .68; hence, the first five figures of the root are 37068. Since the integral part of the given number contains three periods there are three figures in the integral part of the root; therefore, $\sqrt[3]{50,932,676} = 370.68$.

Ans.

EXAMPLE 3.—What is the cube root of .834?

SOLUTION.—There is but one period. Moving the decimal point, the altered number is 834, which falls between 833.238 and 835.897 in the columns headed n^3 on page 9 of the table. The first three figures of the root are 941. The first difference is $835.897 - 833.238 = 2659$; the second difference is $834 - 833.238 = 762$; $762 \div 2659 = .286+$, or .29; hence, the first five figures of the root are 94129. Since the given number is wholly decimal, the root is wholly decimal; and since there is no complete cipher period between the decimal point and the first digit of the given number, there are no ciphers between the decimal point and the first digit of the root. Therefore, $\sqrt[3]{.834} = .94129$.

Ans.

EXAMPLES FOR PRACTICE

Find the cube root of:

(a)	78,347.809639.	(a) 42.79
(b)	2.	(b) 1.2599
(c)	4,180,769,192.462.	(c) 1,611.0
(d)	.696.	Ans. (d) .88621
(e)	.375.	(e) .72112
(f)	513,229.783302144.	(f) 80.064

FOURTH AND FIFTH ROOTS

94. The processes for fourth and fifth roots are exactly the same as for square and cube roots, except that for fourth root the given number is pointed off into periods of *four* figures each and the columns headed n^4 are used, while for fifth root the given number is pointed off into periods of *five* figures each and the columns headed n^5 are used.

EXAMPLE 1.—What is the fourth root of 3,690.72?

SOLUTION.—Pointing off into periods of four figures each, the result is 3690'.7200. In the present case there is no need of moving the decimal point since it already follows the first period containing a digit; and since six figures only are required, throw off the two ciphers on the right and look in the table under the headings n^4 and find between what two numbers 3,690.72 falls. Referring to page 7, the given number falls between 3,682.56 and 3,701.51. The first difference is 3,701.51 − 3,682.56 = 1895; the second difference is 3,690.72 − 3,682.56 = 816; 816 ÷ 1895 = .430+, or .43. The number in the column headed n and opposite 3,682.56 is 7.79; hence, the first five figures of the root are 77943. Since there is but one integral period in the given number, there is but one integral place in the root; therefore, $\sqrt[4]{3,690.72} = 7.7943$. Ans.

Read very carefully Art. 96.

EXAMPLE 2.—What is the fifth root of .7854?

SOLUTION.—Pointing off into periods of five figures each, the result is .78540; moving the decimal point, the altered number is 78540. Referring to the table and looking in the columns headed n^5, 78540 is found to lie between 78196.0 and 78607.6 on page 9. The first difference is 78607.6 − 78196.0 = 4116; the second difference is 78540.0 − 78196.0 = 3440; 3440 ÷ 4116 = .835+, or .84−. The number in the column headed n and opposite 78196.0 is 9.52; hence, the first five significant figures of the root are 95284. Since the given number is a decimal, the root is a decimal; therefore, $\sqrt[5]{.7854} = .95284$. Ans.

EXAMPLE 3.—What is the fifth root of 497.23?

SOLUTION.—Pointing off into periods of five figures each, the result is 497.23000. As only six figures are required, drop the last two, obtaining 497.230. Referring to the table in the columns headed n^5, 497.230 is found to lie between 495.884 and 503.092 on page 3. The first difference is 503.092 − 495.884 = 7208; the second difference is 497.230 − 495.884 = 1346; 1346 ÷ 7208 = .186+, or .19−. The number in the column headed n and opposite 495.884 is 3.46; hence, the first five significant figures of the root are 34619. Since there is but one integral period, $\sqrt[5]{497.23} = 3.4619$. Ans.

95. The following is a general rule for using the table to find the square root, cube root, fourth root, or fifth root of any number.

Rule.—I. *Beginning at the decimal point, and going to the right and to the left, point off the given number whose root is to be found into periods having as many figures in each period as there are units in the index* (see Art. **78**) *of the root.*

II. *If the decimal point does not immediately follow the right-hand figure of the first period containing a digit, move it* *from its position until it does follow the right-hand figure of the first period containing a digit. Call the result the* **altered number.** *If there are more than six figures in the altered number, drop all after the sixth figure, increasing the sixth figure by 1 if the seventh figure is 5 or a greater number. In the case of square root, retain only five figures, when the left-hand period contains but one significant figure.*

III. *Refer to the table of powers that follows the Examination Questions, and looking in the columns having at the head "n" and an exponent of the same value as the index of the root, find between what two numbers in these columns the altered number falls. Subtract the smaller of these two numbers from the larger, and call the result the* **first difference.** *Subtract the smaller of the two numbers from the altered number, and call the result the* **second difference.** *Divide the second difference by the first difference, and find the quotient to three figures, which reduce to two figures, increasing the second figure by one if the third figure is 5 or a greater number. The two figures thus found are the fourth and fifth figures of the root. The first three figures will be found in the column headed "n", opposite the smaller of the two numbers in the table between which the given number falls.*

IV. *Locate the decimal point by means of the principle that there will be as many figures in the root preceding the decimal point as there are periods preceding the decimal point in the given number; if the number is entirely decimal, the root is entirely decimal, and if there are any complete cipher periods immediately following the decimal point, there will be as many ciphers following the decimal point in the root as there are complete cipher periods following the decimal point in the given number.*

96. The student should study Arts. **63** to **96** very thoroughly, particularly the examples. Each example should be carefully considered by itself, as it illustrates some feature not present in the other examples. *The student should do the actual work on a separate sheet of paper performing each operation in the order given in the solution; he will find it advisable to work the Examples for Practice also. Any student* *who follows these instructions will have no difficulty in using the table.*

The student will notice that the reason for the second step, moving the decimal point, is to get the decimal point in the same relative position that it occupies in the corresponding numbers of the table.

ROOTS OF FRACTIONS

97. If the given number is in the form of a fraction, and it is required to find some root of it, the simplest and most exact method is to reduce the fraction to a decimal and extract the required root of the decimal. If, however, the numerator and denominator of the fraction are perfect powers, extract the required root of each separately, and write the root of the numerator for a new numerator, **and** the root of the denominator for a new denominator.

EXAMPLE 1.—What is the square root of $\frac{9}{64}$?

SOLUTION.— $\sqrt{\frac{9}{64}} = \frac{\sqrt{9}}{\sqrt{64}} = \frac{3}{8}$. Ans.

EXAMPLE 2.—What is the square root of $\frac{5}{8}$?

SOLUTION.— $\sqrt{\frac{5}{8}} = \sqrt{.625} = .79057$, since $\frac{5}{8} = .625$. **Ans.**

EXAMPLE 3.—What is the cube root of $\frac{27}{125}$?

SOLUTION.— $\sqrt[3]{\frac{27}{125}} = \frac{\sqrt[3]{27}}{\sqrt[3]{125}} = \frac{3}{5}$. Ans.

EXAMPLE 4.—What is the cube root of $\frac{1}{4}$?

SOLUTION.—Since $\frac{1}{4} = .25$, $\sqrt[3]{\frac{1}{4}} = \sqrt[3]{.25} = .62996$. Ans.

98. Rule.—*Extract the required root of the numerator and denominator separately; or, reduce the fraction to a decimal, and extract the root of the decimal.*

EXAMPLES FOR PRACTICE

(a) $\sqrt{\frac{9}{16}} = ?$

(b) $\sqrt[3]{\frac{27}{1728}} = ?$

(c) $\sqrt[3]{\frac{27}{375}} = ?$

(d) $\sqrt[3]{\frac{560}{125}} = ?$

Ans. $\begin{cases} (a)\ \frac{3}{4} \\ (b)\ \frac{1}{4} \\ (c)\ .41602 \\ (d)\ 1.6355 \end{cases}$

99. On page 10 of the table are given the square, cube, and fourth, and fifth powers of the first nine digits. By aid of this little table, the page on which the first three figures of the required root are to be found is instantly located. Thus, after moving the decimal point (if necessary) in the given number find, in the column in which n has an exponent equal to the index of the root sought, between what two numbers the altered number falls; the number in the left-hand column opposite the smaller of these two numbers is the page of the table sought.

For example, on what pages will the first three figures of the (a) square, (b) cube, (c) fourth, and (d) fifth roots of .00432176 be found?

Pointing off and moving the decimal point the altered numbers, reduced to six figures, become for each case, (a) 43.2176; (b) 4.32176; (c) 43.2176; (d) 432.176. Referring to page 10 of the table, in the column headed n^2, 43.2176 falls between 36 and 49; hence, the first three figures of the square root will be found on page 6. 4.32176 falls between 1 and 8 in the column headed n^3; hence, the first three figures of the cube root will be found on page 1. 43.2176 falls between 16 and 81 in the column headed n^4; hence, the first three figures of the fourth root will be found on page 2. 432.176 falls between 243 and 1,024 in the column headed n^5; hence, the first three figures of the fifth root will be found on page 3.

100. In the following articles will be described how more than five figures of the root can be found, and exact methods for extracting any root, the index being an integer, to any number of figures. *The student may omit everything from this point to the Examination Questions, if he so desires.*

101. If a root has been found to five significant figures and it is desired to obtain more figures, perhaps the easiest way is to proceed as follows: Raise the number indicated by the root to the power indicated by an exponent equal to the index of the root; if the result so obtained is less than the given number, add 1 to the right-hand figure of the root and raise the new number to the same power; but if the result so obtained is greater than the given number, subtract 1 from the right-hand figure of the root and raise the new number to same power. The result of these operations is to obtain powers of two consecutive numbers having *five* significant figures each, one of the powers being a little greater and the other a little less than the given number. Then proceeding exactly as previously described, divide the second difference by the first difference and obtain four more figures of the root.

Consider example 1, Art. **92.** The square root of 31,416 to five significant figures is 177.25. $177.25^2 = 31,417.5625$, which is a little greater than 31,416; hence, subtracting 1 from 177.25, $177.24^2 = 31,414.0176$, which is a little less than 31,416. The first difference is $31,417.5625 - 31,414.0176 = 3.5449$. The second difference is $31,416 - 31,414.0176 = 1.9824$; $1.9824 \div 3.5449 = .55922$, or .5592 to four figures. Therefore, $\sqrt{31,416} = 177.245592$ to nine significant figures.

Suppose it has been found that the cube root of 37,267 is 33.402 to five significant figures, and it is desired to obtain more figures. Proceed exactly as before. $33.402^3 = 37,266.397760808$, which is a little less than 37,267; hence, adding 1 to 33.402, $33.403^3 = 37,269.744941827$. The first difference is $37,269.744941827 - 37,266.397760808 = 3.347181019$; the second difference is $37,267 - 37,266.397760808 = .602239192$; $.602239192 \div 3.347181019 = .17992+$, or .1799 to four figures. Therefore, $\sqrt[3]{37,267} = 33.4021799$ to nine significant figures.

102. As before stated, it is customary to use some kind of a table instead of extracting the roots directly, still the square root is so frequently required that it is well to learn how to extract square root directly. There are several good methods, and none are much harder than long division. The method given here is the simplest and easiest to remember and apply of any. For cube root and higher roots, all exact methods are long and laborious. The method given in the pages that follow is a general one, applicable to any root, the index of which is an integer, and is very easy to remember.

SQUARE ROOT—EXACT METHOD

103. The method is best explained by giving several examples with full explanations of each step. In order to make the work clearer to the student and easier to follow, the figures in the root and the successive numbers resulting from their use are printed in light and heavy-face type alternately.

EXAMPLE 1.—Find the square root of 31,505,769.

SOLUTION.—
```
                                              root
                              3 1'5 0'5 7'6 9 ( 5 6 1 3   Ans.
        (a)    5       (b)    2 5
               5       (c)      6 5 0
        (d)  1 0 0            6 3 6
               6       (e)      1 4 5 7
             1 0 6             1 1 2 1
               6                 3 3 6 6 9
             1 1 2 0             3 3 6 6 9
                 1
             1 1 2 1
                 1
             1 1 2 2 0
                   3
             1 1 2 2 3
```

EXPLANATION.—First point off into periods of two figures each. Now, find the largest single number whose square is less than or equal to 31, the first period. This is evidently 5, since $6^2 = 36$, which is greater than 31. Write it to the right, as in long division, and also to the left, as shown at (a). This is the first figure of the root. Now, multiply the 5 at (a) by the 5 in the root, and write the result under the first period, as shown at (b). Subtract and obtain 6 as a remainder.

Add the root already found to the 5 at (a), getting 10, and annex a cipher to this 10, thus making it 100, as shown at (d), which call the **first trial divisor**. Bring down the next period, 50, and annex it to the remainder 6, as shown at (c), which call the **first dividend**. Divide the first dividend (c) by the first trial divisor (d) and obtain 6, which is *probably* the next figure of the root. Write 6 in the root, as shown, and also add it to 100, the trial divisor, making it 106. This is called the **first complete divisor.**

Multiply the first complete divisor, 106, by 6, the second figure in the root, and subtract the result from the first dividend (c); the remainder is 14. Add the second figure of the root to the complete divisor, 106, and annex a cipher, thus getting 1120, which call the **second trial divisor.** Annex the next period, to the remainder in the second column making it 1457, as shown at (e), which call the **second dividend.** Dividing 1457 by 1120, we get 1 as the next figure of the root. Adding this last figure of the root to 1120, the result is 1121, the **second complete divisor.** Multiplying the second complete divisor by the third figure of the root and subtracting from the second dividend, 1457, the remainder is 336.

Now, adding the last figure of the root to 1121 and annexing a cipher as before, the result is 11220, the **third trial divisor.** Annexing the next and last period, 69, to the remainder in the second column the result is 33669, the **third dividend.** Dividing 33669 by 11220, the result is 3, the fourth figure of the root. Adding the fourth figure of the root to 11220, the result is 11223, the **third complete divisor.** Multiplying the third complete divisor by the fourth figure of the root, the result is 33669. Subtracting the product from the third dividend, there is no remainder; hence, $\sqrt{31,505,769} = 5,613$.

Read very carefully that part of Art. 96 which is printed in Italics.

EXAMPLE 2.—What is the square root of .000576?

SOLUTION.—

$$
\begin{array}{ll}
 & \overset{root}{.00'05'76\,(\,.024\ \ \text{Ans.}} \\
2 & \quad 4 \\
\underline{2} & \quad \overline{176} \\
40 & \quad 176 \\
\underline{4} & \quad \overline{} \\
\overline{44} &
\end{array}
$$

EXPLANATION.—Beginning at the decimal point and pointing off the number into periods of two figures each, it is seen that the first period is composed of ciphers; hence, the first figure of the root must be a cipher. The remaining portion of the solution should be perfectly clear from what has preceded.

104. If the number is not a perfect power, the root will consist of an interminable number of decimal places. The result may be carried to any required number of decimal places by annexing periods of two ciphers each to the number.

EXAMPLE 1.—What is the square root of 3? Find the result to five decimal places.

SOLUTION.—

$$
\begin{array}{ll}
& \overset{root}{3.0\ 0'0\ 0'0\ 0'0\ 0'0\ 0'0\ 0\ (\ 1.7\ 3\ 2\ 0\ 5+\ \ Ans.} \\
1 & 1 \\
\underline{1} & \overline{2\ 0\ 0} \\
2\ 0 & 1\ 8\ 9 \\
\underline{7} & \overline{\ \ 1\ 1\ 0\ 0} \\
2\ 7 & \ \ 1\ 0\ 2\ 9 \\
\underline{7} & \overline{\ \ \ \ 7\ 1\ 0\ 0} \\
3\ 4\ 0 & \ \ \ \ 6\ 9\ 2\ 4 \\
\underline{3} & \overline{\ \ \ \ \ \ 1\ 7\ 6\ 0\ 0\ 0\ 0} \\
3\ 4\ 3 & \ \ \ \ \ \ 1\ 7\ 3\ 2\ 0\ 2\ 5 \\
\underline{3} & \overline{\ \ \ \ \ \ \ \ 2\ 7\ 9\ 7\ 5} \\
3\ 4\ 6\ 0 & \\
\underline{2} & \\
3\ 4\ 6\ 2 & \\
\underline{2} & \\
3\ 4\ 6\ 4\ 0\ 0 & \\
\underline{5} & \\
3\ 4\ 6\ 4\ 0\ 5 & \\
\end{array}
$$

EXPLANATION.—Annex five periods of two ciphers each to the right of the decimal point. The first figure of the root is found to be 1. To get the second figure, we find that, on dividing 200 by 20, it is 10. This is evidently too large.

Trying 9, we add 9 to 20 and multiply 29 by 9; the result is 261, a result which is considerably larger than 200; hence, 9 is too large. In the same way, it is found that 8 is also too large. Trying 7, 7 times 27 is 189, a result smaller than 200; therefore, 7 is the second figure of the root. The next two figures, 3 and 2, are easily found. The fifth figure in the root is a cipher, since the trial divisor, 34640, is greater than the new dividend, 17600. In a case of this kind we annex another cipher to 34640, thereby making it 346400, and bring down the next period, making the 17600, 1760000. Dividing the fourth dividend, 1760000, by the fourth trial divisor, 346400, the result is 5.0+. Hence, the next figure of the root is 5, and, as we now have five decimal places, we stop.

The square root of 3 is, then, 1.73205+.

If the second figure of the quotient last obtained, 5.0+, had been 5 or a greater digit, the figure in the fifth decimal place would have been increased by 1.

EXAMPLE 2.—What is the square root of .3 to five decimal places?

SOLUTION.—

$$.3\,0'0\,0'0\,0'0\,0'0\,0'0\,0\,(.5\,4\,7\,7\,2+\ \text{Ans.}$$

```
        5           2 5
        5          ─────
       ───          5 0 0
      1 0 0         4 1 6
        4          ─────
      ───           8 4 0 0
      1 0 4         7 6 0 9
        4          ─────
      ───           7 9 1 0 0
      1 0 8 0       7 6 6 2 9
        7          ─────
      ───           2 4 7 1 0 0
      1 0 8 7       2 1 9 0 8 4
        7          ─────
      ───           2 8 0 1 6
    1 0 9 4 0
        7
    ───
    1 0 9 4 7
        7
    ───
  1 0 9 5 4 0
        2
  ───
  1 0 9 5 4 2
```

EXPLANATION.—In the above example we annex a cipher to .3, making the first period .30, since every period of a decimal, as was mentioned before, must have two figures in it. The remainder of the work should be perfectly clear.

105. If it is required to find the square root of a mixed number, begin at the decimal point and point off the periods both to the right and to the left. The manner of finding the root will then be exactly the same as in the previous cases.

EXAMPLE.—What is the square root of 258.2449?

SOLUTION.—

$$2'5\ 8.2\ 4'4\ 9\ (1\ 6.0\ 7 \quad \text{Ans.}$$

1	1
1	1 5 8
——	1 5 6
2 0	
6	2 2 4 4 9
——	2 2 4 4 9
2 6	
6	
——	
3 2 0 0	
7	
——	
3 2 0 7	

EXPLANATION.—In the above example, since 320 is greater than 224, we place a cipher for the third figure of the root and annex a cipher to 320, making it 3200. Then, bringing down the next period, 49, 7 is found to be the fourth figure of the root. Since there is no remainder, the square root of 258.2449 is 16.07.

106. PROOF.—To prove square root, square the result obtained. If the number is an exact power, the square of the root will equal it; if it is not an exact power, the square of the root will very nearly equal it.

107. RULE.—I. *Begin at units place and separate the number into periods of two figures each, proceeding from left to right with the decimal part, if there be any.*

II. *Find the greatest number whose square is contained in the first, or left-hand, period. Write this number as the first figure in the root; also, write it at the left of the given number.*

Multiply this number at the left by the first figure of the root, and subtract the result from the first period.

III. *Add the first figure of the root to the number in the first column on the left and annex a cipher to the result; this is the first trial divisor. Annex the second period to the remainder in the second column; this is the first dividend. Divide the dividend by the trial divisor for the second figure in the root and add this figure to the trial divisor to form the complete divisor. Multiply the complete divisor by the second figure in the root and subtract this result from the dividend. (If this result is larger than the dividend, a smaller number must be tried for the second figure of the root.) Add the second figure of the root to the complete divisor. Annex a cipher for a new trial divisor, and bring down the third period and annex it to the last remainder for the second dividend.*

IV. *Continue in this manner to the last period, after which, if any additional places in the root are required, bring down cipher periods and continue the operation.*

V. *If at any time the trial divisor is larger than the dividend, place a cipher in the root, annex a cipher to the trial divisor, and bring down another period.*

VI. *If the root contains an interminable decimal and it is desired to terminate the operation at some point, say, the fourth decimal place, carry the operation one place farther, and if the fifth figure is 5 or greater, increase the fourth figure by 1 and omit the sign +.*

108. **Short Method.**—If the number whose root is to be extracted is not an exact square, the root will be an interminable decimal. It is then usual to extract the root to a certain number of significant figures. In such cases the work may be greatly shortened as follows: Determine to how many significant figures the work is to be carried, say seven, for example; divide this number by 2 and take the next higher number. In the above case, we have $7 \div 2 = 3\frac{1}{2}$; hence, we take 4, the next higher number. Now extract the root in the usual manner until four significant figures have been obtained. Then form the trial divisor in the usual manner, but omitting to annex the cipher; divide the last remainder by the trial divisor, as in long division, obtaining as many figures of the quotient as there are remaining figures of the root, in this case $7 - 4 = 3$. The quotient so obtained is the remaining figures of the root.

Consider example 2, Art. **104.** Here there are five figures in the root. We therefore extract the root to three figures in the usual manner, obtaining .547 for the first three root figures. The next trial divisor is 1094 (with the cipher omitted) and the last remainder is 791. Then, 791 ÷ 1094 = .723, and the next two figures of the root are 72, the whole root being .54772+. Always carry the division one place farther than desired, and if the last figure is 5 or a greater digit, increase the preceding figure by 1. This method should not be used unless the root is to contain five or more figures.

NOTE.—If the last figure of the root found in the regular manner is a cipher, carry the process one place farther before dividing as described above.

EXAMPLES FOR PRACTICE

Find the square root of:

(a)	186,624.		(a)	432
(b)	2,050,624.		(b)	1,432
(c)	29,855,296.		(c)	5,464
(d)	.0116964.		(d)	.10815−
(e)	198.1369.		(e)	14.0761
(f)	994,009.	Ans.	(f)	997
(g)	2.375 to four decimal places.		(g)	1.5411
(h)	1.625 to three decimal places.		(h)	1.275
(i)	.3025.		(i)	.55
(j)	.571428.		(j)	.75593--
(k)	.78125.		(k)	.88388+

CUBE ROOT—EXACT METHOD

109. The process of extracting cube root is very similar to that just described for square root, the work being arranged in three columns instead of two. An example will best illustrate the method.

EXAMPLE.—What is the cube root of 375,741,853,696?

SOLUTION.—

(1)	(2)	(3)	root
		3 7 5'7 4 1'8 5 3'6 9 6 (7 2 1 6	Ans.
7	49	343	
7	98		
14	14700	3 2 7 4 1	
7	4 2 4	3 0 2 4 8	
210	15124	2 4 9 3 8 5 3	
2	4 2 8	1 5 5 7 3 6 1	
212	1 5 5 5 2 0 0	9 3 6 4 9 2 6 9 6	
2	2 1 6 1	9 3 6 4 9 2 6 9 6	
214	1 5 5 7 3 6 1		
2	2 1 6 2		
2 1 6 0	1 5 5 9 5 2 3 0 0		
1	1 2 9 8 1 6		
2 1 6 1	1 5 6 0 8 2 1 1 6		
1			
2 1 6 2			
1			
2 1 6 3 0			
6			
2 1 6 3 6			

EXPLANATION.—Write the work in three columns as follows: On the right place the number whose cube root is to be extracted, and point it off into periods of *three* figures each. Call this column (3). Find the largest number whose cube is less than or equal to the first period, in this case 7. Write the 7 on the right, as shown, for the first figure of the root, and also on the extreme left at the head of column (1). Multiply the 7 in column (1) by the first figure of the root 7, and write the product 49 at the head of column (2). Multiply the number in column (2) by the first figure of the root 7, and write the product 343 under the figures in the first period. Subtract, obtaining 32 for the remainder. Add the first figure of the root to the number in column (1), obtaining 14. Multiply the last number in column (1) by the first figure of the root, add the product to the number in column (2), and obtain 147. Add the first figure of the root to the last number in column (1), and obtain 21. Annex *one* cipher to the number in column (1), and obtain 210. Also, annex *two* ciphers to the number in column (2), and obtain 14,700 for the first trial divisor. Bring down the next period, annexing it to the remainder in column (3), and obtain 32,741 for the first dividend. Dividing the first dividend by the first trial divisor, we obtain $\frac{32741}{14700} = 2+$, and write the 2 as the second figure of the root. Add the 2 to the number in column (1), and obtain 212, which, multiplied by the second figure of the root, and added to the trial divisor, gives 15,124, the first complete divisor. This last result, multiplied by the second figure of the root and subtracted from the first dividend, gives a remainder of 2,493. Adding the second figure of the root to the number in column (1), we get 214; this, multiplied by the second figure of the root and added to complete divisor, gives 15,552. Adding the second figure of the root to the number in column (1) gives 216. Annexing one cipher to the number in column (1) gives 2,160. Annexing two ciphers to the number in column (2) gives 1,555,200, the second trial divisor. Annexing the third period to the remainder in column (3), we obtain 2,493,853 for the second dividend. Dividing the second dividend by the second trial divisor, we obtain $\frac{2493853}{1555200} = 1+$, and write 1 as the third figure of the root. The remainder of the work is continued in the same manner and should be perfectly clear from what has preceded.

110. In extracting the cube root of a decimal, proceed as above, taking care that each period contains *three* figures. Begin the pointing off at the decimal point, going toward the right. If the last period does not contain three figures, annex ciphers until it does.

EXAMPLE 1.—What is the cube root of .009129329?

SOLUTION.—

		root
		.0 0 9′1 2 9′3 2 9 (.2 0 9 Ans.
2	4	8
2	8	‾
‾	‾	1 1 2 9 3 2 9
4	1 2 0 0 0 0	1 1 2 9 3 2 9
2	5 4 8 1	‾‾‾‾‾‾
‾	‾‾‾‾‾	
6 0 0	1 2 5 4 8 1	
9		
‾		
6 0 9		

EXPLANATION.—Beginning at the decimal point, and pointing off as shown, the largest number whose cube is less than 9 is seen to be 2; hence, 2 is the first figure of the root. When finding the second figure, it is seen that the first trial divisor 1,200 is greater than the dividend; hence, write a cipher for the second figure of the root; bring down the next period to form the second dividend; annex two ciphers to the trial divisor to form the second trial divisor; also, annex one cipher to the 60 in column (1). Dividing the second dividend by the second trial divisor, we get $\dfrac{1129329}{120000} = 9+$, and write 9 as the third figure of the root. Complete the work as before.

EXAMPLE 2.—What is the cube root of 78,347.809639?

SOLUTION.—

```
                                                              root
                                        7 8'3 4 7.8 0 9'6 3 9 ( 4 2.7 9
    4          16                       6 4
    4          32                       ─────
   ───        ────                      1 4 3 4 7
    8         4 8 0 0                    1 0 0 8 8
    4          2 4 4                     ─────────
  ─────       ───────                       4 2 5 9 8 0 9
  1 2 0       5 0 4 4                        3 7 6 6 4 8 3
      2         2 4 8                        ───────────
  ─────       ───────                             4 9 3 3 2 6 6 3 9
  1 2 2       5 2 9 2 0 0                          4 9 3 3 2 6 6 3 9
      2           8 8 6 9                          ───────────────
  ─────       ───────────
  1 2 4       5 3 8 0 6 9
      2           8 9 1 8
  ─────       ───────────
  1 2 6 0     5 4 6 9 8 7 0 0
        7         1 1 5 3 7 1
  ───────     ───────────────
  1 2 6 7     5 4 8 1 4 0 7 1
        7
  ───────
  1 2 7 4
        7
  ───────
  1 2 8 1 0
          9
  ─────────
  1 2 8 1 9
```

EXPLANATION.—Since we have a mixed number, begin at the decimal point and point off periods of three figures each, in both directions. The first period contains but two figures, and the largest number whose cube is less than 78 is 4; consequently, 4 is the first figure of the root. The remainder of the work should be perfectly clear. When dividing the second dividend by the second trial divisor for the third figure of the root, the quotient was 8+; but, on trying it, it was found that 8 was too large, the complete divisor being considerably larger than the trial divisor. Therefore, 7 was used instead of 8.

EXAMPLE 3.—What is the cube root of 5 to five decimal places?

root

SOLUTION.—   5.0 0 0′0 0 0′0 0 0′0 0 0′0 0 0(1.7 0 9 9 7 5+

1	1	1
1	2	4 0 0 0
2	3 0 0	3 9 1 3
1	2 5 9	8 7 0 0 0 0 0 0
3 0	5 5 9	7 8 4 4 3 8 2 9
7	3 0 8	8 5 5 6 1 7 1 0 0 0
3 7	8 6 7 0 0 0 0	7 8 8 9 9 9 2 2 9 9
7	4 5 9 8 1	6 6 6 1 7 8 7 0 1 0 0 0
4 4	8 7 1 5 9 8 1	6 1 4 0 1 4 3 1 7 9 7 3
7	4 6 0 6 2	5 2 1 6 4 3 8 3 0 2 7
5 1 0 0	8 7 6 2 0 4 3 0 0	
9	4 6 1 5 1 1	
5 1 0 9	8 7 6 6 6 5 8 1 1	
9	4 6 1 5 9 2	
5 1 1 8	8 7 7 1 2 7 4 0 3 0 0	
9	3 5 9 0 8 3 9	
5 1 2 7 0	8 7 7 1 6 3 3 1 1 3 9	
9		
5 1 2 7 9		
9		
5 1 2 8 8		
9		
5 1 2 9 7 0		
7		
5 1 2 9 7 7		

Root correct to five decimal places is 1.70998−.   Ans.

EXPLANATION.—In the preceding example we annex five periods of ciphers, of three ciphers each, to the 5 for the decimal part of the root, placing the decimal point between the 5 and the first cipher. In practice it is not necessary to write these cipher periods after the given number; when one cipher is added to the number in column (1) and two to the number in column (2), three ciphers would be added to the number in column (3). Since the quotient obtained by

dividing the fourth dividend by the fourth trial divisor is
666178701000 ÷ 87712740300 = 7.5+ the root correct to five
decimal places is 1.70998 —.

EXAMPLE 4.—What is the cube root of .5 to four decimal places?

SOLUTION.—

7	49	.500'000'000'000 (.7937+ Ans.
7	98	34
14	14700	157000
7	1971	150039
210	16671	6961000
9	2052	5638257
219	1872300	1322743000
9	7119	1321748953
228	1879419	994047
9	7128	
2370	188654700	
3	166579	
2373	188821279	
3		
2376		
3		
23790		
7		
23797		

EXPLANATION.—In the above example we annex two
ciphers to the .5 to complete the first period, and three
periods of three ciphers each. The largest number whose
cube is less than 500 is 7; this we write as the first figure of
the root. The remainder of the work should be perfectly
plain from the explanations of the preceding examples.
Since the quotient obtained by dividing the third dividend
by the third trial divisor is 1322743000 ÷ 188654700 = 7.0+,
the root is correct as found to the fourth decimal place.

EXAMPLE 5.—What is the cube root of .05 to four decimal places?

SOLUTION.—

$$.0\,5\,0'0\,0\,0'0\,0\,0'0\,0\,0\ (\ .3\,6\,8\,4+\quad \text{root}$$

3	9	2 7
3	1 8	————
——	————	2 3 0 0 0
6	2 7 0 0	1 9 6 5 6
3	5 7 6	————
——	————	3 3 4 4 0 0 0
9 0	3 2 7 6	3 1 8 0 0 3 2
6	6 1 2	————
——	————	1 6 3 9 6 8 0 0 0
9 6	3 8 8 8 0 0	1 6 2 6 8 5 5 0 4
6	8 7 0 4	————
——	————	1 2 8 2 4 9 6
1 0 2	3 9 7 5 0 4	
6	8 7 6 8	
——	————	
1 0 8 0	4 0 6 2 7 2 0 0	
8	4 4 1 7 6	
——	————	
1 0 8 8	4 0 6 7 1 3 7 6	
8		
——		
1 0 9 6		
8		
——		
1 1 0 4 0		
4		
——		
1 1 0 4 4		

111. PROOF.—To prove cube root, cube the result obtained. If the given number is an exact power, the cube of the root will equal it; if not an exact power, the cube of the root will very nearly equal it.

112. **Rule.**—I. *Arrange the work in three columns, placing the number whose cube root is to be extracted in the third or right-hand column. Begin at units place, and separate the number into periods of three figures each, proceeding from the decimal point toward the right with the decimal part, if there is any.*

II. *Find the greatest number whose cube is not greater than the number expressed by the first period that contains a digit. Write this number as the first figure of the root; also, write it at the head of the first column. Multiply the number in the first column by the first figure in the root, and write the result in the second column. Multiply the number in the second column by the first figure of the root, and subtract the product* *from the first period. Add the first figure of the root to the number in the first column. Multiply the last number in the first column by the first figure of the root, and add the product io the number in the second column. Add the first figure of the root to the number in the first column. Annex one cipher to the last number in the first column, two ciphers to the last number in the second column, and annex the second period to the remainder in the third column. The last numbers in the second and third columns are, respectively, the first trial divisor and the first dividend.*

III. *Divide the first dividend by the first trial divisor to find the second figure of the root. Add the second figure of the root to the number in the first column, multiply the sum by the second figure of the root, and add the result to the first trial divisor to form the first complete divisor. Multiply the first complete divisor by the second figure of the root, and subtract the result from the first dividend in the third column. Add the second figure of the root to the number in the first column; multiply the sum by the second figure of the root, and add the product to the complete divisor. Add the second figure of the root to the number in the first column. Annex one cipher to the number in the first column, and two ciphers to the last number in the second column to form the second trial divisor. Annex the third period to the remainder in the third column for the second dividend.*

IV. *If there are more periods to be brought down, proceed as before. If there is a remainder after the root of the last period has been found, annex cipher periods, and proceed as before. The figures of the root thus obtained will be decimals.*

V. *If the root contains an interminable decimal, and it is desired to terminate the operation at some point, say the fifth significant figure, carry the operation one place farther, and if the sixth figure is 5 or greater, increase the fifth figure by 1 and omit the sign +.*

113. The method of Art. **108** can be applied to cube root (or any other root) as well as to square root. Thus, in example 3, Art. **110**, there are $5 + 1 = 6$ figures in the root

Extracting the root in the usual manner to $6 \div 2 = 3$, say 4 figures, we get for the first four figures 1,709. The last remainder is 8,556,171, and the next trial divisor, with the ciphers omitted, is 8,762,043. Hence, the next two figures of the root are $8,556,171 \div 8,762,043 = .976$, say .98. Therefore, the root is 1.70998.

EXAMPLES FOR PRACTICE

Find the cube root of

(a) $\frac{27}{512}$.
(b)   2 to five decimal places.
(c)   4,180,769,192.462 to five decimal places.
(d) $\frac{87}{125}$.
(e) $\frac{3}{8}$.
(f)   513,229.783302144 to three decimal places.

Ans. $\begin{cases} (a) \ \frac{3}{8} \\ (b) \ 1.25992+ \\ (c) \ 1,610.96238 \\ (d) \ .8862+ \\ (e) \ .7211+ \\ (f) \ 80.064 \end{cases}$

FOURTH, FIFTH, AND OTHER ROOTS

114. If the student has carefully studied the foregoing rules for square and cube root and thoroughly understands their application, he should be able to extend the process to other roots. For instance, consider the last example in Art. **110,** $\sqrt[3]{.05} = ?$ The first step is to point off into periods of *three* figures each. Note: First, the number *three* corresponds in value to the index figure ^{3}; second, the work is arranged in *three* columns, the number of columns corresponding in value to the index; third, the number of operations (additions) in the first column for each figure of the root is *three* (which number again corresponds to the index), in the second column one less than in the first (or two), and in the third column one less than in the second (or one, subtraction); fourth, one cipher is added to the number in the first column, two ciphers to the number in the second column, three ciphers (or a period of three figures) to the number in the third column, the number of operations in all cases corresponding to the number of the column, counting from the right, and the number of ciphers added corresponding to the number of the column, counting from the left. Bearing these facts in mind, it is unnecessary to remember a rule for each root, and by substituting for *three*, in the preceding sentence, *four*, *five*, etc. the fourth, fifth, etc. roots are readily found.

EXAMPLE.—What is the fourth root of .05, that is $\sqrt[4]{.05} = ?$

SOLUTION.—

			.0 5 0 0 (. 4 7 2 8
4	1 6	6 4	2 5 6
4	3 2	1 9 2	
8	4 8	2 5 6 0 0 0	2 4 4 0 0 0 0
4	4 8	7 5 3 8 3	2 3 1 9 6 8 1
1 2	9 6 0 0	3 3 1 3 8 3	1 2 0 3 1 9 0 0 0 0
4	1 1 6 9	8 3 9 0 9	8 3 5 9 0 0 6 5 6
1 6 0	1 0 7 6 9	4 1 5 2 9 2 0 0 0	3 6 7 2 8 9 3 4 4 0 0 0 0
7	1 2 1 8	2 6 5 8 3 2 8	3 3 7 3 4 9 4 1 1 2 2 5 6
1 6 7	1 1 9 8 7	4 1 7 9 5 0 3 2 8	2 9 9 3 9 9 3 2 7 7 4 4
7	1 2 6 7	2 6 6 5 8 6 4	
1 7 4	1 3 2 5 4 0 0	4 2 0 6 1 6 1 9 2 0 0 0	
7	3 7 6 4	1 0 7 0 5 7 2 0 3 2	
1 8 1	1 3 2 9 1 6 4	4 2 1 6 8 6 7 6 4 0 3 2	
7	3 7 6 8	1 0 7 1 7 8 1 3 7 6	
1 8 8 0	1 3 3 2 9 3 2	4 2 2 7 5 8 5 4 5 4 0 8	
2	3 7 7 2		
1 8 8 2	1 3 3 6 7 0 4 0 0		
2	1 5 1 1 0 4		
1 8 8 4	1 3 3 8 2 1 5 0 4		
2	1 5 1 1 6 8		
1 8 8 6	1 3 3 9 7 2 6 7 2		
2	1 5 1 2 3 2		
1 8 8 8 0	1 3 4 1 2 3 9 0 4		
8			
1 8 8 8 8			
8			
1 8 8 9 6			
8			
1 8 9 0 4			
8			
1 8 9 1 2			

$$\frac{2993993277440000}{422758545408000} = \frac{2993993277440}{422758545408} = 7.082+$$

Hence, $\sqrt[4]{.05}$, correct to 7 significant figures, is .4728708+.

Ans.

Explanation.—Since the index is 4 the number must be pointed off into periods of *four* figures each and the work must be arranged in *four* columns. Since the given number is a decimal and contains but two figures it is necessary to annex two ciphers to complete the first period, which must contain *four* figures.

The first figure of the root is 4, for $4^4 = 256$ and $5^4 = 625$, which is greater than 500. Write the first figure of the root at the head of the first column; multiply it by itself and write the product (16) at the head of the second column; multiply this last number by the first figure of the root and write the product (64) at the head of the third column; multiply the last number by the first figure of the root and write the product (256) under the first period in the fourth column. Subtracting 256 from 500 the remainder is 244.

Add the first figure of the root to the number in the first column, multiply the sum (8) by the first figure of the root, and add the product to the number in the second column obtaining 48 for the sum. Multiply this last number by the first figure of the root and add the product to the number in the third column, obtaining 256 for the sum.

Repeat the operations just described for the first and second columns and repeat again for the first column. Now annex one cipher to the number in the first column, two ciphers to the number in the second column, three ciphers to the number in the third column, and four ciphers to the number in the fourth column. The first dividend is 2440000 and the first trial divisor is 256000. The quotient obtained by dividing the first dividend by the first trial divisor is 9+, but on trying 9 for the second figure of the root, it was found to be too large; 8 was also found to be too large, and it was necessary to use 7.

The student will readily follow the remainder of the work. It may be remarked that the most difficult part of the operation is to determine the second figure of the root, but when it has once been determined, the first figure of the quotient obtained by dividing any dividend by its corresponding trial divisor will always be the next figure of the root.

Having obtained four figures of the root three more can be determined by applying the principle of Arts. **108** and **113.** If five figures only had been required the last two could have been obtained by dividing the third dividend by the third trial divisor. Thus, omitting unnecessary ciphers, $\frac{3672893440}{420616192} = 8.73+$. Hence, the fourth and fifth figures are 87.

115. It is usually easier (and there is less liability of making mistakes) to extract the square root and then extract the square root of the result than to extract the fourth root direct. Thus, $\sqrt{\sqrt{.05}} = \sqrt{.22360679} = .4728708$.

As previously stated, the fourth root is very seldom required; the fifth root, however, is required with some frequency in certain calculations (see Art. **75**). The process is here illustrated by two examples.

EXAMPLE 1.— $\sqrt[3]{909,203,700,718,879,776}$ = ?

SOLUTION.—

$909'203'700'718'879'776(3906$ Ans.
243
666 20370
659 24199
6961710718879776
6961710718879776

3	9
3	18
6	27
3	27
9	54
3	36
12	9000
3	1431
150	10431
9	1512
159	11943
9	1593
168	13536
9	1674
177	152100000
9	117036
186	152217036
9	
19500	
6	
19506	

27
81
108
162
270000
93879
363879
107487
471366
121824
593190000000
913302216
594103302216

81
324
4050000
3274911
7324911
4242294
1156720500000000
3564619813296
11602851119813296

EXPLANATION.—Since the index is 5 the given number is pointed off into periods of five figures each and the work is arranged in five columns. The first figure of the root is 3, since $3^5 = 243$ and $4^5 = 1,024$. The work should be evident from what has preceded. Note that the first dividend contains the first trial divisor 16 + times; hence, 9 was tried for the second figure of the root. Note further that the second dividend 69617107188 will not contain the second trial divisor 115672050000; hence, another cipher was annexed to the number in the first column, two more to the number in the second column, three more to the number in the third column, four more to the number in the fourth column, and the next period was annexed to the number in the fifth column. As will be seen, the given number is a perfect fifth power.

EXAMPLE 2.— $\sqrt[5]{.00009}$ = ?

SOLUTION.— .00009(.1551

1	1	1	1	1
1	2	3	4	800000
2	3	4	50000	659375
1	3	6	81875	
3	6	10000	131875	14062500000
1	4	6375	121250	13528596875
4	1000	16375	2531250000	
1	275	7875	174469375	53390312500000
50	1275	24250	2705719375	28897294032751
5	300	9500	180283750	
55	1575	33750000	28860031250000	24493018467249
5	325	1143875	37262782751	
60	1900	34893875	28897294032751	
5	350	1162875	37286823254	
65	225000	36056750	28934580856005	
5	3775	1182000		
70	228775	37238750000		
5	3800	24032751		
750	232575	37262782751		
5	3825	24040503		
755	236400	37286823254		
5	3850	24048256		
760	24025000	37310871510		
5	7751			
765	24032751			
5	7752			
770	24040503			
5	7753			
7750	24048256			
1	7754			
7751	24056010			
1				
7752				
1				
7753				
1				
7754				
1				
7755				

$$\frac{244930184672490}{28934580856005} = 8.464+.$$

Hence, $\sqrt[5]{.00009}$ = .1551846+. Ans.

EXPLANATION.—The quotient obtained by dividing the first dividend by the first trial divisor is 16; hence, 9 was tried for the second figure of the root and was found to be too large; 8, 7, and 6 were successively tried and all found to be too large, and 5 was found to be the second figure of the root. The remainder of the work should be evident.

ARITHMETIC.

(SECTION 6.)

INTRODUCTION.

116. The subject of ratio and proportion is one of the most useful of all the subjects that are taught in Arithmetic. The student will find frequent use for the principles treated of in the following pages, and is requested to study them with great care.

The student should carefully study the definitions, constantly referring to them from time to time as he progresses with the subject; he should note particularly those articles relating to inverse ratio and inverse proportion. The idea of inverse proportion is usually a difficult one for the student to grasp, but a careful study of Art. **149** and of the examples in Arts. **150** and **151** will make the matter clear to him.

Although some of the examples included between Arts. **130** and **153,** inclusive, may be solved by other methods than the use of proportion, all the examples included between the above articles, and those of similar nature included in the Examination Questions, must be solved by applying the principles of proportion; no other method of solution will be accepted. The student should study very carefully Arts. **128, 129, 143,** and **144;** they are very important, and they should be thoroughly understood.

The subject of compound proportion as treated in ordinary textbooks on Arithmetic usually proves of considerable difficulty to the student. The method here given, while not entirely new, presents the matter in a clearer light, we believe, than any other we have ever seen.

RATIO.

117. Suppose that it is desired to compare two numbers, say 20 and 4. If we wish to know how many times larger 20 is than 4, we divide 20 by 4 and obtain 5 for the quotient; thus, $20 \div 4 = 5$. Hence, we say that 20 is 5 times as large as 4, i. e., 20 contains 5 times as many units as 4. Again, suppose we desire to know what part of 20 is 4. We then divide 4 by 20 and obtain $\frac{1}{5}$; thus, $4 \div 20 = \frac{1}{5}$, or .2. Hence, 4 is $\frac{1}{5}$ or .2 of 20. This operation of comparing two numbers is termed *finding the ratio* of the two numbers. Ratio, then, is a comparison. It is evident that the two numbers to be compared must be expressed in the same unit; in other words, the two numbers must both be abstract numbers or concrete numbers of the same kind. For example, it would be absurd to compare 20 horses with 4 birds, or 20 horses with 4. Hence, **ratio** may be defined as a comparison between two numbers of the same kind.

118. A ratio may be expressed in three ways; thus, if it is desired to compare 20 and 4, and express this comparison as a ratio, it may be done as follows: $20 \div 4$, $20:4$, or $\frac{20}{4}$. All three are read *the ratio of 20 to 4*. The ratio of 4 to 20 would be expressed thus: $4 \div 20$, $4:20$, or $\frac{4}{20}$. The first method of expressing a ratio, although correct, is seldom or never used; the second form is the one oftenest met with, while the third is rapidly growing in favor, and is likely to supersede the second. The third form, called the fractional form, is preferred by modern mathematicians, and possesses great advantages to students of algebra and of higher mathematical subjects. The second form seems to be better adapted to arithmetical subjects, and is the one we shall ordinarily adopt. There is still another way of expressing a ratio, though seldom or never used in the case of a simple ratio like that given above. Instead of the colon, a straight vertical line is used; thus, $20 \mid 4$.

119. The **terms** of a ratio are the two numbers to be compared; thus, in the above ratio, 20 and 4 are the terms. When both terms are considered together they are called a **couplet;** when considered separately, the first term is called the **antecedent,** and the second term, the **consequent.** Thus, in the ratio 20 : 4, 20 and 4 form a couplet, and 20 is the antecedent, and 4, the consequent.

120. A ratio may be **direct** or **inverse.** The *direct ratio* of 20 to 4 is 20 : 4, while the *inverse ratio* of 20 to 4 is 4 : 20. The direct ratio of 4 to 20 is 4 : 20, and the inverse ratio is 20 : 4. An inverse ratio is sometimes called a **reciprocal** ratio. The **reciprocal** of a number is 1 divided by the number. Thus, the reciprocal of 17 is $\frac{1}{17}$; of $\frac{3}{8}$ is $1 \div \frac{3}{8} = \frac{8}{3}$; i. e., the reciprocal of a fraction is the fraction inverted. Hence, the inverse ratio of 20 to 4 may be expressed as 4 : 20 or as $\frac{1}{20} : \frac{1}{4}$. Both have equal values; for,

$$4 \div 20 = \tfrac{1}{5}, \text{ and } \frac{1}{20} \div \frac{1}{4} = \frac{1}{20} \times \frac{4}{1} = \tfrac{1}{5}.$$

121. The term **vary** implies a ratio. When we say that two numbers vary as some other two numbers, we mean that the ratio between the first two numbers is the same as the ratio between the other two numbers.

122. The **value** of a ratio is the result obtained by performing the division indicated. Thus, the value of the ratio 20 : 4 is 5; it is the quotient obtained by dividing the antecedent by the consequent.

123. By expressing the ratio in the fractional form, for example, the ratio of 20 to 4 as $\frac{20}{4}$, it is easy to see, from the laws of fractions, that if both terms be multiplied or both divided by the same number it will not alter the value of the ratio. Thus,

$$\frac{20}{4} = \frac{20 \times 5}{4 \times 5} = \frac{100}{20}; \text{ and } \frac{20}{4} = \frac{20 \div 4}{4 \div 4} = \frac{5}{1}.$$

124. It is also evident, from the laws of fractions, that multiplying the antecedent or dividing the consequent multiplies the ratio, and dividing the antecedent or multiplying the consequent divides the ratio.

125. When a ratio is expressed in words, as the ratio of 20 to 4, the first number named is always regarded as the antecedent and the second as the consequent, without regard to whether the ratio itself is direct or inverse. *When not otherwise specified, all ratios are understood to be direct.* To express an inverse ratio the simplest way of doing it is to express it as if it were a direct ratio, with the first number named as the antecedent, and then transpose the antecedent to the place occupied by the consequent and the consequent to the place occupied by the antecedent; or if expressed in the fractional form, invert the fraction. Thus, to express the inverse ratio of 20 to 4, first write it $20:4$, and then, transposing the terms, as $4:20$; or as $\frac{20}{4}$, and then inverting, as $\frac{4}{20}$. Or, the reciprocals of the numbers may be taken, as explained above. To **invert** a ratio is to transpose its terms.

EXAMPLES FOR PRACTICE.

126. What is the value of the ratio of:

(a) $98:49$?

(b) $\$45 : \$9$?

(c) $6\frac{1}{4} : \frac{3}{4}$?

(d) $3.5 : 4.5$?

(e) The inverse ratio of 76 to 19 ?

(f) The inverse ratio of 49 to 98 ?

(g) The inverse ratio of 18 to 24 ?

(h) The inverse ratio of 9 to 15 ?

(i) The ratio of 10 to 3, multiplied by 3 ?

(j) The ratio of 35 to 49, multiplied by 7 ?

(k) The ratio of 18 to 64, divided by 9 ?

(l) The ratio of 14 to 28, divided by 5 ?

Ans.

(a) 2.

(b) 5.

(c) $12\frac{1}{2}$.

(d) $.77\frac{7}{9}$.

(e) $\frac{1}{4}$.

(f) 2.

(g) $1\frac{1}{3}$.

(h) $1\frac{2}{3}$.

(i) 10.

(j) 5.

(k) $\frac{1}{32}$.

(l) $\frac{1}{10}$.

---

127. Instead of expressing the value of a ratio by a single number as above, it is customary to express it by means of another ratio in which the consequent is 1. Thus, suppose that it is desired to find the ratio of the weights of two pieces of iron, one weighing 45 pounds and the other weighing 30 pounds. The ratio of the heavier to the lighter is then 45 : 30, an inconvenient expression. Using the fractional form, we have $\frac{45}{30}$. Dividing both terms by 30, the consequent, we obtain $\frac{1\frac{1}{2}}{1}$ or $1\frac{1}{2} : 1$. This is the same result as obtained above, for $1\frac{1}{2} \div 1 = 1\frac{1}{2}$, and $45 \div 30 = 1\frac{1}{2}$.

128. A ratio may be squared, cubed, or raised to any power, or any root of it may be taken. Thus, if the ratio of two numbers is $105 : 63$, and it is desired to cube this ratio, the cube may be expressed as $105^3 : 63^3$. That this is correct is readily seen; for, expressing the ratio in the fractional form, it becomes $\frac{105}{63}$, and the cube is $\left(\frac{105}{63}\right)^3 = \frac{105^3}{63^3}$ $= 105^3 : 63^3$. Also, if it is desired to extract the cube root of the ratio $105^3 : 63^3$, it may be done by simply dividing the exponents by 3, obtaining $105 : 63$. This may be proved in the same way as in the case of cubing the ratio. Thus,

$$105^3 : 63^3 = \left(\frac{105}{63}\right)^3, \text{ and } \sqrt[3]{\left(\frac{105}{63}\right)^3} = \frac{105}{63} = 105 : 63.$$

129. Since $\left(\frac{105}{63}\right)^3 = \left(\frac{5}{3}\right)^3$, it follows that $105^3 : 63^3$ $= 5^3 : 3^3$ (this expression is read, the ratio of 105 cubed to 63 cubed equals the ratio of 5 cubed to 3 cubed), and, hence, that the antecedent and consequent may both be multiplied or both divided by the same number, irrespective of any indicated powers or roots, without altering the value of the ratio. Thus, $24^2 : 18^2 = 4^2 : 3^2$. For, performing the operations indicated by the exponents, $24^2 = 576$ and $18^2 = 324$. Hence, $576 : 324 = 1\frac{7}{9}$ or $1\frac{7}{9} : 1$. Also, 4^2 $= 16$ and $3^2 = 9$; hence, $16 : 9 = 1\frac{7}{9}$ or $1\frac{7}{9} : 1$, the same result as before. Also, $24^2 : 18^2 = \frac{24^2}{18^2} = \left(\frac{24}{18}\right)^2 = \left(\frac{4}{3}\right)^2$ $= \frac{4^2}{3^2} = 4^2 : 3^2$.

The statement may be proved for roots in the same manner. Thus $\sqrt[3]{24^3} : \sqrt[3]{18^3} = \sqrt[3]{4^3} : \sqrt[3]{3^3}$. For, the $\sqrt[3]{24^3}$ = 24 and $\sqrt[3]{18^3}$ = 18; and, $24 : 18 = 1\frac{1}{3}$ or $1\frac{1}{3} : 1$. Also, $\sqrt[3]{4^3} = 4$ and $\sqrt[3]{3^3} = 3$; $4 : 3 = 1\frac{1}{3}$ or $1\frac{1}{3} : 1$.

If the numbers composing the antecedent and consequent have different exponents, or if different roots of those numbers are indicated, the operations above described cannot be performed. This is evident; for, consider the ratio of $4^2 : 8^3$. When expressed in the fractional form it becomes $\frac{4^2}{8^3}$, which cannot be expressed either as $\left(\frac{4}{8}\right)^2$ or as $\left(\frac{4}{8}\right)^3$, and, hence, cannot be reduced as described above.

———

PROPORTION.

130. **Proportion** is an equality of ratios, the equality being indicated by the double colon (::) or by the sign of equality (=). Thus, to write in the form of a proportion the two equal ratios, $8 : 4$ and $6 : 3$, which both have the same value, 2, we may employ one of the three following forms:

$$8 : 4 :: 6 : 3 \qquad (1)$$
$$8 : 4 = 6 : 3 \qquad (2)$$
$$\frac{8}{4} = \frac{6}{3} \qquad (3)$$

131. The first form is the one most extensively used, by reason of its having been exclusively employed in all the older works on mathematics. The second and third forms are being adopted by all modern writers on mathematical subjects, and, in time, will probably entirely supersede the first form. In this subject we shall adopt the second form, unless some statement can be made clearer by using the third form.

132. A proportion may be read in two ways. The old way to read the above proportion was—*8 is to 4 as 6 is to 3;* the new way is—*the ratio of 8 to 4 equals the ratio of 6 to 3.* The student may read it either way, but we recommend the latter.

133. Each ratio of a proportion is termed a **couplet.** In the above proportion, $8:4$ is a couplet, and so is $6:3$.

134. The numbers forming the proportion are called **terms;** and they are numbered consecutively from left to right, thus: *first   second   third   fourth*
$$8 \ : \ 4 \ = \ 6 \ : \ 3$$
Hence, in any proportion, the ratio of the first term to the second term equals the ratio of the third term to the fourth term.

135. The first and fourth terms of a proportion are called the **extremes,** and the second and third terms, the **means.** Thus, in the foregoing proportion, 8 and 3 are the extremes and 4 and 6 are the means.

136. A **direct proportion** is one in which both couplets are direct ratios.

137. An **inverse proportion** is one which requires one of the couplets to be expressed as an inverse ratio. Thus, 8 is to 4 inversely as 3 is to 6 must be written $8:4 = 6:3$; i. e., the second ratio (couplet) must be inverted.

138. Proportion forms one of the most useful sections of arithmetic. In our grandfathers' arithmetics, it was called " The rule of three."

139. **Rule I.**—*In any proportion, the product of the extremes equals the product of the means.*
Thus, in the proportion,
$$17:51 = 14:42.$$
$17 \times 42 = 51 \times 14$, since both products equal 714.

140. **Rule II.**—*The product of the extremes divided by either mean gives the other mean.*

EXAMPLE.—What is the third term of the proportion $17 : 51 = \ :42$?
SOLUTION.—Applying rule II, $17 \times 42 = 714$, and $714 \div 51 = 14$. Ans.

141. **Rule III.**—*The product of the means divided by either extreme gives the other extreme.*

EXAMPLE.—What is the first term of the proportion $:51 = 14:42$?
SOLUTION.—Applying rule III, $51 \times 14 = 714$, and $714 \div 42 = 17$.
Ans.

142. When stating a proportion in which one of the terms is unknown, represent the missing term by a letter, as x. Thus, the last example would be written,

$$x:51 = 14:42$$

and for the value of x we have $x = \dfrac{51 \times 14}{42} = 17$.

143. If the same operations (addition and subtraction excepted) be performed upon *all* the terms of a proportion, the proportion is not thereby destroyed. In other words, if all the terms of a proportion be (1) multiplied or (2) divided by the same number; (3) if all the terms be raised to the same power; (4) if the same root of all the terms be taken, or (5) if both couplets be inverted, the proportion still holds. We will prove these statements by a numerical example, and the student can satisfy himself by other similar ones. The fractional form will be used, as it is better suited to the purpose. Consider the proportion $8:4 = 6:3$. Expressing it in the third form, it becomes $\dfrac{8}{4} = \dfrac{6}{3}$. What we are to prove is that if any of the five operations enumerated above be performed upon all the terms of the proportion, the first fraction will still equal the second fraction.

1. Multiplying all the terms by any number, say 7, $\dfrac{8 \times 7}{4 \times 7}$ $= \dfrac{6 \times 7}{3 \times 7}$; or $\dfrac{56}{28} = \dfrac{42}{21}$. Now $\dfrac{56}{28}$ evidently equals $\dfrac{42}{21}$, since the value of either ratio is 2, and the same is true of the original proportion.

2. Dividing all the terms by any number, say 7, $\dfrac{8 \div 7}{4 \div 7}$ $= \dfrac{6 \div 7}{3 \div 7}$; or $\dfrac{\frac{8}{7}}{\frac{4}{7}} = \dfrac{\frac{6}{7}}{\frac{3}{7}}$. But $\dfrac{8}{7} \div \dfrac{4}{7} = 2$, and $\dfrac{6}{7} \div \dfrac{3}{7} = 2$ also, the same as in the original proportion.

3. Raising all the terms to the same power, say the cube, $\dfrac{8^3}{4^3} = \dfrac{6^3}{3^3}$. This is evidently true, since $\dfrac{8^3}{4^3} = \left(\dfrac{8}{4}\right)^3 = 2^3 = 8$, and $\dfrac{6^3}{3^3} = \left(\dfrac{6}{3}\right)^3 = 2^3 = 8$ also.

4.   Extracting the same root of all the terms, say the cube root, $\dfrac{\sqrt[3]{8}}{\sqrt[3]{4}} = \dfrac{\sqrt[3]{6}}{\sqrt[3]{3}}$.   It is evident that this is likewise true, since $\dfrac{\sqrt[3]{8}}{\sqrt[3]{4}} = \sqrt[3]{\dfrac{8}{4}} = \sqrt[3]{2}$, and $\dfrac{\sqrt[3]{6}}{\sqrt[3]{3}} = \sqrt[3]{\dfrac{6}{3}} = \sqrt[3]{2}$ also.

5.   Inverting both couplets, $\dfrac{4}{8} = \dfrac{3}{6}$, which is true, since both equal $\frac{1}{2}$.

144.   If both terms of either couplet be multiplied or both divided by the same number, the proportion is not destroyed.   This should be evident from the preceding article, and also from Art. **123.**   Hence, in any proportion, equal factors may be canceled from the terms of a couplet, before applying rule II or III.   Thus, the proportion $45 : 9 = x : 7.1$, we may divide both terms of the first couplet by 9 (that is, cancel 9 from both terms), obtaining $5 : 1 = x : 7.1$, whence $x = 7.1 \times 5 \div 1 = 35.5$.   (See Art. **129.**)

145.   The principle of all calculations in proportion is this: *Three of the terms are always given, and the remaining one is to be found.*

146.   EXAMPLE.—If 4 men can earn $25 in one week, how much can 12 men earn in the same time?

SOLUTION.—The required term must bear the same relation to the given term of the same kind, as one of the remaining terms bears to the other remaining term. We can then form a proportion by which the required term may be found.

The first question the student must ask himself in every calculation by proportion is:

"What is it I want to find?"

In this case it is dollars. We have two sets of men, one set earning $25, and we want to know how many dollars the other set earns. It is evident that the amount 12 men earn bears the same relation to the amount 4 men earn as 12 men bear to 4 men. Hence, we have the proportion, the amount 12 men earn is to $25 as 12 men are to 4 men, or, since either extreme equals the product of the means divided by the other extreme, we have

The amount 12 men earn : $25 :: 12 men : 4 men,

or the amount 12 men earn $= \dfrac{\$25 \times 12}{4} = \$75$.   Ans.

Since it matters not which place x, or the required term, occupies, the problem could be stated in any of the following forms, the value of x being the same in each:

(*a*) $25 : the amount 12 men earn = 4 men : 12 men; or the amount 12 men earn $= \dfrac{\$25 \times 12}{4}$, or $75, since either mean equals the product of the extremes divided by the other mean.

(*b*) 4 men : 12 men = $25 : the amount that 12 men earn; or the amount that 12 men earn $= \dfrac{\$25 \times 12}{4}$, or $75, since either extreme equals the product of the means divided by the other extreme.

(*c*) 12 men : 4 men = the amount 12 men earn : $25; or the amount that 12 men earn $= \dfrac{\$25 \times 12}{4}$, or $75, since either mean equals the product of the extremes divided by the other mean.

147. If the proportion is an inverse one, first form it as though it were a direct proportion, and then invert one of the couplets.

EXAMPLES FOR PRACTICE.

148. Find the value of x in each of the following:

(*a*)	$16 : $64 :: x : $4.		(*a*)	$x = $1.
(*b*)	x : 85 :: 10 : 17.		(*b*)	$x = 50$.
(*c*)	24 : x :: 15 : 40.		(*c*)	$x = 64$.
(*d*)	18 : 94 :: 2 : x.	Ans.	(*d*)	$x = 10\frac{4}{9}$.
(*e*)	$75 : $100 = x : 100.		(*e*)	$x = 75$.
(*f*)	15 pwt. : x = 21 : 10.		(*f*)	$x = 7\frac{1}{7}$ pwt.
(*g*)	x : 75 yd. = $15 : $5.		(*g*)	$x = 225$ yd.

1. If 75 pounds of lead cost $2.10, what would 125 pounds cost at the same rate ?   Ans. $3.50.

2. If A does a piece of work in 4 days and B does it in 7 days, how long will it take A to do what B does in 63 days ?   Ans. 36 days.

3. The circumferences of any two circles are to each other as their diameters. If the circumference of a circle 7 inches in diameter is 22 inches, what will be the circumference of a circle 31 inches in diameter ?
                                          Ans. $97\frac{3}{7}$ inches.

INVERSE PROPORTION.

149. In Art. **137,** an inverse proportion was defined as one which required one of the couplets to be expressed as an inverse ratio. Sometimes the word *inverse* occurs in the statement of the example; in such cases, the proportion can be written directly, merely inverting one of the couplets. But it frequently happens that only by carefully studying the conditions of the example, can it be ascertained whether the proportion is direct or inverse. When in doubt, the student can always satisfy himself as to whether the proportion is direct or inverse by first ascertaining what is required, and stating the proportion as a direct proportion. Then, in order that the proportion may be true, if the first term is smaller than the second term, the third term must be smaller than the fourth; or if the first term is larger than the second term, the third term must be larger than the fourth term. Keeping this in mind, the student can always tell whether the required term will be larger or smaller than the other term of the couplet to which the required term belongs. Having determined this, the student then refers to the example, and ascertains from its conditions whether the required term is to be larger or smaller than the other term of the same kind. If the two determinations agree, the proportion is direct, otherwise it is inverse, and one of the couplets must be inverted.

150. EXAMPLE.—If A's *rate* of doing work is to B's as $5 : 7$, and A does a piece of work in 42 days, in what time will B do it?

SOLUTION.—The required term is the number of days it will take B to do the work. Hence, stating as a direct proportion,

$$5 : 7 = 42 : x.$$

Now, since 7 is greater than 5, x will be greater than 42. But, referring to the statement of the example, it is easy to see that B works faster than A; hence it will take B a less number of days to do the work than A. Therefore, the proportion is an inverse one, and should be stated

$$5 : 7 = x : 42$$

from which $x = \dfrac{5 \times 42}{7} = 30$ days. Ans.

Had the example been stated thus: The time that A requires to do a piece of work is to the time that B requires, as $5 : 7$; A can do it in 42 days, in what time can B do it? it is evident that it would take B a longer time to do the work than it would A; hence, x would be greater than 42, and the proportion would be direct, the value of x being $\dfrac{7 \times 42}{5}$ = 58.8 days.

40—10

151. Solve the following:

1. If a pump which discharges 4 gal. of water per min. can fill a tank in 20 hr., how long will it take a pump discharging 12 gal. per min. to fill it? Ans. $6\frac{2}{3}$ hr.

2. If a pump discharges 90 gal. of water in 20 hr., in what time will it discharge 144 gal.? Ans. 32 hr.

3. The weight of any gas (the volume and pressure remaining the same) varies inversely as the absolute temperature. If a certain quantity of some gas weighs 2.927 lb. when the absolute temperature is 525°, what will the same volume of gas weigh when the absolute temperature is 600°, the pressure remaining the same? Ans. 2.561+ lb.

4. If 50 cu. ft. of air weigh 4.2 pounds when the absolute temperature is 562°, what will be the absolute temperature when the same volume weighs 5.8 pounds, the pressure being the same in both cases? Ans. 407°, very nearly.

POWERS AND ROOTS IN PROPORTION.

152. It was stated in Art. **128** that a ratio could be raised to any power or any root of it might be taken. A proportion is frequently stated in such a manner that one of the couplets must be raised to some power or some root of it must be taken. In all such cases, both terms of the couplet so affected *must be raised to the same power or the same root of both terms must be taken.*

153. EXAMPLE.—Knowing that the weight of a sphere varies as the cube of its diameter, what is the weight of a sphere 6 inches in diameter if a sphere 8 inches in diameter of the same material weighs 180 pounds?

SOLUTION.—This is evidently a direct proportion. Hence, we write
$$6^3 : 8^3 = x : 180.$$
Dividing both terms of the first couplet by 2^3 (see Art. **129**)
$$3^3 : 4^3 = x : 180, \text{ or } 27 : 64 = x : 180;$$
whence, $x = \dfrac{27 \times 180}{64} = 75\frac{15}{16}$ pounds. Ans.

EXAMPLE.—A sphere 8 inches in diameter weighs 180 pounds; what is the diameter of another sphere of the same material which weighs $75\frac{15}{16}$ pounds?

SOLUTION.—Since the weights of any two spheres are to each other as the cubes of their diameters, we have the proportion
$$180 : 75\frac{15}{16} = 8^3 : x^3.$$

The required term, x, must be cubed, because the other term of the couplet is cubed. But, $8^3 = 512$; hence,

$$180 : 75\tfrac{15}{16} = 512 : x^3, \text{ or } x^3 = \frac{75\tfrac{15}{16} \times 512}{180} = 216;$$

whence, $x = \sqrt[3]{216} = 6$ inches. Ans.

154. Since taking the same root of all the terms of a proportion does not change its value (Art. **143**), the above example might have been solved by extracting the cube root of all the numbers, thus obtaining $\sqrt[3]{180} : \sqrt[3]{75\tfrac{15}{16}} = 8 : x$;

whence, $x = \dfrac{8 \times \sqrt[3]{75\tfrac{15}{16}}}{\sqrt[3]{180}} = 8 \times \sqrt[3]{\dfrac{75\tfrac{15}{16}}{180}} = 8\sqrt[3]{\dfrac{1,215}{2,880}} = 8\sqrt[3]{\dfrac{27}{64}}$

$= 8 \times \tfrac{3}{4} = 6$ inches. The process, however, is longer and is not so direct, and the first method is to be preferred.

155. If two cylinders have equal volumes, but different diameters, the diameters are to each other inversely as the square roots of their lengths. Hence, if it is desired to find the diameter of a cylinder that is to be 15 inches long, and which shall have the same volume as one that is 9 inches in diameter and 12 inches long, we write the proportion

$$9 : x = \sqrt{15} : \sqrt{12}.$$

Since neither 12 nor 15 are perfect squares, we square all the terms (Arts. **154** and **143**) and obtain

$$81 : x^2 = 15 : 12; \text{ whence, } x^2 = \frac{81 \times 12}{15} = 64.8,$$

and $x = \sqrt{64.8} = 8.05$ inches = diameter of **15**-inch cylinder.

EXAMPLES FOR PRACTICE.

156. Solve the following examples:

1. The intensity of light varies inversely as the square of the distance from the source of light. If a gas jet illuminates an object 30 feet away with a certain distinctness, how much brighter will the object be at a distance of 20 feet ?   Ans. $2\tfrac{1}{4}$ times as bright.

2. In the last example, suppose that the object had been 40 feet from the gas jet; how bright would it have been, compared with its brightness at 30 feet from the gas jet ?   Ans. $\tfrac{9}{16}$ as bright.

3. When comparing one light with another, the intensities of their illuminating powers vary as the squares of their distances from the

source. If a man can just distinguish the time indicated by his watch, 50 feet from a certain light, at what distance could he distinguish the time from a light 3 times as powerful ?   Ans. 86.6+ feet.

4. The quantity of air flowing through a mine varies directly as the square root of the pressure. If 60,000 cubic feet of air flow per min. ute when the pressure is 2.8 pounds per square foot, how much wil' flow when the pressure is 3.6 pounds per square foot ?
                    Ans. 68,034 cu. ft. per min., nearly.

5. In the last example, suppose that 70,000 cubic feet per minute had been required; what would be the pressure necessary for this quantity ?   Ans. 3.81+ lb. per sq. ft.

CAUSES AND EFFECTS.

157. Many examples in proportion may be more easily solved by using the principle of *cause and effect*. That which may be regarded as producing a change or alteration in something, or as accomplishing something, may be called a **cause,** and the change or alteration, or thing accomplished, as the **effect.**

158. *Like causes produce like effects.* Hence, when two causes of the same kind produce two effects of the same kind, the ratio of the causes equals the ratio of the effects; in other words the first cause is to the second cause as the first effect is to the second effect. Thus, in the question— if 3 men can lift 1,400 pounds, how many pounds can 7 men lift?—we call 3 men and 7 men the *causes* (since they accomplish something, viz., the lifting of the weight), the number of pounds lifted, viz., 1,400 pounds and x pounds, are the effects. If we call 3 men the first cause, 1,400 pounds is the first effect; 7 men is the second cause, and x pounds is the second effect. Hence, we may write

$$\underset{\text{1st cause}}{3} : \underset{\text{2d cause}}{7} = \underset{\text{1st effect}}{1,400} : \underset{\text{2d effect}}{x}$$

whence $x = \dfrac{7 \times 1,400}{3} = 3,266\tfrac{2}{3}$ pounds.

159. The principle of cause and effect is extremely useful in the solution of examples in compound proportion, as we shall now show.

COMPOUND PROPORTION.

160. All the cases of proportion so far considered have been cases of **simple proportion ;** i. e., each term has been composed of but one number. There are many cases, however, in which two or all the terms have more than one number in them; all such cases belong to **compound proportion.** In all·examples in compound proportion, both causes or both effects or all four consist of more than two numbers. We will illustrate this by an

EXAMPLE.—If 40 men earn $1,280 in 16 days, how much will 36 men earn in 31 days?

SOLUTION.—Since 40 men earn something, 40 men is a cause, and since they take 16 days in which to earn something, 16 days is also a cause. ·For the same reason 36 men and 31 days are also causes. The effects, that which is earned, are 1,280 dollars and x dollars. Then, 40 men and 16 days make up the first cause, and 36 men and 31 days make up the second cause. $1,280 is the first effect, and $$x$ is the second effect. Hence, we write

$$\begin{array}{cc} \textit{1st cause} & \textit{2d cause} \\ 40 & 36 \\ 16 & 31 \end{array} \quad \begin{array}{cc} \textit{1st effect} & \textit{2d effect} \\ 1{,}280 & x \end{array}$$

$$\frac{40}{16} : \frac{36}{31} = 1{,}280 : x$$

Now, instead of using the colon to express the ratio, we shall use the vertical line (see Art. **118**), and the above becomes

$$\left.\frac{40}{16}\right|\frac{36}{31} = 1{,}280 \left|\ x.\right.$$

In the last expression, the product of all the numbers included between the vertical lines must equal the product of all the numbers without them; i. e., $36 \times 31 \times 1{,}280 = 40 \times 16 \times x$.

$$\text{Or } x = \frac{36 \times 31 \times \overset{\overset{2}{80}}{\cancel{1280}}}{\cancel{40} \times \cancel{16}} = \$2{,}232. \text{ Ans.}$$

161. The above might have been solved by canceling factors of the numbers in the original proportion. For, if any number within the lines has a factor common to any number without the lines, that factor may be canceled from both numbers. Thus,

$$\left.\frac{\cancel{40}}{\cancel{16}}\right|\frac{36}{31} = \frac{\overset{\overset{2}{80}}{\cancel{1280}}}{}\left|\ x.\right.$$

16 is contained in 1,280, 80 times. Cancel 16 and 1,280, and write 80 above 1,280. 40 is contained in 80, 2 times. Cancel

40 and 80, and write 2 above 80. Now, since there are no more numbers that can be canceled, $x = 36 \times 31 \times 2 = \$2,232$, the same result as was obtained in the preceding article.

162. Rule.—*Write all the numbers forming the first cause in a vertical column, and draw a vertical line ; on the other side of this line write in a vertical column all the numbers forming the second cause. Write the sign of equality to the right of the second column, and on the right of this form a third column of the numbers composing the first effect, drawing a vertical line to the right ; on the other side of this line, write for a fourth column, the numbers composing the second effect. There must be as many numbers in the second cause as in the first cause, and in the second effect as in the first effect ; hence, if any term is wanting, write x in its place. Multiply together all the numbers within the vertical lines, and also all those without the lines (canceling previously, if possible), and divide the product of those numbers which do not contain x by the product of the others in which x occurs, and the result will be the value of x.*

163. Example.—If 40 men can dig a ditch 720 feet long, 5 feet wide, and 4 feet deep in a certain time, how long a ditch 6 feet deep and 3 feet wide could 24 men dig in the same time ?

Solution.—Here 40 men and 24 men are the causes, and the two ditches are the effects. Hence,

$$
\begin{array}{c|c|c}
 & & \cancel{3} \\
 & & \cancel{18} \\
 & & \cancel{720} \quad x \\
\cancel{40} \;\Big|\; 24 = & & 5 \quad \cancel{3} \text{ whence, } x = 24 \times 5 \times 4 = 480 \text{ feet. Ans.} \\
 & & 4 \quad \cancel{6}
\end{array}
$$

164. Example.—The volume of a cylinder varies directly as its length and directly as the square of its diameter. If the volume of a cylinder 10 inches in diameter and 20 inches long is 1,570.8 cubic inches, what is the volume of another cylinder 16 inches in diameter and 24 inches long ?

Solution.—In this example, either the dimensions or the volumes may be considered the causes ; say we take the dimensions for the causes. Then, squaring the diameters,

$$
\begin{array}{c|c}
10^2 & 16^2 \\
20 & 24
\end{array} = 1,570.8 \quad
\begin{array}{c|c}
& \\
x, \text{ or }
\end{array}
\begin{array}{c|c}
100 & 256 \\
\cancel{20} & \cancel{24} \\
5 & 6
\end{array} = 1,570.8 \quad \Big| \; x;
$$

whence, $x = \dfrac{256 \times 6 \times 1,570.8}{5 \times 100} = 4,825.4976$ cubic inches. Ans.

165. EXAMPLE.—If a block of granite 8 ft. long, 5 ft. wide, and 3 ft. thick weighs 7,200 lb., what will be the weight of a block of granite 12 ft. long, 8 ft. wide, and 5 ft. thick ?

SOLUTION.—Taking the weights as the effects, we have

$$
\begin{array}{c|c|c}
 & 4 & \\
\not8 & \not{12} & \\
\not5 & \not8 = 7{,}200 & x, \text{ or } x = 4 \times 7{,}200 = 28{,}800 \text{ pounds. Ans.} \\
\not3 & \not5 &
\end{array}
$$

166. EXAMPLE.—If 12 compositors in 30 days of 10 hours each set up 25 sheets of 16 pages each, 32 lines to the page, in how many days 8 hours long can 18 compositors set up, in the same type, 64 sheets of 12 pages each, 40 lines to the page ?

SOLUTION.—Here compositors, days, and hours compose the causes, and sheets, pages, and lines the effects.   Hence,

$$
\begin{array}{c|c|c|c}
3 & \not3 & \not5 & 2 \\
\not{12} \cdot & \not{18} & \not{25} & \not{64} \\
 & & 4 & \\
\not{30} & x = \not{16} & & \not{12}, \text{ or } x = 3 \times 10 \times 2 = 60 \text{ days. Ans.} \\
\not6 & & & 4 \\
10 & \not8 & \not{32} & \not{40} \\
 & & & \not5
\end{array}
$$

167. In examples stated like that in Art. **164,** should an inverse proportion occur, write the various numbers as in the preceding examples, and then transpose from one side of the vertical line to the other side those numbers which are said to vary inversely.

EXAMPLE.—The centrifugal force of a revolving body varies directly as its weight, as the square of its velocity, and inversely as the radius of the circle described by the center of the body.   If the centrifugal force of a body weighing 15 pounds is 187 pounds when the body revolves in a circle having a radius of 12 inches, with a velocity of 20 feet per second, what will be the centrifugal force of the same body when the radius is increased to 18 inches and the speed is increased to 24 feet per second ?

SOLUTION.—Calling the centrifugal force the effect, we have

$$
\begin{array}{c|c|c}
15 & 15 & \\
20^2 & 24^2 = 187 & x. \\
12 & 18 &
\end{array}
$$

Transposing 12 and 18 (since the radii are to vary inversely) and squaring 20 and 24,

$$
\begin{array}{c|c|c}
\not{15} & \not{15} & \\
 & 2 & \\
25 & \not{36} = 187 & x, \text{ or } x = \dfrac{12 \times 2 \times 187}{25} = 179.52 \text{ pounds.   Ans.} \\
\not{400} & \not{576} & \\
\not{18} & 12 &
\end{array}
$$

EXAMPLES FOR PRACTICE.

168. Solve the following by compound proportion:

1. If 12 men dig a trench 40 rods long in 24 days of 10 hours each, how many rods can 16 men dig in 18 days of 9 hours each?

Ans. 36 rods.

2. If a piece of iron 7 feet long, 4 inches wide, and 6 inches thick weighs 600 pounds, how much will a piece of iron weigh that is 16 feet long, 8 inches wide, and 4 inches thick? Ans. 1,828$\frac{4}{7}$ lb.

3. If 24 men can build a wall 72 rods long, 6 feet wide, and 5 feet high in 60 days of 10 hours each, how many days will it take 32 men to build a wall 96 rods long, 4 feet wide, and 8 feet high, working 8 hours a day? Ans. 80 days.

4. The horsepower of an engine varies as the mean effective pressure, as the piston speed, and as the square of the diameter of the cylinder. If an engine having a cylinder 14 inches in diameter develops 112 horsepower when the mean effective pressure is 48 pounds per square inch and the piston speed is 500 feet per minute, what horsepower will another engine develop if the cylinder is 16 inches in diameter, piston speed is 600 feet per minute, and mean effective pressure is 56 pounds per square inch? Ans. 204.8 horsepower.

5. Referring to the example in Art. **164,** what will be the volume of a cylinder 20 inches in diameter and 24 inches long?

Ans. 7,539.84 cubic inches.

6. Knowing that the product of $3 \times 5 \times 7 \times 9$ is 945, what is the product of $6 \times 15 \times 14 \times 36$? Ans. 45,360.

ELEMENTS OF ALGEBRA

(PART 1)

FUNDAMENTAL OPERATIONS

USE OF LETTERS

1. In arithmetic, numbers are represented by the figures
1, 2, 3, 4, etc. There is no reason, however, why numbers
may not be represented by other symbols, such as letters, if
rules are provided for their use.

In algebra, numbers are represented by both figures and
letters. It will be seen later that the use of letters often
simplifies the solution of examples and shortens calculations.

The principal advantage of letters is that they are general
in their meaning. Thus, unlike figures, the letter a does
not stand for the number 1, the letter b for 2, c for 3, etc.,
but *any* letter may be taken to represent *any* number, it
being only necessary that a letter shall always stand for the
same number *in the same example.*

2. To illustrate this difference between letters and
figures, consider an example, as follows: If a farmer
exchanges 20 bushels of oats, worth 40 cents per bushel,
for 8 bushels of wheat, what is the price of the wheat per
bushel? Working this example by arithmetic, it is necessary to find first the value of the oats, which is 20×40 cents
$= 800$ cents, and then divide this result by 8 to find the

§ 3

price per bushel of the wheat, obtaining 800 cents ÷ 8 = 100 cents. Any other similar example would be worked in the same manner. If, however, letters are used instead of figures, the final expression will be a formula (which, when expressed in words, becomes a rule), which can be applied to *any* example of this kind by substituting for the letters the numerical values assigned to them in the particular example under consideration. Thus,

Let a = number of bushels of oats;
           b = price per bushel of oats;
           c = number of bushels of wheat;
           d = price per bushel of wheat.

The price of the oats is then $a \times b$; dividing this product by c, the price of the wheat per bushel is $\dfrac{a \times b}{c}$, which is denoted by d. Therefore, d equals $\dfrac{a \times b}{c}$, or

$$d = \frac{a \times b}{c}$$

This last expression is called an *equation* in algebra, but when used to solve examples like the foregoing, it is called a *formula*. As given here, this formula is perfectly general; a may represent any number of bushels of oats; b, any price of oats per bushel; c, any number of bushels of wheat; and d, the resulting price per bushel of wheat. Expressing the formula in words,

The price paid per bushel of wheat is equal to the number of bushels of oats multiplied by the price of oats per bushel, and the product divided by the number of bushels of wheat received in exchange.

The words in Italics constitute a general rule and apply to any similar exchange of any two commodities, by merely changing the words *oats* and *wheat* to whatever else is bartered, and *bushels* to whatever other units of measure are used.

3. Standing by itself the equation $d = \dfrac{a \times b}{c}$ has practically no meaning, except as indicating that certain opera-
tions are to be performed. When meanings are given to
the letters, the equation becomes intelligible at once, and
when numerical values are assigned to the quantities represented by the letters a, b, and c, the value of d can be
determined. For example, if a and c represent the number
of bushels of oats and wheat, respectively, involved in any
exchange and b and d their respective prices per bushel,
then from the equation (formula) it is seen at once that the
price of the wheat is to be found by multiplying the number
of bushels of oats by the price per bushel and dividing the
product by the number of bushels of wheat exchanged. In
other words, it is known just what operations are required
to find the price per bushel of the wheat. If, further, the
number of bushels of oats involved in the transaction is 20
and of wheat is 8, and the price of the oats is 40 cents per
bushel, then these values are substituted for the quantities
the letters represent, thus,

$$d = \frac{20 \times 40}{8} = 100 \text{ cents}$$

4. The foregoing is a very simple example; it has been
introduced merely to give some idea of what algebra is used
for and a reason for studying it. The conditions involved
in any particular problem require that the quantities
involved be subjected to various operations, arrangements,
and combinations, in order that the final expression may be
reduced to as simple a form as possible. The operations
are practically the same as in arithmetic, only more general;
viz., addition, subtraction, multiplication, division, involution, evolution, and factoring. The operation of factoring
is a particularly important one in algebra, as will be pointed
out later.

Many practical problems can be solved by algebra that are
incapable of solution by arithmetic, and many others are
readily solved that can be solved only with great difficulty
by arithmetic.

5. An **equation** is a statement of equality between two expressions. Thus, $x + y = 8$ is an equation, and means that the sum of the numbers represented by x and y is equal to 8. Examples are solved in algebra by the aid of equations, in which numbers are represented both by letters and by figures. The following simple example will give an idea of the method of solution:

EXAMPLE.—If an iron rail 30 feet long is cut in two so that one part is four times as long as the other, how long is the shorter part?

SOLUTION.—Any letter may represent any number, therefore:

Let x = length of shorter part

Then, $4 \times x$ (written $4x$) = length of longer part

But the sum of the two parts must equal the total length, 30 ft.

Hence, $x + 4x = 30$

Adding x and $4x$, $5x = 30$

Whence, dividing by 5, $x = 6$ ft. Ans.

6. The student has probably noticed the similarity between an equation and a **formula.** All formulas are equations, and the same rules apply to both. An equation is not called a formula, however, unless it is a statement of a general rule.

7. **Algebra** treats of the equation and its use. Since the use of equations involves the use of letters, it will be necessary, before considering equations, to take up addition, subtraction, multiplication, etc. of expressions in which letters are used.

NOTATION

8. The term **quantity** is used to designate any number that is to be subjected to mathematical processes. A quantity is strictly a concrete number; as, 6 books, 5 pounds, 10 yards. *Symbols* used to *represent* numbers, and expressions containing two or more such symbols, as ax, $10bd$, $(c + 12)$, etc., are often called *quantities*, the term being a convenient one to use.

9. The **signs** $+$, $-$, $\times$, $\div$ are the same in algebra as in arithmetic. The sign of multiplication $\times$ is usually omitted, however, multiplication being indicated by simply writing the quantities together. Thus, abc means $a \times b \times c$; $2xy$ means $2 \times x \times y$. Evidently, the sign $\times$ cannot be omitted between two *figures*, as addition instead of multiplication would then be indicated. Thus, 24 means $20 + 4$ instead of 2×4.

10. A **coefficient** is a figure or letter prefixed to a quantity; it shows how many times the latter is to be taken. Thus, in the expression $4a$, 4 is the coefficient of a and indicates that a is to be taken 4 times; that is, $4a$ is equal to $a + a + a + a$. When several quantities are multiplied together, any of them may be regarded as the coefficient of the others. Thus, in $6axy$, 6 is the coefficient of axy; $6a$, of xy; $6ax$, of y; etc. In general, however, when a coefficient is spoken of, the numerical coefficient only is meant, as the 6 above. When no numerical coefficient is written, it is understood to be 1. Thus, cd is the same as $1cd$.

11. The **factors** of a quantity are the quantities that, when multiplied together, will produce it. Thus, 2, 3, and 3 are the factors of 18, since $2 \times 3 \times 3 = 18$; 2, a, and b are the factors of $2ab$, since $2 \times a \times b = 2ab$.

12. An **exponent** is a small figure placed at the right and a little above a quantity; it shows how many times the latter is to be taken *as a factor*. Thus, $4^3 = 4 \times 4 \times 4 = 64$, the exponent 3 showing that the number 4 is to be used 3 times as a factor; likewise, $a^5 = aaaaa$. Any quantity written without an exponent is understood to have the exponent 1; thus, $b^1 = b$.

13. The difference between a coefficient and an exponent should be clearly understood. A coefficient *multiplies* the quantity which it precedes; it shows that the quantity is to be *added to itself*. Thus, $3a = 3 \times a$, or $a + a + a$. An exponent indicates that a quantity is to be *multiplied by itself.* Thus, $a^3 = a \times a \times a$. A more complete definition of an exponent will be given later.

14. A **power** is the result obtained by taking a quantity two or more times *as a factor.* For example, 16 is the fourth power of 2, because 2 multiplied by itself until it has been taken four times as a factor produces 16; a^3 is the third power of a, because $a \times a \times a = a^3$.

15. A **root** of a quantity is one of its equal factors. Thus, 2 is a root of 4, of 8, and of 16, since $2 \times 2 = 4$, $2 \times 2 \times 2 = 8$, and $2 \times 2 \times 2 \times 2 = 16$, 2 being one of the equal factors in each case. In like manner, a is a root of a^2, a^3, a^5, etc. The symbol that denotes that the second, or square, root is to be extracted is $\sqrt{}$; it is called the **radical sign,** and the quantity under the sign is called the **radical.** For other roots, the same symbol is used but with a figure, called the *index* of the root, written above it to indicate the root. Thus, $\sqrt{a}$, $\sqrt[3]{a}$, $\sqrt[4]{a}$, etc. signify the square root, cube root, fourth root, etc. of a. The vinculum is generally used in combination with the radical sign to indicate how much of the expression is governed by the sign. Thus, in an expression like $\sqrt{a} + b$ it is understood that the square root of a only is wanted. If, however, it were desired to write the square root of the sum of a and b, the expression would be written $\sqrt{a+b}$, the vinculum extending as far as necessary to indicate how much of the expression was governed by the radical sign. Occasionally, the parenthesis is used instead of the vinculum, but seldom in American textbooks; thus, instead of $\sqrt{a+b}$, it would be written $\sqrt{(a+b)}$.

16. The use of the parenthesis, bracket, brace, and vinculum was explained in *Arithmetic.* These symbols are called **symbols of aggregation,** meaning that the quantities enclosed within them are aggregated, or collected, into one quantity.

17. The **terms** of an algebraic expression are those parts that are connected by the signs $+$ and $-$. Thus, x^2, $- 2xy$, and y^2 are terms of the expression $x^2 - 2xy + y^2$. When a term contains both figures and letters, the part consisting of letters is called the **literal** part of the term; thus, xy is the literal part of the term $2xy$.

18. **Like terms** are those that differ only in their numerical coefficients; all others are **unlike terms.** Thus, $2ab^2$ and $5ab^2$ are like terms; $5ab$ and $5ab^2$ are unlike terms, because one contains b and the other b^2.

19. A **monomial** is an expression consisting of only one term; as, $4abc$, $3x^2$, $2ax^3$, etc.

20. A **binomial** is an expression consisting of two terms; as, $a + b$, $2a + 5b$, etc.

21. A **trinomial** is an expression consisting of three terms; as, $a^2 + 2ab + b^2$, $(a + x)^2 - 2(a + x)y + y^2$, etc., the expression $(a + x)$ being treated as one quantity.

22. A **polynomial** is an expression consisting of more than two terms. The name is usually applied only to an expression consisting of four or more terms.

23. The polynomial $a + a^2b + 2a^3 - 3a^4b - a^5$ is said to be arranged according to the *increasing* or *ascending powers* of a, because the exponents of a increase from left to right, the exponent of the first a being 1 understood. (Art. **12.**) The polynomial $a^3b^3 + ab^2 + 4a^4b + 1$ is arranged according to the *decreasing* or *descending powers* of b, the exponents of b decreasing in order from left to right.

24. The arrangement of the terms of a polynomial does not affect its value. Thus, $x^2 + 2xy + y^2$ has the same value as $2xy + y^2 + x^2$, just as $2 + 6 + 4$ has the same value as $6 + 4 + 2$.

READING ALGEBRAIC EXPRESSIONS

25. Quantities like a, x, b^2, etc. are read "a," "x," "b square," etc. In reading monomials in which multiplication is indicated, the word "times" is not used. Thus, abc is read "abc"; $7ad^2b^3$ is read "$7ad$ square b cube."

26. The polynomial $a + a^2b + 2a^3 - 3a^4b - a^5$ is read "a, plus a square b, plus $2a$ cube, minus $3a$ fourth b, minus a fifth." Considerable care is required when reading expressions containing polynomials. Thus, if $4(a - b)$ were read "$4a$ minus b," the binomial $4a - b$ would be understood. It *should* be read "4 times $a - b$," or "4 times the parenthesis a minus b," in which case it will be understood that 4 multiplies the whole quantity $a - b$, since the word "times" is not used with monomials. Again, $m(m^2 + 2mn + n^2)$ and $m(m^2 + 2mn) + n^2$ should each be so read that there can be no doubt as to whether the n^2 is to be multiplied by m or not.

Let the distinction to be made in reading the following be observed:

$$\sqrt{\frac{m+n}{x-y^2}} \text{ and } \sqrt{m + \frac{n}{x-y^2}}$$

In the first case, the whole quantity $m + n$ is divided by $x - y^2$, and it would be clear to say, "the square root of the fraction $m + n$ over $x - y^2$." In the second case, where the n only is divided by $x - y^2$, it may be read, "the square root of the quantity m plus the fraction n over $x - y^2$." The word "quantity" shows that the square root of the whole expression is taken, and the word "fraction" after "plus" shows that only the n is divided by $x - y^2$.

27. When a polynomial is affected by an exponent, it should be clearly indicated. Thus,

$$(3a - d^2)\ (3a - d)^2\ (3a - d^2)^2$$

should be read, "$3a - d$ square, times the square of $3a - d$, times the square of $3a - d$ square."

28. Sometimes expressions like A', B'', c', d'', C_1, a_2, etc. appear in formulas or elsewhere in algebraic problems when it is desirable to have the same letter represent different quantities that are similar, or correspond to one another. The marks $'$, $''$, $'''$, $_1$, $_2$, etc. serve to distinguish the letters. The expressions are also used to designate similar or corresponding lines in geometrical figures. A', B'', C''' etc. are read "*a major prime, b major second, c major third,*" etc.; a', b'', c''', etc. are read "*a minor prime, b minor second, c minor third,*" etc.; a_1, B_2, C_3, d_4, etc. are read "*a minor sub-one, b major sub-two, c major sub-three, d minor sub-four,*" etc.

The words *major* and *minor* are used only when capitals and small letters are used in the same problem. Otherwise they are dropped, and a', b_2, for example, are read "*a prime, b sub-two.*"

POSITIVE AND NEGATIVE QUANTITIES

29. One of the chief differences between arithmetic and algebra is the use in the latter of the negative quantity. In arithmetic all quantities are positive, but in algebra negative quantities are used with the same frequency as positive quantities.

Positive and **negative** are terms applied to quantities of opposite character; as, money earned and money owed, water running into a tank and water running out, a distance up stream and a distance down stream, the height of a tower and the depth of a well, the pull on a lifting rope and the weight of the load, etc.

30. Positive quantities are preceded by the sign plus, as $+2xy$, $+ab$, etc., and negative quantities by the sign minus, as $-2xy$, $-ab$, etc. Thus, if money earned is $+\$50$, a like amount owed is $-\$50$. If the quantity of water running into a tank is denoted by $+a$, the same quantity running out should be denoted by $-a$.

40—11

31. It really does not matter which quantity is taken as positive and which as negative, so long as the two are opposite in character; but it is customary to call something gained positive and something lost negative. Thus, money earned is usually regarded as positive, money owed as negative; distance up, positive, distance down, negative.

32. The signs $+$ and $-$ may be used in two entirely different senses; heretofore, they have been used exclusively as symbols of operation; thus, $+$ placed between two quantities indicates that they are to be added, etc. In the distinction between positive and negative quantities, however, the positive quantity is denoted by the sign $+$ and the negative quantity by the sign $-$. Hence, under different circumstances, these signs may denote addition and subtraction, or they may denote positive and negative quantities. Suppose we write the expression $\$500 - \$200 = \$300$; this may mean either $\$500 - (+\$200) = \$300$, or $\$500 + (-\$200) = \$300$. In the first case, $\$200$ is *positive* and is *subtracted* from $\$500$; in the second case, $\$200$ is *negative* and is *added* to $\$500$. The result of the operation, $\$300$ is the same in either case, as will be shown later. For convenience, therefore, it is always assumed that any algebraic expression consisting of two or more terms invariably represents the *addition of those terms.* Thus, an expression like $a^2 - 2ab + b^2$ is always understood to mean $+a^2 + (-2ab) + (+b^2)$. This fact should be kept in mind, as it will be of assistance later.

33. It is usual to consider that quantities *increase* in a positive direction and *decrease* in a negative direction. For example, when the mercury in a thermometer goes up (rises), the temperature increases, but when the mercury falls, the temperature decreases. This distinction is made, however, only in the manner here indicated ; it has nothing to do with the actual numerical value of the quantities. But when, for any purpose, the distinction is made, *any positive quantity, no matter how small, is greater than any* *negative quantity; also, of any two negative quantities, the smaller is the greater.* This point is illustrated very nicely by reference to Fig. 1. From various points on the circle draw perpendiculars to the diameter AB. Call any perpendicular above AB positive and any below negative. If the point selected corresponds with A or B, the length of the perpendicular is zero. Now if we consider that the chief object is to reach the highest point possible above AB without going beyond

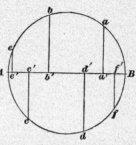

FIG. 1

the circle, it is evident that any perpendicular above AB, as $a\,a'$, $b\,b'$, or $e\,e'$, is greater than any perpendicular below AB, as $c\,c'$, $d\,d'$, or $f\,f'$; it is also evident that $f\,f'$ is greater than $c\,c'$ or $d\,d'$, since the point f is nearer the highest point of the circle than c or d. Furthermore, the figure shows that zero is greater than any negative quantity.

34. When writing algebraic expressions, if a positive term stands alone, or if the first term of an expression is positive, the plus sign is omitted, it being understood that the term is positive. Thus, $3a$ means the same as $+3a$, and $a - b$ the same as $+a - b$. The minus sign must never be omitted.

EXAMPLES FOR PRACTICE

Express the following algebraically:

1. Three x square y square, minus two cd times the quantity a plus b.
   Ans. $3x^2y^2 - 2cd(a + b)$

2. The quantity m square plus two mn plus n square in parenthesis, times a square b cube c fourth.   Ans. $(m^2 + 2mn + n^2)a^2b^3c^4$

3. A, plus the square root of D, times the parenthesis X plus Y.
   Ans. $A + \sqrt{D}(X + Y)$

4. A, plus the square root of D times the parenthesis X plus Y.
   Ans. $A + \sqrt{D(X + Y)}$

5.   Ten x plus y, minus 7 times the quantity x minus the fraction y over 4 in parenthesis, plus the fraction x square minus y square over two cd.

$$\text{Ans. } 10x + y - 7\left(x - \frac{y}{4}\right) + \frac{x^2 - y^2}{2cd}$$

When $a = 6$, $b = 5$, and $c = 4$, find the numerical values of

6. $a^2 + 2ab + b^2$.   Ans. $6^2 + 2 \times 6 \times 5 + 5^2 = 121$

7. $2a^2 + 3bc - 5$.   Ans. $72 + 60 - 5 = 127$

8. $2ac^5 - a^2(a + b)$.   Ans. 11,892

9. $abc^2 + ab^2c - a^2bc$.   Ans. 360

When $x = 8$ and $y = 6$, what do the following equal:

10. $(x+y)(x-y) - \sqrt{\dfrac{x+y^2}{11}}$?   Ans. $(8+6)(8-6) - \sqrt{\dfrac{8+6^2}{11}} = 26$

11. $\sqrt{(x+y^2)(x^2+y)} - (x-y)(\sqrt[3]{x} + y)$?   Ans. 39.5

12. $\dfrac{x^2y^2}{x+y} + \dfrac{x^2y(x+y^2)}{\sqrt{3xy}}$?   Ans. 1,572.57

———

ADDITION

———

ADDITION OF MONOMIALS

35.   The operations of addition, subtraction, multiplication, and division performed with algebraic expressions are each based on the same operations performed with monomials; hence, if the latter are clearly understood no trouble will be experienced with the former.

36.   There are four cases in connection with addition of two monomials: when both are positive, when the first is positive and the second is negative, when the first is negative and the second is positive, and when both are negative. Let the monomials be the numbers 11 and 6; then the four cases are represented as follows:

$$
\begin{aligned}
(+11) + (+6) &= \quad 11 + 6 = +17 \qquad \textbf{(1)}\\
(+11) + (-6) &= \quad 11 - 6 = + \ 5 \qquad \textbf{(2)}\\
(-11) + (+6) &= -11 + 6 = - \ 5 \qquad \textbf{(3)}\\
(-11) + (-6) &= -11 - 6 = -17 \qquad \textbf{(4)}
\end{aligned}
$$

The second form of the above equations follows from the assumption made in Art. **32.**

37. To interpret these results, and, also, those which are obtained from the operations of subtraction, multiplication,

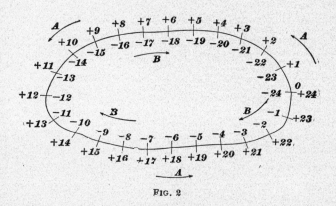

FIG. 2

and division, suppose that a man has a plot of ground, as represented in Fig. 2, and that the distance around it is 24 steps of 3 feet each. Suppose, further, that the man is to walk around the plot and that if his face is turned to walk ahead in the direction of the arrows marked A, the action is positive; while if his face is turned to walk ahead in the direction of the arrows marked B, the action is negative. Again, he may walk forwards or backwards; if he walks forwards call the action positive, and if he walks backwards call the action negative.

Having made these assumptions, consider the four cases in order.

Case (1),

$$(+11) + (+6) = +17$$

Referring to Fig. 2, the man walks from O to $+11$; the sign in parenthesis, which is plus, indicates that he is to face to walk in the direction of the arrows marked A, and the sign between the terms, which is plus, indicates that he walked forwards as many steps as are indicated by the second term, that is, 6. As a result he stops at $+17$. Hence, $(+11) + (+6) = 11 + 6 = 17$.

Case (2),
$$(+11) + (-6) = +5$$

He walks from O to $+11$, as before; the minus sign in parenthesis indicates that he is to walk in the direction of the arrows marked B, and the plus sign between the terms indicates that he is to walk forwards 6 steps. He therefore stops at $+5$. Hence, $(+11) + (-6) = 11 - 6 = +5$.

Case (3),
$$(-11) + (+6) = -5$$

He walks from O to -11; the plus sign in parenthesis indicates that he is to walk in the direction of the arrows marked A, and the plus sign between the terms indicates that he is to walk forwards 6 steps. He therefore stops at -5. Hence, $(-11) + (+6) = -11 + 6 = -5$.

Case (4),
$$(-11) + (-6) = -17$$

He walks from O to -11; the minus sign in parenthesis indicates that he is to walk in the direction of the arrows marked B, and the plus sign between the terms indicates that he is to walk forwards 6 steps. He therefore stops at -17. Hence, $(-11) + (-6) = -11 - 6 = -17$.

38. An inspection of the results obtained in four cases just given shows that when the two numbers have like signs, the sum is found by adding, as in arithmetic, and prefixing the common sign; and that when the two numbers have unlike signs, the sum is found by subtracting, as in arithmetic, and prefixing to the result the sign of the greater number.

39. To add two like quantities, as $11a$ and $6a$, whatever the signs may be, simply add the numerical coefficients as above directed and prefix the result to the letters forming the monomial. For example, the sum of $-11a$ and $6a$ is $-5a$, of $-11a$ and $-6a$ is $-17a$, etc.; also, of $-11ab$

and $6ab$ is $-5ab$, of $11ab$ and $6ab$ is $17ab$, etc. That this is so will be readily seen by referring again to Fig. 2. The distance around the plot is 24 steps, and each step is 3 feet long (see Art. **37**); the distance in feet for 11 steps is 33 feet and for 6 steps 18 feet. Instead of writing 33 feet and 18 feet, the number of feet in a step may be represented by a, in which case 33 feet becomes $11a$ and 18 feet, $6a$. If, therefore, $11a$ and $6a$ are added, the result must be equal to the sum of 33 feet and 18 feet. Now, as stated above, $11a + 6a = 17a$; substituting for a its value, 3 feet, $17a = 17 \times 3$ feet $= 51$ feet. Also, 33 feet $+ 18$ feet $= 51$ feet. A little reasoning will show that the law holds good whatever the signs of the two quantities.

Again, in 1 foot there are 12 inches; hence 33 feet $= 396$ inches, and 18 feet $= 216$ inches. Letting a represent the number of feet in a step and b the number of inches in a foot, $a \times b$, or ab, represents the number of inches in a step. Therefore, $11ab + 6ab$ $= 17ab = 17 \times 3 \times 12$ inches $= 612$ inches $= 396$ inches $+ 216$ inches.

40. Only quantities having the same letters affected with the same exponents can be added, i. e., combined into a single term. For example, 7 and -9, $-ab$ and $8ab$, $4a^2b$ and $-2a^2b$, etc. can be added; but 7^2 and -9, $-a^2b$ and $8ab$, $4a^2b$ and $-2ab^2$, etc. cannot be added. The only way in which 7^2 and -9 can be added, is to change the form of 7^2 so as to get rid of the exponent; this is done by raising 7 to the power indicated, obtaining 49, a number having the exponent 1, the same as the exponent of -9. When this is done, $7^2 + (-9) = 7^2 - 9 = 49 - 9 = 40$. When the unlike terms contain letters, however, it is very seldom possible to change the form so as to make them alike, and it then becomes necessary to indicate the addition. Thus, the sum of $-a^2b$ and $8ab$ is written either $-a^2b + 8ab$ or $8ab - a^2b$, according to which arrangement of terms is desired; so also, the sum of $4a^2b$ and $-2ab^2$ is written either $4a^2b - 2ab^2$ or $-2ab^2 + 4a^2b$. But when no

particular arrangement of terms is desired, a positive term
is always written first.

Suppose it were required to add the following monomials,
a^2b, $-4a^2b$, $-2a^2b$, and $3a^2b$. The sum of the first two is
$a^2b - 4a^2b = -3a^2b$, since when no numerical coefficient is
written, it is always understood to be 1. Adding to this
result the third monomial, the sum is $-3a^2b - 2a^2b$
$= -5a^2b$. Adding to this result the fourth monomial, the
sum is $-5a^2b + 3a^2b = -2a^2b$, the sum of all the monomials.
The addition may be performed more rapidly and conveniently by adding all the positive and all the negative
monomials separately, and then adding the two sums.
Thus, $a^2b + 3a^2b = 4a^2b$; $-4a^2b - 2a^2b = -6a^2b$; $-6a^2b$
$+ 4a^2b = -2a^2b$.

41. From these illustrations, the following important
principle is derived. *If all the terms to be added are positive, the sum is positive; if all are negative, the sum is
negative. If one term is positive and the other is negative,
the sum has the sign of the numerically greater.* If there
are several terms to be added, part of which are positive
and part negative, the sum is positive or negative according
as the sum of the positive terms is numerically greater or
less than the sum of the negative terms.

To add like quantities having the same sign:

Rule I.—*Add the coefficients, give the sum the common
sign, and annex the common literal part.*

To add like quantities having different signs:

Rule II.—*Add the positive and the negative coefficients separately, and from the greater sum subtract the lesser. Give
the remainder the sign of the greater sum, and annex the
common literal part.*

EXAMPLE 1.—Find the sum of $-2abxy$, $-abxy$, $-3abxy$, and $-6abxy$.

SOLUTION.—The sum of the coefficients is 12 (remember that the
coefficient of $-abxy$ is 1), and the common sign is $-$. The common
literal part, $abxy$, annexed to these gives as the result $-12abxy$.
(Rule I.)

EXAMPLE 2.—Add xy^2, $-2xy^2$, $8xy^2$, and $-4xy^2$.

SOLUTION.—The sum of the coefficients of the positive terms is 9, and of the negative terms, 6. Their difference is 3, and the sign of the greater sum is $+$. The common literal part, xy^2, annexed to these gives as the result $3xy^2$. (Rule II.)

EXAMPLES FOR PRACTICE

Find the sum of the following:

1. $-6a^2$, $2a^2$, $-5a^2$, $4a^2$, $-3a^2$, and a^2.   Ans. $-7a^2$
2. $2a^2b$, $-a^2b$, $11a^2b$, $-5a^2b$, $4a^2b$, and $-9a^2b$.   Ans. $2a^2b$
3. $2x^2$, $3xy$, $-x^2$, $8y^2$, $-5xy$, and $-7y^2$.   Ans. $x^2 - 2xy + y^2$

NOTE.—Combine like terms and connect with respective signs.

4. a^2bc, $-2ab^2c$, $3abc^2$, $-4a^2bc$, and $5ab^2c$.

Ans. $3ab^2c - 3a^2bc + 3abc^2$

ADDITION OF POLYNOMIALS

42. Addition of polynomials is merely an extension of addition of monomials.

Rule.—*Write the expressions underneath one another, with like terms in the same vertical column. Add each column separately, and connect the sums by their proper signs.*

EXAMPLE 1.—Find the sum of $5a^2 + 6ac - 3b^2 - 2xy$, $7ac - 3a^2 + 4b^2 + 3xy$, and $4xy - 5b^2 + 8ac - a^2$.

SOLUTION.—Writing like terms in the same vertical column, we have

$$5a^2 + 6ac - 3b^2 - 2xy$$
$$-3a^2 + 7ac + 4b^2 + 3xy$$
$$-a^2 + 8ac - 5b^2 + 4xy$$
$$sum \quad a^2 + 21ac - 4b^2 + 5xy \quad \text{Ans.}$$

EXAMPLE 2.—Find the sum of $a^2x - ax^2 - x^2$, $ax - x^2 - a^2$, $-2a^2 - 2a^2x - 2ax^2$, and $3a^2 - 3a^2x + 3ax^2$.

SOLUTION.—

$$a^2x - ax^2 - x^2$$
$$- x^2 - a^2 + ax$$
$$-2a^2x - 2ax^2 \qquad -2a^2$$
$$-3a^2x + 3ax^2 \qquad + 3a^2$$
$$sum \quad -4a^2x + 0 \quad -2x^2 + 0 \quad + ax$$
$$= ax - 4a^2x - 2x^2 \quad \text{Ans. (Arts. 23 and 24.)}$$

EXAMPLES FOR PRACTICE

Find the sum of the following:

1. $ax + 2bx + 4by - 3ay$, $2ax + bx + 2ay - by$, and $4ax + 3by$.

           Ans. $7ax + 3bx + 6by - ay$

2. $a - x + 4y - 3z + w$, $z + 3a - 2x - y - w$, and $x + y + z$.

           Ans. $4a - 2x + 4y - z$

3. $2a - 3b + 4d$, $2b - 3d + 4c$, $2d - 3c + 4a$, and $2c - 3a + 4b$.

           Ans. $3a + 3b + 3c + 3d$

4. $6x - 3y + 7m$, $2n - x + y$, $2y - 4x - 5m$, and $m + n - y$.

           Ans. $x - y + 3m + 3n$

SUBTRACTION

SUBTRACTION OF MONOMIALS

43. As in addition, there are four cases, as follows, using the same numbers as in Art. **36.**

$$(+11) - (+6) = \quad 11 - 6 = +\ 5 \qquad \textbf{(1)}$$
$$(+11) - (-6) = \quad 11 + 6 = +17 \qquad \textbf{(2)}$$
$$(-11) - (+6) = -11 - 6 = -17 \qquad \textbf{(3)}$$
$$(-11) - (-6) = -11 + 6 = -\ 5 \qquad \textbf{(4)}$$

To interpret these results, refer again to Fig. 2. As before, the sign of the first term, or minuend, indicates whether the man walks first in the direction of the arrows marked A or those marked B, and the number 11 indicates where he stops; the sign of the second term, or subtrahend, indicates whether he is *then* to walk in the direction of the arrows A or the arrows B; and the sign between the terms indicates whether the walk is to be forwards or backwards.

Case (1),

$$(+11) - (+6) = +5$$

He walks from O to $+11$; the sign of the second term being plus, indicates that he is to face so as to walk in the direction of the arrows marked A; the sign between the terms indicates that he is to walk backwards 6 steps. He therefore stops at $+5$. Hence, $(+11) - (+6) = 5$.

Had the subtrahend been numerically greater than the minuend, that is, had the operation been $(+6) - (+11)$, he would have walked first to $+6$ and then backwards 11 steps to -5. Hence, $(+6) - (+11) = -5$.

Case (2),
$$+11 - (-6) = +17$$

He walks first to $+11$; turns around to face as though to walk in the direction of the arrows marked B; then walks backwards 6 steps, stopping at $+17$. Hence, $(+11) - (-6) = +17$. Also, $(+6) - (-11) = +17$.

Case (3),
$$(-11) - (+6) = -17$$

He walks first to -11, turns around to face as though to walk in the direction of the arrows marked A (indicated by the plus sign of the second term); then walks backwards 6 steps, stopping at -17. Hence, $(-11) - (+6) = -17$. Also, $(-6) - (+11) = -17$.

Case (4),
$$(-11) - (-6) = -5$$

He walks to -11; the minus sign of second term indicates he is to face so as to walk in the direction of the arrows marked B; the minus sign between the terms indicates that he is to walk backwards 6 steps. He therefore stops at -5. Hence, $(-11) - (-6) = -5$.

Had the subtrahend been greater numerically than the minuend, that is, had the operation been $(-6) - (-11)$, he would have walked first to -6, and then walked backwards 11 steps, stopping at $+5$. Hence, $(-6) - (-11) = +5$.

44. An inspection of these results shows: first, that when the signs are alike, as in cases (1) and (4), the difference is equal to the *difference* between the two numbers, and the sign of the difference is the same as the sign of the larger number; second, that when the signs are unlike, as in cases (2) and (3), the difference is equal to the *sum* of the two numbers, and the sign of the difference is the same as the sign of the minuend.

45. Consider further the four cases of subtraction. The result obtained in each case might also be obtained by changing the sign of the subtrahend and proceeding as in addition, as follows :

$$(+11) - (+6) = (+11) + (-6) = \quad 11 - 6 = +5$$
$$(+11) - (-6) = (+11) + (+6) = \quad 11 + 6 = +17$$
$$(-11) - (+6) = (-11) + (-6) = -11 - 6 = -17$$
$$(-11) - (-6) = (-11) + (+6) = -11 + 6 = -5$$

Moreover, this method will always produce the same results as will be obtained by applying the law for subtraction stated in Art. **44.** Hence, the following rule for the subtraction of like monomials :

Rule.—*Change the sign of the subtrahend, and proceed as in addition.*

EXAMPLE.—From $-3ab^2x$ take $7ab^2x$.

SOLUTION.—Changing the sign of the subtrahend, $7ab^2x$, and *adding*, we have

$$
\begin{array}{ll}
-3ab^2x & \quad -3ab^2x \\
\underline{7ab^2x} & \quad \underline{-7ab^2x \text{ (sign changed)}} \\
& \quad -10ab^2x \quad \text{Ans.}
\end{array}
$$

If the monomials are unlike, the difference cannot be expressed as a single term. Thus, to subtract $5ab^2x$ from $3a^2bx$, change sign of $5ab^2x$ and add it to $3a^2bx$, obtaining $3a^2bx + (-5ab^2x) = 3a^2bx - 5ab^2x$.

46. In arithmetic, subtraction consists in finding how much greater (or less) some number is than another. In algebra, subtraction has an entirely different meaning on account of the use of negative quantities. In algebra, subtraction consists in finding what quantity must be added to the subtrahend to produce the minuend, and the subtrahend may be greater than or less than the minuend, and either may be positive or negative. The result of the subtraction must in all cases be the actual difference, and its sign must show whether the subtrahend must be increased or decreased to produce the minuend. For example, if A has $11 and B has $6, $+$ $5 must be *added* to B's money to make the amount the same as A's; also, — $5 must be added to A's money to make the amount the same as B's. In one case the subtrahend is increased, and in the other it is decreased, and the sign of difference shows which occurred. Hence, $11 - 6 = 5$, and $6 - 11 = -5$.

Further, if A has $11 and B owes $6, i. e., has — $6, it is necessary to increase the amount B has + $17 to make the amount equal to A's, since it would take $6 to pay what B owes and $11 more to reach the amount A has. Since the amount B had was increased, the sign of the difference is +. Hence, $11 - (-6) = +17$.

If A owes $11 and B has $6, B must lose $17 in order to owe the same amount as A. Hence, $-11 - 6 = -17$.

If A owes $11 and B owes $6, B must lose $5 more to owe as much as A, and A must gain $5 to owe as little as B. Hence, $-11 - (-6) = -5$, and $-6 - (-11) = +5$.

EXAMPLES FOR PRACTICE

Solve the following:

1. From $17a$ take $-11a$.   Ans. $28a$
2. From $-11a$ take $17a$.   Ans. $-28a$
3. Subtract $5cd$ from $-4cd$.   Ans. $-9cd$
4. Subtract $-10b^2$ from $-10b^2$.   Ans. 0
5. What quantity added to $10xy$ will produce $-12xy$?
                                    Ans. $-22xy$
6. What does $10xy$ subtracted from $-12xy$ equal?   Ans. $-22xy$

SUBTRACTION OF POLYNOMIALS

47. To subtract one polynomial from another:

Rule.—*Write the subtrahend underneath the minuend, with like terms in the same vertical column. Change the sign of each term of the subtrahend, or imagine the sign of each term to be changed, and proceed as in addition.*

EXAMPLE 1.—From $3ac - 2b$ subtract $ac - b - d$.

SOLUTION.— $3ac - 2b$
               $-ac + b + d$ (subtrahend with signs changed)
    difference $2ac - b + d$ Ans.

EXAMPLE 2.—From $2x^3 - 3x^2y + 2xy^2$ subtract $x^3 - xy^2 + y^3$.

SOLUTION.—

$$2x^3 - 3x^2y + 2xy^2$$
$$- \ x^3 \qquad\quad + \ xy^2 - y^3 \text{ (subtrahend with signs changed)}$$

difference $x^3 - 3x^2y + 3xy^2 - y^3$.   Ans.

EXAMPLES FOR PRACTICE

Solve the following:

1. From $7a + 5b - 3c$ take $a - 7b + 5c - 4$.   Ans. $6a + 12b - 8c + 4$
2. From $3m - 5n + r - 2s$ take $2r + 3n - m - 5s$.
                                        Ans. $4m - 8n - r + 3s$
3. Subtract $2x - 2y + 2$ from $y - x$.   Ans. $3y - 3x - 2$
4. Subtract $3x^3 + 4x^2y - 7xy^2 + y^3 - xy^3$ from $5x^3 + x^2y - 6xy^2 + y^3$.
                                   Ans. $2x^3 - 3x^2y + xy^2 + xy^3$

SYMBOLS OF AGGREGATION

48. Parentheses, brackets, etc. being used to enclose expressions that are to be treated as one quantity, the sign before the symbol affects the *entire expression*, not the first term only. Thus, $-(a^2 - 2ab + b^2)$ signifies that all the terms are to be subtracted from what precedes, not a^2 only.

49. When combining the terms of any expression without parentheses, proceed as in addition of monomials. When a parenthesis is preceded by a minus sign, the expression within the parenthesis must be considered as a subtrahend, and all signs must be changed before removing the parenthesis.

50. If, on the contrary, the sign before the parenthesis is plus, the signs of the terms within the parenthesis must not be changed when the parenthesis is removed, because the signs of the terms are not changed in addition.

51. When a quantity is enclosed by a parenthesis, the first term is understood to have the plus sign, unless the minus sign is given; thus, in the expression $-(8x + 5 - 2b)$, the minus sign refers to the whole quantity. The sign of $8x$ is $+$, and the expression, if written in full, would be $-(+8x + 5 - 2b)$.

EXAMPLE 1.—Remove the parenthesis from $4c - (3a + 4ab - d)$.

SOLUTION.—Changing the sign of each enclosed term, and remembering that the sign of $3a$ is $+$, understood, the result is $4c - 3a - 4ab + d$. Ans.

EXAMPLE 2.—Remove the parentheses from $4a - 5x - (a - 4x) + (x - 8a)$.

SOLUTION.— $4a - 5x - (a - 4x) + (x - 8a) = 4a - 5x - a + 4x + x - 8a$.
Adding the like terms,

$$
\begin{array}{r}
4a - 5x \\
-\ a + 4x \\
-8a +\ x \\
\hline
-5a + 0 = -5a \quad \text{Ans.}
\end{array}
$$

52. Symbols of aggregation will often be found enclosing others. In such cases they may be removed in succession, *always beginning with the innermost pair.*

EXAMPLE.—Remove all the symbols of aggregation from $6a - \{b - [7cd - 4a + (2cd - \overline{a - b})]\}$.

SOLUTION.—First remove the vinculum. This being in effect the same as the parenthesis, the minus sign before the a indicates that $+ a$ and $- b$ are to be subtracted.
The expression is then

$$6a - \{b - [7cd - 4a + (2cd - a + b)]\}$$

Removing the parenthesis, the expression becomes

$$6a - \{b - [7cd - 4a + 2cd - a + b]\}$$

This, with the brackets removed, is equal to

$$6a - \{b - 7cd + 4a - 2cd + a - b\}$$

which, in turn, is equal to

$$6a - b + 7cd - 4a + 2cd - a + b$$

Combining like terms

$$6a - 4a - a - b + b + 7cd + 2cd = a + 9cd \quad \text{Ans.}$$

53. If it is desired to enclose several terms in parenthesis or some other symbol of aggregation, and the sign of
the first term to be so enclosed is plus, simply write the
symbol so as to enclose the desired terms. But if the sign
of the first term is minus, it is customary to change· the
signs of all the terms enclosed and write the minus sign
before the parenthesis, so that the first term within the
parenthesis may be positive. Thus, if it were desired to
enclose the last two terms of $x^2 - 2ax + a^2$ in parenthesis, it
would be written $x^2 - (2ax - a^2)$; while if the first two
terms were to be enclosed, it would be written $(x^2 - 2ax) + a^2$.

EXAMPLES FOR PRACTICE

Remove the parentheses from the following :

1. $- (2mn - m^2 - n^2)$.   Ans. $m^2 - 2mn + n^2$

2. $1 - (- b + c + 3)$.   Ans. $b - c - 2$

3. $5a - 4b + 3c - (- 3a + 2b - c)$.   Ans. $8a - 6b + 4c$

4. $3x - (2x - 5) + (7 - x)$.   Ans. 12

Remove the symbols of aggregation from the following :

5. $m - [4n - k - (m + n - 2k)]$.   Ans. $2m - 3n - k$

6. $5x - (2x - 3y) - (x + 5y)$.   Ans. $2x - 2y$

7. $3a - [7a - (5a - b - a)] - (- a - 4b)$.   Ans. $a + 3b$

8. $3x + \{2y - [5x - (3y + \overline{x - 4y})]\}$.   Ans. $y - x$

9. $100x - \{200x - [500x - (- 100x) - 300x] - 400x\}$.   Ans. $600x$

10. $7cx - \{4cy - [(4cx + 3cy) + cy - cx]\}$.   Ans. $10cx$

NOTE.—Observe that the sign before the parenthesis is $+$ understood.

11.   Enclose within parenthesis the second, third, and fourth terms
of $x^4 - 4x^3 + 6x^2 - 4x + 1$.   Ans. $x^4 - (4x^3 - 6x^2 + 4x) + 1$

12.   Enclose the last two terms of $x^4 - 4x^3 + 6x^2 - 4x + 1$ in
parenthesis, the last three terms in brackets, and the last four terms
in braces.   Ans. $x^4 - \{4x^3 - [6x^2 - (4x - 1)]\}$

MULTIPLICATION

MULTIPLICATION OF MONOMIALS

54. Multiplication of algebraic quantities consists of two distinct operations; first, the multiplication of the coefficients, and, second, the multiplication of the literal parts. The second operation will be treated first.

Consider two quantities as a and b; their product is evidently $a \times b = ab$, the sign of multiplication being understood. The product of ab and c is evidently $ab \times c = a \times b \times c = abc$. The product of a and a is $a \times a = a^2$; of a^2 and a, is $a^2 \times a = a \times a \times a = a^3$; of a^2 and b is $a^2 \times b = a^2b$; of a^2b and bc is $a^2b \times bc = a \times a \times b \times b \times c = a^2b^2c$; and of a^3b^2 and a^2b^3c is $a \times a \times a \times b \times b \times a \times a \times b \times b \times b \times c = a \times a \times a \times a \times a \times b \times b \times b \times b \times b \times c = a^5b^5c$. An inspection of these results shows that the product consists of all the letters occurring in both multiplicand and multiplier and that the exponents of the letters in the product are equal to the *sum* of the exponents of the corresponding letters in the multiplicand and multiplier. The law is perfectly general, whether the exponents are positive (as above) or negative, integral (as above) or fractional, provided that the 'word sum is understood to mean *algebraic sum*.

55. The coefficients are multiplied separately and in the same manner as in arithmetic. For example, $5a^2b^2 \times 3ab^2 = 5 \times a^2b^2 \times 3 \times ab^2 = 5 \times 3 \times a^2b^2 \times ab^2 = 15a^3b^4$; $4ab \times bc = 4 \times ab \times 1 \times bc = 4 \times 1 \times ab \times bc = 4ab^2c$, etc.

56. All that now remains is to determine the sign of the product. As in addition and subtraction. there are four cases as follows:

$$(+11) \times (+6) = +66 \qquad \textbf{(1)}$$
$$(+11) \times (-6) = -66 \qquad \textbf{(2)}$$
$$(-11) \times (+6) = -66 \qquad \textbf{(3)}$$
$$(-11) \times (-6) = +66 \qquad \textbf{(4)}$$

40—12

Referring to Fig. 3, which is Fig. 2 repeated here for convenience, the man starts walking in all cases at the zero point O. Call 11 in all four cases the multiplicand and 6

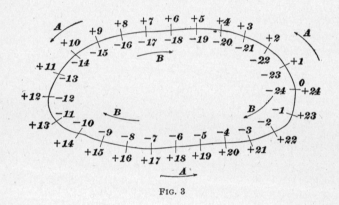

FIG. 3

the multiplier. Let the sign of the multiplicand indicate the direction faced and the sign of the multiplier indicate whether the walk is forwards or backwards.

Case (1),

$$(+11) \times (+6) = +66$$

The man starts at O, faces to walk in the direction of the arrows marked A, and takes 66 steps forwards, going twice around the plot and stopping at $+18$. Hence, $(+11) \times (+6) = 11 \times 6 = 66$.

Case (2),

$$(+11) \times (-6) = -66$$

He starts at O, faces to walk in the direction of the arrows marked A, and takes 66 steps backwards, going twice around the plot and stopping at -18. Hence, $(+11) \times (-6) = 11 \times -6 = -66$.

Case (3),

$$(-11) \times (+6) = -66$$

He starts at O, faces to walk in the direction of the arrows marked B, takes 66 steps forwards, going twice around the plot and stopping at -18. Hence, (-11) $\times (+6) = -11 \times 6 = -66$.

Case (4),

$$(-11) \times (-6) = +66$$

He starts at O, faces to walk in the direction of the arrows marked B, takes 66 steps backwards, going twice around the plot, and stopping at $+18$. Hence, (-11) $\times (-6) = -11 \times -6 = +66$.

57. An inspection of the results obtained shows that when the signs of the multiplicand and multiplier are alike, the product is positive, and when the signs are unlike, the product is negative.

58. A little consideration will show, further, that when a series of monomials are to be multiplied together to form a single term, the sign of the product will depend on the number of minus signs, being positive when the number of negative monomials is even and negative when the number of negative monomials is odd. For example, the product $a \times -b \times c \times -a^2$ is positive, since the number of minus signs is *two*, an even number. This can be shown by actual multiplication; thus, $a \times -b \times c \times -a^2 = -ab \times c$ $\times -a^2 = -abc \times -a^2 = a^3bc$. Again, the product a $\times -b \times c \times -a^2 \times -b$ is negative, since the number of minus signs is *three*, an odd number. This can also be shown by actual multiplication; thus, $a \times -b \times c \times -a^2$ $\times -b = -ab \times c \times -a^2 \times -b = -abc \times -a^2 \times -b$ $= a^3bc \times -b = -a^3b^2c$.

59. From the foregoing the following rule is obtained for the multiplication of monomials:

Rule.—*To the product of the coefficients, annex the letters of both monomials; give each letter an exponent equal to the sum of the exponents of that letter.*

Make the sign of the product plus, when the signs of the multiplicand and multiplier are alike; and minus, when they are unlike.

EXAMPLE.—Multiply $4a^2b$ by $-5a^3bc$.

SOLUTION.—The product of the coefficients is 20, and the letters to be annexed are a, b, and c. The new exponent of a is 5, and of b, 2, since $a^{2+3} = a^5$, and $b^{1+1} = b^2$. The sign of the product is minus, since the two factors have different signs.

Hence, $4a^2b \times -5a^3bc = -20a^5b^2c$ Ans.

60. When there are more than two factors, there are simply three or more examples in multiplication to solve in succession, each to be performed by the foregoing rule. Or, multiply the coefficients as in arithmetic, write all the letters that occur in the factors, and give to each an exponent equal to the sum of the exponents of the letters in the factors. Determine the sign by the principle given in Art. **58.**

EXAMPLE.—Find the continued product of $6x^2yz^3$, $-9x^2y^2z^2$, and $-3x^4yz$.

SOLUTION.—*First:* $6x^2yz^3 \times -9x^2y^2z^2 = -54x^{2+2}y^{1+2}z^{3+2}$, or $-54x^4y^3z^5$. Now, multiplying this product by $-3x^4yz$, we have $-54x^4y^3z^5 \times -3x^4yz = 162x^8y^4z^6$. Ans.

Second: The product of the coefficients is $6 \times 9 \times 3 = 162$. The sum of the exponents of x is $2 + 2 + 4 = 8$, of y is $1 + 2 + 1 = 4$, and of z is $3 + 2 + 1 = 6$. Since the number of minus signs is even, the sign of the product is $+$. Hence, the product is $162x^8y^4z^6$. Ans.

EXAMPLES FOR PRACTICE

Find the product of:

1. a^3b^2 and $-5abd$.   Ans. $-5a^4b^3d$

2. $-7xy$ and $-7x^2y^2$.   Ans. $49x^3y^3$

3. $-15m^5n^6$ and $3mn$.   Ans. $-45m^6n^7$

4. $3a(x-y)^2$ and $2a^2(x-y)$.   Ans. $6a^3(x-y)^3$

SUGGESTION.—Treat the $(x-y)$ as though it were a single letter.

5. Find the continued product of $2a^3m^2x$, $-3a^2mx^3$, and $4am^3x^2$.
                                     Ans. $-24a^6m^6x^6$

6. What does $-a^2bn \times -2cdn \times -3bdc^2 \times -2acn^2$ equal?
                                 Ans. $12a^3b^2c^4d^2n^4$

MULTIPLICATION OF POLYNOMIALS

61. There are two cases, (1) when the multiplier is a monomial, and (2) when it contains more than one term. The first case will be considered first. The process is best illustrated by an example.

EXAMPLE.—Multiply $3a^2b^2 - 3a^4b - b^4 + a^5 - 4ab^3$ by $-5ab^2$.

SOLUTION.—*First:*

$$3a^2b^2 - 3a^4b - b^4 + a^5 - 4ab^3$$
$$-\ 5ab^2$$
$$\overline{-15a^3b^4 + 15a^5b^3 + 5ab^6 - 5a^6b^2 + 20a^2b^5}$$

Arranging terms according to descending powers of a, the product is $-5a^6b^2 + 15a^5b^3 - 15a^3b^4 + 20a^2b^5 + 5ab^6$. Ans.

Second: Arranging the multiplicand according to descending powers of a, before multiplying,

$$a^5 - 3a^4b + 3a^2b^2 - 4ab^3 - b^4$$
$$-\ 5ab^2$$
$$\overline{-5a^6b^2 + 15a^5b^3 - 15a^3b^4 + 20a^2b^5 + 5ab^6}\quad \text{Ans.}$$

EXPLANATION.—For convenience, the multiplication is begun with the left-hand term of the multiplicand instead of at the right, as in arithmetic, and the multiplier is written at the left also. Each term of the multiplicand is then treated as a monomial and multiplied by the multiplier, according to the rule of Art. **59,** and the various results are added algebraically, as indicated. As it is more convenient, and in most cases necessary, to have the resulting product arranged according to the descending or ascending powers of one of the letters, the terms are then rearranged according to the descending powers of a.

A better way to obtain the result indicated by the answer is to arrange the multiplicand according to the descending or ascending powers of the letter selected, by which means the product will not require to be rearranged; this is indicated by the second solution. Here, $a^5 \times -5ab^2 = -5a^6b^2$, $-3a^4b \times -5ab^2 = 15a^5b^3$, $3a^2b^2 \times -5ab^2 = -15a^3b^4$, $-4ab^3 \times -5ab^2 = 20a^2b^5$, and $-b^4 \times -5ab^2 = 5ab^6$.

62. From the foregoing, the following rule is derived:

Rule.—*Arrange the terms of the multiplicand according to the descending or ascending powers of some letter, and multiply each term of the multiplicand by the monomial multiplier; the algebraic sum of the results will be the product sought.*

63. When the multiplier consists of more than one term:

Rule.—*The terms of the multiplicand are arranged according to the descending or ascending powers of one of the letters, and the terms of the multiplier are arranged similarly, with the left-hand term of the multipiier under the left-hand term of the multiplicand. Each term of the multiplicand is then multiplied by the first (left-hand) term of the multiplier, proceeding from left to right, and the successive results are written underneath, connected by their proper signs, for the first partial product. Each term of the multiplicand is then multiplied by the second term of the multiplier for the second partial product, the terms similar to those in the first partial product being placed underneath to form a column. The multiplication is thus continued with the third and remaining terms until all the terms of the multiplier have been used as monomial multipliers. The various columns are then added and the result is the product sought.*

EXAMPLE 1.—Multiply $6a - 4b$ by $4a - 2b$.

SOLUTION.—Write the multiplier under the multiplicand, and begin to multiply *at the left.*

$$6a - 4b \qquad (1)$$
$$4a - 2b$$

Multiplying (1) by $4a$ gives $\overline{24a^2 - 16ab}$ (2)

Multiplying (1) by $-2b$ gives $\quad -12ab + 8b^2$ (3)

Adding (2) and (3) gives $\overline{24a^2 - 28ab + 8b^2}$ Ans.

The like terms, $-16ab$ and $-12ab$, are written under each other, so that it will be easier to add them.

EXAMPLE 2.—Multiply $x^3 - x + 1 + x^2$ by $1 - x^2 + x$.

SOLUTION.—Arrange both multiplicand and multiplier according to the increasing or the decreasing powers of the same letter, in this case according to the increasing powers of x.

$$1 - x + x^2 + x^3 \qquad (1)$$

$$\underline{1 + x - x}$$

Multiplying (1) by 1 gives $1 - x + x^2 + x^3 \qquad (2)$

Multiplying (1) by $+ x$ gives $x - x^2 + x^3 + x^4 \qquad (3)$

Multiplying (1) by $- x^2$ gives $\underline{ - x^2 + x^3 - x\ - x^5} \qquad (4)$

Adding (2), (3), and (4) gives $1 - x^2 + 3x^3 - x^5$ Ans.

EXAMPLE 3.—Find the product of $3a^2b + a^3 + 3ab^2 + b^3$ and $a^3 - b^3 + 3ab^2 - 3a^2b$.

SOLUTION.—Arranging the terms according to the descending powers of a and multiplying,

$$a^3 + 3a^2b + 3ab^2\ + b^3$$
$$\underline{a^3 - 3a^2b + 3ab^2\ -\ b^3}$$
$$a^6 + 3a^5b + 3a^4b^2 +\ a^3b^3$$
$$ - 3a^5b - 9a^4b^2 - 9a^3b^3 - 3a^2b^4$$
$$ 3a^4b^2 + 9a^3b^3 + 9a^2b^4 + 3ab^5$$
$$\underline{ -\ a^3b^3 - 3a^2b^4 - 3ab^5 - b^6}$$
$$a^6 + 0 - 3a^4b^2 + 0 + 3a^2b^4 + 0 - b^6$$

Hence, the product is $a^6 - 3a^4b^2 + 3a^2b^4 - b^6$.   Ans.

64. Multiplication is frequently indicated by enclosing each of the quantities to be multiplied in a parenthesis. The sign of multiplication is not placed between the parentheses, multiplication being understood. When the quantities are multiplied together, the expression is said to be **expanded.**

For example, in the expression $(m - 2n)(2m - n)$, the binomial $m - 2n$ is to be multiplied by the binomial $2m - n$. Performing the multiplication, the product is $2m^2 - 5mn + 2n^2$, which is the expanded form of the expression.

EXAMPLES FOR PRACTICE

Multiply the following:

1. $x^2 + 2xy + y^2$ by $x + y$.   Ans. $x^3 + 3x^2y + 3xy^2 + y^3$

2. $3ab^2m^3 + 4a^2b - 2$ by $a^6b^7m^8$.   Ans. $3a^7b^9m^{11} + 4a^8b^8m^8 - 2a^6b^7m^8$

3. $c^2 - d^2$ by $c^2 + d^2$.   Ans. $c^4 - d^4$

4. $x^4 + x^2y^2 + y^4$ by $x^2 - y^2$.   Ans. $x^6 - y^6$

5. $3a^2 - 7a + 4$ by $2a^2 + 9a - 5$.   Ans. $6a^4 + 13a^3 - 70a^2 + 71a - 20$

Expand the following:

6. $(2a - 3c)(4 - 3a)$.   Ans. $8a - 12c - 6a^2 + 9ac$

7. $(x + 2)(x - 2)(x^2 + 4)$.   Ans. $x^4 - 16$

8. $[x(x^2 - y^2) - 2][x(x^2 + y^2) + 2]$.

NOTE.—The expressions in the brackets reduce to $x^3 - xy^2 - 2$ and $x^3 + xy^2 + 2$. The product of these is $x^6 - x^2y^4 - 4xy^2 - 4$. Ans.

DIVISION

DIVISION OF MONOMIALS

65. The law of signs for division is the same as for multiplication; i. e., *when the dividend and divisor have like signs, the sign of the quotient is plus, and when they have unlike signs, the sign of the quotient is minus.* This may be proved (1) directly or (2) as following from the law of signs for multiplication. It will first be proved directly.

66. There are four cases as follows:

$$(+ 66) \div (+ 11) = + 6 \qquad \textbf{(1)}$$
$$(+ 66) \div (- 11) = - 6 \qquad \textbf{(2)}$$
$$(- 66) \div (+ 11) = - 6 \qquad \textbf{(3)}$$
$$(- 66) \div (- 11) = + 6 \qquad \textbf{(4)}$$

Referring to Fig. 3, suppose our man to start from O in all cases. He is to walk 11 steps and count 1, walk 11 steps more and count 2, and so on until he has walked 66 steps. The number of 11-step periods counted will be the quotient. If he walks around the plot in the direction of the arrows A, the quotient will be plus, while if the walk is in the direction of the arrows B, the quotient will be minus. Let the sign of the dividend indicate the direction he is to face, and let the sign of the divisor indicate whether he is to walk forwards or backwards.

Case (1),

$$(+ 66) \div (+ 11) = + 6$$

The plus sign of the dividend shows that he is to face to walk in the direction of the arrows marked A; the plus sign of the divisor shows he is to walk forwards; hence, he walks around the plot in the direction of the arrows A, and the sign of the quotient is plus.   Therefore, $66 \div 11 = 6$.

Case (2),
$$(+66) \div (-11) = -6$$

He faces to walk in the direction of the arrows marked A; the minus sign of the divisor indicates he is to walk backwards; hence, he walks around the plot in the direction of the arrows B, and the sign of the quotient is minus.   Therefore, $66 \div -11 = -6$.

Case (3),
$$(-66) \div (+11) = -6$$

The minus sign of the dividend shows he is to face to walk in the direction of the arrows marked B; the plus sign of the divisor indicates he is to walk forwards; hence, he walks around the plot in the direction of the arrows B, and the sign of the quotient is minus.   Therefore, $-66 \div 11 = -6$.

Case (4),
$$(-66) \div (-11) = +6$$

He faces to walk in the direction of the arrows B; the minus sign of the divisor indicates he is to walk backwards; hence, he walks around the plot in the direction of the arrows A, and the sign of the quotient is plus.   Therefore, $-66 \div -11 = 6$.

67.   The second proof follows directly from the laws of multiplication and the fact that the product of the divisor and quotient plus the remainder, if any, must equal the dividend.

Case (1),
$$(+66) \div (+11) = +6$$

Here the product of the divisor 11 and the quotient 6 must equal $+66$.   Since only the product of like signs is positive and the sign of the divisor is plus, the sign of the quotient must also be plus.

Case (2),

$$(+ 66) \div (- 11) = - 6$$

Here the sign of the divisor is minus; hence, the sign of the quotient must also be minus, that the product may be positive.

Case (3),

$$(- 66) \div (+ 11) = - 6$$

Case (4),

$$(- 66) \div (- 11) = + 6$$

Since the sign of the dividend is minus, the divisor and quotient must have opposite signs in order that their product may be negative.

68. In multiplication of monomials the exponents of the common letters are added, in division the exponents are subtracted. Thus, since $a^3 \times a^2 = a^{3+2} = a^5$, it follows that $a^5 \div a^2 = a^{5-2} = a^3$, and $a^5 \div a^3 = a^{5-3} = a^2$. This may also be proved by direct division; thus, $a^5 \div a^3$

$$= \frac{a \times a \times a \times a \times a}{a \times a \times a} = \frac{\not a \times \not a \times \not a \times a \times a}{\not a \times \not a \times \not a} = a^2.$$

Hence, also, $- 20x^3y^2z^5 \div 4xyz^2 = - 5x^2yz^3$. That this result is true is proved by multiplying the divisor by the quotient, or by direct division and cancelation; thus, $4xyz^2 \times - 5x^2yz^3 = - 20x^3y^2z^5$, or

$$\frac{\overset{-5}{-\cancel{20}} \times \not x \times x \times x \times \not y \times y \times \not z \times \not z \times z \times z \times z}{\cancel{4} \times \not x \times \not y \times \not z \times \not z}$$

$$= \frac{-5 \times x \times x \times y \times z \times z \times \cancel{z}}{1} = - 5x^2yz^3$$

69. From these facts the following laws are evident:

If the dividend and the divisor have like signs, the quotient will have the plus sign; if they have unlike signs, the quotient will have the minus sign.

The coefficient of the quotient is equal to the coefficient of the dividend divided by the coefficient of the divisor.

The exponent of a letter in the quotient is equal to its exponent in the dividend minus its exponent in the divisor.

70. If a letter has the same exponent in the dividend and divisor, the exponent of that letter in the quotient is 0; thus, $a^3 \div a^3 = a^{3-3} = a^0 = 1$. When the dividend and divisor are equal, the quotient is always 1; since the exponent of the quotient when the dividend and divisor are equal is always zero, and since the dividend and divisor may be any two equal quantities whatever, it follows that any number or quantity having zero for an exponent is equal to **1**. In other words, $a^0 = 1$, $592^0 = 1$, $a^0b^0c^0 = 1$, etc.

71. The **reciprocal** of a number is 1 divided by the number; thus, the reciprocal of 8 is $\frac{1}{8}$, of a is $\frac{1}{a}$, of x^2 is $\frac{1}{x^2}$, etc. The reciprocal of a fraction is the fraction inverted; thus, the reciprocal of $\frac{7}{12}$ is $\frac{12}{7}$, since $1 \div \frac{7}{12} = 1 \times \frac{12}{7} = \frac{12}{7}$. So, also, the reciprocal of $\frac{a-b}{c}$ is $\frac{c}{a-b}$.

72. When a letter in the divisor has a higher exponent than the same letter in the dividend the exponent of that letter in the quotient is negative; thus, $a^3 \div a^5 = a^{-2}$; $20x^2y^nz^2 \div 4xy^2z^3 = 5xz^{-1}$, etc. The negative exponent is interpreted as follows: Dividing a^3 by a^5, the result is

$$\frac{a \times a \times a}{a \times a \times a \times a \times a} = \frac{\cancel{a} \times \cancel{a} \times \cancel{a}}{\cancel{a} \times \cancel{a} \times \cancel{a} \times a \times a} = \frac{1}{a^2}; \text{ but } a^3 \div a^5$$

$= a^{-2}$. Hence, $a^{-2} = \frac{1}{a^2}$; that is, *a quantity having a negative exponent is equal to the reciprocal of the quantity having an equal positive exponent.* Further, $20x^2y^2z^2 \div 4xy^2z^3$

$$= \frac{20 \times x \times x \times y \times y \times z \times z}{4 \times x \times x \times y \times y \times z \times z \times z} = \frac{5x}{z}; \text{ but } 20x^2y^2z^2 \text{ divided}$$

by $4xy^2z^3$ also equals $5xz^{-1}$; and, hence, *if it be desired to transfer a factor,* as z in $\dfrac{5x}{z}$, *from the divisor to the dividend, it may be done by canceling the factor from the divisor and writing it in the dividend with the sign of its exponent changed.*

73. From the foregoing, the following rule is derived for division of monomials:

Rule.—*Divide the coefficient of the dividend by the coefficient of the divisor and to the quotient annex the letters of the dividend, each with an exponent equal to its exponent in the dividend minus its exponent in the divisor, omitting those letters whose exponents become zero.*

Make the sign of the quotient plus when the dividend and divisor have like signs, and minus when they have unlike signs.

EXAMPLE 1.—Divide $6a^5b^4c^3$ by $-3a^2bc^3$.

SOLUTION.—The quotient of $6 \div 3$ is 2. The letters to be annexed, and their exponents, are $a^{5-2} = a^3$, and $b^{4-1} = b^3$. The c has an exponent of $3 - 3 = 0$, so that it becomes equal to 1, and is omitted. The sign of the quotient is minus.

Hence, $\qquad 6a^5b^4c^3 \div -3a^2bc^3 = -2a^3b^3$ Ans.

PROOF.— $\qquad -3a^2bc^3 \times -2a^3b^3 = 6a^5b^4c^3$

EXAMPLE 2.—Divide $-10a^6b^3c^2d$ by $-2ab^3c$.

SOLUTION.— $-10a^6b^3c^2d \div -2ab^3c = 5a^{6-1}b^{3-3}c^{2-1}d = 5a^5cd$.

$\qquad\qquad\qquad\qquad\qquad\qquad\qquad\qquad$ Ans.

EXAMPLES FOR PRACTICE

Divide the following:

1. $12m^2n$ by $4n$. $\qquad\qquad\qquad\qquad\qquad$ Ans. $3m^2$
2. $30x^6y^5bc^3$ by $-6x^5y^5c^2$. $\qquad\qquad\quad$ Ans. $-5xbc$
3. $-44a^3b^3c^3$ by $-11ab^2c^3$. $\qquad\quad$ Ans. $4a^2b$
4. $-100x^4y^3z^2$ by x^3y^2. $\qquad\quad$ Ans. $-100xyz^2$
5. $75pq^2x^3m^4$ by $75x^3$. $\qquad\qquad$ Ans. pq^2m^4

DIVISION OF POLYNOMIALS

74. When the divisor is a monomial:

Rule.—*Divide each term of the dividend by the divisor, and connect the partial quotients by their proper signs.*

EXAMPLE.—Divide $12a^2b^4 - 9ab^3 + 6a^3b^4$ by $3ab^3$.

SOLUTION.— $\qquad 3ab^3)\overline{12a^2b^4 - 9ab^3 + 6a^3b^4}$

$\qquad\qquad$ quotient $4ab \quad -3 \quad\ + 2a^2b$ Ans.

EXAMPLES FOR PRACTICE

Divide the following:

1. $64m^2n^3 - 32mn^2 + 8m^2n$ by $8mn$.   Ans. $8mn^2 - 4n + m$
2. $27x^3y^2z - 9x^3yz^2 - 333x^3y^2z^2$ by $-3x^3yz$.

                         Ans. $-9y + 3z + 111yz$

3. $10(x + y)^2 - 5a(x + y) + 5a^2(x + y)$ by $5(x + y)$.

                         Ans. $2(x + y) - a + a^2$

75. The division of a polynomial by a polynomial is performed in the same manner as is the operation called *long division* in arithmetic. The work is performed to the best advantage if the dividend and divisor are arranged according to the ascending or descending powers of the same letter. The process is shown in the following example:

EXAMPLE.—Divide $x^3 - 9x^2 + x^4 - 16x - 4$ by $4 + x^2 + 4x$.

SOLUTION.—Arrange the dividend and divisor according to descending powers of x.

$$
\begin{array}{l}
\textit{dividend} \quad\quad x^4 + \ x^3 - \ 9x^2 - 16x - 4 \underline{|\ x^2 + 4x + 4\ } \textit{divisor} \\
\quad\quad\quad\quad\quad\quad \underline{x^4 + 4x^3 + \ 4x^2} \quad\quad\quad\quad (x^2 - 3x - 1\ \textit{quotient} \\
\textit{first new dividend} \quad -3x^3 - 13x^2 - 16x \\
\quad\quad\quad\quad\quad\quad \underline{-3x^3 - 12x^2 - 12x} \\
\textit{second new dividend} \quad\quad -x^2 - \ 4x - 4 \\
\quad\quad\quad\quad\quad\quad\quad\quad \underline{-x^2 - \ 4x - 4}
\end{array}
$$

Divide the first term of the dividend x^4 by the first term of the divisor x^2 for the first term x^2 of the quotient. Multiply the whole divisor by x^2 and the product is $x^4 + 4x^3 + 4x^2$. Subtract this from the dividend and the remainder is the first new dividend $-3x^3 - 13x^2 - 16x - 4$. The term -4 need not be brought down, since the divisor consists of three terms only.

Divide the first term of the remainder $-3x^3$ by the first term of the divisor x^2 and the result is $-3x$, the second term of the quotient. Again, multiply the whole divisor by this term of the quotient and subtract the product, $-3x^3 - 12x^2 - 12x$, from the first remainder. The remainder is $-x^2 - 4x - 4$, the term -4 being brought down from the original dividend. Divide the first term of this remainder $-x^2$ by the first term of the divisor x^2 and the quotient -1 is the third term of the quotient. Multiply the whole divisor by this term of the quotient and the product is $-x^2 - 4x - 4$. When this product is subtracted from the remainder, $-x^2 - 4x - 4$, there is no remainder.

The sum of the various products plus the remainder, if any, $x^4 + 4x^3 + 4x^2$, $-3x^3 - 12x^2 - 12x$, and $-x^2 - 4x - 4$, is the original dividend.

76. The student will find it advantageous to place the divisor on the right of the dividend, with the quotient below, as shown in the last example. It will then be easier to multiply each term of the divisor by the new term of the quotient and there will be less liability of mistakes. The solution will also require less space.

77. To divide one polynomial by another:

Rule.—I. *Arrange both dividend and divisor according to ascending or descending powers of some common letter.*

II. *Divide the first term of the dividend by the first term of the divisor to obtain the first term of the quotient.*

III. *Multiply the entire divisor by the first term of the quotient; write the product under the dividend and subtract it from the dividend for the first remainder.*

IV. *Regard the remainder as a new dividend and divide its first term by the first term of the divisor for the second term of the quotient.*

V. *Multiply the whole divisor by the second term of the quotient; write the product under the first remainder and subtract as before.*

VI. *So continue until the remainder is 0, or until the first term of the remainder cannot be divided by the first term of the divisor without a change of sign in the exponent of the quotient.*

Note.—When there is a final remainder, it is to be written over the divisor and annexed to the quotient.

Example 1.—Divide $x^4 + 57x - 70$ by $x^2 + 3x - 5$.

Solution.—

dividend	$x^4 \qquad\qquad + 57x - 70($	$x^2 + 3x - 5$ *divisor*
$(x^2 + 3x - 5) \times x^2$	$= x^4 + 3x^3 - 5x^2$	$(x^2 - 3x + 14$ *quotient*
first new dividend	$-3x^3 + 5x^2 + 57x$	
$(x^2 + 3x - 5) \times (-3x) =$	$-3x^3 - 9x^2 + 15x$	
second new dividend	$+ 14x^2 + 42x - 70$	
$(x^2 + 3x - 5) \times 14 \quad =$	$+ 14x^2 + 42x - 70$	

CHECK.—By the definition of division the dividend is the product of the divisor and quotient; therefore, to check a division, multiply the divisor by the quotient, and if the product is the dividend, the work is probably correct. Thus, example 1 may be checked as follows:

divisor $\qquad x^2 + 3x - 5$

quotient $\qquad x^2 -- 3x + 14$

$$\begin{array}{l} \overline{x^4 + 3x^3 - 5x^2} \\ \quad\ - 3x^3 - 9x^2 + 15x \\ \quad\qquad\quad + 14x^2 + 42x - 70 \end{array}$$

product $\qquad x^4 \qquad\qquad\quad + 57x - 70$ *dividend*

EXAMPLE 2.—Divide (*a*) $x^2 - y^2$ by $x - y$; also, (*b*) $a^4 - x^4$ by $a + x$.

SOLUTION.—

(*a*)

$$\begin{array}{l} x^2 - y^2 \underline{(x - y} \\ \underline{x^2 - xy}\ \ (x + y \\ \quad + xy - y^2 \\ \quad \underline{+ xy - y^2} \end{array}$$

(*b*)

$$\begin{array}{l} a^4 - x^4 \underline{(a + x} \\ \underline{a^4 + a^3x}\ \ (a^3 - a^2x + ax^2 - x^3 \\ \quad - a^3x - x^4 \\ \quad \underline{- a^3x - a^2x^2} \\ \qquad\quad a^2x^2 - x^4 \\ \qquad\quad \underline{a^2x^2 + ax^3} \\ \qquad\qquad\quad - ax^3 - x^4 \\ \qquad\qquad\quad \underline{- ax^3 - x^4} \end{array}$$

Ans. $\begin{cases} (a) & x + y \\ (b) & a^3 - a^2x + ax^2 - x^3 \end{cases}$

EXAMPLE 3.—Divide $a^5 - 9 + 7a^2 - 17a^3$ by $3 + a^2 + 5a$.

SOLUTION.—

$$\begin{array}{l} a^5 \qquad - 17a^3 + 7a^2 - 9 \underline{(a^2 + 5a + 3} \\ \underline{a^5 + 5a^4 + 3a^3} \qquad\quad (a^3 - 5a^2 + 5a - 3 \ \ \text{Ans.} \\ \ - 5a^4 - 20a^3 + 7a^2 \\ \ \underline{- 5a^4 - 25a^3 - 15a^2} \\ \qquad\quad 5a^3 + 22a^2 - 9 \\ \qquad\quad \underline{5a^3 + 25a^2 + 15a} \\ \qquad\qquad\ - 3a^2 - 15a - 9 \\ \qquad\qquad\ \underline{- 3a^2 - 15a - 9} \end{array}$$

EXAMPLES FOR PRACTICE

Divide:

1. $a^2 + 2ab + b^2$ by $a + b$.   Ans. $a + b$
2. $a^2 - 2ab + b^2$ by $a - b$.   Ans. $a - b$
3. $a^3 - 3a^2b + 3ab^2 - b^3$ by $a - b$.   Ans. $a^2 - 2ab + b^2$

4. $a^3 + a^2 + 4a - 20$ by $a - 2$.   Ans. $a^2 + 3a + 10$

5. $8x^2 - 26xy + 15y^2$ by $4x - 3y$.   Ans. $2x - 5y$

6. $x^4 - x^2y^2 - 12y^4$ by $x^2 + 3y^2$.   Ans. $x^2 - 4y^2$

7. $a^4 + 64$ by $a^2 + 4a + 8$.   Ans. $a^2 - 4a + 8$

8. $x^2y^2 + 2xy^2z - x^2z^2 + y^2z^2$ by $xy + xz + yz$. Ans. $xy - xz + yz$

9. $12x^4 - 26x^3y - 8x^2y^2 + 10xy^3 - 8y^4$ by $3x^2 - 2xy + y^2$.

Ans. $4x^2 - 6xy - 8y^2$

10. $a^{10} - 29a^4 + 62a^3 + 3a^2 + 16a - 352$ by $a^4 + 2a^3 - 5a - 11$.

Ans. $a^6 - 2a^5 + 4a^4 - 3a^3 + 7a^2 - 16a + 32$

ELEMENTS OF ALGEBRA

(PART 2)

FACTORS AND MULTIPLES

FACTORING

1. It was stated in Art. **4,** Part 1, that factoring is **a** particularly important operation. The reason that this is so is that terms cannot be combined in algebra as in arithmetic, because the equivalence of the terms is not known. The idea can be best illustrated by an example.

Suppose it is required to multiply 5,402 by 136. The number 5,402 is equal to $5,000 + 400 + 2 = 5\,(10^3) + 4\,(10^2) + 2$. Similarly, 136 is equal to $10^2 + 3\,(10) + 6$. If now a be substituted for 10, the two numbers become $5a^3 + 4a^2 + 2$ and $a^2 + 3a + 6$. Multiplying these two algebraic expressions, the product is

$$
\begin{array}{l}
5a^3 + 4a^2 + 2 \\
\underline{a^2 + 3a\ + 6} \\
5a^5 + 4a^4 \qquad\quad + 2a^2 \\
\quad\ 15a^4 + 12a^3 \qquad\quad + 6a \\
\quad\qquad\ \underline{30a^3 + 24a^2 \qquad\quad + 12} \\
5a^5 + 19a^4 + 42a^3 + 26a^2 + 6a + 12
\end{array}
$$

That this result is correct can be seen at once by substituting 10 for a, thus:

§4

40—13

The product of 5,402 and 136 by arithmetic is

$$5\,4\,0\,2$$
$$1\,3\,6$$
$$\overline{3\,2\,4\,1\,2}$$
$$1\,6\,2\,0\,6$$
$$5\,4\,0\,2$$
$$\overline{7\,3\,4\,6\,7\,2}$$

$$5a^5 = 5\,0\,0\,0\,0\,0$$
$$19a^4 = 1\,9\,0\,0\,0\,0$$
$$42a^3 = 4\,2\,0\,0\,0$$
$$26a^2 = 2\,6\,0\,0$$
$$6a = 6\,0$$
$$12 = 1\,2$$
$$sum = 7\,3\,4\,6\,7\,2$$

Since the two products agree, it is evident that both methods are correct. In the case of the arithmetical operation, it will be noted that the different terms obtained are merged into one another, while in the algebraic operation it was necessary to connect the various terms by signs, as it was not known what relation they bore to one another. The product is a long, unwieldy expression of six terms and cannot be used conveniently in future operations. If, however, the expression can be factored, it then becomes available for future use, and operations can be performed that would otherwise in many cases be impossible.

2. Any quantity, as A, that is exactly divisible by another quantity, as B, is said to be a **multiple** of B, and B is said to be a **factor** of A; for example, 12 is a multiple of 2, 3, 4, and 6, and 2, 3, 4, and 6 are each a factor of 12; $a^2 - b^2$ is a multiple of $a - b$ and of $a + b$, and $a - b$ and $a + b$ are both factors of $a^2 - b^2$.

3. The process of finding the factors of a quantity is called **factoring**; but before a quantity can be factored, it must be shown that it is a multiple; that is, that it can be divided by some quantity besides 1 or itself without a remainder. Many ingenious methods have been devised for determining whether quantities were multiples and, if so, how to factor them. Binomial factors or those having a binomial form are the ones principally sought. A few of the simplest and most generally used methods will now be described.

4. Every number has two exact divisors, viz., the number itself and unity. For, if x denotes any number, $x \div x = 1$, and $x \div 1 = x$. But neither of these two divisors of a number is regarded as a factor.

5. A **prime number,** or simply a **prime,** is a number that has no factors except itself and unity.

Thus, 2, 3, 5, 7, 11, 13, 17, etc. are primes.

6. A prime number that is a factor of another number is a **prime factor** of that number.

Thus, 2 and 3 are prime factors of 6; 7 is a prime factor of 14, 21, etc.

7. Every number not a prime can be resolved into prime factors, and this resolution can give only one set of prime factors.

Thus, $3 \times 7 \times 13$ is the only set of prime factors of 273; also, $2 \times 5 \times 7 \times 11$ are the only prime factors of 770.

8. A **composite number** is a number that can be separated into two or more factors besides itself and unity.

Thus, 8, 12, 20, 36, etc. are composite numbers.

9. The multiples of 2 are **even** numbers; all other numbers are **odd.**

Thus, 2, 4, 6, 8, etc. are even numbers; while 1, 3, 5, 7, etc. are odd numbers.

10. The prime factors of a given number must be found by trial. Beginning with 2 and taking each of the prime numbers in succession, we determine which of them are exact divisors of the given number.

EXAMPLE 1.—Find the prime factors of 534.

SOLUTION.—Dividing by 2 and then by 3,

$$534 = 2 \times 3 \times 89$$

$$\begin{array}{r} 2\,)\,5\,3\,4 \\ 3\,)\,2\,6\,7 \\ \hline 8\,9 \end{array}$$

As 2, 3, and 89 are primes, they are the prime factors of 534

Thus, $534 = 2 \times 3 \times 89$ Ans.

EXAMPLE 2.—Find the prime factors of 862.

SOLUTION.—After dividing 862 by 2, try to divide 431   2)8 6 2
by 2, 3, 5, 7, 11, 13, 17, and 19. It is unnecessary to try   4 3 1
any prime number greater than 19, for 431 divided by 19
gives a quotient less than 23, the next prime number. Therefore,
if 431 were divisible by 23 or any number greater than 23, the quotient
would be less than 19, and 431 would have a factor less than 19. But
by trial it is found that 431 has no factor less than 19, and is, therefore,
a prime number. Thus,

$$862 = 2 \times 431 \quad \text{Ans.}$$

EXAMPLES FOR PRACTICE

Find the prime factors of:

1. 35.   Ans. 5×7
2. 117.   Ans. $3^2 \times 13$
3. 3,575.   Ans. $5^2 \times 11 \times 13$
4. 13,260.   Ans. $2^2 \times 3 \times 5 \times 13 \times 17$

FACTORS OF ALGEBRAIC EXPRESSIONS

11. An algebraic term is **integral** if it does not contain
a *letter* as a *divisor ;* otherwise it is **fractional.**

Thus, ab, x^2, $3mn^2x$, $\frac{2}{3}xy$ are integral terms; while $a \div b$,
$\frac{x}{y}$, $\frac{3m}{4n}$ are fractional. An integral term may have either an
integral or a fractional value; so also may a fractional term.

The classification of terms into integral and fractional
has reference to their literal part, not to their numerical
part or to their numerical value.

An **integral expression** is an expression of which all the
terms are integral.

Thus, $5x + 3x^2 + 6x^3 + 3acx^4$ is an integral expression.
But $\frac{x}{y} + \frac{3a}{b} + \frac{4m}{x}$ is a fractional expression.

An expression is said to be *integral with respect to a certain letter* when that letter does not occur as a divisor in
any term.

Thus, $\dfrac{x}{a} + \dfrac{x^2y}{a^2} + \dfrac{x^3y^2}{a^3}$ is integral with respect to x, but fractional with respect to a. In the following discussion of factors and multiples, only integral expressions are treated.

12. Factors of Monomials.—Since monomials containing more than one element are simply indicated multiplications, the factors of a monomial are found by mere inspection. Thus,

$$11a^4x^2 = 11 \times a \times a \times a \times a \times x \times x$$

13. Factors of Polynomials.—The product of two or more binomials or trinomials often assumes a certain type form, and when these type forms appear, it is easy to find the factors. Some of the simplest methods of finding these factors are given in the following articles.

CASE I

14. To factor a polynomial when all of its terms have a common factor.—The common factor is found by inspection and the other factor is found by dividing the polynomial by the common factor.

EXAMPLE.—Find the factors of $16x^2y^2 + 4x^3y^2 - 12xy^4$.

SOLUTION.—It is evident that each term contains the common factor $4xy^2$. Dividing the number by $4xy^2$, the quotient is $4x + x^2 - 3y^2$, which is the other factor.

Hence, $16x^2y^2 + 4x^3y^2 - 12xy^4 = 4xy^2(4x + x^2 - 3y^2)$ Ans.

15. To discover the monomial factor of a polynomial, first ascertain the factors common to all the numerical coefficients. This is done by ascertaining if the smallest numerical coefficient is contained in the coefficients of *all* the other terms, and if so, reserve it for the coefficient of the monomial factor; if not, and it is not a prime number, resolve it into its prime factors and see if any are factors of all the remaining terms, multiplying all the common prime factors for the numerical coefficient of the monomial factor sought. Then examine the polynomial to find the letters common to every term, take each of these common letters with the lowest exponent it has in any term of the polynomial. The product of the letters so chosen and the common factors of the numerical coefficients is the monomial factor.

EXAMPLE 1. — Find the factors of $12ab^2c^3 - 18a^3c^2y + 24a^2c^4 - 36a^4bc^5y^2$.

SOLUTION.—The numerical coefficients are 12, 18, 24, and 36. The smallest coefficient, 12, is not a factor of 18; hence, it is resolved into its prime factors, which are $2 \times 2 \times 3$. Since 18 is divisible by one 2 and by 3, and the other coefficients, 24 and 36, are divisible by 12, the numerical coefficient of the monomial factor is $2 \times 3 = 6$, the largest factor common to 12, 18, 24, and 36. The letters a and c are common to all the terms, and the lowest power of a is the first, and of c the square. Therefore, the monomial factor is $2 \times 3 \times a \times c^2$, or $6ac^2$. Dividing the polynomial by $6ac^2$, the quotient is $2b^2c - 3a^2y + 4ac^2 - 6a^3bc^3y^2$. Hence,

$$12ab^2c^3 - 18a^3c^2y + 24a^2c^4 - 36a^4bc^5y^2 = 6ac^2(2b^2c - 3a^2y + 4ac^2 - 6a^3bc^3y^2)$$
Ans.

EXAMPLE 2.—Factor $2ax - bx$.

SOLUTION.—The only letter or number common to the two terms is x.

Hence, $2ax - bx = (2a - b)x$ Ans.

EXAMPLES FOR PRACTICE

Factor the following expressions:

1. $a^4 + ax$.   Ans. $a(a^3 + x)$

2. $12a^5 - 2a^3 + 4a^4$.   Ans. $2a^3(6a^2 - 1 + 2a)$

3. $30m^4n^2 - 6n^3$.   Ans. $6n^2(5m^4 - n)$

4. $16x^2y^3 - 8x^5 + 8$.   Ans. $8(2x^2y^3 - x^5 + 1)$

5. $4x^3y - 12x^2y^2 + 8xy^3$.   Ans. $4xy(x^2 - 3xy + 2y^2)$

6. $49a^2b^3c^4 - 63a^3b^2c^4 + 7a^4b^2c^3$.   Ans. $7a^2b^2c^3(7bc - 9ac + a^2)$

EQUAL FACTORS

16. **Equal factors** are those whose terms have the same letters, and whose letters have the same exponents and the same signs. Thus, $5a(2y - x)$ and $5a(2y - x)$ are equal factors of $5a(2y - x) \times 5a(2y - x) = 25a^2(2y - x)^2$; but $5a(2y - x)$ and $-5a(2y - x)$ are unequal factors, since the signs of $5a$ are not the same in both expressions.

17. A product of two equal factors is a **perfect square.** Either of the equal factors of a quantity is called its **square root.**

18. A product of three equal factors is a **perfect cube.** Any one of the equal factors of a quantity is called its **cube root.**

19. In factoring, it is important to be able to easily distinguish quantities that are perfect squares and cubes, and to determine their roots. By definition, $9a^2b^2$ is a perfect square because $3ab \times 3ab = 9a^2b^2$, and $3ab$ is its square root. Also, $8a^6$ is a perfect cube because $2a^2 \times 2a^2 \times 2a^2 = 8a^6$, and $2a^2$ is its cube root. In each of these cases the coefficients of the roots are multiplied together, and the exponents added, to produce a perfect power. *Hence, a quantity is a perfect square when its coefficient is a perfect square, and the exponents of all its letters can be divided by 2.* For example, $36x^{10}$, $49b^2c^4d^8$, $16a^6b^{12}$, and 1 are all perfect squares, whose roots are $6x^5$, $7bc^2d^4$, $4a^3b^6$, and 1, respectively. No perfect square, however, can have a minus sign; for, let $a =$ any quantity, $-a \times -a = a^2$, and $a \times a = a^2$. The square root of a^2 may be $-a$, or a, and a square root is often written $\pm a$, read plus or minus a.

A quantity is a perfect cube when its coefficient is a perfect cube, and the exponents of all its letters can be divided by 3. Thus, $27x^{12}$, $-64b^3c^9d^6$, $8a^{15}b^{18}$, and 1 are all perfect cubes, whose roots are $3x^4$, $-4bc^3d^2$, $2a^5b^6$, and 1, respectively. The sign of the cube root is always the same as that of its cube.

CASE II

20. **To factor a trinomial that is a perfect square.**

Any trinomial is a perfect square when the first and the last terms are perfect squares and positive, and the second term is twice the product of their square roots.

Thus, let x and y represent any two quantities whatever, and we have the general forms of the square as follows:

$$(x+y)^2 = (x+y)(x+y) = x^2 + 2xy + y^2 \qquad \textbf{(1)}$$
$$(x-y)^2 = (x-y)(x-y) = x^2 - 2xy + y^2 \qquad \textbf{(2)}$$

The sign of the second term of the square always determines the sign of the second term of the root, y in this particular case.

21. Since x may represent any quantity and $\dot{y}$ any other quantity, it is evident that *any* trinomial having the form $x^2 + 2xy + y^2$ or $x^2 - 2xy + y^2$ is a perfect square.

Rule.—*Extract the square roots of the first and the last term of the trinomial, and connect the results by the sign of the second term.*

EXAMPLE 1.—Factor $x^2 + 6xy + 9y^2$.

SOLUTION.—First see if the trinomial has the form stated in Art. **20.** The first and the last terms are seen to be perfect squares, and their roots to be x and $3y$. The second term is also twice the product of the roots x and $3y$, and, since it has the plus sign, the binomial root must be $x + 3y$. Hence, the given expression is a square of the form $x^2 + 2xy + y^2$, and

$$x^2 + 6xy + 9y^2 = (x + 3y)(x + 3y) = (x + 3y)^2 \quad \text{Ans.}$$

EXAMPLE 2.—Factor $16m^4 + 9n^6 - 24m^2n^3$.

SOLUTION.—The first term of the expression is a perfect square, but the last term is not. Inspecting the second term, it is found to be the square of $3n^3$, and the third term to be twice the product of $3n^3$ and the square root, $4m^2$, of the first term. Arranging the trinomial so that the first and the last term are perfect squares, it becomes $16m^4$

$- 24m^2n^3 + 9n^6$ (a square of the form $x^2 - 2xy + y^2$); hence, $16m^4 + 9n^6 - 24m^2n^3 = 16m^4 - 24m^2n^3 + 9n^6 = (4m^2 - 3n^3)(4m^2 - 3n^3) = (4m^2 - 3n^3)^2$. Ans.

EXAMPLE 3.—Factor $4x^2 + x^2y^2 + 2x^2y$.

SOLUTION.—Arranging the trinomial so that the first term and the last term are perfect squares, it becomes $4x^2 + 2x^2y + x^2y^2$. Now, although the first and the last term are perfect squares with roots $2x$ and xy, respectively, the second term is only equal to the product of the roots; hence, the trinomial is *not* a perfect square, and can only be factored by Case I. Each term contains x^2, and

$$4x^2 + x^2y^2 + 2x^2y = x^2(4 + y^2 + 2y) \text{ Ans.}$$

22. *When two of the terms of a trinomial are perfect squares, and have like signs, and the other term is twice the product of their roots, the trinomial is a perfect square.*

Compare this statement with Art. **20.** Thus, $2ab - a^2 - b^2$, if divided by -1, becomes $- 2ab + a^2 + b^2 = a^2 - 2ab + b^2$; hence, $2ab - a^2 - b^2 = - (a^2 - 2ab + b^2) = - (a - b)^2$.

EXAMPLE 1.—Factor $4pq - 4p^2 - q^2$.

SOLUTION.—Dividing first by -1, we have $- 4pq + 4p^2 + q^2 = 4p^2 - 4pq + q^2 = (2p - q)^2$.
Hence, $4pq - 4p^2 - q^2 = - (4p^2 - 4pq + q^2) = - (2p - q)^2$ Ans.

EXAMPLE 2.—Factor $16r^2s^2 + 16r^4 + 4s^4$.

SOLUTION.—The expression contains three squares, but, by careful inspection, we see that the first term is also twice the product of the square roots of the other two.
Thus, $16r^2s^2 + 16r^4 + 4s^4 = 16r^4 + 16r^2s^2 + 4s^4 = (4r^2 + 2s^2)^2$ Ans.

23. The two formulas given in Art. **20** are also used to write out the square of the sum or the difference of two quantities in place of actually performing the multiplication. These are expressed in words as follows:

The square of the sum of two quantities is equal to the square of the first, plus twice the product of the first and the second, plus the square of the second.

The square of the difference of two quantities is equal to the square of the first, minus twice the product of the first and the second, plus the square of the second.

EXAMPLE 1.—What is the value of $(2ax + 3b^2)^2$?

SOLUTION.—Here x in formula **1,** Art. **20,** equals $2ax$ and $y = 3b^2$; hence, $x^2 = 4a^2x^2$, $2xy = 2 \times 2ax \times 3b^2 = 12ab^2x$, and $y^2 = 9b^4$. Therefore, $(2ax + 3b^2)^2 = 4a^2x^2 + 12ab^2x + 9b^4$ Ans.

EXAMPLE 2.—What is the square of $x^2 - 2ax + a^2$?

SOLUTION.— $x^2 - 2ax + a^2 = (x^2 - 2ax) + a^2$. Now treating the two terms in parenthesis as a single term, let x in formula **2** equal $x^2 - 2ax$ and y equal a^2. $x^2 = (x^2 - 2ax)^2 = x^4 - 4ax^3 + 4a^2x^2$ (applying formula **2**); $2xy = 2 \times (x^2 - 2ax) \times a^2 = 2a^2x^2 - 4a^3x$; and $y^2 = a^4$. Therefore,

$$(x^2 - 2ax + a^2)^2 = x^4 - 4ax^3 + 4a^2x^2 + 2a^2x^2 - 4a^3x$$
$$+ a^4 = x^4 - 4ax^3 + 6a^2x^2 - 4a^3x + a^4 \quad \text{Ans.}$$

The same result will be obtained if the second and third terms are included in parenthesis and treated as one term. Thus, $x^2 - 2ax + a^2 = x^2 - (2ax - a^2)$. See Art. **53,** Part 1. Let x in formula **2** equal x^2 and $y = 2ax - a^2$. Then, $x^2 = (x^2)^2 = x^4$; $2xy = 2 \times x^2 \times (2ax - a^2) = 4ax^3 - 2a^2x^2$; and $y^2 = (2ax - a^2)^2 = 4a^2x^2 - 4a^3x + a^4$. Therefore, $(x^2 - 2ax + a^2)^2 = x^4 - (4ax^3 - 2a^2x^2) + 4a^2x^2 - 4a^3x + a^4 = x^4 - 4ax^3 + 6a^2x^2 - 4a^3x + a^4$. Ans.

24. After a little practice, simple expansions like those in the last two examples can be written directly. Formulas **1** and **2** are very important and should be thoroughly memorized.

EXAMPLES FOR PRACTICE

Factor the following trinomials:

1. $x^2 - 16x + 64$.   Ans. $(x - 8)^2$
2. $n^6 - 26n^3 + 169$.   Ans. $(n^3 - 13)^2$
3. $25x^2 + 70xyz + 49y^2z^2$.   Ans. $(5x + 7yz)^2$
4. $16c^2 + b^2 - 8bc$.   Ans. $(4c - b)^2$
5. $2mx - m^2 - x^2$.   Ans. $-(m - x)^2$
6. $a^2b^4c^6 - 2ab^2c^3 + 1$.   Ans. $(ab^2c^3 - 1)^2$

Square the following:

7. $m + n$.   Ans. $m^2 + 2mn + n^2$
8. $4x + 2$.   Ans. $16x^2 + 16x + 4$
9. $3a - 5b$.   Ans. $9a^2 - 30ab + 25b^2$
10. Square $2c^2 - c + d$.

NOTE.—First separate $2c^2 - c + d$ into two terms by enclosing $c + d$ in parenthesis; then the expression becomes $2c^2 - (c - d)$, and considering this as a binomial, the square is $4c^4 - 4c^2(c - d) + (c - d)^2$.

$$- 4c^2(c - d) = - 4c^3 + 4c^2d$$
$$(c - d)^2 = c^2 - 2cd + d^2$$

Adding these results to $4c^4$, the final result is $4c^4 - 4c^3 + 4c^2d + c^2 - 2cd + d^2$. Ans.

25. **To factor an expression that is the difference between two perfect squares:**

Formula,

$$(x + y)(x - y) = x^2 - y^2$$

26. Since x may represent any quantity and y any other quantity, it is evident from the formula that any expression that is the difference between two perfect squares may be factored by the following:

Rule.—*Extract the square roots of the first and last terms. Add these roots for the first factor, and subtract the second from the first for the second factor.*

EXAMPLE 1.—Factor $9x^8y^6 - 4$.

SOLUTION.—The square roots of the first and last terms are $3x^4y^3$ and 2. The sum of these roots is $3x^4y^3 + 2$, and the second subtracted from the first is $3x^4y^3 - 2$.

Hence, $\qquad 9x^8y^6 - 4 = (3x^4y^3 + 2)(3x^4y^3 - 2)$　Ans.

EXAMPLE 2.—Factor $(a + b)^2 - m^2n^2$.

SOLUTION.—The square roots of the first and last terms are $a + b$ and mn. The sum of these roots is $a + b + mn$, and the second subtracted from the first is $a + b - mn$.

Hence,

$$(a + b)^2 - m^2n^2 = (a + b + mn)(a + b - mn)　\text{Ans.}$$

27. The formula in Art. **25** is also generally used to write out the product of the sum and difference of two quantities, without actually performing the multiplication. The formula is stated in words as follows:

The product of the sum and difference of two quantities is equal to the difference of their squares.

EXAMPLE 1.—Expand $(x^2 + 3)(x^2 - 3)$.

SOLUTION.—The square of the first term is x^4, and of the second, 9.

Hence, $\qquad (x^2 + 3)(x^2 - 3) = x^4 - 9$　Ans.

EXAMPLE 2.—Expand $(ax^2 + bx - 1)(ax^2 + bx + 1)$.

SOLUTION.— $ax^2 + bx - 1 = (ax^2 + bx) - 1$, $ax^2 + bx + 1 = (ax^2 + bx) + 1$; their product is, therefore, $(ax^2 + bx)^2 - 1$, the two terms in parenthesis being treated as one term. If desired to expand further, the expression becomes, applying formula **1,** Art. **20,** $a^2x^4 + 2abx^3 + b^2x^2 - 1$. Ans.

EXAMPLE 3.—Factor the expression obtained for the answer to the last example.

SOLUTION.—On examining the expression $a^2x^4 + 2abx^3 + b^2x^2 - 1$, it is seen that the first three terms are composed of descending powers of x with but two literal coefficients. Hence, these terms are separated from the last term, -1, for investigation, thus obtaining $(a^2x^4 + 2abx^3 + b^2x^2) - 1$, which equals $x^2(a^2x^2 + 2abx + b^2) - 1$. The expression in parenthesis is evidently the square of $ax + b$; hence, the expression becomes $x^2(ax + b)^2 - 1$. In this last expression the first term is a perfect square, and since the second term is also a perfect square, $x^2(ax + b)^2 - 1 = [x(ax + b) + 1] [x(ax + b) - 1] = (ax^2 + bx + 1)(ax^2 + bx - 1)$. Ans.

EXAMPLES FOR PRACTICE

Factor the following expressions:

1. $a^2 - 16$.   Ans. $(a + 4)(a - 4)$
2. $a^2 - 49c^8$.   Ans. $(a + 7c^4)(a - 7c^4)$
3. $81x^6y^4 - 1$.   Ans. $(9x^3y^2 + 1)(9x^3y^2 - 1)$
4. $(ax + by)^2 - 1$.   Ans. $(ax + by + 1)(ax + by - 1)$
5. $25x^4y^2 - (bx + 1)^2$.   Ans. $[5x^2y + (bx + 1)] [5x^2y - (bx + 1)]$
    $= (5x^2y + bx + 1)(5x^2y - bx - 1)$
6. $1 - 169x^2y^4z^6$.   Ans. $(1 + 13xy^2z^3)(1 - 13xy^2z^3)$

Expand the following:

7. $(m + 1)(m - 1)$.   Ans. $m^2 - 1$
8. $(x^2 + y^2)(x^2 - y^2)$.   Ans. $x^4 - y^4$
9. $(4a + 4b^2)(4a - 4b^2)$.   Ans. $16a^2 - 16b^4$

---

28. In example 5, the expression $(bx + 1)^2$ should be regarded as a single term; in fact, any number of terms may be regarded as a single term by enclosing them in parenthesis and operating on them as though they were a single letter.

When solving any examples requiring the application of the rules in Art. **26** or **29,** first ascertain if the numerical coefficients of the two terms are perfect squares or perfect cubes; if not, there is no use of examining further.

CASE IV

29. **To factor an expression that is the sum or difference of two perfect cubes.**

Letting x represent one quantity and y some other quantity, the sum and the difference of two perfect cubes will be represented by $x^3 + y^3$ and $x^3 - y^3$. By actual division it may be shown that

$$(x^3 + y^3) \div (x + y) = x^2 - xy + y^2 \qquad (1)$$
$$\text{and} \quad (x^3 - y^3) \div (x - y) = x^2 + xy + y^2 \qquad (2)$$

Hence, any expression that is the sum or difference of two perfect cubes may be factored as follows:

Rule.—*Extract the cube root of each term. Connect the results by the sign of the second term for the first factor, and obtain the second factor by division.*

It is to be noticed that the second factor will not be a perfect square, because its second term will not be twice the product of the square roots of the other two.

EXAMPLE.—Factor $8x^6 - 27y^9$.

SOLUTION.—The cube root of the first term is $2x^2$, and of the second term $3y^3$; the sign of the second term is minus. Consequently, the first factor is $2x^2 - 3y^3$. The second factor is found by division to be $4x^4 + 6x^2y^3 + 9y^6$. Hence, the factors are $2x^2 - 3y^3$ and $4x^4 + 6x^2y^3 + 9y^6$. Ans.

EXAMPLES FOR PRACTICE

Factor the following expressions:

1. $x^3 - 8y^3$. 　　　　　Ans. $(x - 2y)(x^2 + 2xy + 4y^2)$
2. $m^3 + 64n^6$. 　　　　Ans. $(m + 4n^2)(m^2 - 4mn^2 + 16n^4)$
3. $27a^3 - 8x^3$. 　　　　Ans. $(3a - 2x)(9a^2 + 6ax + 4x^2)$
4. $1,000 - 27a^6b^3$. 　　Ans. $(10 - 3a^2b)(100 + 30a^2b + 9a^4b^2)$
5. $1 + 729m^{12}n^{15}$. 　　Ans. $(1 + 9m^4n^5)(1 - 9m^4n^5 + 81m^8n^{10})$
6. $512a^3 - 64b^3$. 　　　Ans. $(8a - 4b)(64a^2 + 32ab + 16b^2)$

CASE V

30. Sometimes expressions may be resolved into two or more factors by the application of more than one of the given rules. The student should make himself so familiar with the first four cases that he will be able to determine readily when any of them may be applied.

When Case I is to be used in connection with other cases, it should be applied first.

EXAMPLE 1.—Factor $3mx^2y^3 - 12my^7$.

SOLUTION.—By Case I, $3mx^2y^3 - 12my^7 = 3my^3(x^2 - 4y^4)$. Factoring the expression in the parenthesis by Case III, $x^2 - 4y^4 = (x + 2y^2)(x - 2y^2)$.

Hence, $3mx^2y^3 - 12my^7 = 3my^3(x + 2y^2)(x - 2y^2)$ Ans.

EXAMPLE 2.—Factor $80a^2x^2 - 40ax^2 + 5x^2$.

SOLUTION.—By Case I, $80a^2x^2 - 40ax^2 + 5x^2 = 5x^2(16a^2 - 8a + 1)$. Factoring the expression in the parenthesis by Case II, $16a^2 - 8a + 1 = (4a - 1)^2$.

Hence, $80a^2x^2 - 40ax^2 + 5x^2 = 5x^2(4a - 1)^2$ Ans.

EXAMPLE 3.—Factor $2mn + 1 - m^2 - n^2$.

SOLUTION.—Arrange the expression as follows: $1 - m^2 + 2mn - n^2 = 1 - (m^2 - 2mn + n^2)$. By Case II, this equals $1 - (m - n)^2$. By Case III, this equals $[1 + (m - n)][1 - (m - n)] = (1 + m - n)(1 - m + n)$. Ans.

EXAMPLE 4.—Factor $a^6 - b^6$.

SOLUTION.—By Case III, $a^6 - b^6 = (a^3 + b^3)(a^3 - b^3)$. By Case IV, $a^3 + b^3 = (a + b)(a^2 - ab + b^2)$, and $a^3 - b^3 = (a - b)(a^2 + ab + b^2)$.
Hence,

$$a^6 - b^6 = (a + b)(a - b)(a^2 - ab + b^2)(a^2 + ab + b^2)\ \text{Ans.}$$

EXAMPLE 5.—Factor $4a^2 + x^4 - c^2 + 2cd + 4ax^2 - d^2$.

SOLUTION.—This may be arranged as follows: $4a^2 + 4ax^2 + x^4 - c^2 + 2cd - d^2 = 4a^2 + 4ax^2 + x^4 - (c^2 - 2cd + d^2)$.

By Case II, this equals $(2a + x^2)^2 - (c - d)^2$. Hence, by Case III, $4a^2 + x^4 - c^2 + 2cd + 4ax^2 - d^2 = (2a + x^2 + c - d)(2a + x^2 - c + d)$
Ans.

EXAMPLE 6.—Factor $ac - bc + ad - bd$.

SOLUTION.—We observe that, if the first two and last two terms be factored by Case I, they will each show the same binomial factor, $a - b$. Thus, $ac - bc + ad - bd = (ac - bc) + (ad - bd) = c(a - b) + d(a - b)$. Applying Case I again, we have (dividing by $a - b$) for the factors $(a - b)(c + d)$. Ans.

EXAMPLE 7.—Factor $x^2 + ax - bx - ab$.

SOLUTION.—This example is like the last. Here, $x^2 + ax - bx - ab$ $= (x^2 + ax) - (bx + ab) = x(x + a) - b(x + a) = (x + a)(x - b)$. Ans.

31. When factoring polynomials which come under Case V, first ascertain whether there is a monomial factor in the expression. If there is one, divide it out and reserve it. If the remaining terms cannot apparently be factored by Cases II, III, and IV, endeavor to so arrange the various terms that they may be factored by application of some of the preceding rules. No fixed rules can be given that will cover all the different expressions which fall under Case V, and the results depend entirely on the ingenuity of the student, who must have considerable practice before he can factor polynomials successfully. It is important, however, that he should have some knowledge of the process. The explanations to the following examples are more full than those given above, and will probably afford some assistance to the understanding of the solutions given under Case V.

EXAMPLE 1.—Factor $ax^6 - ay^6 + b^2x^6 - b^2y^6$.

SOLUTION.—It is readily seen that a is a factor of the first two terms, and b^2 a factor of the last two. Enclosing the first two and last two terms in parentheses, the polynomial becomes $(ax^6 - ay^6) + (b^2x^6 - b^2y^6)$, which of course equals $a(x^6 - y^6) + b^2(x^6 - y^6)$. It is now seen that both terms of this binomial have the common factor $(x^6 - y^6)$. Dividing it out, the quotient is $a + b^2$. Hence, the required factors are $(a + b^2)$ and $(x^6 - y^6)$. But, since x^6 and y^6 are perfect squares, the quantity $x^6 - y^6$ may be factored by Case III. Thus, $x^6 - y^6 = (x^3 + y^3)(x^3 - y^3)$. Both of the factors last obtained may be factored by Case IV. Thus, $x^3 + y^3 = (x^2 - xy + y^2)(x + y)$ and $x^3 - y^3 = (x^2 + xy + y^2)(x - y)$. Therefore, since it is impossible to factor any further, $ax^6 - ay^6 + b^2x^6 - b^2y^6 = (a + b^2)(x^2 - xy + y^2)(x^2 + xy + y^2)(x + y)(x - y)$. Ans.

EXAMPLE 2.—Factor $4 - 9m^2 - n^2 + 6mn$.

SOLUTION.—Apparently, none of the rules will apply here; hence, the chief dependence must be placed on the proper arrangement of the terms. Noticing that the terms $9m^2$ and n^2 are both perfect squares and have like signs, and that the term $6mn$ is twice the product of the square roots of $9m^2$ and n^2, the last three terms are enclosed in parenthesis, and the expression becomes $4 - (9m^2 + n^2 - 6mn)$.

The second term of this binomial is a perfect square, according to Art. **20,** and the binomial may be written $4 - (3m - n)^2$, since $(3m - n)^2 = 9m^2 - 6mn + n^2$. The binomial $4 - (3m - n)^2$ may now be factored by Case III, since both terms are perfect squares. Therefore, $4 - (3m - n)^2 =$

$$[2 + (3m - n)] [2 - (3m - n)] = (2 + 3m - n)(2 - 3m + n) \quad \text{Ans.}$$

If the student will carefully study the following Examples for Practice in connection with the foregoing, he should experience no great difficulty in factoring. Until he has become accustomed to factoring, the student should prove his work by multiplying the factors together, and comparing the result with the original expression.

EXAMPLES FOR PRACTICE

Factor the following expressions:

1. $x^4 - y^4$. Apply Case III twice.   Ans. $(x^2 + y^2)(x + y)(x - y)$
2. $3abx^2 + 3ay^2b + 6axyb$. Apply Cases I and II. Ans. $3ab(x + y)^2$
3. $a^4b^2 - ab^5$. Apply Cases I and IV. Ans. $ab^2(a - b)(a^2 + ab + b^2)$
4. $2bc - b^2 - c^2 + 4$.   Ans. $(2 + b - c)(2 - b + c)$
5. $16m^2 - 25d^4 + 4n^2 + 16mn$. Ans. $(4m + 2n + 5d^2)(4m + 2n - 5d^2)$
6. $y^2 - ay + by - ab$.   Ans. $(y - a)(y + b)$
7. $c^2 - 1 + 4x - 4x^2 - 2cd^2 + d^4$. Apply Cases II and III after arranging the terms as follows: $(c^2 - 2cd^2 + d^4) - (4x^2 - 4x + 1)$.
      Ans. $(c - d^2 + 2x - 1)(c - d^2 - 2x + 1)$
8. $a^2 - x^2 - 1 + 2x$. Apply Cases II and III.
      Ans. $(a + 1 - x)(a - 1 + x)$
9. $4b^3 - 16ab^3 + 16a^2b^3$. Apply Cases I and II. Ans. $4b^3(1 - 2a)^2$
10. $x^8 - m^8$.   Ans. $(x^4 + m^4)(x^2 + m^2)(x + m)(x - m)$

CASE VI

32. Expressions of the form $x^n \pm y^n$ frequently occur, in which n is an integer (whole number). The sign $\pm$ is read *plus or minus*, and means that either sign may be used. *One of the factors will be $x + y$, when n is an even number (2, 4, 6, etc.) and the connecting sign is $-$, or when n is an odd number (3, 5, 7, etc.) and the connecting sign is $+$. When the connecting sign is $-$, $x - y$ is **always** a factor.*

$x^n + y^n$ cannot be factored when n is even unless n is exactly divisible by some odd number that is greater than 1.

Thus, $x^4 - y^4$ may be divided by $x + y$, and also by $x - y$; $x^4 + y^4$ cannot be factored; $x^5 + y^5$ may be divided by $x + y$; $x^5 - y^5$ may be divided by $x - y$. $x^6 + y^6$ can be factored, since it equals $x^{2 \times 3} + y^{2 \times 3}$; it is divisible by $x^2 + y^2$. Since 1 with any exponent equals 1 (that is $1^2 = 1$, $1^3 = 1$, $1^{10} = 1$, etc.), any root of 1 will also equal 1. Therefore, in the above expressions, 1 may be substituted for either x or y. Thus, $x^4 - 1$ is divisible by $x + 1$ and $x - 1$; $1 - y^4$ is divisible by $1 + y$ and $1 - y$, etc.

FRACTIONS

REDUCTION OF FRACTIONS

DEFINITIONS

33. A **fraction,** in algebra, is considered as an expression indicating division. The sign $\div$ is seldom used, it being more convenient to write the dividend, or quantity to be divided, above a horizontal line, with the divisor below it, in the form of a fraction.

Thus, the fraction $\dfrac{a + b}{c - d}$ means that $a + b$ is to be divided by $c - d$, and is the same as $(a + b) \div (c - d)$. It is read "$a + b$ divided by $c - d$" or "$a + b$ over $c - d$." All fractions are read in this way in algebra, except simple numerical fractions, as $\frac{1}{2}$, $\frac{25}{32}$, etc., which are read as in arithmetic.

34. The quantities above and below the line are called the **numerator** and the **denominator,** respectively, as in the case of numerical fractions. They are known as the **terms** of a fraction.

35. Since dividing any quantity by 1 does not change its value, we may write any quantity as a fraction by making the quantity itself the numerator and 1 the denominator. Thus, $7x^2y$ may be written $\dfrac{7\,x^2y}{1}$ and not be altered in value.

36. The **three signs of a fraction** are: the sign before the dividing line, which affects the entire fraction; the sign of the numerator; and the sign of the denominator. When any one of these signs is omitted, it is understood to be plus. *Any two signs of a fraction may be changed without altering its value, but if any one, or all three, be changed, the value of the fraction will be changed from + to − or from − to +.*

When either the numerator or the denominator has more than one term, it should be enclosed in a parenthesis when performing operations affecting it as a whole. The parenthesis may be removed after the operations are completed.

Take the fraction $-\dfrac{a-b}{c-d}$; placing numerator and denominator in parentheses, we have $-\dfrac{(a-b)}{(c-d)}$. The signs of the numerator and denominator are each + and that of the fraction −.

Let the quotient of $(a-b)\div(c-d)=q$; then,

$$-\frac{+\,(a-b)}{+\,(c-d)}=-\,(+q)=-q \qquad \textbf{(1)}$$

$$-\frac{-\,(a-b)}{-\,(c-d)}=-\,(+q)=-q \qquad \textbf{(2)}$$

$$-\frac{+\,(a-b)}{-\,(c-d)}=-\,(-q)=+q \qquad \textbf{(3)}$$

$$-\frac{-\,(a-b)}{+\,(c-d)}=-\,(-q)=+q \qquad \textbf{(4)}$$

$$+\frac{+\,(a-b)}{+\,(c-d)}=+\,(+q)=+q \qquad \textbf{(5)}$$

$$+\frac{-\,(a-b)}{-\,(c-d)}=+\,(+q)=+q \qquad \textbf{(6)}$$

$$+\frac{+\,(a-b)}{-\,(c-d)}=+\,(-q)=-q \qquad \textbf{(7)}$$

$$+\frac{-\,(a-b)}{+\,(c-d)}=+\,(-q)=-q \qquad \textbf{(8)}$$

Taking equation (1) as the standard, the sign of the quotient is minus. In equations (2), (7), and (8) *two* of the signs were changed, but the sign of the quotient remained unchanged. In equations (3), (4), and (5) only *one* sign was changed, with the result that the sign of the quotient was changed from minus to plus. In equation (6) all *three* signs were changed, resulting in a change in the sign of the quotient from minus to plus.

PRINCIPLES USED IN REDUCTION

37. To *reduce* a fraction is to change its form without changing its value. Thus, $\dfrac{10x}{5}$ and $\dfrac{20x}{10}$ have different forms, but like values, since $10x \div 5$ and $20x \div 10$ are each equal to $2x$.

The terms of a fraction may both be multiplied, or may both be divided by the same quantity without changing their value.

38. To reduce a fraction to its simplest form:

Rule.—*Resolve each term into its factors, and cancel those factors that appear in both terms.*

39. *In performing all operations on fractions, the student must learn to use a polynomial factor as a single quantity, like a monomial factor.*

This is illustrated in the following examples, where there are polynomial factors in both numerator and denominator that can be canceled.

EXAMPLE 1.—Reduce $\dfrac{x^2 + 2xy + y^2}{x^2 - y^2}$ to its simplest form.

SOLUTION.—Factoring both numerator and denominator

$$\frac{x^2 + 2xy + y^2}{x^2 - y^2} = \frac{(x+y)(x+y)}{(x+y)(x-y)}$$

Canceling the common factor $x + y$ from both gives, as the result,

$$\frac{\cancel{(x+y)}(x+y)}{\cancel{(x+y)}(x-y)} = \frac{x+y}{x-y} \quad \textbf{Ans.}$$

EXAMPLE 2.—Reduce $\dfrac{3x^5 - 6x^4y}{6x^2y^2 - 12xy^3}$ to its simplest form.

SOLUTION.— $\dfrac{3x^5 - 6x^4y}{6x^2y^2 - 12xy^3} = \dfrac{3x^4(x - 2y)}{6xy^2(x - 2y)}$, when factored.

Canceling the common factors, the result is

$$\dfrac{\cancel{3x^4}(\cancel{x - 2y})}{\cancel{6xy^2}(\cancel{x - 2y})} = \dfrac{x^3}{2y^2} \quad \textbf{Ans.}$$

40. Sometimes the whole numerator is contained in the denominator, or the denominator in the numerator. The numerator or denominator will then reduce to the number 1.

EXAMPLE 1.—Reduce $\dfrac{b + 3c^2}{2b^2 + 6bc^2}$ to its simplest form.

SOLUTION.— $\dfrac{b + 3c^2}{2b^2 + 6bc^2} = \dfrac{\cancel{b + 3c^2}}{2b(\cancel{b + 3c^2})} = \dfrac{1}{2b} \quad \textbf{Ans.}$

EXAMPLE 2.—Reduce $\dfrac{x^6 - 1}{x^3 - 1}$ to its simplest form.

SOLUTION.— $\dfrac{x^6 - 1}{x^3 - 1} = \dfrac{(x^3 + 1)(\cancel{x^3 - 1})}{\cancel{x^3 - 1}} = \dfrac{x^3 + 1}{1} = x^3 + 1 \quad \textbf{Ans.}$
(Art. **35.**)

41. From the last example it will be seen that division may sometimes be performed by cancelation. Thus, $\dfrac{x^6 - 1}{x^3 - 1}$ means $(x^6 - 1) \div (x^3 - 1)$, and the divisor $x^3 - 1$ canceled from the dividend $x^6 - 1$ gives the quotient $x^3 + 1$.

A factor must be common to each term of the numerator and to each term of the denominator in order to be canceled. Thus, the factor x cannot be canceled from $\dfrac{3ax}{x + 4m}$ because it is not common to both terms of the denominator.

EXAMPLES FOR PRACTICE

Reduce the following to their simplest form:

1. $\dfrac{3a + 3b}{a^2 - b^2}$.   Ans. $\dfrac{3}{a - b}$

2. $\dfrac{x^4 - y^4}{x^2 - y^2}$.   Ans. $x^2 + y^2$

3. $\dfrac{54a^3b^5c^2}{72a^2b^2c}$.   Ans. $\dfrac{3ab^3c}{4}$

4. $\dfrac{12a^2x^3}{36a^3x^5}$.   Ans. $\dfrac{1}{3ax^2}$

5. $\dfrac{n^3 - 2n^2}{n^2 - 4n + 4}$.   Ans. $\dfrac{n^2}{n - 2}$

REDUCING FRACTIONS TO A COMMON DENOMINATOR

42. When fractions are to be added or subtracted, it is necessary to so reduce them that all the denominators will be alike. This is called **reducing them to a common denominator.**

43. To reduce fractions to a common denominator:

Rule.—*Resolve each denominator into its factors.*

Take each factor the greatest number of times it occurs in any denominator, and find the product of these factors.

Divide this product by each of the denominators. Multiply the corresponding numerators by these quotients, for new numerators. Write each new numerator with the common denominator beneath it.

Example.—Reduce $\dfrac{7a}{x + y}$, $\dfrac{3ab}{x^2 - y^2}$, and $\dfrac{2b}{(x + y)^2}$ to a common denominator.

Solution.—Factoring the denominators, $x + y$ is not factorable. $x^2 - y^2 = (x + y)(x - y)$, and $(x + y)^2 = (x + y)(x + y)$. Now here are two separate factors, $x + y$ and $x - y$, of which $x + y$ occurs twice in $(x + y)^2$. Hence, the common denominator is $(x + y)(x + y)(x - y) = (x + y)^2(x - y)$. Dividing this product by $x + y$, the quotient is $(x + y)(x - y) = x^2 - y^2$. Hence, the first new numerator is $7a(x^2 - y^2)$ and the new fraction is $\dfrac{7a(x^2 - y^2)}{(x + y)^2(x - y)}$. Similarly, $\dfrac{3ab}{x^2 - y^2}$ becomes $\dfrac{3ab(x + y)}{(x + y)^2(x - y)}$, and $\dfrac{2b}{(x + y)^2}$ becomes $\dfrac{2b(x - y)}{(x + y)^2(x - y)}$. Ans.

The student should note that this denominator can be written in several different ways, and he should not become confused if his work does not always agree with the answer.

Besides $(x+y)(x+y)(x-y)$ and $(x+y)^2(x-y)$, it may be written $(x^2-y^2)(x+y)$, $(x^2+2xy+y^2)(x-y)$, or $x^3 + x^2y - xy^2 - y^3$. These five expressions have exactly the same value. The student should prove this statement by substituting numbers for x and y.

EXAMPLES FOR PRACTICE

Reduce the following to common denominators:

1. $\dfrac{3yz}{2x}$, $\dfrac{4xz}{3y}$, and $\dfrac{5xy}{4z}$.   Ans. $\dfrac{18y^2z^2}{12xyz}$, $\dfrac{16x^2z^2}{12xyz}$, and $\dfrac{15x^2y^2}{12xyz}$

2. $\dfrac{x^2y}{10}$, $\dfrac{xyz}{15}$, and $\dfrac{7yz^2}{30}$.   Ans. $\dfrac{3x^2y}{30}$, $\dfrac{2xyz}{30}$, and $\dfrac{7yz^2}{30}$

3. $\dfrac{2}{a^3x^3}$, $\dfrac{3}{ax^3}$, and $\dfrac{4}{a^2x}$.   Ans. $\dfrac{2}{a^3x^3}$, $\dfrac{3a^2}{a^3x^3}$, and $\dfrac{4ax^2}{a^3x^3}$

4. $\dfrac{m+n}{m-n}$, and $\dfrac{m-n}{m+n}$.   Ans. $\dfrac{m^2+2mn+n^2}{m^2-n^2}$, and $\dfrac{m^2-2mn+n^2}{m^2-n^2}$

5. $\dfrac{2}{x}$, $\dfrac{3}{2x-1}$, and $\dfrac{2x-1}{4x^2-1}$.

Ans. $\dfrac{2(4x^2-1)}{x(4x^2-1)}$, $\dfrac{3x(2x+1)}{x(4x^2-1)}$, and $\dfrac{x(2x-1)}{x(4x^2-1)}$

OPERATIONS WITH FRACTIONS

ADDITION AND SUBTRACTION OF FRACTIONS

44. To add or subtract fractions:

Rule.—*Reduce the fractions, if necessary, to a common denominator. Add or subtract the numerators, and write the result over the common denominator.*

EXAMPLE 1.—Find the sum of $\dfrac{2a-b}{5}$ and $\dfrac{a+b}{4}$.

SOLUTION.— $\dfrac{2a-b}{5}$ and $\dfrac{a+b}{4}$, reduced to a common denominator,

become $\dfrac{4(2a-b)}{20}$ and $\dfrac{5(a+b)}{20}$, which are equal, respectively, to

$\dfrac{8a-4b}{20}$ and $\dfrac{5a+5b}{20}$. Adding the numerators, the result is $8a-4b$

$+ 5a + 5b = 13a + b$, which written over the common denominator gives as the sum, $\dfrac{13a + b}{20}$. The work is written as follows:

$$\frac{2a - b}{5} + \frac{a + b}{4} = \frac{8a - 4b}{20} + \frac{5a + 5b}{20}$$

$$= \frac{8a - 4b + 5a + 5b}{20} = \frac{13a + b}{20} \text{ Ans.}$$

EXAMPLE 2.—Subtract $\dfrac{6b - 2}{3b}$ from $\dfrac{4a - 1}{2a}$.

SOLUTION.—Reducing the fractions to a common denominator, $\dfrac{4a - 1}{2a}$

$- \dfrac{6b - 2}{3b} = \dfrac{12ab - 3b}{6ab} - \dfrac{12ab - 4a}{6ab}$. Subtracting the second numerator from the first, and writing the result over the common denominator, $\dfrac{12ab - 3b}{6ab} - \dfrac{12ab - 4a}{6ab} = \dfrac{(12ab - 3b) - (12ab - 4a)}{6ab}$

$= \dfrac{12ab - 3b - 12ab + 4a}{6ab}$, with the parentheses removed. Combining like terms in the numerator gives as the result $\dfrac{4a - 3b}{6ab}$. Ans.

45. *If, as in the example just given, the numerator of the fraction to be subtracted has more than one term,* care must be taken *to change the sign of every term before combining.* It will usually be convenient to enclose the whole numerator in a parenthesis before combining. The parenthesis may then be removed by the principles of Arts. **49, 50,** and **51,** Part 1.

EXAMPLE 1.—Simplify $\dfrac{x^3}{x - 1} - \dfrac{x^2}{x + 1} - \dfrac{x}{x - 1} + \dfrac{1}{x + 1}$.

SOLUTION.—Reducing to the common denominator $x^2 - 1$,

$$\frac{x^3}{x - 1} - \frac{x^2}{x + 1} - \frac{x}{x - 1} + \frac{1}{x + 1} = \frac{x^4 + x^3}{x^2 - 1} - \frac{x^3 - x^2}{x^2 - 1} - \frac{x^2 + x}{x^2 - 1} + \frac{x - 1}{x^2 - 1}$$

Adding or subtracting the numerators as required,

$$\frac{(x^4 + x^3) - (x^3 - x^2) - (x^2 + x) + (x - 1)}{x^2 - 1}$$

which, with the parentheses removed,

$$= \frac{x^4 + x^3 - x^3 + x^2 - x^2 - x + x - 1}{x^2 - 1}$$

Combining like terms, the result is

$$\frac{x^4 - 1}{x^2 - 1} = x^2 + 1 \ \text{Ans.}$$

EXAMPLE 2.—Simplify $\dfrac{1}{(x-2)^2} + \dfrac{1}{2-x}$.

SOLUTION.—If the denominator of the second fraction were written $x - 2$ instead of $2 - x$, $(x-2)^2$ would be the common denominator. By Art. **36,** the signs of the denominator and the sign before the fraction $\dfrac{1}{2-x}$ may be changed, giving $-\dfrac{1}{-2+x} = -\dfrac{1}{x-2}$. (Art. **24,** Part 1.) Hence, $\dfrac{1}{(x-2)^2} + \dfrac{1}{2-x} = \dfrac{1}{(x-2)^2} - \dfrac{1}{x-2}$, which, when reduced to a common denominator,

$$= \frac{1}{(x-2)^2} - \frac{x-2}{(x-2)^2} = \frac{1-(x-2)}{(x-2)^2} = \frac{1-x+2}{(x-2)^2} = \frac{3-x}{(x-2)^2} \ \text{Ans.}$$

EXAMPLES FOR PRACTICE

Simplify the following by reducing to simple fractions:

1. $\dfrac{x}{3} + \dfrac{x}{4} + \dfrac{x}{5}$. 　　　　　　　　　　Ans. $\dfrac{47x}{60}$

2. $\dfrac{4x-3}{5} + \dfrac{7x+1}{3} + \dfrac{3x}{2}$. 　　　　　Ans. $\dfrac{139x-8}{30}$

3. $\dfrac{1}{x-y} - \dfrac{1}{x^2-y^2}$. 　　　　　　　Ans. $\dfrac{x+y-1}{x^2-y^2}$

4. $\dfrac{a^2+b^2}{2} - \dfrac{(a+b)^2}{4}$. Ans. $\dfrac{2(a^2+b^2)-(a^2+2ab+b^2)}{4} = \dfrac{(a-b)^2}{4}$, after removing parentheses and combining.

5. $\dfrac{a^2}{a^2-1} + \dfrac{a}{a-1} - \dfrac{a}{a+1}$. 　　　　　Ans. $\dfrac{a^2+2a}{a^2-1}$

6. $\dfrac{4m^2+1}{4m^2} - \dfrac{3m-1}{12m^3} + \dfrac{1-12n}{12n}$. 　　Ans. $\dfrac{n+m^3}{12m^3n}$

7. $\dfrac{y}{(x+y)^2} + \dfrac{y}{x^2-y^2} - \dfrac{1}{x+y}$.
　　　　Ans. $\dfrac{y(x-y)+y(x+y)-(x^2-y^2)}{(x+y)^2(x-y)} = \dfrac{2xy-x^2+y^2}{x^3+x^2y-xy^2-y^3}$

8. $\dfrac{x}{x+1} + \dfrac{x}{1-x} + \dfrac{3x}{x^2-1}$. 　　　　　Ans. $\dfrac{x}{x^2-1}$

MULTIPLICATION OF FRACTIONS

46. To multiply fractions:

Rule.—*Multiply the numerators together for the numerator of the product, and the denominators together for the denominator of the product.*

47. Any number of fractions may be multiplied together. The operation may be very much shortened by resolving the terms of the fractions into their factors, and canceling. The product should be reduced to its simplest form.

EXAMPLE 1.—Find the product of $\dfrac{6a^2}{5}$, $\dfrac{2ab}{3c}$, and $\dfrac{2ac}{b^2}$.

SOLUTION. — The product of the numerators is $6a^2 \times 2ab \times 2ac$ $= 24a^4bc$, and of the denominators, $5 \times 3c \times b^2 = 15b^2c$. Writing $24a^4bc$ over $15b^2c$, the product of the fractions is $\dfrac{24a^4bc}{15b^2c} = \dfrac{8a^4}{5b}$, when reduced to its lowest terms. The work is written as follows:

$$\frac{\overset{2}{\cancel{8a^2}}}{5} \times \frac{2a\cancel{b}}{\cancel{3c}} \times \frac{2a\cancel{c}}{\underset{b}{\cancel{b^2}}} = \frac{8a^4}{5b} \quad \textbf{Ans.}$$

EXAMPLE 2.—Find the product of $\dfrac{x^2 + 2x}{(x-1)^2}$, $x^2 - 1$, and $\dfrac{x^2 - 4x + 4}{x^2 - 4}$.

SOLUTION. — First make $x^2 - 1$ a fraction by writing 1 for its denominator, thus, $\dfrac{x^2 - 1}{1}$; then, factoring both terms of each fraction,

$$\frac{x^2 + 2x}{(x-1)^2} \times \frac{x^2 - 1}{1} \times \frac{x^2 - 4x + 4}{x^2 - 4}$$

$$= \frac{x(\cancel{x+2})(x+1)(\cancel{x-1})(\cancel{x-2})(x-2)}{(\cancel{x-1})(x-1)(\cancel{x-2})(\cancel{x+2})} = \frac{x(x+1)(x-2)}{x-1} \quad \textbf{Ans.}$$

EXAMPLE 3.—Find the product of $\dfrac{1}{a^3} - \dfrac{4c^2}{a}$, and $\dfrac{a^3}{1 + 2ac}$.

SOLUTION.—Performing the subtraction, $\dfrac{1}{a^3} - \dfrac{4c^2}{a} = \dfrac{1 - 4a^2c^2}{a^3}$.

Multiplying, $\dfrac{1 - 4a^2c^2}{a^3} \times \dfrac{a^3}{1 + 2ac} = \dfrac{\overset{1-2ac}{(\cancel{1 - 4a^2c^2})}\cancel{a^3}}{(\cancel{1 + 2ac})\cancel{a^3}} = 1 - 2ac \quad \textbf{Ans.}$

EXAMPLES FOR PRACTICE

Multiply the following:

1. $\dfrac{3a^2bc}{5abc^2}$ by $\dfrac{10ab^2c}{3abc}$. Ans. $\dfrac{2ab}{c}$

2. $\dfrac{5x^2y}{7x}$ by $21xy$. Ans. $15x^2y^2$

Find the product of:

3. $\dfrac{3x^2y}{4xz^2}$, $\dfrac{5y^2z}{6xy}$, and $\dfrac{-12x^2}{2xy^2}$. Ans. $-\dfrac{15x}{4z}$

4. $\dfrac{x^2-y^2}{c^3-d^3}$, $\dfrac{c-d}{(x+y)^2}$, and $\dfrac{x^3+y^3}{x-y}$. Ans. $\dfrac{x^2-xy+y^2}{c^2+cd+d^2}$

5. $\dfrac{4y}{x}-\dfrac{16}{xy}$, and $\dfrac{1}{2y+4}$. Ans. $\dfrac{2y-4}{xy}$

6. $\dfrac{a+b}{2}+\dfrac{a-b}{4}$, and $\dfrac{4}{9a^2+6ab+b^2}$. Ans. $\dfrac{1}{3a+b}$

DIVISION OF FRACTIONS

48. Division, in fractions, is the reverse of multiplication, and is the process employed when, given one of two fractions and their product, it is required to find the other. For example, it is required to divide $\dfrac{a}{4}$ by $\dfrac{1}{2}$. Find such a fraction that, multiplied by $\dfrac{1}{2}$, will give $\dfrac{a}{4}$, for the product. This fraction is $\dfrac{a}{2}$, for $\dfrac{a}{2}\times\dfrac{1}{2}=\dfrac{a}{4}$. Also, $\dfrac{x}{5}\div\dfrac{x}{7}=\dfrac{7}{5}$, since $\dfrac{7}{5}\times\dfrac{x}{7}=\dfrac{x}{5}$. If, in this case, the divisor had been inverted and the fractions multiplied, the result would have been $\dfrac{x}{5}\times\dfrac{7}{x}=\dfrac{7}{5}$.

49. Hence, to divide by a fraction:

Rule.—*Invert the divisor and proceed as in multiplication.*

EXAMPLE 1.—Divide $\dfrac{3a^2b}{5x^3y}$ by $\dfrac{9ab^3}{10x^4y^2}$.

SOLUTION.—The divisor inverted $=\dfrac{10x^4y^2}{9ab^3}$.

Hence, $\dfrac{3a^2b}{5x^3y} \div \dfrac{9ab^3}{10x^4y^7} = \dfrac{3a^2b}{5x^3y} \times \dfrac{10x^4y^3}{9ab^3} = \dfrac{\overset{2a}{\cancel{3}} \times \overset{x}{\cancel{10}}\cancel{a^2}\overset{y}{\cancel{b}}\cancel{x^4}\cancel{y^3}}{\underset{3}{\cancel{5}} \times \underset{b^2}{\cancel{9}}\cancel{a}\cancel{b^3}\cancel{x^3}\cancel{y}} = \dfrac{2axy}{3b^2}$ **Ans.**

EXAMPLE 2.—Divide $x^2 + 2x + 1$ by $\dfrac{x+1}{x-1}$.

SOLUTION.—By Art. **35,**

$$\frac{x^2 + 2x + 1}{1} \times \frac{x-1}{x+1} = \frac{(\cancel{x+1})(x+1)(x-1)}{\cancel{x+1}} = x^2 - 1 \quad \textbf{Ans.}$$

EXAMPLES FOR PRACTICE

Divide the following:

1. $\dfrac{9x^3 - 3x^4}{24}$ by $\dfrac{3x}{8}$.   Ans. $\dfrac{3x^2 - x^3}{3}$

2. $\dfrac{ab - bx}{a+z}$ by $\dfrac{ac - cx}{a+z}$.   Ans. $\dfrac{b}{c}$

3. $\dfrac{1 - 8b^2 + 16b^4}{1 + 2b}$ by $\dfrac{1 - 4b^2}{3a}$.   Ans. $3a(1 - 2b)$

4. $6a^2cd - 6abcd$ by $\dfrac{6acd}{a^2 + ab + b^2}$.   Ans. $a^3 - b^3$

MIXED QUANTITIES AND COMPLEX FRACTIONS

50. An integral expression (see Art. **11**) is one containing neither fractions nor negative exponents. The expression $a^2 + 2ab$ is integral, but the expressions $a^2 + \dfrac{1}{2ab}$, $2a^{-2}$, $\dfrac{3}{a^2 + b}$ are not. The expression $2a^{-2}$ is only another way of writing $\dfrac{2}{a^2}$.

51. The **integral part** of an expression is that part which, if taken by itself, would be an integral expression.

52. A **mixed quantity** is an expression containing both integral and fractional parts, as $2a^2 - \dfrac{c+d}{4a}$. Considering the integral part, $2a^2$, as a fraction with a denominator 1 (see Art. **35**), a mixed quantity becomes simply the indicated addition or subtraction of two fractions; thus,

$$2a^2 - \frac{c+d}{4a} = \frac{2a^2}{1} - \frac{c+d}{4a}.$$

53. A fraction may be reduced to either an entire or a mixed quantity by dividing the numerator by the denominator, provided the division be possible. It frequently happens that by performing the indicated division, the fraction will be reduced to a simpler form. The case of reducing a fraction to an entire quantity was taken up in Art. **40.**

EXAMPLE.—Simplify $\dfrac{4x^2 + 12x - 1}{2x + 3}$.

SOLUTION.—Performing the indicated division,

$$2x+3 \overline{)4x^2 + 12x - 1}\,(2x + 3 - \frac{10}{2x+3} \quad \text{Ans.}$$
$$\underline{4x^2 + 6x}$$
$$6x - 1$$
$$\underline{6x + 9}$$
$$- 10$$

54. Mixed quantities are frequently more convenient to handle as fractions.

To reduce a mixed quantity to a fraction:

Rule.—*Write the integral part with a denominator 1, and perform the indicated addition or subtraction.*

EXAMPLE.—Reduce $x^2 + xy + y^2 - \dfrac{b}{x - y}$ to a fraction.

SOLUTION.—

$$x^2 + xy + y^2 - \frac{b}{x-y} = \frac{x^2 + xy + y^2}{1} - \frac{b}{x-y}$$

Subtracting the second fraction from the first gives

$$\frac{(x^2 + xy + y^2)(x-y) - b}{x-y} = \frac{x^3 - y^3 - b}{x-y} \quad \text{Ans.}$$

EXAMPLES FOR PRACTICE

Solve the following:

1. Reduce $\dfrac{a^2c + b^2}{c}$ to a mixed quantity.   Ans. $a^2 + \dfrac{b^2}{c}$

2. Simplify $\dfrac{x^2 + 4xy + 5y^2 - 3x}{x + 2y}$.   Ans. $x + 2y - 3 + \dfrac{y^2 + 6y}{x + 2y}$

3. Reduce $x + 3 - \dfrac{7x + 3}{2x + 1}$ to a fraction.   Ans. $\dfrac{2x^2}{2x + 1}$

4. From $3a + \dfrac{a + b}{d}$ subtract $a - \dfrac{a - b}{d}$.

$$\text{Ans. } 2a + \frac{2a}{d} = \frac{2a(d + 1)}{d}$$

5. Divide $m + n - \dfrac{2n}{m - n}$ by $m - n - \dfrac{2n}{m + n}$.   Ans. $\dfrac{m + n}{m - n}$

SUGGESTION.—First reduce the mixed quantities to fractions.

COMPLEX FRACTIONS

55. A **complex fraction** is one that contains fractions in one or both of its terms. Thus, $\dfrac{a + \dfrac{x}{y}}{a + x}$, $\dfrac{a - b}{\dfrac{x}{y}}$, and $\dfrac{\dfrac{a}{b}}{\dfrac{c}{d}}$ are complex fractions.

56. Complex fractions can be reduced by performing the indicated division; thus, $\dfrac{\frac{5}{8}}{\frac{3}{4}} = \dfrac{5}{8} \div \dfrac{3}{4} = \dfrac{5}{8} \times \dfrac{4}{3} = \dfrac{5}{6}$. A much simpler way is to multiply both terms by the least common denominator of the fractions contained. Thus, $\dfrac{\frac{5}{8} \times 8}{\frac{3}{4} \times 8} = \dfrac{5}{6}$.

57. Hence, to simplify a complex fraction:

Rule.—*Multiply both terms by the common denominator of the fractional parts.*

EXAMPLE 1.—Simplify $\dfrac{\dfrac{x}{y} - \dfrac{y}{x}}{\dfrac{1}{y} - \dfrac{1}{x}}$.

SOLUTION.—The common denominator of the fractional parts is xy. Multiplying each term by this,

$$\frac{\dfrac{x}{y} \times xy - \dfrac{y}{x} \times xy}{\dfrac{1}{y} \times xy - \dfrac{1}{x} \times xy} = \frac{x^2 - y^2}{x - y} = x + y \quad \text{Ans.}$$

The multiplication can frequently be performed mentally, without writing the common denominator, at the same time canceling common factors.

EXAMPLE 2.—Simplify $\dfrac{1}{1 + \dfrac{a}{1 + a + \dfrac{2a^2}{1 - a}}}$.

SOLUTION.—This is the case of a complex fraction in which the denominator is itself a complex fraction.

First, consider the part $\dfrac{a}{1 + a + \dfrac{2a^2}{1 - a}}$.

Multiplying both terms by $1 - a$,

$$\frac{a(1-a)}{(1+a)(1-a) + 2a^2} = \frac{a - a^2}{1 - a^2 + 2a^2} = \frac{a - a^2}{1 + a^2}$$

The fraction thus becomes $\dfrac{1}{1 + \dfrac{a - a^2}{1 + a^2}}$.

Multiplying both terms by $1 + a^2$,

$$\frac{1 + a^2}{1 + a^2 + a - a^2} = \frac{1 + a^2}{1 + a} \quad \textbf{Ans.}$$

EXAMPLES FOR PRACTICE

Simplify the following:

1. $\dfrac{\dfrac{3ac^2}{16}}{24}$.   Ans. $\dfrac{ac^2}{128}$

2. $\dfrac{1 + \dfrac{a}{c}}{c - \dfrac{a^2}{c}}$.   Ans. $\dfrac{1}{c - a}$

3. $\dfrac{2\frac{7}{8}}{8 - 2x + \dfrac{x^2}{8}}$.   Ans. $\dfrac{23}{(8 - x)^2}$

SUGGESTION.— $2\frac{7}{8}$ means $2 + \frac{7}{8}$. Hence, for the numerator multiply 2 by the least common denominator 8, and add 7.

4. $\dfrac{1}{x + \dfrac{1}{1 + \dfrac{x + 1}{3 - x}}}$.   Ans. $\dfrac{4}{3x + 3}$

THEORY OF EXPONENTS

58. An **exponent** may be a number, a letter, or a combination of both; it may be integral, fractional, or zero; and it may be positive or negative.

59. When the exponent is a letter, it is called a **literal exponent.** Exponents may involve several letters and terms. The following are examples of exponents: x^3, x^a, x^{3a}, $x^{\frac{3}{4}}$, $x^{-\frac{2a}{3}}$, x^o, x^{2p-q}, etc.

60. It has been shown before (see Art. **70**, Part 1) that any quantity with zero for an exponent is equal to 1. It has also been shown that any quantity having a negative exponent is equal to the reciprocal of the quantity with an equal positive exponent; that is, for example, $x^{-\frac{2a}{3}} = \dfrac{1}{x^{\frac{2a}{3}}}$.

An expression like x^{2p-q} arises from dividing x^{2p} by x^q; thus, $x^{2p} \div x^q = x^{2p-q}$.

61. As it is frequently necessary in algebraic operations to use letters for exponents—as an example see Art. **32**—it also becomes necessary to affect such quantities with exponents and to extract roots. For example, the square of x^n may be written either $(x^n)^2$ or x^{2n}, the latter being a simplified form of the former. An expression of this kind can be best understood by a numerical example. Thus, consider the expression $5^{2\times2\times2}$; this is equivalent to $[(5^2)^2]^2$ and also to 5^8. The advantage of writing it $5^{2\times2\times2}$ is that it indicates how the multiplication may be simplified. For example, instead of multiplying 5 by 5 and this product by 5 and so on until 5 has been used eight times as a factor, simply square 5, then square the product, and then square the last product; this results in three multiplications instead of seven.

Since $(x^m)^3 = (x^m) \times (x^m) \times (x^m) = x^{3m}$, and $(x^m)^n$ evidently equals x^{nm}, all that is necessary to do in raising an expression like x^m to any power is to multiply the exponent of the given expression by the exponent denoting the power to which the expression is to be raised. An expression like x^{3m} must not be considered as equivalent to $x^m \times x^3$, for the latter expression is equal to x^{m+3}.

62. If an expression like x^{6m} occurs and it is desired to extract, say, the cube root of it, divide the exponent of the expression by the index of the root. Thus, $\sqrt[3]{x^{6m}} = x^{6m \div 3} = x^{2m}$; this is necessarily true since $(x^{2m})^3 = x^{6m}$. But when the exponent is not exactly divisible by the index, the division is indicated by a fraction. Thus, $\sqrt[n]{x^m} = x^{m \div n}$

$= x^{\frac{m}{n}}$; $\sqrt[3]{x^{2a}} = x^{\frac{2a}{3}}$; $\sqrt[4]{x} = x^{\frac{1}{4}}$; $\sqrt[3]{\dfrac{1}{x^a}} = \dfrac{\sqrt[3]{1}}{\sqrt[3]{x^a}} = \dfrac{1}{\sqrt[3]{x^a}}$

$= \dfrac{1}{x^{\frac{a}{3}}} = x^{-\frac{a}{3}}$, etc.

63. From the foregoing the following rules are evident:

Rule I.—*To raise a monomial to any power, raise the numerical coefficient to the desired power and multiply the exponent of each letter by the exponent denoting the power to which the monomial is to be raised. If the sign of the monomial is plus, or if the sign is minus and the exponent denoting the power is even, the sign of the power will be plus; but if the sign is minus and the exponent denoting the power is odd, the sign of the power will be minus.*

Rule II.—*To extract any root of a monomial, extract the required root of the numerical coefficient and divide the exponent of each letter by the index of the root. If the index is odd, the sign of the root will be the same as the sign of the monomial; but if the index of the root is even and the sign of the monomial is plus, the sign of the root will be ±, while if* *the sign of the monomial is minus, the root must be indicated, as it is impossible to extract an even root of a negative quantity.*

64. These two rules should be readily understood from what has preceded, but a further discussion of the law of signs will be given. For this purpose consider the two expressions $(\pm x)^n$ and $\sqrt[n]{\pm x}$. These give rise to the following eight cases:

$$\text{When } n \text{ is even } (+x)^n = +x^n \qquad \textbf{(1)}$$
$$\text{When } n \text{ is odd } (+x)^n = +x^n \qquad \textbf{(2)}$$
$$\text{When } n \text{ is even } (-x)^n = +x^n \qquad \textbf{(3)}$$
$$\text{When } n \text{ is odd } (-x)^n = -x^n \qquad \textbf{(4)}$$
$$\text{When } n \text{ is odd } \sqrt[n]{+x} = +\sqrt[n]{x} \qquad \textbf{(5)}$$
$$\text{When } n \text{ is odd } \sqrt[n]{-x} = -\sqrt[n]{x} \qquad \textbf{(6)}$$
$$\text{When } n \text{ is even } \sqrt[n]{+x} = \pm\sqrt[n]{x} \qquad \textbf{(7)}$$
$$\text{When } n \text{ is even } \sqrt[n]{-x} = \sqrt[n]{-x} \qquad \textbf{(8)}$$

Cases (1) and (2) are evident, since any positive quantity raised to any power must be positive. Cases (3) and (4) follow from Art. **58,** Part 1. Case (5) is the converse of Case (2), and Case (6) is the converse of Case (4). Case (7) gives an ambiguous result because when n is even $(+x)^n$ and $(-x)^n$ are both equal to $+x^n$, and unless there is something else in the conditions of the problem to determine which sign to use, it is necessary to use the double sign. Case (8) can only be indicated as shown. This can virtually be restricted to $\sqrt{-x}$, in which the index is 2. The square root of a negative quantity is called an **imaginary quantity.** There is no integral or fractional quantity whose square will equal a negative quantity; hence, the square root of such a quantity must be indicated as shown in Case (8).

EXAMPLE 1.—Find the values of the following: $(a^{-1})^{-\frac{1}{2}}$; $(cd^{-2})^{\frac{2}{3}}$; $(x^a)^{-b} \div (x^{-a})^{-b}$.

SOLUTION.—In the first, multiplying the exponents, $-1 \times -\frac{1}{2} = \frac{1}{2}$.
Hence, $(a^{-1})^{-\frac{1}{2}} = a^{\frac{1}{2}}$, or $\sqrt{a}$ Ans.

In like manner,

$(c\,d^{-2})^{\frac{5}{2}} = c^{\frac{5}{2}}d^{-5}$, Ans., since $1 \times \frac{5}{2} = \frac{5}{2}$, and $-2 \times \frac{5}{2} = -5$

In the next one,

$$(x^a)^{-b} = x^{-ab} \text{ and } (x^{-a})^{-b} = x^{ab}$$

Dividing, $x^{-ab} \div x^{ab} = x^{-ab-ab} = x^{-2ab}$ Ans.

EXAMPLE 2.—Find the value of $\sqrt[4]{256a^4b^{12}c^8}$.

SOLUTION.—The 4th root of 256 is 4. The exponent of a in the root is $4 \div 4 = 1$; of b, $12 \div 4 = 3$; and of c, $8 \div 4 = 2$. As this is an even root of a positive quantity, the sign should be $\pm$.

Hence, $\sqrt[4]{256a^4b^{12}c^8} = \pm 4ab^3c^2$ Ans.

EXAMPLE 3.—Find the value of $\sqrt[3]{\dfrac{27m^3x^9}{a^9b^6c^{12}}}$.

SOLUTION.— $\sqrt[3]{27m^3x^9} = 3mx^3$; $\sqrt[3]{a^9b^6c^{12}} = a^3b^2c^4$. The quantity is positive, and, as this is an odd root, its sign must be the same, or positive.

Hence, $\sqrt[3]{\dfrac{27m^3x^9}{a^9b^6c^{12}}} = \dfrac{3m\,x^3}{a^3b^2c^4}$ Ans.

65. Since in $\dfrac{1}{a^2} = a^{-2}$, a^{-2} changes to a^2 when placed in the denominator, we may state the following principle:

A factor may be changed from the numerator to the denominator, or from the denominator to the numerator, if the sign of its exponent be changed.

For example, $\dfrac{n^{-3}}{ab} = \dfrac{1}{abn^3}$; $\dfrac{n}{ab^{-\frac{1}{2}}} = \dfrac{nb^{\frac{1}{2}}}{a}$; $\dfrac{x^{-\frac{2}{3}}}{5y^{-1}} = \dfrac{y}{5x^{\frac{2}{3}}}$, etc.

In the last, the positive exponent 1 of the y is not written.

EXAMPLE.—Express, with positive exponents,

$$a^{-1}b^{-2}c^3 + a^{-2}b^{-\frac{3}{4}}c^{-\frac{1}{3}} + a^3b^{-2}$$

SOLUTION.—Since these terms may be taken as fractions, with 1 for the denominators, transfer the letters with negative exponents to the denominators, obtaining

$$a^{-1}b^{-2}c^3 + a^{-2}b^{-\frac{3}{4}}c^{-\frac{1}{3}} + a^3b^{-2} = \dfrac{c^3}{ab^2} + \dfrac{1}{a^2b^{\frac{3}{4}}c^{\frac{1}{3}}} + \dfrac{a^3}{b^2}\ \text{Ans.}$$

66. The student must note very carefully that factors of an entire term only can be changed from numerator to denominator, or vice versa, and that when thus changed they become factors of the whole of the other term. Thus, in $\dfrac{a}{bc^{-2}+d}$, c^{-2} *cannot* be transferred to the numerator by merely changing the sign of the exponent. The exponent may, however, be made positive by multiplying both terms by c^2; thus, $\dfrac{a \times c^2}{(bc^{-2}+d)\times c^2} = \dfrac{ac^2}{b+c^2d}$. In $\dfrac{ac^{-2}}{b+d}$, if we transfer the c^{-2}, it becomes $\dfrac{a}{c^2(b+d)}$, c^2 becoming a factor of the *entire* denominator.

EXAMPLE 1.—Clear $x^2y^{-2}z^{-1} + \dfrac{2xy}{y^{-1}-x^3} - \dfrac{3a^{-1}b^{-2}c^3}{a^2+b}$ of negative exponents.

SOLUTION.—Treat each term of the expression separately. $x^2y^{-2}z^{-1} = \dfrac{x^2y^{-2}z^{-1}}{1}$; changing the factors with negative exponents to the denominator, and at the same time changing the signs of the exponents, the result is $\dfrac{x^2}{y^2z}$. In $\dfrac{2xy}{y^{-1}-x^3}$, y^{-1} is not a factor of the whole denominator; hence, multiply both terms of the fraction by the reciprocal of y^{-1} or y; thus, $\dfrac{2xy \times y}{(y^{-1}-x^3)\times y} = \dfrac{2xy^2}{1-x^3y}$. In $\dfrac{3a^{-1}b^{-2}c^3}{a^2+b}$, a^{-1} and b^{-2} are factors of the entire numerator, so we write them as factors of the entire denominator, with the signs of the exponents changed; thus,

$$\frac{3a^{-1}b^{-2}c^3}{a^2+b} = \frac{3c^3}{ab^2(a^2+b)} = \frac{3c^3}{a^3b^2+ab^3}$$

Hence,

$$x^2y^{-2}z^{-1} + \frac{2xy}{y^{-1}-x^3} - \frac{3a^{-1}b^{-2}c^3}{a^2+b} = \frac{x^2}{y^2z} + \frac{2xy^2}{1-x^3y} - \frac{3c^3}{a^3b^2+ab^3} \quad \text{Ans.}$$

EXAMPLE 2.—Solve the following:

$$a^3 \times a^{-1}; \; n \times n^{-\frac{1}{4}}; \; 2c^{-\frac{2}{3}} \times \frac{1}{-3\sqrt[3]{c^2}}; \; c^{\frac{n}{m}} \div c^{\frac{2n}{m}}; \; x^2 \div \sqrt[5]{x^2}$$

Write the answers with positive exponents.

SOLUTION.— $a^3 \times a^{-1} = a^{3+(-1)} = a^{3-1} = a^2$ Ans.

$$n \times n^{-\frac{1}{4}} = n^{1+(-\frac{1}{4})} = n^{1-\frac{1}{4}} = n^{\frac{3}{4}} \quad \text{Ans.}$$

$$2c^{-\frac{2}{3}} \times \frac{1}{-3\sqrt[3]{c^2}} = \frac{2c^{-\frac{2}{3}}}{1} \times -\frac{1}{3\sqrt[3]{c^2}} = \frac{2}{c^{\frac{2}{3}}} \times -\frac{1}{3c^{\frac{2}{3}}} = -\frac{2 \times 1}{c^{\frac{2}{3}} \times 3c^{\frac{2}{3}}}$$

$$= -\frac{2}{3c^{\frac{2}{3}+\frac{2}{3}}} = -\frac{2}{3c^{\frac{4}{3}}} \text{ Ans.}$$

$$c^{\frac{n}{m}} \div c^{\frac{2n}{m}} = c^{\frac{n}{m}-\frac{2n}{m}} = c^{\frac{n-2n}{m}} = c^{\frac{-n}{m}} = c^{-\frac{n}{m}} = \frac{1}{c^{\frac{n}{m}}} \text{ Ans.}$$

$$x^2 \div \sqrt[5]{x^2} = x^2 \div x^{\frac{2}{5}} = x^{2-\frac{2}{5}} = x^{\frac{10}{5}-\frac{2}{5}} = x^{\frac{8}{5}} \text{ Ans.}$$

EXAMPLES FOR PRACTICE

Clear the following of negative exponents:

1. $x^2 y^{-2} z^{-\frac{1}{4}}$.   Ans. $\dfrac{x^2}{y^2 z^{\frac{1}{4}}}$

2. $3a^{-1}b + \dfrac{2a}{b^{-3}c^{-1}} + c^{-1}$.   Ans. $\dfrac{3b}{a} + 2ab^3c + \dfrac{1}{c}$

3. $\dfrac{4a^{-2}(c+d)}{2c+d}$.   Ans. $\dfrac{4(c+d)}{a^2(2c+d)}$

Express the following without radical signs:

4. $\sqrt[3]{b^{-2}}$.   Ans. $(b^{-2})^{\frac{1}{3}}$ or $b^{-\frac{2}{3}}$
5. $4a\sqrt{a^{-1}b^{-3}}$.   Ans. $4aa^{-\frac{1}{2}}b^{-\frac{3}{2}} = 4a^{\frac{1}{2}}b^{-\frac{3}{2}}$

Find the values of the following:

6. $m^{\frac{1}{2}} \times m^{-\frac{1}{6}}$.   Ans. $m^{\frac{1}{3}}$

7. $2ab^{\frac{1}{2}} \times a^{-\frac{1}{2}}b$.   Ans. $2a^{\frac{1}{2}}b^{\frac{3}{2}}$

8. $c^{\frac{n}{2}} \div \sqrt{c^{-n}}$.   Ans. c^n

9. $2x^{-2} \div (x^2)^{-\frac{1}{2}}$.   Ans. $2x^{-1}$

10. $\left(cd^{-\frac{n}{m}}\right)^{2m} \times \sqrt{d^{4n}}$.   Ans. c^{2m}

ELEMENTS OF ALGEBRA

(PART 3)

EQUATIONS

1. As defined in Art. **5,** Part 1, an **equation** is a statement of equality between two expressions, as $x + 6 = 14$.

2. Every equation has two parts, called the **first** and **second members.** The first member is the part on the left of the sign of equality, and the second member the part on the right of that sign. In $x + 6 = 14$, $x + 6$ is the first member, and 14 is the second member.

3. Equations usually consist of **known** and **unknown quantities**; that is, of quantities whose values are given, and of quantities whose values are not given, but are to be found. Thus, in $x + 6 = 14$, 6 and 14 are known quantities, and x is unknown; but since by the statement of the equation, $x + 6$ must equal 14, x must have such a value that when added to 6 the sum will be 14. Hence, the value of x is fixed for this particular case, and in a similar manner the value of a single unknown quantity in any equation is fixed by the relations that it bears to the known quantities, and this value can usually be found.

§ 5

4. **To solve an equation** is to find the value of the unknown quantity. This is done by a series of **transformations** by which the first member becomes the unknown quantity, and the second member becomes a known quantity, which is, therefore, the value of the unknown quantity.

TRANSFORMATIONS

5. In transforming an equation, the equality of its members must be preserved; otherwise the existing relations between the known and unknown quantities will be destroyed. Transformations are based upon the following principles:

6. In any equation:

I. The same quantity may be added to both members. For example, if 2 be added to both members of $x^2 = 16$, the members of the resulting equation, $x^2 + 2 = 18$, will be equal.

II. The same quantity may be subtracted from both members. Thus, if $x^2 = 16$, then $x^2 - 2 = 14$.

III. Both members may be multiplied or both divided by the same quantity. Thus, if $x^2 = 16$, then $2x^2 = 32$ and $\frac{x^2}{2} = 8$.

IV. Both members may be raised to the same power. Thus, if $x^2 = 16$, then $x^4 = 256$.

V. Like roots of both members may be extracted. Thus, if $x^2 = 16$, then $x = 4$.

A little thought will show that none of these operations will destroy the equality of the members. In the equation $16 = 16$, for example, by I, $16 + 2 = 16 + 2$; by II, $16 - 2 = 16 - 2$; by III, $16 \times 2 = 16 \times 2$, etc. It is to be observed, however, that after any transformation, the *members* do not equal their original values. In transforming an equation, it is not permissible to multiply or divide the given equation by 0, or by any expression containing the quantity whose value is to be found.

7. Transposition.—In transforming an equation, it is frequently necessary to transpose, or change, a term from one member to the other. For example, in the equation $3x + 5 = 12$, let it be required to transpose the $+5$ to the second member. This may be done by *subtracting* $+5$ from both members, which, by Art. **6,** II, will not destroy the equality; thus,

$$3x + 5 = 12$$

Subtracting $+5$ from both members, $\quad\quad 5 \quad\quad 5$

$$\overline{}$$

$$3x \quad\quad = 12 - 5 = 7$$

Again, let it be required to transpose the -5 in $3x - 5 = 12$ to the second member. This may be done by *adding* $+5$ to both members, which, by Art. **6,** I, will not destroy the equality; thus,

$$3x - 5 = 12$$

Adding $+5$ to both members, $\quad\quad 5 \quad\quad 5$

$$\overline{}$$

$$3x \quad\quad = 12 + 5 = 17$$

Now, what was really accomplished in each case was to transpose 5 from the first to the second member, *with its sign changed;* and in changing a term from the second to the first member, the same operation would be performed. Hence,

8. *Any term may be transposed from either member of an equation to the other, if its sign be changed.*

9. Cancelation.—*When the same term appears with the same sign in both members of an equation, it may be canceled from both.* For, in the equation $x + a = 6 + a$, we have, by transposing the a in the first member, to the second member, $x = 6 + a - a$; whence, the a's cancel, leaving $x = 6$. It must be observed that terms will not cancel from both members unless they have the *same* sign.   Thus, in $x - a = 6 + a$, we have, by transposing the $-a$, $x = 6 + 2a$.

10. Changing Signs. — It is sometimes desirable to change the sign of a quantity in an equation from $-$ to $+$ or from $+$ to $-$.   To change it, we use the following principle: *the signs of all the terms of both members of an equation may be changed without destroying the equality.*   For, in the equation $-x + 4 = 10 - a$, both members may be multiplied by -1 (Art. **6**, III), giving $x - 4 = -10 + a$, or $a - 10$.

11. Clearing of Fractions. — When an equation contains fractions it must be cleared of them in order to find the value of the unknown quantity.

EXAMPLE. — Clear the equation $x + \dfrac{x}{2} + \dfrac{3x}{4} + \dfrac{2x}{6} = 100$ of fractions.

SOLUTION. — The least common denominator of the fractions is 12. By Art. **6**, III, both members may be multiplied by the same quantity.   Hence, multiplying each term by 12, we have $12x + \dfrac{12x}{2} + \dfrac{36x}{4} + \dfrac{24x}{6} = 1{,}200$.   Now, reducing each fraction to its simplest form, which will not alter its value, and so will not destroy the equality of the members, we have $12x + 6x + 9x + 4x = 1{,}200$, the denominators of all the fractions having canceled.

12. *Hence, to clear an equation of fractions, multiply each term of the equation by the least common denominator.*

13. Instead of multiplying the numerators by the least common denominator and then reducing the fractions to their simplest forms, it is easier to divide the least common denominator by each denominator, and then multiply the corresponding numerators by the quotients.

EXAMPLE. — Clear the equation $\dfrac{2x}{x + 2} = \dfrac{1}{2} - \dfrac{3x + 2}{x^2 - 4}$ of fractions.

SOLUTION. — The least common denominator is $2(x^2 - 4)$.   Dividing this by $x + 2$ and multiplying $2x$ by the quotient, $2(x - 2)$, gives

$4x(x-2)$, or $4x^2-8x$; dividing $2(x^2-4)$ by 2 and multiplying 1 by the quotient, x^2-4, gives x^2-4; and dividing $2(x^2-4)$ by x^2-4 and multiplying $-(3x+2)$ by the quotient, 2, gives $-6x-4$. Hence, the equation becomes $4x^2-8x = x^2-4-6x-4$, all the denominators having canceled in the process.

14. *Where a fraction is preceded by a minus sign, care must be taken to change the sign of every term of the numerator when clearing of fractions.*

EXAMPLES FOR PRACTICE

Clear the following equations of fractions:

1. $x + \dfrac{3x}{4} + \dfrac{5}{7} = 16 - \dfrac{2}{x}$.   Ans. $28x^2 + 21x^2 + 20x = 448x - 56$

2. $\dfrac{x}{4} - \dfrac{x-3}{2} = \dfrac{a}{6}$.   Ans. $3x - 6x + 18 = 2a$

3. $\dfrac{x}{a-b} - x = \dfrac{a-b}{a+b} - 1$.

     Ans. $ax + bx - a^2x + b^2x = a^2 - 2ab + b^2 - a^2 + b^2$

4. $\dfrac{1}{(a-b)} = \dfrac{x}{a-b} - \dfrac{a+b}{x}$.   Ans. $x = x^2 - a^2 + b^2$

SOLUTION OF SIMPLE EQUATIONS

15. A **simple equation** is one containing only the first power of the unknown quantity, when cleared of radical and aggregation signs and fractions. It is also called an equation of the **first degree.**

16. The unknown quantity in a simple equation containing but one unknown quantity is usually represented by the letter x. Known quantities are represented by figures and by the *first* letters of the alphabet. Equations containing known quantities represented by letters are called **literal equations,** and if any literal equation be solved (Art. **4**), the value of the unknown quantity will usually contain one or more of the first letters of the alphabet.

17. To solve a simple equation:

Rule.—*Clear the equation of fractions, if it has any.*

Transpose the terms containing unknown quantities to the first member, and the known terms to the second member.

Combine the terms containing the unknown quantity into one term and reduce the second member to its simplest form.

Divide both members of the resulting equation by the coefficient of the unknown quantity (Art. **6,** *III), and the second member of this last equation will be the value of the unknown quantity.*

This rule does not hold absolutely in all cases, since special methods are often used, of which the student can learn only by practice.

18. To verify the result, substitute the value of the unknown quantity in the original equation, which should then reduce so that both members will be alike. When this occurs the equation is said to be **satisfied.**

19. A **root** of an equation is the number or quantity which, when substituted for the unknown quantity, satisfies the equation. After an equation has been solved the root so obtained should always be substituted for the unknown quantity to see if it satisfies the equation; if it does the root found is correct; otherwise the work must be repeated to find the error.

20. In the following examples, the value of the unknown quantity x is to be determined. The transformations used all depend on principles explained in Arts. **5–14.**

EXAMPLE 1.—Solve the equation $20 + 5x - 3x - 18 = 10$.

SOLUTION.—Transposing 20 and -18 to the second member,
$$5x - 3x = 10 - 20 + 18$$
Combining like terms, $2x = 8$
Dividing both members by 2 (Art. **6,** III),
$$x = 4 \quad \text{Ans.}$$

To verify the result, substitute 4 for x in the original equation. (Art. **18**.) Thus,

$$20 + 5 \times 4 - 3 \times 4 - 18 = 10$$

or,
$$20 + 20 - 12 - 18 = 10$$

Combining, $10 = 10$, which proves the result

EXAMPLE 2.—Solve the equation $5x - (10 - x) = 5x + 4(x - 1)$.

SOLUTION.—Removing the parentheses,

$$5x - 10 + x = 5x + 4x - 4$$

or
$$6x - 10 = 9x - 4$$

Transposing -10 to the second member and $9x$ to the first member,

$$6x - 9x = 10 - 4$$

Combining like terms, $-3x = 6$

Changing signs to make the term containing x positive,

$$3x = -6 \quad \text{(Art. 10.)}$$

Dividing both members by 3, $x = -2$. Ans.

PROOF.— $5 \times -2 - (10 + 2) = 5 \times -2 + 4(-2 - 1)$

or
$$-10 - 10 - 2 = -10 - 8 - 4$$

Combining, $-22 = -22$, which proves the result

EXAMPLE 3.—Solve the equation

$$16 - x - \{7x - [8x - (9x - \overline{3x - 6x})]\} = 0$$

SOLUTION.—Removing the aggregation signs,

$$16 - x - 7x + 8x - 9x + 3x - 6x = 0$$

or
$$-12x + 16 = 0$$

Transposing 16 to the second member,

$$-12x = -16$$

Dividing both members by -12,

$$x = \tfrac{16}{12} = 1\tfrac{1}{3} \quad \text{Ans.}$$

EXAMPLE 4.—Solve the equation

$$\frac{2x + 2}{2} + \frac{1}{4} = \frac{8 - 6x}{5} + \frac{2(6x + 7)}{8}$$

SOLUTION.—Reducing the first term of the first member and the last term of the second member to a simpler form, the equation becomes

$$x + 1 + \frac{1}{4} = \frac{8 - 6x}{5} + \frac{6x + 7}{4}$$

Clearing of fractions by multiplying each term of both members by 20, the least common denominator, we have

$$20x + 20 + 5 = 32 - 24x + 30x + 35$$

or
$$20x + 25 = 6x + 67$$

Transposing and uniting terms,

$$14x = 42$$

Dividing by 14, $x = 3$ **Ans.**

EXAMPLE 5.—Solve the equation $x + \dfrac{x+4}{2} - \dfrac{3x-4}{5} - \dfrac{x}{8} = 9$.

SOLUTION.—Clearing of fractions by multiplying each term by 40, the least common denominator, and remembering that the sign of the second fraction is minus (Art. **14**),

$$40x + 20x + 80 - (24x - 32) - 5x = 360$$

Removing parenthesis, transposing and uniting terms,

$$31x = 248$$

Dividing by 31, $x = 8$ **Ans.**

EXAMPLE 6.—Solve the equation $\dfrac{3}{1-x} - \dfrac{2}{1+x} + \dfrac{1}{1-x^2} = 0$.

SOLUTION.—Clearing of fractions by multiplying by $1 - x^2$, the least common denominator,

$$3(1+x) - 2(1-x) + 1 = 0$$
$$3 + 3x - 2 + 2x + 1 = 0$$

Uniting and transposing terms,

$$5x = -2$$
$$x = -.4 \quad \textbf{Ans.}$$

NOTE.— 0 multiplied or divided by any number = 0.

21. If the denominators in a fractional equation are partly monomial and partly polynomial, it will be easier to clear of fractions at first partially by multiplying by the least common denominator of the *monomial* denominators.

EXAMPLE 1.—Solve the equation $\dfrac{8x+5}{14} = \dfrac{4x+6}{7} - \dfrac{7x-3}{6x+2}$.

SOLUTION.—Clearing of fractions partially, by multiplying each term by 14, and noticing that 2 may be canceled from the denominator of the second fraction of the second member when multiplying by 14,

$$8x + 5 = 8x + 12 - \frac{49x - 21}{3x + 1}$$

Transposing and uniting the terms (Art. **9**),

$$\frac{49x - 21}{3x + 1} = 7$$

Clearing of fractions by multiplying each term by $3x + 1$,

$$49x - 21 = 21x + 7$$
$$28x = 28$$
$$x = 1 \quad \text{Ans.}$$

EXAMPLE 2.—Solve the equation $1 + \dfrac{3}{x - 1} = \dfrac{3 + \dfrac{4 - x}{1 - x}}{3}$.

SOLUTION.—Simplifying the second member by multiplying both numerator and denominator of the fraction by $1 - x$,

$$1 + \frac{3}{x - 1} = \frac{3(1 - x) + 4 - x}{3(1 - x)}$$

Changing the signs of the first fraction so as to make the denominator $1 - x$, and clearing of fractions by multiplying by $3(1 - x)$,

$$3(1 - x) - 9 = 3(1 - x) + 4 - x$$

Canceling $3(1 - x)$ from both members and transposing,

$$x = 13 \quad \text{Ans.}$$

22. When powers of the unknown quantity higher than the first appear in an equation, they will often cancel, the equation thus reducing to a simple one.

EXAMPLE.—Solve the equation

$$(x + 3)^2 - 3x(4x + 1) = 5x^2 - (4x - 5)^2$$

SOLUTION.—Performing the operations indicated,

$$x^2 + 6x + 9 - 12x^2 - 3x = 5x^2 - (16x^2 - 40x + 25)$$

Removing the parenthesis and transposing terms,

$$x^2 + 6x - 12x^2 - 3x - 5x^2 + 16x^2 - 40x = -25 - 9$$

Combining like terms, $\quad -37x = -34$
Dividing by -37, $\qquad x = \frac{34}{37} \quad \text{Ans.}$

23. In **literal equations** (Art. **16**), the terms containing known or unknown quantities cannot always be combined into one. In solving, all terms containing unknown quantities must be brought into the first member without regard to whether they contain known quantities.

EXAMPLE 1.—Solve the literal equation $2ax - 3b = x + c - 3ax$.

SOLUTION.—Transposing the terms containing the unknown quantities to the first member and the remaining terms to the second member, and combining like terms,

$$5ax - x = 3b + c$$

Factoring $5ax - x$ with a view to bringing x alone in the first member,

$$(5a - 1)x = 3b + c$$

The coefficient of x is now $5a - 1$, this being considered as one quantity.

Dividing by $5a - 1$, $x = \dfrac{3b + c}{5a - 1}$ Ans.

PROOF.—Since the original equation is equivalent to $5ax - x = 3b + c$, it will be sufficient to satisfy this equation. Hence, substituting the value of x,

$$\frac{5a(3b + c)}{5a - 1} - \frac{3b + c}{5a - 1} = 3b + c$$

or
$$\frac{(5a - 1)\,(3b + c)}{5a - 1} = 3b + c$$

Canceling the $5a - 1$,
$$3b + c = 3b + c$$

EXAMPLE 2.—Solve the equation

$$(x + a)\,(x - b) - (x - a)\,(x + b) = a^2 - b^2$$

SOLUTION.—Performing the operations indicated,

$$x^2 + ax - bx - ab - (x^2 - ax + bx - ab) = a^2 - b^2$$

Combining like terms, $2ax - 2bx = a^2 - b^2$
whence, $2(a - b)x = a^2 - b^2$

or $x = \dfrac{a^2 - b^2}{2(a - b)} = \dfrac{(a + b)\,(a - b)}{2(a - b)} = \dfrac{(a + b)}{2}$ Ans.

EXAMPLE 3.—Solve the equation, $\dfrac{3x + 1}{x + 1} = \dfrac{3bx - 2a + c}{b(x + 1) - a}.$

SOLUTION.—Clearing of fractions,

$$(3x + 1)\,[b(x + 1) - a] = (x + 1)\,(3bx - 2a + c)$$

or
$$3bx(x + 1) - 3ax + b(x + 1) - a = 3bx(x + 1) - (2d - c)\,(x + 1)$$

Canceling $3bx(x + 1)$ from both members,

$$-3ax + bx + b - a = -2ax + cx - 2a + c$$

Transposing and uniting terms,

$$-ax + bx - cx = -a - b + c$$

Changing signs and factoring,

$$(a - b + c)x = a + b - c$$

whence, $x = \dfrac{a + b - c}{a - b + c}$ Ans.

EXAMPLES FOR PRACTICE

Solve the following equations:

1. $16 - 3x = 13 - 6x.$ Ans. $x = -1$

2. $3(4x - 5) + 6 = 1 + 2x.$ Ans. $x = 1$

3. $6(5 - 2x) = 6 - 2(x - 2).$ Ans. $x = 2$

4. $\dfrac{2x}{3} - \dfrac{4x}{3} = 5 - \dfrac{3x}{4}.$ Ans. $x = 60$

5. $\dfrac{x+1}{3} - \dfrac{x+4}{5} = 16 - \dfrac{x+3}{4}.$ Ans. $x = 41$

6. $\dfrac{x}{3} - \dfrac{x^2 - 5x}{3x - 7} = \dfrac{2}{3}.$ Ans. $x = -7$

7. $\dfrac{5 - 2x}{x + 1} - \dfrac{3 - 2x}{x + 4} = 0.$ Ans. $x = 4\frac{1}{4}$

8. $2x - 4a = 3ax + a^2 - a^2 x.$ Ans. $x = \dfrac{a^2 + 4a}{a^2 - 3a + 2}$

9. $\dfrac{ax + 2x}{5a} - \dfrac{a^2 + 4a + 4}{4b} = 0.$ Ans. $x = \dfrac{5a^2 + 10a}{4b}$

SUGGESTION.—Transposing the second term to the second member,

$$\frac{ax + 2x}{5a} = \frac{a^2 + 4a + 4}{4b} = \frac{(a + 2)^2}{4b}$$

Multiplying both sides by $5a$,

$$ax + 2x = \frac{5a(a + 2)^2}{4b}$$

Solving for x,

$$x = \frac{5a(a + 2)^2}{(a + 2)4b} = \frac{5a(a + 2)}{4b} = \frac{5a^2 + 10a}{4b}$$

10. $\dfrac{a(c^2 + x^2)}{cx} = ab + \dfrac{ax}{c}.$ Ans. $x = \dfrac{c}{b}$

PROBLEMS LEADING TO SIMPLE EQUATIONS WITH ONE UNKNOWN QUANTITY

24. There are two steps in the solution of problems by algebra:

First.—The relations which exist between the known and the unknown quantities, that is, between those whose values are given in the problem and those whose values are required, must be stated by one or more equations. This is called the **statement** of the problem.

Second.—The resulting equation or equations must be solved, giving the values of the required quantities.

25.   The ability to state a problem by means of an equation depends upon the ingenuity of the operator and his ability to reason, rather than upon his knowledge of algebra. No definite rule can be given for making the statement, but in general, where there is only one unknown quantity in a problem:

Decide what quantity it is whose value is to be found. This will be the unknown quantity, or the answer. Then represent the unknown quantity by x and form an equation that will indicate the relations between the known and the unknown quantities as stated in the problem.

It will thus be seen that by the algebraic method, the answer to a problem is used in the solution and operated upon as though it were a known quantity, which is one great advantage over the arithmetical method.

Note.—The equation will also indicate the operations that would be performed in proving the statement made in the problem, were the answer known.   Hence, the equation may often be formed by noticing what operations would be performed upon the answer in proving.

Example 1.—Find such a number that, when 14 is added to its double, the sum shall be 30.

Solution.—The quantity whose value is required is the number itself.   As this is the unknown quantity, let x = the number, whence $2x$ must be double the number.   Now the problem states that when 14 is added to double the number the sum will be 30.   In other words, when 14 is added to $2x$, the sum will be 30.   Hence, the statement of the problem in the form of an equation is

$$2x + 14 = 30$$

Whence, solving, $x = 8$ Ans.

Example 2.—Find a number which, when multiplied by 4, will exceed 40 as much as it is now below 40.

Solution.—Let x = the required number, which, when multiplied by 4, becomes $4x$.   According to the conditions of the problem, the amount by which 4 times the required number, or $4x$, exceeds 40 is equal to the amount that the number itself, or x, is below 40.

But $4x - 40$ is the amount by which $4x$ exceeds 40, and $40 - x$ is the amount by which x is below 40.

Hence, by the conditions, we have the statement,

$$4x - 40 = 40 - x$$

Transposing and uniting, $5x = 80$

or $x = 16$ Ans.

EXAMPLE 3.—Two loads of brick together weigh 4,000 lb.; but if 500 lb. be transferred from the smaller to the larger load, the latter will weigh 7 times as much as the former. How much does each load weigh ?

SOLUTION.—If the weights of the two loads were known and it was desired to prove the correctness of the example, we should add 500 lb. to the weight of the larger load and subtract 500 lb. from the weight of the smaller load, as stated in the example. The larger load should then weigh 7 times as much as the smaller. To obtain the equation, the same thing is done by letting $x = $ the weight of one load, whence $4,000 - x$ equals the weight of the other load.

Let $x = $ the weight of the smaller load.

Then, $4,000 - x = $ the weight of the larger load.

Also, $x - 500 = $ the weight of the smaller load after transferring 500 lb.

And $4,000 - x + 500 = $ the weight of the larger load after transferring 500 lb.

By the conditions, the larger load now weighs 7 times as much as the smaller.

Hence, $7(x - 500) = 4,000 - x + 500$

Solving, $7x - 3,500 = 4,500 - x$

or $8x = 8,000$

whence, $x = 1,000$ lb. $= $ weight of smaller load $\big\}$ Ans.

and $4,000 - x = 3,000$ lb. $= $ weight of larger load

PROOF.— $1,000 - 500 = 500 = $ weight of the smaller load, and $3,000 + 500 = 3,500 = $ weight of the larger load after the 500 pounds have been transferred; $3,500 \div 500 = 7$.

EXAMPLE 4.—The circumference of the fore wheel of a carriage is 10 feet, and of the hind wheel 12 feet. What distance has the carriage traveled, when the fore wheel has made 8 more turns than the hind wheel ?

SOLUTION.—In this example the distance traveled is not known, but is required to be found. Suppose that the distance is known, and that it equals x feet, and that we wish to see whether the statement is true that the fore wheel makes 8 more revolutions than the hind wheel in passing over x feet. The number of revolutions of the fore wheel is evidently $\frac{x}{10}$, and of the hind wheel, $\frac{x}{12}$. The example states that the difference between them equals 8.

Hence,
$$\frac{x}{10} - \frac{x}{12} = 8 \quad (1)$$

Solving for x.
$$12x - 10x = 960$$
or
$$2x = 960$$
and
$$x = 480 \text{ ft. \ Ans.}$$

Proof.—
$$\frac{480}{10} = 48 = \text{revolutions of fore wheel}$$
$$\frac{480}{12} = 40 = \text{revolutions of hind wheel}$$
$$48 - 40 = 8. \quad \text{Compare this proof with (1)}$$

Example 5.—A water cistern connected with three pipes can be filled by one of them in 80 minutes, by another in 200 minutes, and by the third in 300 minutes. In what time will the cistern be filled when all three pipes are open at once?

Solution.—Here the unknown quantity is the number of minutes required to fill the cistern by all three pipes together. Supposing this to be x minutes, the example may be proved by noticing that the sum of the quantities of water flowing through each pipe separately in a given length of time, as 1 minute, must be equal to the quantity flowing through all three together in the same length of time. According to the problem, the quantity discharged by the first pipe in one minute would be $\frac{1}{80}$, by the second $\frac{1}{200}$, and by the third $\frac{1}{300}$ of the contents of the cistern. In like manner the quantity discharged by all three at once in one minute would be $\frac{1}{x}$. Then, if the example is stated correctly,
$$\frac{1}{80} + \frac{1}{200} + \frac{1}{300} = \frac{1}{x}$$

Clearing of fractions,
$$x(30 + 12 + 8) = 2,400$$
or
$$50x = 2,400$$
whence,
$$x = 48 \text{ minutes \ Ans.}$$

Example 6.—A man rows a boat a certain distance *with* the tide, at the rate of $6\frac{2}{3}$ miles an hour, and returns at the rate of $3\frac{1}{3}$ miles an hour, *against* a tide half as strong. If the man is pulling at a uniform rate, what is the velocity of the stronger tide?

Solution.—If the following statement is not clear, the student should reason it out for himself in a manner similar to that used in the last three examples.

Let x = number of miles per hour that the stronger tide is running, then $\frac{x}{2}$ = number of miles per hour that the weaker tide is running.

Hence, $6\frac{2}{3} - x$ and $3\frac{1}{3} + \frac{x}{2}$ are expressions for the rate at which the man is pulling. But, as he is pulling at a constant rate all the time, these expressions must be equal. Hence,

$$6\frac{2}{3} - x = 3\frac{1}{3} + \frac{x}{2}$$

or

$$\frac{20}{3} - x = \frac{10}{3} + \frac{x}{2}$$

Clearing of fractions, $40 - 6x = 20 + 3x$

or $-9x = -20$

whence, $x = 2\frac{2}{9}$ miles per hour   Ans.

EXAMPLES FOR PRACTICE

Solve the following examples:

1. The greater of two numbers is four times the lesser number, and their sum is 400; what are the numbers?   Ans. 80 and 320

2. A farmer has 108 animals, consisting of horses, sheep, and cows. He has four times as many cows as horses, lacking 8, and five times as many sheep as horses, lacking 4; how many has he of each kind?

Ans. $\left\{\begin{array}{l} \text{12 horses} \\ \text{40 cows} \\ \text{56 sheep} \end{array}\right.$

3. A can do a piece of work in 8 days, and B can do it in 10 days; in what time can they do it working together?   Ans. $4\frac{4}{9}$ days

4. Find five consecutive numbers whose sum is 150.

Ans. $28 + 29 + 30 + 31 + 32$

5. A boat whose rate of sailing is 6 miles per hour in still water moves down a stream which flows at the rate of 3 miles per hour, and returns, making the round trip in 8 hours; how far did it go down the stream?   Ans. 18 mi.

QUADRATIC EQUATIONS

26. A **quadratic equation** is one in which the *square* is the highest power of the unknown quantity when simplified as stated in Art. **15.** It is also called an equation of the **second degree.**

27. A **pure quadratic equation** is one which contains the square only of the unknown quantity, as $x^2 + 2ab = 10$.

28. An **affected quadratic equation** is one containing both the square and the first power of the unknown quantity, as $x^2 + 2x = 6$.

29. By the processes used to reduce simple equations, any pure quadratic equation may be reduced to an equation having the square of the unknown quantity alone in the first member, and some known quantity in the second member, as in $x^2 = a$, where x^2 is the square of the unknown quantity and a is a known quantity. The value of the unknown quantity may then be found by extracting the square root of both members, which, by Art. **6,** V, will not destroy the equality of the equation. By referring to Case (7), Art. **64,** Part 2, it will be seen that after extracting the square root, each member should be written with the $\pm$ sign. Thus, extracting the square root of both members of $x^2 = a$, we have $\pm x = \pm \sqrt{a}$. This may be taken in four ways, namely, that

$$+ x = + \sqrt{a}$$
$$+ x = - \sqrt{a}$$
$$- x = - \sqrt{a}$$
$$- x = + \sqrt{a}$$

But by Art. **10,** the signs of both members of the last two equations may be changed, making $+ x = + \sqrt{a}$ and

$+ x = - \sqrt{a}$, the same as in the first two equations. Hence, the equation $x^2 = a$ has the two values,

$$x = + \sqrt{a}$$
and
$$x = - \sqrt{a}$$

and these may be expressed by writing x in the first member without any sign (plus understood), and writing the square root of a in the second member with the $\pm$ sign, thus,

$$x = \pm \sqrt{a}$$

30. From the foregoing, we have the following rule for solving a pure quadratic equation:

Rule.—*Reduce the given equation to the form of $x^2 = a$ (Art. 29), and extract the square root of both members, writing the $\pm$ sign before the square root of the second member.*

NOTE.—The **root** of an equation is the value of the unknown quantity. From this it will be seen that a simple equation has one root, and a quadratic equation has two roots. In general, any equation has as many roots as there are units in the exponent of the unknown quantity.

EXAMPLE 1.—Solve the equation $\dfrac{x^2}{16} - \dfrac{x^2 - 3}{5} = \dfrac{1}{20}$.

SOLUTION.—Clearing of fractions by multiplying each term by 80,
$$5x^2 - 16(x^2 - 3) = 4$$

Transposing and uniting, $- 11x^2 = - 44$,
or $x^2 = 4$

Extracting the square root of both members,
$$x = \pm 2 \quad \text{Ans.}$$

EXAMPLE 2.—Solve the equation

$$\frac{\sqrt{x-2}}{\sqrt{x+2}} + \frac{\sqrt{x+2}}{\sqrt{x-2}} = 4$$

SOLUTION.—Clearing of fractions by multiplying each term by $\sqrt{x+2} \times \sqrt{x-2}$,
$$x - 2 + x + 2 = 4\sqrt{x+2} \times \sqrt{x-2}$$
or, $2x = 4\sqrt{x^2 - 4}$
Dividing by 2, $x = 2\sqrt{x^2 - 4}$
Squaring, $x^2 = 4(x^2 - 4)$
or $x^2 = 4x^2 - 16$
whence, $- 3x^2 = - 16$
and $x^2 = \frac{16}{3}$

Extracting the square root of both members,

$$x = \pm 4\sqrt{\tfrac{1}{3}} \quad \text{Ans.}$$

NOTE.—That $\sqrt{x+2} \times \sqrt{x-2} = \sqrt{x^2-4}$ is readily seen from the following: Using fractional exponents $\sqrt{x-2} \times \sqrt{x+2} = (x-2)^{\frac{1}{2}}(x+2)^{\frac{1}{2}}$. Since $25^{\frac{1}{2}} \times 36^{\frac{1}{2}} = 5 \times 6 = 30$ and since $(25 \times 36)^{\frac{1}{2}} = 900^{\frac{1}{2}} = 30$, it follows that $25^{\frac{1}{2}} \times 36^{\frac{1}{2}} = (25 \times 36)^{\frac{1}{2}}$; and since any numbers whatever may be substituted for 25 and 36, a and b may be substituted also, and $a^{\frac{1}{2}} \times b^{\frac{1}{2}} = (ab)^{\frac{1}{2}}$. Now letting $a = x-2$ and $b = x+2$, $a^{\frac{1}{2}} \times b^{\frac{1}{2}} = (x-2)^{\frac{1}{2}}(x+2)^{\frac{1}{2}} = [(x-2)(x+2)]^{\frac{1}{2}} = (x^2-4)^{\frac{1}{2}} = \sqrt{x^2-4}$.

EXAMPLES FOR PRACTICE

Solve the following equations:

1. $3x^2 - 57 - 4x^2 = -8x^2 + 6.$ Ans. $x = \pm 3$

2. $\dfrac{1}{2x^2} + 7 = \dfrac{9}{4x^2}.$ Ans. $x = \pm \tfrac{1}{2}$

3. $35 - \dfrac{x^2+50}{5} = x^2 - \dfrac{x^2-10}{3}.$ Ans. $x = \pm 5$

4. $x\sqrt{6+x^2} = 1 + x^2.$ Ans. $x = \pm \tfrac{1}{2}$

AFFECTED QUADRATIC EQUATIONS

31. Every affected quadratic equation may be reduced to the form

$$x^2 \pm px = \pm q$$

in which the term containing x^2 is positive and the coefficient is 1; the term containing x is positive or negative and the coefficient has any value; and the remaining term q has any value and is positive or negative. For example, suppose it is required to bring the equation $ax^2 - bx + cx - x^2 + 3 = d$ into the required form. First collect the terms containing x^2 and factor; then the terms containing x and factor; then the terms that do not contain x^2 or x after transposing them to the second member. Lastly divide by the coefficient of x^2. Thus,

$$ax^2 - x^2 + cx - bx = d - 3$$
$$(a-1)x^2 + (c-b)x = d - 3$$
$$x^2 + \frac{c-b}{a-1}x = \frac{d-3}{a-1}$$

Here x^2 is positive, and the coefficient is 1; the coefficient of x is $\dfrac{c-b}{a-1}$, which may be put equal to p; and the known term (usually called the **absolute term,** because it does not change for any value of x) is $\dfrac{d-3}{a-1}$, which may be represented by q. The equation is now of the required form.

32. Any equation of the form $x^2 \pm px = \pm q$ may be solved, that is, the values of x (the *roots* of the equation) may be found, whether the coefficients are numerical or literal, by the following formula:

$$x \;=\; \mp \tfrac{1}{2}(p \pm \sqrt{p^2 \pm 4q})^{*}$$

The $\mp$ sign is read *minus or plus*, and is a combination of the minus and plus signs. In this formula, *the minus sign before the parenthesis is used if the coefficient of x in the original equation is positive, and the positive sign is used if this coefficient is negative;* the plus sign between p^2 and $4q$ is used if q in the original equation is positive, and the negative sign is used if q is negative. The double sign before the radical indicates that there are two values of x, one of which is equal to one-half of p plus the radical, and the other to one-half of p minus the radical.

EXAMPLE.—Solve the equation $4x^2 - 16x - 128 = 0$.

SOLUTION.— $4x^2 - 16x - 128 = 0$
Transposing 128, $4x^2 - 16x = 128$
Dividing by 4, $x^2 - 4x = 32$

The equation is now in the required form, and p in the formula equals 4, while $q = 32$. Since p is negative, use the positive sign before the parenthesis, and since q is positive, use the positive sign under the radical sign. Substituting,

$$x = \tfrac{1}{2}(4 \pm \sqrt{4^2 + 4 \times 32})$$
$$= \tfrac{1}{2}(4 \pm \sqrt{16 + 128})$$
$$= \tfrac{1}{2}(4 \pm \sqrt{144})$$
$$= \tfrac{1}{2}(4 \pm 12)$$
$$= \tfrac{1}{2}(4 + 12), \text{ or } \tfrac{1}{2}(4 - 12)$$
$$= 8 \text{ or } -4 \quad \text{Ans.}$$

---

* For proof see page 40.

33. The result just obtained may be proved in two ways: *First*, by substituting the values found for x in the original equation; if both satisfy the equation, the results are correct. *Second*, put the original equation in the form $x^2 \pm px \pm q = 0$, by transposing the absolute term; then form two binomial factors by adding to x the roots *with their signs changed;* the product of these factors must equal the first member of the equation, if the work is correct.

Applying the first proof to the last example,

$$4(+8)^2 - 16(+8) - 128 = 256 - 128 - 128 = 0$$
$$4(-4)^2 - 16(-4) - 128 = 64 + 64 - 128 = 0$$

Applying the second proof to the same example, the roots with their signs are -8 and 4; adding these to x, the sums are $x - 8$ and $x + 4$. Treating these binomials as factors and expanding $(x - 8)(x + 4) = x^2 - 4x - 32$, which is the value of the first member of the equation $4x^2 - 16x - 128 = 0$ when reduced to the form $x^2 \pm px \pm q = 0$, by dividing both members by 4. It is to be noted that 0 multiplied or divided by any finite quantity is zero.

34. If any equation of the form $x^2 \pm px \pm q = 0$ can be factored (and every such equation can be factored), either factor can be placed equal to zero, and by transposing the absolute term the value of x can be found. For example, in the last article $x^2 - 4x - 32 = 0$; hence $(x - 8)(x + 4) = 0$, from which $x - 8 = \dfrac{0}{x + 4} = 0$, and $x = 8$, or $x + 4 = \dfrac{0}{x - 8} = 0$, and $x = -4$.

This fact gives an easy method of determining the roots by inspection when the equation has numerical coefficients and the roots are integral or fractional. It is evident, as will be seen by actual multiplication, that the product of the absolute terms of the factors must equal the absolute term of the given equation; also that the sum of the absolute terms of the factors must be equal to the coefficient of x; in both cases the sign of the term is supposed to be included in the statement. Consider now the equation

$$x^2 - 4x - 32 = 0$$

The absolute term -32 is obtained by multiplying two numbers with unlike signs; the coefficient of x, which is -4, is obtained by adding either two negative quantities or a positive and a negative quantity, the negative quantity being the greater to obtain the minus sign. The following are all the pairs of integral factors of -32, whose product will equal -32, together with their sums:

Product	Sum	Product	Sum
$-1 \times 32 = -32$	$-1 + 32 = 31$	$1 \times -32 = -32$	$1 + (-32) = -31$
$-2 \times 16 = -32$	$-2 + 16 = 14$	$2 \times -16 = -32$	$2 + (-16) = -14$
$-4 \times 8 = -32$	$-4 + 8 = 4$	$4 \times -8 = -32$	$4 + (-8) = -4$

In the last case, both conditions are fulfilled; hence, $x^2 - 4x - 32 = (x - 8)(x + 4) = 0$, from which $x = 8$ or -4. It is well in all cases to attempt the solution by inspection before applying the formula, since if a solution is possible by this method the work is greatly reduced. This method also proves the work by simply multiplying the factors.

EXAMPLE.—Solve by inspection $13x - x^2 = -14$.

SOLUTION.—Bring the equation into the required form by changing all the signs and transposing the absolute term.

$$x^2 - 13x - 14 = 0$$

The only pairs of integral factors of 14 are 1×14 and 2×7. The coefficient of x is -13, and since $-14 + 1 = -13$, the factors are evidently -14×1. Hence,

$$(x - 14)(x + 1) = 0, \text{ and } x = 14 \text{ or } -1 \quad \text{Ans.}$$

REMARK.—If the formula had been used in solving the last example the work would have been as follows:

$$x^2 - 13x = 14$$
$$x = \tfrac{1}{2}(13 \pm \sqrt{13^2 + 4 \times 14})$$
$$= \tfrac{1}{2}(13 \pm \sqrt{225})$$
$$= \tfrac{1}{2}(13 \pm 15)$$
$$= 14 \text{ or } -1$$

35. The principles given in Art. **34** may be obtained directly from the following data for writing out the product of any two binomials, the first terms of which are alike:

Add the square of the first term, the product of the first term and the sum of the second terms, and the product of the second terms.

EXAMPLE.—Write out the products of $x-3$ and $x-6$; also, of $x^2 - a$ and $x^2 + b$.

SOLUTION.—For the first case, the square of the first term is x^2; the sum of the second terms is $-3-6 = -9$; and the product of the second terms is $-3 \times -6 = 18$; hence, $(x-3)(x-6) = x^2 - 9x + 18.$
Ans.

For the second case, the square of the first term is x^4; the sum of the second term is $-a+b = -(a-b)$ or $(b-a)$; the product of the second terms is $-ab$; hence,

$$(x^2 - a)(x^2 + b) = x^4 - (a-b)x^2 - ab \text{ or } x^4 + (b-a)x^2 - ab \text{ Ans.}$$

36. Several examples will now be given showing the application of the foregoing methods to the solution of typical examples.

EXAMPLE 1.—Solve the equation $-3x^2 - 7x = \frac{10}{3}$.

SOLUTION.—Dividing both members by -3 to make x^2 stand alone and positive, $x^2 + \frac{7}{3}x = -\frac{10}{9}$.

From the formula, $x = -\frac{1}{2}(\frac{7}{3} \pm \sqrt{\frac{49}{9} - \frac{40}{9}})$
$= -\frac{1}{2}(\frac{7}{3} \pm 1)$
$= -\frac{5}{3} \text{ or } -\frac{2}{3}$ Ans.

The example may also be solved by inspection, as follows:
$$x^2 + \frac{7}{3}x + \frac{10}{9} = 0$$

The absolute term $\frac{10}{9}$ is equal to $\frac{2 \times 5}{3 \times 3} = \frac{2}{3} \times \frac{5}{3}$, and $\frac{2}{3} + \frac{5}{3} = \frac{7}{3}$; hence, $(x + \frac{2}{3})(x + \frac{5}{3}) = 0$, and $x = -\frac{2}{3} \text{ or } -\frac{5}{3}$. Ans.

EXAMPLE 2.—Solve the equation $x - \dfrac{x^3 - 8}{x^2 + 5} = 2$.

SOLUTION.—Clearing of fractions,
$$x^3 + 5x - x^3 + 8 = 2x^2 + 10$$

Transposing and uniting terms,
$$-2x^2 + 5x = 2$$
Dividing by -2, $x^2 - \frac{5}{2}x = -1$

From the formula, $\quad x = \frac{1}{2}\left(\frac{5}{2} \pm \sqrt{\frac{25}{4} - 4}\right)$

$$= 2 \text{ or } \tfrac{1}{2} \quad \text{Ans.}$$

Solving by inspection,

$$x^2 - \tfrac{5}{2}x + 1 = 0$$

$$1 = \tfrac{2}{2} = \frac{2 \times 1}{1 \times 2} = 2 \times \tfrac{1}{2}; \; -2 + (-\tfrac{1}{2}) = -2\tfrac{1}{2} = -\tfrac{5}{2}$$

hence, $\quad (x - 2)(x - \tfrac{1}{2}) = 0$, and $x = 2$ or $\tfrac{1}{2}$ Ans.

EXAMPLE 3.—Solve the literal equation $acx^2 - bcx + adx = bd$.

SOLUTION.—Reducing the equation so that the first member will contain two terms, one with x^2 and one with x,

$$acx^2 - (bc - ad)x = bd$$

Dividing by ac, $x^2 - \dfrac{bc - ad}{ac} x = \dfrac{bd}{ac}$

From the formula,

$$x = \tfrac{1}{2}\left(\frac{bc - ad}{ac} \pm \sqrt{\left(\frac{bc - ad}{ac}\right)^2 + \frac{4bd}{ac}}\right)$$

$$= \tfrac{1}{2}\left(\frac{bc - ad}{ac} \pm \sqrt{\frac{b^2c^2 - 2bcad + a^2d^2}{a^2c^2} + \frac{4bdac}{a^2c^2}}\right)$$

$$= \tfrac{1}{2}\left(\frac{bc - ad}{ac} \pm \sqrt{\frac{b^2c^2 + 2bcad + a^2d^2}{a^2c^2}}\right)$$

$$= \tfrac{1}{2}\left(\frac{bc - ad}{ac} \pm \sqrt{\frac{(bc + ad)^2}{(ac)^2}}\right)$$

$$= \tfrac{1}{2}\left(\frac{bc - ad}{ac} \pm \frac{bc + ad}{ac}\right)$$

$$= \tfrac{1}{2}\left(\frac{2bc}{ac}\right) = \frac{b}{a} \text{ or } \tfrac{1}{2}\left(-\frac{2ad}{ac}\right) = -\frac{d}{c} \quad \text{Ans.}$$

The example may also be solved by inspection.

$$x^2 - \frac{bc - ad}{ac} x - \frac{bd}{ac} = 0$$

The coefficient of x is $-\dfrac{bc - ad}{ac}$, which is equal to $-\left(\dfrac{bc}{ac} - \dfrac{ad}{ac}\right)$

$= -\left(\dfrac{b}{a} - \dfrac{d}{c}\right) = -\dfrac{b}{a} + \dfrac{d}{c};$ the product of these two fractions is

$-\dfrac{b}{a} \times \dfrac{d}{c} = -\dfrac{bd}{ac}$, which is the same as the absolute term; hence,

$$\left(x - \frac{b}{a}\right)\left(x + \frac{d}{c}\right) = 0, \text{ and } x = \frac{b}{a} \text{ or } -\frac{d}{c} \quad \text{Ans.}$$

EXAMPLE 4.—Solve for x in the equation $80 - 3x^2 - 2x = -5$.

SOLUTION.—Transposing the known term in the left-hand member, $-3x^2 - 2x = -85$. Dividing by the coefficient of x (which is -3 in this case), the equation becomes $x^2 + \tfrac{2}{3}x = \tfrac{85}{3}$.

From the formula, $x = -\frac{1}{2}(\frac{2}{3} \pm \sqrt{\frac{4}{9} + \frac{340}{3}})$
$= -\frac{1}{2}(\frac{2}{3} \pm \frac{32}{3})$
$= -\frac{17}{3}$ or $\frac{15}{3} = 5$ Ans.

By inspection, the factors of $\frac{85}{3}$ are $\frac{17}{3}$ and 5; but $5 = \frac{15}{3}$; and since $\frac{17}{3} + (-\frac{15}{3}) = \frac{2}{3}$, it is evident that $x^2 + \frac{2}{3}x - \frac{85}{3} = (x + \frac{17}{3})(x - 5) = 0$, and $x = -\frac{17}{3}$ or 5. Ans.

EXAMPLE 5.—Find the value of x in the equation $\dfrac{x}{x + a} = \dfrac{b}{x - b}$.

SOLUTION.—Clearing of fractions, $x(x - b) = b(x + a)$ or $x^2 - bx = bx + ab$. The term bx in the right-hand member must be transposed to the other side so that only the known term shall be on the right. The equation then becomes $x^2 - bx - bx = ab$, or

$$x^2 - 2bx = ab$$

From the formula,

$$x = \frac{1}{2}(2b \pm \sqrt{4b^2 + 4ab})$$
$$= \frac{1}{2}(2b \pm \sqrt{4(b^2 + ab)})$$
$$= \frac{1}{2}(2b \pm 2\sqrt{b^2 + ab})$$
$$= b \pm \sqrt{b^2 + ab} \quad \text{Ans.}$$

This example cannot be solved by inspection, since the required factors, which are $x - b + \sqrt{b^2 + ab}$ and $x - b - \sqrt{b^2 + ab}$ can be determined only by the aid of the formula. That the result is correct may be proved by multiplying the factor. Thus, $(x - b + \sqrt{b^2 + ab})(x - b - \sqrt{b^2 + ab}) = [x - (b - \sqrt{b^2 + ab})] \times [x - (b + \sqrt{b^2 + ab})] = x^2 - (b - \sqrt{b^2 + ab} + b + \sqrt{b^2 + ab})x + (b - \sqrt{b^2 + ab})(b + \sqrt{b^2 + ab})$ (see Art. **35**) $= x^2 - 2bx + b^2 - (b^2 + ab)$ (see Art. **27**, Part 2) $= x^2 - 2bx - ab$, which is the same as the original equation with the absolute term transposed to the first member.

EXAMPLE 6.—Find the positive value of T in the equation

$$2.03222 = 6.1007 - \frac{2,719.78}{T} - \frac{400,215}{T^2}$$

SOLUTION.—Clearing of fractions and transposing,

$$4.06848\,T^2 - 2,719.78\,T = 400,215$$

Dividing by 4.06848, $T^2 - 668.500\,T = 98,369.7$

Applying the formula,

$$T = \frac{1}{2}(668.5 \pm \sqrt{668.5^2 + 4 \times 98,369.7}) = 792.609 \quad \text{Ans.}$$

EXAMPLES FOR PRACTICE

Solve the following equations:

1. $x^2 + 2x = 35$.   Ans. $x = 5$ or -7

2. $9x^2 + 6x = 15$.   Ans. $x = 1$ or $-1\frac{2}{3}$

3. $5x^2 - 24x = 5$.   Ans. $x = 5$ or $-\frac{1}{5}$

4. $x + \dfrac{24}{x-1} = 3x - 4$.   Ans. $x = 5$ or -2

5. $-5x^2 + 9x = 2\frac{1}{4}$.   Ans. $x = \frac{3}{2}$ or $\frac{3}{10}$

6. $\dfrac{x}{x+1} + \dfrac{x+1}{x} = 1\frac{3}{6}$.   Ans. $x = 2$ or -3

7. $\dfrac{9x}{12x+6b} = \dfrac{3b}{4x-2b}$.   Ans. $x = \dfrac{b}{4}\left(3 \pm \sqrt{17}\right)$

8. $\dfrac{2x(a-x)}{3a-2x} = \dfrac{a}{4}$.   Ans. $x = \dfrac{3a}{4}$ or $\dfrac{a}{2}$

EQUATIONS IN THE QUADRATIC FORM

37. An equation is in the *quadratic form* when it contains only two powers of the unknown quantity, *and the exponent of one power is twice as great as the exponent of the other.* Such equations are solved by the rules for quadratics.

EXAMPLE 1.—Solve the equation $x^4 + 4x^2 = 12$.

SOLUTION.—By inspection,

$$x^4 + 4x^2 - 12 = (x^2 - 2)(x^2 + 6) = 0$$

whence, $x^2 = 2$ or -6.

Extracting the square root,

$$x = \pm \sqrt{2} \text{ or } \pm \sqrt{-6} \quad \text{Ans.}$$

EXAMPLE 2.—Solve the equation $x^6 + 20x^3 - 10 = 59$.

SOLUTION.—Transposing the 59,

$$x^6 + 20x^3 - 69 = 0$$

By inspection, $x^6 + 20x^3 - 69 = (x^3 + 23)(x^3 - 3) = 0$;

whence, $x^3 = 3$ or -23

Extracting the cube root,

$$x = \sqrt[3]{3} \text{ or } \sqrt[3]{-23} = -\sqrt[3]{23} \quad \text{Ans.}$$

EXAMPLE 3.—Solve the equation $x^{\frac{2}{5}} + x^{\frac{1}{5}} = 756$.

SOLUTION.—Using the formula, because the factors are not easily found,

$$x^{\frac{1}{5}} = -\tfrac{1}{2}\left(1 \pm \sqrt{1 + 3{,}024}\right) = -\tfrac{1}{2}(1 \pm 55) = -28 \text{ or } 27$$

Now, to obtain a value for x, we must extract the cube root of both members and then raise both members to the 5th power. This will clear x of its fractional exponent.

Extracting the cube root, $x^{\frac{1}{5}} = 3$ or $- \sqrt[3]{28}$.

Raising to the fifth power, $x = 243$ or $- \sqrt[3]{28^5}$. Ans.

EXAMPLES FOR PRACTICE

Solve the following equations:

1.	$x^4 + 4x^2 = 117.$	Ans. $x = \pm 3$ or $\pm \sqrt{-13}$
2.	$x^6 - 2x^3 = 48.$	Ans. $x = 2$ or $- \sqrt[3]{6}$
3.	$x^6 - 8x^3 = 513.$	Ans. $x = 3$ or $- \sqrt[3]{19}$
4.	$x^3 - x^{\frac{3}{2}} = 56.$	Ans. $x = 4$ or $(-7)^{\frac{2}{3}}$

PROBLEMS LEADING TO QUADRATIC EQUATIONS

38. In quadratics, where two answers are obtained by solving equations, it is usually the case that only one answer, the positive value, is required. In some instances, however, the negative value is the one sought. In works treating on higher mathematics, the negative value is used as frequently as the positive value.

EXAMPLE 1.—There are two numbers whose sum is 40, and the sum of their squares is 818. What are the numbers?

SOLUTION.—Let $x =$ one number, and $40 - x =$ the other number.

Then, by the conditions, $x^2 + (40 - x)^2 = 818$

whence, $\qquad x^2 + 1{,}600 - 80x + x^2 = 818$

Combining, $\qquad\qquad 2x^2 - 80x = -782$

or $\qquad\qquad\qquad x^2 - 40x = -391$

From the formula, $x = \tfrac{1}{2}\left(40 \pm \sqrt{40^2 - 4 \times 391}\right) = 23$ or **17**

whence, $\qquad\qquad x = 23$ or 17 $\Big\}$ Ans.

and $\qquad\qquad 40 - x = 17$ or 23

Both answers fulfil the conditions.

EXAMPLE 2.—An iron bar weighs 36 pounds. If it had been 1 foot longer, each foot would have weighed $\frac{1}{2}$ a pound less. Find the length of the bar.

SOLUTION.—Let $x =$ the length of the bar in feet.

Then, $\dfrac{36}{x} =$ the weight per foot, and

$\dfrac{36}{x+1} =$ the weight per foot if the bar were 1 foot longer.

By the conditions, $\dfrac{36}{x} - \dfrac{36}{x+1} = \frac{1}{2}$

Clearing of fractions, $72x + 72 - 72x = x^2 + x$
or $x^2 + x - 72 = 0$

By inspection, $x^2 + x - 72 = (x+9)(x-8) = 0$
whence, $x = 8$ ft. or -9 ft.   Ans.

PROOF.— $\dfrac{36}{8} = 4\frac{1}{2}$; $\dfrac{36}{8+1} = 4$; $4\frac{1}{2} - 4 = \dfrac{1}{2}$

Or $\dfrac{36}{-9} = -4$; $\dfrac{36}{-9+1} = -4\frac{1}{2}$; $-4 - (-4\frac{1}{2}) = \dfrac{1}{2}$

Only the positive value is required, although both values will satisfy the equation.

EXAMPLE 3.—A number of men ordered a yacht to be built for $6,300. Each man was to pay the same amount, but two of them withdrew, making it necessary for those remaining to advance $200 more than they otherwise would have done. How many men were there at first ?

SOLUTION.—Let $x =$ the number of men at first.

Then, $\dfrac{6,300}{x} =$ what each was to have paid, and

$\dfrac{6,300}{x-2} =$ what each finally paid.

By the conditions, $\dfrac{6,300}{x-2} - \dfrac{6,300}{x} = 200$

Clearing of fractions and combining,

$$200x^2 - 400x = 12,600$$
or $x^2 - 2x - 63 = 0$

By inspection, $x^2 - 2x - 63 = (x-9)(x+7) = 0$
whence, $x = 9$ or -7 Ans.

PROOF.— $\dfrac{6,300}{9} = 700$; $\dfrac{6,300}{9-2} = 900$; $900 - 700 = 200$

Or $\dfrac{6,300}{-7} = -900$; $\dfrac{6,300}{-7-2} = -700$; $-700 - (-900) = 200$

Only the positive value can be used.

EXAMPLE 4.—A and B start at the same time to travel 150 miles. A travels 3 miles an hour faster than B, and finishes his journey $8\frac{1}{3}$ hours before him. How many miles did each travel per hour ?

SOLUTION.—Let x = number of miles A traveled per hour, and

$$x - 3 = \text{number of miles B traveled per hour.}$$

Then, $\dfrac{150}{x}$ = the time in which A performs the journey, and

$\dfrac{150}{x-3}$ = the time in which B performs the journey.

By the conditions, $\dfrac{150}{x-3} - \dfrac{150}{x} = 8\frac{1}{3}$

Clearing of fractions and combining,

$$25x^2 - 75x = 1,350$$

or $$x^2 - 3x - 54 = 0$$

By inspection, $x^2 - 3x - 54 = (x-9)(x+6) = 0$;

whence, $x = 9 \text{ or } -6$

and $x - 3 = 6 \text{ or } -9$

Using the positive values, A traveled 9 miles per hour and B traveled 6 miles per hour. Ans.

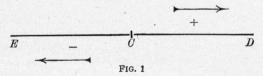

FIG. 1

39. As an illustration of the use of the negative values, consider the following explanation, which refers to the preceding example. In Fig. 1 let C be the starting point. Call any advance in the direction of the upper arrow, or from C toward D, positive, and in the opposite direction, negative. Let E and D be each 150 miles from C. Suppose that a train of cars 150 miles long has one end at C and the other end at D, and that the train is moving in the direction from C to E at the rate of 15 miles per hour. Now, if A and B start toward D, running on the train at the rate of 9 and 6 miles per hour, respectively, while the train moves 15 miles per hour toward E, the rate of travel of A toward D is $9 - 15 = -6$ miles per hour, and of B, $6 - 15 = -9$ miles per hour. It is now evident that A is traveling toward D 3 miles per hour faster than B. When A has traveled 150 miles, in other words, when he has reached the end of the train, B has reached the point E; he has traveled negatively farther than A, but if he travels to the end of the train, it will take him $8\frac{1}{3}$ hours longer than it did A.

The preceding paragraph is also an illustration of the statement, that of two negative values, the one which has the less value numerically is the greater.

EQUATIONS CONTAINING TWO UNKNOWN QUANTITIES

40. In the third problem in Art. **25,** it was shown how, under certain conditions, more than one unknown quantity *in an example* may be represented *in an equation*, by expressing the value of each quantity in terms of x, thus producing only the *one unknown quantity x in the equation.*

Sometimes, however, each quantity is represented by a different letter, as x, y, or z, in which case, it is necessary to have as many equations as there are unknown quantities, in order to effect a solution. For example, if it were required to find the value of x in the equation $x + y = 10$, x and y being unknown quantities, we should have $x = 10 - y$, x being still undetermined because its value is in terms of the unknown quantity y. There must be another equation, therefore, expressing some other relation between the unknown quantities x and y, in order to fix their values. The equations which fix the values of the unknown quantities must be *independent and simultaneous.*

41. Independent equations are those which express different relations between the unknown quantities. Thus, $x + y = 4$, and $xy = 6$ express different relations between x and y, and are independent. But $x + y = 4$, and $3x + 3y = 12$, are not independent, because, by dividing both members of the second equation by 3, it reduces to the first equation, and thus expresses the *same* relations between the unknown quantities

42. **Simultaneous equations** are such as will be satisfied (Art. **18**) by substituting the same values for the same unknown quantities in each equation.

43. Equations containing more than one unknown quantity are solved by so combining them as to obtain a single equation containing but one unknown quantity. This process is called **elimination.** In what follows, equations containing two unknown quantities will be considered.

44. **To eliminate by substitution:**

Rule.—*From one equation, find the value of one of the unknown quantities in terms of the other. Substitute this value for the same unknown quantity in the other equation.*

EXAMPLE.—Solve the equations

$$2x + 3y = 18 \qquad (1)$$
$$3x - 2y = 1 \qquad (2)$$

SOLUTION.—It will be more convenient to first find the value of x in (2), since, after transposing $-2y$ to the second member, it will become positive.

Transposing $-2y$ in (2), $3x = 1 + 2y$.

Dividing both members by 3,

$$x = \frac{1 + 2y}{3} \qquad (3)$$

This gives the value of x in terms of y.

Substituting this value of x for the x in (1),

$$\frac{2(1 + 2y)}{3} + 3y = 18$$

Removing the parenthesis,

$$\frac{2 + 4y}{3} + 3y = 18$$

Clearing of fractions, $2 + 4y + 9y = 54$

Transposing the 2 and uniting the $4y$ and $9y$,

$$13y = 52$$

whence, $\qquad\qquad y = 4$ Ans.

Now, having the value of y, we may substitute it for y in any of the above equations containing both x and y, and thus obtain a value for x.

Substituting this value in equation (3),

$$x = \frac{1 + 2 \times 4}{3}$$

whence,　　　　　　　$x = 3$　Ans.

45. To eliminate by comparison :

Rule.—*From each equation find the value of one of the unknown quantities in terms of the other. Form a new equation by placing these two values equal to each other and solve.*

Elimination by comparison depends upon the principle that quantities which are equal to the same or two equal quantities are equal to each other. Thus, if $y = 2$ and $x = 2$, y is evidently equal to x.

EXAMPLE.—Solve the same equations as before,

$$2x + 3y = 18 \qquad (1)$$
$$3x - 2y = 1 \qquad (2)$$

SOLUTION.—First obtain the value of x in each equation, it being more convenient to obtain in this case than y.

Transposing $3y$ in (1),　　$2x = 18 - 3y$

or　　　　　　　　　$x = \dfrac{18 - 3y}{2}$　　(3)

Transposing $- 2y$ in (2),　　$3x = 1 + 2y$

or　　　　　　　　　$x = \dfrac{1 + 2y}{3}$　　(4)

Placing the values of x in (3) and (4) equal to each other,

$$\frac{18 - 3y}{2} = \frac{1 + 2y}{3}$$

Clearing of fractions,　　$54 - 9y = 2 + 4y$

Transposing and uniting terms,

$$- 13y = - 52$$

whence,　　　　　　　$y = 4$　Ans.

Substituting this value in (4),

$$x = \frac{1 + 8}{3} = 3 \quad \text{Ans.}$$

46. **To eliminate by addition or subtraction :**

Rule.—*Select the unknown quantity to be eliminated, and multiply the equations by such numbers as will make the coefficients of this quantity equal in the resulting equations. If the signs of the terms having the same coefficient are alike, subtract one equation from the other; if unlike, add the two equations.*

It is evident that this will not destroy the equality, because adding or subtracting two equations is equivalent to adding the same quantity to, or subtracting it from, both members.

EXAMPLE.—Solve the same equations as before,

$$2x + 3y = 18 \qquad (1)$$
$$3x - 2y = 1 \qquad (2)$$

FIRST SOLUTION.—Since the signs of the terms containing x in each equation are alike, x may be eliminated by subtraction. If the first equation be multiplied by 3 and the second by 2, the coefficients of x in each equation will become equal. Hence,

Multiplying (1) by 3,	$6x + 9y = 54$	(3)
Multiplying (2) by 2,	$6x - 4y = 2$	(4)
Subtracting (4) from (3),	$13y = 52$	
whence,	$y = 4$ Ans.	

Substituting this value of y for the y in (2),

	$3x - 8 = 1$
Transposing,	$3x = 9$
or	$x = 3$ Ans.

SECOND SOLUTION.—

$$2x + 3y = 18 \qquad (1)$$
$$3x - 2y = 1 \qquad (2)$$

Since the signs of the terms containing y in each equation are unlike, y may be eliminated by addition.

Multiplying (1) by 2,	$4x + 6y = 36$	(3)
Multiplying (2) by 3,	$9x - 6y = 3$	(4)
Adding (3) and (4),	$13x = 39$	
whence,	$x = 3$ Ans.	
Substituting in (1),	$6 + 3y = 18$	
	$3y = 12$	
	$y = 4$ Ans.	

MISCELLANEOUS EXAMPLES

47. From the foregoing it will be seen that any one, of the three methods of elimination can be applied to the solution of equations. The student must use his judgment as to which is the best one to apply in any case.

EXAMPLE 1.—Solve the equations

$$\frac{3}{x} + \frac{1}{y} = \frac{5}{4} \qquad (1)$$

$$\frac{2}{x} - \frac{3}{y} = -1 \qquad (2)$$

SOLUTION.—Multiplying (1) by 3,

$$\frac{9}{x} + \frac{3}{y} = \frac{15}{4} \qquad (3)$$

Adding (2) and (3),

$$\frac{11}{x} = \frac{15}{4} - 1 = \frac{11}{4}$$

Clearing of fractions $\qquad 44 = 11x$

or $\qquad\qquad\qquad\qquad x = 4 \ $ Ans.

Substituting this value of x in (1),

$$\frac{3}{4} + \frac{1}{y} = \frac{5}{4}$$

Clearing of fractions, $\qquad 3y + 4 = 5y$

Transposing, $\qquad\qquad\quad -2y = -4$

or $\qquad\qquad\qquad\qquad\quad y = 2 \ $ Ans.

EXAMPLE 2.—Solve the equations

$$x + 36y = 900 \qquad (1)$$
$$36x + y = 1{,}320 \qquad (2)$$

SOLUTION.—Adding (1) and (2),

$$37x + 37y = 2{,}220 \qquad (3)$$

Dividing by 37, $\qquad\quad x + y = 60 \qquad (4)$

Subtracting (4) from (1), $\quad 35y = 840$

$$y = 24 \ \text{Ans.}$$

Substituting this value in (4),

$$x + 24 = 60$$
$$x = 36 \ \text{Ans.}$$

EXAMPLE 3.—Solve the equations

$$\frac{m}{x} + \frac{n}{y} = a \qquad (1)$$

$$\frac{n}{x} + \frac{m}{y} = b \qquad (2)$$

SOLUTION.—Multiplying (1) by m,

$$\frac{m^2}{x} + \frac{mn}{y} = am \qquad (3)$$

Multiplying (2) by n, $\qquad \frac{n^2}{x} + \frac{mn}{y} = bn \qquad (4)$

Subtracting (4) from (3),

$$\frac{m^2 - n^2}{x} = am - bn$$

Clearing of fractions, $m^2 - n^2 = (am - bn)x$

whence, $\qquad\qquad x = \frac{m^2 - n^2}{am - bn}$ Ans.

Multiplying (1) by n, $\qquad \frac{mn}{x} + \frac{n^2}{y} = an \qquad (5)$

Multiplying (2) by m, $\qquad \frac{mn}{x} + \frac{m^2}{y} = bm \qquad (6)$

Subtracting (6) from (5),

$$\frac{n^2 - m^2}{y} = an - bm$$

Clearing of fractions, $n^2 - m^2 = (an - bm)y$

whence, $\qquad\qquad y = \frac{n^2 - m^2}{an - bm}$, or $\frac{m^2 - n^2}{bm - an}$ Ans.

EXAMPLES FOR PRACTICE

Solve the following equations:

1. $3x + 7y = 33.$
   $2x + 4y = 20.$
   Ans. $\begin{cases} x = 4 \\ y = 3 \end{cases}$

2. $8y + 12x = 116.$
   $2x - y = 3.$
   Ans. $\begin{cases} x = 5 \\ y = 7 \end{cases}$

3. $ax + by = m.$
   $cx + dy = n.$
   Ans. $\begin{cases} x = \dfrac{dm - bn}{ad - bc} \\ y = \dfrac{an - cm}{ad - bc} \end{cases}$

4. $\dfrac{a}{x} + \dfrac{b}{y} = m.$

$\dfrac{c}{x} + \dfrac{d}{y} = n.$

Ans. $\begin{cases} x = \dfrac{ad - bc}{dm - bn} \\ y = \dfrac{bc - ad}{cm - an} \end{cases}$

5. $\dfrac{6}{x} - \dfrac{3}{y} = 4.$

$\dfrac{8}{x} + \dfrac{15}{y} = -1.$

Ans. $\begin{cases} x = 2 \\ y = -3 \end{cases}$

QUADRATIC EQUATIONS CONTAINING TWO UNKNOWN QUANTITIES

48. The methods of solving will be illustrated by the solution of a few examples.

Case I.—*When elimination may be performed by the methods given for simple equations in Arts.* **44–46.**

EXAMPLE 1.—Solve the equations

$$x^2 + y^2 = 13 \qquad (1)$$
$$x + y = 1 \qquad (2)$$

SOLUTION.—Transposing the x in (2),

$$y = 1 - x \qquad (3)$$

Substituting the value of y in (1),

$$x^2 + (1 - x)^2 = 13$$

or $\qquad x^2 + 1 - 2x + x^2 = 13$

Transposing and uniting terms,

$$2x^2 - 2x = 12$$

or $\qquad x^2 - x - 6 = 0$

By inspection, $x^2 - x - 6 = (x - 3)(x + 2) = 0$

whence, $\qquad x = 3 \text{ or } -2$

Now, two values must be found for y which will satisfy the equations when $x = 3$ and $x = -2$.

Substituting these values of x in (3),

when $x = 3$, $y = -2$
when $x = -2$, $y = 3$ Ans.

This is the form in which answers to simultaneous quadratic equations should always be written.

EXAMPLE 2.—Solve the equations

$$4x^2 - 3y^2 = -11 \qquad (1)$$
$$11x^2 + 5y^2 = 301 \qquad (2)$$

SOLUTION.—Multiplying (1) by 5,

$$20x^2 - 15y^2 = -55 \qquad (3)$$

Multiplying (2) by (3),

$$33x^2 + 15y^2 = 903 \qquad (4)$$

Adding (3) and (4), $\qquad 53x^2 = 848$

or $\qquad\qquad\qquad\qquad x^2 = 16$

Extracting the square root, $\quad x = \pm 4$
Substituting $+4$ for x in (2),

$$11 \times 16 + 5y^2 = 301,$$
or $\qquad\qquad\qquad 5y^2 = 125$
$$y^2 = 25$$
$$y = \pm 5$$

Substituting -4 for x in (2) will evidently give the same result, since $(-4)^2 = 16$, the same as 4^2. Hence,

$$\left. \begin{matrix} \text{when } x = 4, y = \pm 5 \\ \text{when } x = -4, y = \pm 5 \end{matrix} \right\} \text{ Ans.}$$

49. Case II.—*When the equations may be so combined or reduced as to produce an equation having for the first member an expression of the form $x^2 + 2xy + y^2$ or $x^2 - 2xy + y^2$.*

No rule can be given for solving examples under this case. The student must depend upon his own ingenuity.

EXAMPLE 1.—Solve the equations

$$x^2 + y^2 = 25 \qquad (1)$$
$$xy = 12 \qquad (2)$$

SOLUTION.—Multiplying (2) by 2,

$$2xy = 24 \qquad (3)$$
Adding (1) and (3), $\quad x^2 + 2xy + y^2 = 49 \qquad (4)$
Subtracting (3) from (1),

$$x^2 - 2xy + y^2 = 1 \qquad (5)$$

Extracting the square root of both terms of (4), see Art. **20,** Part 2,

$$x + y = \pm 7 \qquad (6)$$

Extracting the square root of both terms of (5),

$$x - y = \pm 1 \qquad (7)$$

This gives two simple equations, from which either x or y may be eliminated by addition or subtraction. Adding (6) and (7), the first member of the new equation will be $2x$, and the second member may have four values as follows:

$$7 + 1, \ 7 - 1, \ -7 + 1 \text{ or } -7 - 1$$

or $2x = 8, \ 6, \ -6 \text{ or } -8$

whence, $x = 4, 3, \ -3 \text{ or } -4$

By substituting these values in (2) we have for the corresponding values of y, $y = 3, 4, -4,$ or -3.

These values may also be obtained by subtracting (7) from (6). The answers would be written,

$$\left. \begin{array}{l} \text{when} \quad x = 4, y = 3; \ x = 3, y = 4 \\ \qquad x = -3, y = -4; \ x = -4, y = -3 \end{array} \right\} \text{ Ans.}$$

NOTE.—In solving examples under this case, the object is always to produce two equations, one with $x+y$ and one with $x-y$ for the first member, from which the value of x or y can easily be found.

EXAMPLE 2.—Solve the equations

$$x^3 + y^3 = 133 \qquad (1)$$
$$x^2 - xy + y^2 = 19 \qquad (2)$$

SOLUTION.— $x^3 + y^3$ is divisible by $x + y$ (see Art. **32**, Part 2); hence, $x^3 + y^3 = (x + y)(x^2 - xy + y^2) = 133$. Transposing the first factor to the second member,

$$x^2 - xy + y^2 = \frac{133}{x + y}$$

Therefore, $\dfrac{133}{x + y} = 19$

and $x + y = \frac{133}{19} = 7 \qquad (3)$

This gives at once an equation with $x + y$ for the first member. To obtain a value for $x - y$, it will be noticed that the first member of (2) lacks only one $-xy$ of being $x^2 - 2xy + y^2$, from which $x - y$ may be obtained; hence, proceed to obtain a value for $-xy$, to add to (2).

Squaring (3), $x^2 + 2xy + y^2 = 49 \qquad (4)$

Writing (2) under (4), $x^2 \ \ - xy + y^2 = 19$

and subtracting, $3xy \ \ \ \ = 30$

or $xy \ \ \ \ = 10 \qquad (5)$

Subtracting (5) from (2),

$$x^2 - 2xy + y^2 = 9$$

Extracting the square root (see Art. **20**, Part 2),

$$x - y = \pm 3 \qquad (6)$$

Adding (6) and (3), $2x = 10 \text{ or } 4$

                     $x = 5 \text{ or } 2$

Subtracting (6) from (3), $2y = 4 \text{ or } 10$

                     $y = 2 \text{ or } 5$

Or, solving (5) for x, $\qquad\qquad x = \dfrac{10}{y}$

Substituting the value of x in (3),

$$\frac{10}{y} + y = 7$$

Clearing of fractions and changing signs,

$$y^2 - 7y = -10$$

Solving for y, $\qquad\qquad y = 5 \text{ or } 2$

Substituting their values in (3),

$$x = 2 \text{ or } 5$$

Hence, when $\qquad\qquad \left.\begin{array}{l} x = 5, y = 2 \\ x = 2, y = 5 \end{array}\right\}$ Ans.

EXAMPLES FOR PRACTICE

Solve the following equations:

1. $\left.\begin{array}{l} x^2 + y^2 = 29. \\ x + y = 3. \end{array}\right\}$ Ans. $\left\{\begin{array}{l} x = 5, \ y = -2 \\ x = -2, \ y = 5 \end{array}\right.$

2. $\left.\begin{array}{l} 2x^2 + y^2 = 9. \\ 5x^2 + 6y^2 = 26. \end{array}\right\}$ Ans. $\left\{\begin{array}{l} x = 2, y = \pm 1, \\ x = -2, y = \pm 1 \end{array}\right.$

3. $\left.\begin{array}{l} x + y = -1. \\ xy = -56. \end{array}\right\}$ Ans. $\left\{\begin{array}{l} x = 7, \ y = -8 \\ x = -8, \ y = 7 \end{array}\right.$

PROBLEMS LEADING TO EQUATIONS WITH TWO UNKNOWN QUANTITIES

50. A few examples involving equations with two unknown quantities will now be given. The student should pay particular attention to the manner in which the equations are formed from the conditions given.

EXAMPLE 1.—A certain fraction becomes equal to $\frac{1}{2}$ if 3 is added to its numerator, and equal to $\frac{2}{7}$ if 3 is added to its denominator. What is the fraction?

SOLUTION.—Let $\dfrac{x}{y}$ = the required fraction.

By the conditions, $\qquad\qquad \dfrac{x+3}{y} = \dfrac{1}{2}$

and $\qquad\qquad\qquad\qquad \dfrac{x}{y+3} = \dfrac{2}{7}$

Solving these equations, $x = 6$ and $y = 18$

That is, the fraction is $\frac{6}{18}$. Ans.

EXAMPLE 2.—A crew can row 20 miles in 2 hours down stream, and 12 miles in 3 hours up stream. Required, the rate per hour of the current, and the rate per hour at which the crew would row in still water.

Let $x =$ rate per hour of crew in still water

and $y =$ rate per hour of current.

Then, $x + y =$ rate per hour rowing down stream

and $x - y =$ rate per hour rowing up stream.

Since they row 20 miles in two hours down stream, in one hour, they would row $\frac{20}{2} = 10$ miles, or at the rate of 10 miles per hour. Also, in rowing up stream, they would row at the rate of $\frac{12}{3} = 4$ miles per hour.

Consequently,	$x + y = 10$	(1)
	$x - y = 4$	(2)
Adding,	$2x = 14$	
or	$x = 7$	
Subtracting,	$2y = 6$	
or	$y = 3$	

Hence, the rate of the crew is 7 miles per hour, and of the current, 3 miles per hour. Ans.

EXAMPLE 3.—A wine merchant has two kinds of wine, which cost 72 cents and 40 cents a quart, respectively. How much of each must he take to make a mixture of 50 quarts worth 60 cents a quart ?

SOLUTION.—Let $x =$ required number of quarts at 72 cents

and $y =$ required number of quarts at 40 cents.

Then, $72x =$ cost in cents of the first kind,

$40y =$ cost in cents of the second kind

and $60 \times 50 = 3,000 =$ cost in cents of the mixture.

By the conditions, $x + y = 50$

and $72x + 40y = 3,000$

Solving, $x = 31\frac{1}{4}$ qt. and $y = 18\frac{3}{4}$ qt. Ans.

NOTE.—The equation, $x^2 \pm px = \pm q$ is equivalent to the four equations

$$x^2 + px = \quad q, \text{ or } x^2 + px - q = 0 \qquad (1)$$
$$x^2 - px = \quad q, \text{ or } x^2 - px - q = 0 \qquad (2)$$
$$x^2 + px = -q, \text{ or } x^2 + px + q = 0 \qquad (3)$$
$$x^2 - px = -q, \text{ or } x^2 - px + q = 0 \qquad (4)$$

EQUATION (1).—By Art. **32,** the roots of equation (1) are $-\frac{1}{2}(p + \sqrt{p^2 + 4q})$ and $-\frac{1}{2}(p - \sqrt{p^2 + 4q})$. Applying the principle of Art. **33,** $[x + \frac{1}{2}(p + \sqrt{p^2 + 4q})] \times [x + \frac{1}{2}(p - \sqrt{p^2 + 4q})] = x^2 + px - q$, as here shown by actual multiplication.

$$
\begin{array}{l}
x + \tfrac{1}{2}p + \tfrac{1}{2}\sqrt{p^2 + 4q} \\
\underline{x + \tfrac{1}{2}p - \tfrac{1}{2}\sqrt{p^2 + 4q}} \\
x^2 + \tfrac{1}{2}px + \tfrac{1}{2}x\sqrt{p^2 + 4q} \\
\quad + \tfrac{1}{2}px \qquad\qquad\qquad + \tfrac{1}{4}p^2 + \tfrac{1}{4}p\sqrt{p^2 + 4q} \\
\qquad\qquad - \tfrac{1}{2}x\sqrt{p^2 + 4q} \qquad - \tfrac{1}{4}p\sqrt{p^2 + 4q} - \tfrac{1}{4}p^2 - q \\
\overline{x^2 + px \qquad 0 \qquad + \tfrac{1}{4}p^2 \qquad 0 \qquad - \tfrac{1}{4}p^2 - q} \\
\text{or } x^2 + px - q
\end{array}
$$

REMARK.— $\tfrac{1}{2}\sqrt{p^2 + 4q} \times -\tfrac{1}{2}\sqrt{p^2 + 4q} = \tfrac{1}{2}(p^2 + 4q)^{\frac{1}{2}} \times -\tfrac{1}{2}(p^2 + 4q)^{\frac{1}{2}} = -\tfrac{1}{4}(p^2 + 4q) = -\tfrac{1}{4}p^2 - q.$

EQUATION (2).—The roots of equation (2) are $\tfrac{1}{2}(p + \sqrt{p^2 + 4q})$ and $\tfrac{1}{2}(p - \sqrt{p^2 + 4q})$, and $[x - \tfrac{1}{2}(p + \sqrt{p^2 + 4q})] \times [x - \tfrac{1}{2}(p - \sqrt{p^2 + 4q})] = x^2 - px - q.$

$$
\begin{array}{l}
x - \tfrac{1}{2}p - \tfrac{1}{2}\sqrt{p^2 + 4q} \\
\underline{x - \tfrac{1}{2}p + \tfrac{1}{2}\sqrt{p^2 + 4q}} \\
x^2 - \tfrac{1}{2}px - \tfrac{1}{2}x\sqrt{p^2 + 4q} \\
\quad - \tfrac{1}{2}px \qquad\qquad\qquad + \tfrac{1}{4}p^2 + \tfrac{1}{4}p\sqrt{p^2 + 4q} \\
\qquad\qquad + \tfrac{1}{2}x\sqrt{p^2 + 4q} \qquad - \tfrac{1}{4}p\sqrt{p^2 + 4q} - \tfrac{1}{4}p^2 - q \\
\overline{x^2 - px \qquad 0 \qquad + \tfrac{1}{4}p^2 \qquad 0 \qquad - \tfrac{1}{4}p^2 - q} \\
\text{or } x^2 - px - q
\end{array}
$$

EQUATIONS (3) AND (4).—Equations (3) and (4) can be produced in the same manner, by multiplying its roots, which are : for (3), $-\tfrac{1}{2}(p + \sqrt{p^2 - 4q})$ and $-\tfrac{1}{2}(p - \sqrt{p^2 - 4q})$; for (4), $\tfrac{1}{2}(p + \sqrt{p^2 - 4q})$ and $\tfrac{1}{2}(p - \sqrt{p^2 - 4q})$. Since these are all the cases that can arise, the formula of Art. **32** is correct.

LOGARITHMS

EXPONENTS

1. By the use of logarithms, the processes of multiplication, division, involution, and evolution are greatly shortened, and some operations may be performed that would be impossible without them. Ordinary logarithms cannot be applied to addition and subtraction.

2. The **logarithm** of a number is that *exponent* by which some fixed number, called the **base,** must be affected in order to equal the number. Any number may be taken as the base. Suppose we choose 4. Then the logarithm of 16 is 2, because 2 is the exponent by which 4 (the base) must be affected in order to equal 16, since $4^2 = 16$. In this case, instead of reading 4^2 as 4 square, read it 4 exponent 2. With the same base, the logarithms of 64 and 8 would be 3 and 1.5, respectively, since $4^3 = 64$, and $4^{1.5} = 4^{\frac{3}{2}} = 8$. In these cases, as in the preceding, read 4^3 and $4^{1.5}$ as 4 exponent 3, and 4 exponent 1.5, respectively.

3. Although the base *can* be any positive number except 1, and a table of logarithms calculated, but two bases have been employed. For all arithmetical operations (except addition and subtraction), the logarithms used are called the **Briggs,** or **common,** logarithms, and the base used is 10. In abstract mathematical analysis, the logarithms used are variously called **hyperbolic, Napierian,** or **natural** logarithms, and the base is $2.718281828+$. The common logarithm of any number may be converted into a Napierian logarithm by multiplying the common logarithm by $2.30258508+$, which is usually abbreviated to 2.3026, and sometimes to 2.3. Only the common system of logarithms will be considered in this Course.

§ 5

4. Since in the common system the base is 10, it follows that, since $10^1 = 10$; $10^2 = 100$; $10^3 = 1,000$; etc., the logarithm (exponent) of 10 is 1; of 100 is 2; of 1,000 is 3; etc. For the sake of brevity in writing, the words "logarithm of" are abbreviated to "log." Thus, instead of writing logarithm of $100 = 2$, write log $100 = 2$. When speaking, however, the words for which "log" stands should always be pronounced in full.

5. From the above it will be seen (see *Elementary Algebra*, Arts. **71** and **132**) that, when the base is 10,

since $10^0 =$ 1, the exponent $0 = \log$ 1;

since $10^1 =$ 10, the exponent $1 = \log$ 10;

since $10^2 =$ 100, the exponent $2 = \log$ 100;

since $10^3 = 1,000$, the exponent $3 = \log 1,000$; etc.

Also,

since $10^{-1} = \frac{1}{10} = .1$,   the exponent $-1 = \log .1$;

since $10^{-2} = \frac{1}{100} = .01$, the exponent $-2 = \log .01$;

since $10^{-3} = \frac{1}{1000} = .001$, the exponent $-3 = \log .001$; etc.

From this it will be seen that the logarithms of exact powers of 10 and of decimals like .1, .01, and .001 are the whole numbers 1, 2, 3, etc., and -1, -2, -3, etc., respectively. *Only numbers consisting of 1 and one or more ciphers have whole numbers for logarithms.*

6. Now, it is evident that to produce a number between 1 and 10, the exponent of 10 must be a fraction; to produce a number between 10 and 100, it must be 1 plus a fraction; to produce a number between 100 and 1,000, it must be 2 plus a fraction, etc. Hence, the logarithm of any number between 1 and 10 is a fraction; of any number between 10 and 100, 1 plus a fraction; of any number between 100 and 1,000, 2 plus a fraction; etc. A logarithm, therefore, usually consists of two parts: a whole number, called the **characteristic,** and a fraction called the **mantissa.** The mantissa is always expressed as a decimal. For example, to produce 20, 10 must have an exponent of *approximately* 1.30103, or

$10^{1.30103} = 20$, very nearly, the degree of exactness depending on the number of decimal places used. Hence, log $20 =$ 1.30103, 1 being the characteristic and .30103 the mantissa.

7. Referring to the second part of the table, Art. **5,** it is clear that the logarithms of all numbers less than 1 are negative, the logarithms of those between 1 and .1 being $- 1$ plus a fraction. For, since log $.1 = - 1$, the logarithms of .2, .3, etc. (which are all greater than .1, but less than 1) must be greater than $- 1$; i. e., they must equal $- 1$ *plus* a fraction. For the same reason, to produce a number between .1 and .01 the logarithm (exponent of 10) would be equal to $- 2$ plus a fraction, and for a number between .01 and .001 it would be equal to $- 3$ plus a fraction. Hence, the logarithm of any number between 1 and .1 has a negative characteristic of 1 and a positive mantissa; of a number between .1 and .01, a negative characteristic of 2, and a positive mantissa; of a number between .01 and .001, a negative characteristic of 3 and a positive mantissa; of a number between .001 and .0001, a negative characteristic of 4 and a positive mantissa; etc. *The negative characteristics are distinguished from the positive by the $-$ written over the characteristic.* Thus, $\bar{3}$ indicates that 3 is negative.

It must be remembered that in all cases the mantissa is positive. Thus the logarithm 1.30103 means $+ 1 + .30103$, and the logarithm $\bar{1}.30103$ means $- 1 + .30103$. Were the minus sign written in front of the characteristic, it would indicate that the entire logarithm was negative. Thus, $- 1.30103 = - 1 - .30103$.

8. Rules for Characteristic.—From Art. **7,** it follows that:

I. *For a number greater than 1, the characteristic is one less than the number of integral places in the number.*

By "integral places" is meant the figures (including ciphers) to the left of the decimal point.

II. *For a number wholly decimal, the characteristic is negative, and is numerically one greater than the number of ciphers between the decimal point and the first digit of the decimal.*

For example, the characteristics of the logarithms of 256, 31.24, 7.53, and 1,728.0036 are 2, 1, 0, and 3, respectively, or *one less* than the number of integral places in each case; the characteristics of the logarithms of .0005, .0674, and .50072 are $\overline{4}$, $\overline{2}$, and $\overline{1}$, respectively, or numerically *one greater* than the number of ciphers immediately following the decimal point. It will be noticed that in the last number there are no ciphers, and the characteristic is $0 + \overline{1} = \overline{1}$.

THE LOGARITHMIC TABLE

TO FIND THE LOGARITHM OF A NUMBER

9. To aid in obtaining the mantissas of logarithms, *tables of logarithms* have been calculated, some of which are very elaborate and convenient. In the Table of Logarithms accompanying this text, the mantissas of the logarithms of numbers from 1 to 9,999 are given to five places of decimals, and the mantissas of logarithms of larger numbers can be found by interpolation. It will be noticed that the table contains the *mantissas only;* the characteristics must be determined, in all cases, by applying the rules given in the preceding article.

The table depends on the principle, which will be explained later, that all numbers having the same figures in the same order have their mantissas alike, without regard to the position of the decimal point, which affects the characteristic only. To illustrate, if log 206 = 2.31387, then,

$$\log 20.6 \ = 1.31387; \quad \log .206 \ = \overline{1}.31387;$$
$$\log \ 2.06 = \ .31387; \quad \log .0206 = \overline{2}.31387; \text{ etc.}$$

10. To find the logarithm of a number not having more than four figures:

Rule.—*Find the first three significant figures of the number whose logarithm is desired, in the left-hand column; find the fourth figure in the column at the top (or bottom) of the page; and in the column under (or above) this figure, and opposite the first three figures previously found, will be the mantissa, or* *decimal part, of the logarithm. The characteristic being found as described in Art.* **8,** *write it at the left of the mantissa, and the resulting expression will be the logarithm of the required number.*

11. EXAMPLE.—Find the logarithm (*a*) of 476; (*b*) of 25.47; (*c*) of 1.073; and (*d*) of .06313.

SOLUTION.—(*a*) In order to economize space and make the labor of finding the logarithms easier, the first two figures of the mantissa are given only in the column headed 0. The last three figures of the mantissa opposite 476 in the column headed N. (N. stands for number), page 9, of the tables, are 761, found in the column headed 0; glancing upwards, we find the first two figures of the mantissa, viz., 67. The characteristic is 2; hence, log 476 = 2.67761. Ans.

NOTE.—Since all numbers in the table are decimal fractions, the decimal point is omitted throughout; this is customary in all tables of logarithms.

(*b*) To find the logarithm of 25.47, we find the first three figures 254 in the column headed N. on page 5, and on the same horizontal line, under the column headed 7 (the fourth figure of the given number), will be found the last three figures of the mantissa, viz., 603. The first two figures are evidently 40, and the characteristic is 1; hence, log 25.47 = 1.40603. Ans.

(*c*) For 1.073, the last three figures of the mantissa are found in the usual manner in the column headed 3, opposite 107 in the column headed N. on page 2, to be 060. It will be noticed that these figures are printed *060, the star meaning that instead of glancing *upwards* in the column headed 0, and taking 02 for the first two figures, we must glance *downwards* and take the two figures opposite the number 108 in the left-hand column, i. e., 03. The characteristic being 0, log 1.073 = 0.03060, or more simply, .03060.

(*d*) For .06313, the last three figures of the mantissa are found, opposite 631, in column headed 3 on page 12, to be 024. In this case, the first two figures occur in the same row, and are 80. Since the characteristic is $\bar{2}$, log .06313 = $\bar{2}$.80024. Ans.

12. If the original number contains but one digit (a cipher is not a digit) annex mentally two ciphers to the right of the digit; if the number contains but two digits (with no ciphers between, as in 4008) annex mentally one cipher on the right, before seeking the mantissa. Thus, if the logarithm of 7 is wanted, seek the mantissa for 700, which is .84510; or, if the logarithm of 48 is wanted, seek the mantissa for 480, which is .68124.   Or, find the mantissas of logarithms of numbers between 0 and 100, on the first page of the tables.

The process of finding the logarithm of a number from the table is technically called **taking out the logarithm.**

13.   To take out the logarithm of a number consisting of more than four figures, it is inexpedient to use more than five figures of the number when using five-place logarithms (the logarithms given in the accompanying table are five-place).   Hence, if the number consists of more than five figures, and the sixth figure is less than 5, replace all figures after the fifth with ciphers; if the sixth figure is 5 or more, increase the fifth figure by 1, and replace the remaining figures with ciphers.   Thus, if the number is 31,415,926, find the logarithm of 31,416,000; if 31,415,426, find the logarithm of 31,415,000.

14.   EXAMPLE.—Find log 31,416.

SOLUTION.—Find the mantissa of the logarithm of the first four figures, as explained above.   This is, in the present case, .49707 (see page 6).   Now, subtract the number in the column headed 1, opposite 314 (the first three figures of the given number), from the next greater consecutive number, in this case 721 in the column headed 2.   721 − 707 = 14; this number is called the **difference.**   At the extreme right of the page will be found a secondary table headed P. P., and at the top of one of these columns in this table, in bold-face type, will be found the difference.   It will be noticed that each column is divided into two parts by a vertical line, and that the figures on the left of this line run in sequence from 1 to 9.   Considering the difference column headed 14, we see opposite the number 6 (6 is the last, or fifth, figure of the number whose logarithm we are taking out) the number 8.4, and we add this number to the mantissa found above, disregarding the decimal point in the mantissa, obtaining 49707 + 8.4 = 49715.4.   Now, since 4 is less than 5, we reject it and obtain for our complete mantissa .49715.   Since the characteristic of the logarithm of 31,416 is 4, log 31,416 = 4.49715.   Ans.

15.   EXAMPLE.—Find log 380.93.

SOLUTION.—Proceeding in exactly the same manner as above, the mantissa for 3,809 is 58081 (the star directs us to take 58 instead of 57 for the first two figures); the next greater mantissa is 58092, found in the column headed 0, opposite 381 in column headed N.   The difference is 092 − 081 = 11.   Looking in the section headed P. P. for column headed 11, we find 3.3 opposite 3; neglecting the .3, since it is less than 5, 3 is the amount to be added to the mantissa of the logarithm of 3809 to form the logarithm of 380.93. Hence, $58081 + 3 = 58084$, and since the characteristic is 2, log $380.93 = 2.58084$. Ans.

16. EXAMPLE.— Find log 1,296,728.

SOLUTION.—Since this number consists of more than five figures and the sixth figure is less than 5, we find the logarithm of 1,296,700 and call it the logarithm of 1,296,728. The mantissa of log 1,296 is found on page 2 to be 11261. The difference is $294 - 261 = 33$. Looking in the P.P. section for column headed 33, we find opposite 7 on the extreme left, 23.1; neglecting the .1, the amount to be added to the above mantissa is 23. Hence, the mantissa of log $1,296,728 = 11,261 + 23 = 11,284$; since the characteristic is 6, log $1,296,728 = 6.11284$. Ans.

17. EXAMPLE.—Find log 89.126.

SOLUTION.—Log $89.12 = 1.94998$. Difference between this and log $89.13 = 1.95002 - 1.94998 = 4$. The P. P. (proportional part) for the fifth figure of the number, 6, is 2.4, or 2. Hence, log $89.126 = 1.94998 + .00002 = 1.95000$. Ans.

18. EXAMPLE.—Find log .096725.

SOLUTION.—   Log $.09672 = \bar{2}.98552$.   Difference $= 4$.

                           P. P. for $5 = $ 2

Hence,   log $.096725 = \bar{2}.98554$. Ans.

19. To find the logarithm of a number consisting of five or more figures:

Rule.—I. *If the number consists of more than five figures and the sixth figure is 5 or greater, increase the fifth figure by 1, and write ciphers in place of the sixth and remaining figures.*

II. *Find the mantissa corresponding to the logarithm of the first four figures, and subtract this mantissa from the next greater mantissa in the table; the remainder is the difference.*

III. *Find in the secondary table headed P. P. a column headed by the same number as that just found for the difference, and in this column opposite the number corresponding to the fifth figure (or fifth figure increased by 1) of the given number (this figure is always situated at the left of the dividing line of the column) will be found the P. P. (proportional part) for that number. The P. P. thus found is to be added to the mantissa* *found in* **II**, *as in the preceding examples, and the result is the mantissa of the logarithm of the given number, as nearly as may be found with five-place tables.*

EXAMPLES FOR PRACTICE

20.　Find the logarithms of the following numbers:

1.	.062.	Ans. $\bar{2}$.79239.
2.	620.	Ans. 2.79239.
3.	21.4.	Ans. 1.33041.
4.	.000067.	Ans. $\bar{5}$.82607.
5.	89.42.	Ans. 1.95143.
6.	.785398.	Ans. $\bar{1}$.89509.
7.	.0010823.	Ans. $\bar{3}$.03435.
8.	10,000.	Ans. 4.
9.	1,923.208.	Ans. 3.28403.
10.	3.00026.	Ans. .47717.

TO FIND A NUMBER WHOSE LOGARITHM IS GIVEN

21.　**Rule.—I.**　*Consider the mantissa first. Glance along the different columns of the table which are headed 0 until the first two figures of the mantissa are found. Then glance down the same column until the third figure is found (or 1 less than the third figure). Having found the first three figures, glance to the right along the row in which they are situated until the last three figures of the mantissa are found. Then, the number that heads the column in which the last three figures of the mantissa are found is the fourth figure of the required number, and the first three figures lie in the column headed N., and in the same row in which lie the last three figures of the mantissa.*

II.　*If the mantissa cannot be found in the table, find the mantissa which is nearest to, but less than, the given mantissa, and which call the* **next less mantissa.** *Subtract the next less mantissa from the next greater mantissa in the table to obtain the difference. Also subtract the next less mantissa from the mantissa of the given logarithm, and call the remainder the P. P. Looking in the secondary table headed P. P. for the column headed by the difference just found, find the number opposite the P. P. just found (or the P. P. corresponding most* *nearly to that just found); this number is the fifth figure of the required number; the fourth figure will be found at the top of the column containing the next less mantissa, and the first three figures in the column headed N. and in the same row which contains the next less mantissa.*

III. *Having found the figures of the number as directed in* I *and* II, *locate the decimal point by the rules for the characteristic, annexing ciphers to bring the number up to the required number of figures if the characteristic is greater than 4.*

22. EXAMPLE.—Find the number whose logarithm is 3.56867.

SOLUTION.—The first two figures of the mantissa, 56, are found on page 7; glancing down the column, we find the third figure, 8 (in connection with 820), opposite 370 in the N. column. Glancing to the right along the row containing 820, the last three figures of the mantissa, 867, are found in the column headed 4; hence, the fourth figure of the required number is 4, and the first three figures are 370, making the figures of the required number 3704. Since the characteristic is 3, there are four figures to the left of the decimal point, and the number whose logarithm is 3.56867 is 3,704. Ans.

23. EXAMPLE.—Find the number whose logarithm is 3.56871.

SOLUTION.—The mantissa is not found in the table. The next less mantissa is 56867; the difference between this and the next greater mantissa is $879 - 867 = 12$, and the P. P. is $56871 - 56867 = 4$. Looking in the P. P. section for the column headed 12, we do not find 4, but we do find 3.6 and 4.8. Since 3.6 is nearer 4 than 4.8, we take the number opposite 3.6 for the fifth figure of the required number; this is 3. Hence, the fourth figure is 4, the first three figures 370, and the figures of the number are 37043. The characteristic being 3, the number is 3,704.3. Ans.

24. EXAMPLE.—Find the number whose logarithm is 5.95424.

SOLUTION.—The mantissa is found in the column headed 0 on page 18, opposite 900 in the column headed N. Hence, the fourth figure is 0, and the number is 900,000, the characteristic being 5. Ans. Had the logarithm been $\bar{5}.95424$, the number would have been .00009.

25. EXAMPLE.—Find the number whose logarithm is .93036.

SOLUTION.—The first three figures of the mantissa, 930, are found in the 0 column opposite 852 in the N. column, but since the last two figures of all the mantissas in this row are greater than 36, we must seek the next less mantissa in the preceding row. We find it to be

93034 (the star directing us to use 93 instead of 92 for the first two figures) in the column headed 8. The difference for this case is $039 - 034 = 5$, and the P. P. is $036 - 034 = 2$. Looking in the P. P. section for the column headed 5, we find the P. P., 2, opposite 4. Hence, the fifth figure is 4; the fourth figure is 8; the first three figures 851, and the number is 8.5184, the characteristic being 0. Ans.

26. EXAMPLE.—Find the number whose logarithm is $\bar{2}.05753$.

SOLUTION.—The next less mantissa is found in column headed 1 opposite 114 in the N. column, page 2; hence, the first four figures are 1141. The difference for this case is $767 - 729 = 38$, and the P. P. is $753 - 729 = 24$. Looking in the P. P. section for the column headed 38, we find that 24 falls between 22.8 and 26.6. The difference between 24 and 22.8 is 1.2, and between 24 and 26.6 is 2.6; hence, 24 is nearer 22.8 than it is to 26.6, and 6, opposite 22.8, is the fifth figure of the number. Hence, the number whose logarithm is $\bar{2}.05753 = .011416$. Ans.

EXAMPLES FOR PRACTICE

27. Find the numbers corresponding to the following logarithms:

1.	.74429.	Ans. 5.55.
2.	4.38202.	Ans. 24,100.
3.	$\bar{1}.84510$.	Ans. .7.
4.	1.84510.	Ans. 70.
5.	$\bar{4}.96047$.	Ans. .000913.
6.	3.78942.	Ans. 6,157.7.
7.	.50210.	Ans. 3.1776.
8.	$\bar{3}.63491$.	Ans. .0043143.
9.	$\bar{1}.07619$.	Ans. .11918.
10.	$\bar{3}.23417$.	Ans. .0017146.

---

28. In order to calculate by means of logarithms, a table is absolutely necessary. Hence, for this reason, we do not explain the method of calculating a logarithm. The work involved in calculating even a single logarithm is very great, and no method has yet been demonstrated, of which we are aware, by which the logarithm of a number like 121 can be calculated directly. Moreover, even if the logarithm could be readily obtained, it would be useless without a complete table, such as that which forms part of this text, for the reason that after having used it, say to extract a root, the number corresponding to the logarithm of the result could not be found.

MULTIPLICATION BY LOGARITHMS

29. The principle on which the process is based may be illustrated as follows: Let X and Y represent two numbers whose logarithms are x and y. To find the logarithm of their product, we have, from the definition of a logarithm,

$$10^x = X, \qquad (1)$$

and
$$10^y = Y. \qquad (2)$$

Since both members of (1) may be multiplied by the same quantity without destroying the equality, they evidently may be multiplied by equal quantities like 10^y and Y. Hence, multiplying (1) by (2), member by member,

$$10^x \times 10^y = 10^{x+y} = X Y; \quad (\textit{Elementary Algebra, Art. } \mathbf{57.})$$

or, by the definition of a logarithm, $x + y = \log X Y$. But $X Y$ is the product of X and Y, and $x + y$ is the sum of their logarithms; from which it follows that the sum of the logarithms of two numbers is equal to the logarithm of their product. Hence,

30. To multiply two or more numbers by using logarithms:

Rule.—*Add the logarithms of the several numbers, and the sum will be the logarithm of the product. Find the number corresponding to this logarithm, and the result will be the number sought.*

EXAMPLE.—Multiply 4.38, 5.217, and 83 together.

SOLUTION.—   Log 4.38 = .64147
            Log 5.217 = .71742
            Log   83 = 1.91908

Adding,   3.27797 = log (4.38 × 5.217 × 83).

Number corresponding to 3.27797 = 1,896.6.   Hence, 4.38 × 5.217 × 83 = 1,896.6, nearly.   Ans.

By actual multiplication, the product is 1,896.58818, showing that the result obtained by using logarithms was correct to five figures.

31. When adding logarithms, their *algebraic* sum is always to be found. Hence, if some of their numbers multiplied together are wholly decimal, the algebraic sum of the characteristics will be the characteristic of the product. It must be remembered that the mantissas are always positive.

EXAMPLE.—Multiply 49.82, .00243, 17, and .97 together.

SOLUTION.— Log 49.82 = 1.69740
              Log .00243 = $\bar{3}$.38561
              Log   17 = 1.23045
              Log   .97 = $\bar{1}$.98677

Adding,   0.30023 = log (49.82 × .00243 × 17 × .97).

Number corresponding to 0.30023 = 1.9963. Hence, 49.82 × .00243 × 17 × .97 = 1.9963. Ans.

In this case the sum of the mantissas was 2.30023. The integral 2 added to the positive characteristics makes their sum = 2 + 1 + 1 = 4; sum of negative characteristics = $\bar{3}$ + $\bar{1}$ = $\bar{4}$, whence, 4 + (− 4) = 0. If, instead of 17, the number had been .17 in the above example, the logarithm of .17 would have been $\bar{1}$.23045, and the sum of the logarithms would have been $\bar{2}$.30023; the product would then have been .019963.

32. It can now be shown why, as stated in Art. **9,** all numbers with figures in the same order have the same mantissa without regard to the decimal point. Thus, suppose it were known that log 2.06 = .31387. Then, log 20.6 = log (2.06 × 10) = log 2.06 + log 10 = .31387 + 1 = 1.31387. And so it might be proved with the decimal point in any other position.

EXAMPLES FOR PRACTICE

33. Find the products of the following by the use of logarithms:
1. 100, 32, and 31.64.   Ans. 101,250.
2. 23.1, 59.64, and 7.863.   Ans. 10,833.
3. .00354, .275, and .0198.   Ans. .000019275.
4. 2.763, 59.87, .264, and .001702.   Ans. .074328.

DIVISION BY LOGARITHMS

34. As before, let X and Y represent two numbers, whose logarithms are x and y. To find the logarithm of their quotient, we have, from the definition of a logarithm,

$$10^x = X, \qquad (1)$$

and
$$10^y = Y. \qquad (2)$$

Dividing (1) by (2), $10^{x-y} = \dfrac{X}{Y}$ (*Elementary Algebra*, Art. **70**), or by the definition of a logarithm, $x - y = \log \dfrac{X}{Y}$.

But $\dfrac{X}{Y}$ is the quotient of $X \div Y$, and $x - y$ is the difference of their logarithms, from which it follows that the *difference between the logarithms of two numbers is equal to the logarithm of their quotient.* Hence,

35. To divide one number by another by means of logarithms:

Rule.—*Subtract the logarithm of the divisor from the logarithm of the dividend and the result will be the logarithm of the quotient.*

EXAMPLE.—Divide 6,784.2 by 27.42.

SOLUTION.—

$$\begin{aligned}
\text{Log } 6{,}784.2 &= 3.83150 \\
\text{Log } \quad 27.42 &= 1.43807 \\
\hline
\textit{difference} &= 2.39343 = \log(6{,}784.2 \div 27.42).
\end{aligned}$$

Number corresponding to 2.39343 = 247.42. Hence, 6,784.2 ÷ 27.42 = 247.42. Ans.

36. When subtracting logarithms, their *algebraic* difference is to be found. The operation may sometimes be confusing, because the mantissa is always positive, and the characteristic may be either positive or negative. *When the logarithm to be subtracted is greater than the logarithm from which it is to be taken, or when negative characteristics appear, subtract the mantissa first, and then the characteristic, by changing its sign and adding.* (*Elementary Algebra* Art. **43.**)

EXAMPLE 1.—Divide 274.2 by 6,784.2.

SOLUTION.—

$$\begin{aligned}
\text{Log } \quad 274.2 &= 2.43807 \\
\text{Log } 6{,}784.2 &= 3.83150 \\
\hline
&\overline{2}.60657
\end{aligned}$$

First subtracting the mantissa .83150 gives .60657 for the mantissa of the quotient. In subtracting, 1 had to be taken from the characteristic of the minuend, leaving a characteristic of 1. Subtract the characteristic 3 from this, by changing its sign and adding $1 - 3 = \overline{2}$, the characteristic of the quotient. Number corresponding to $\overline{2}.60657$ = .040418. Hence, 274.2 ÷ 6,784.2 = .040418. Ans.

EXAMPLE 2.—Divide .067842 by .002742.

SOLUTION.—
$$\text{Log } .067842 = \bar{2}.83150$$
$$\text{Log } .002742 = \bar{3}.43807$$
$$\text{difference} = 1.39343$$

Subtracting, .83150 − .43807 = .39343 and − 2 + 3 = 1. Number corresponding to 1.39343 = 24.742. Hence, .067842 ÷ .002742 = 24.742. Ans.

37. The only case that need cause trouble in subtracting is where the logarithm of the minuend has a negative characteristic, or none at all, and a mantissa less than the mantissa of the subtrahend. For example, let it be required to subtract the logarithm 3.74036 from the logarithm $\bar{3}$.55145. The logarithm $\bar{3}$.55145 is equivalent to − 3 + .55145. Now, if we add both + 1 and − 1 to this logarithm, it will not change its value. Hence, $\bar{3}$.55145 = − 3 − 1 + 1 + .55145 = $\bar{4}$ + 1.55145. Therefore, $\bar{3}$.55145 − 3.74036 =

$$\bar{4} + 1.55145$$
$$3 + .74036$$
$$\text{difference} = \bar{7} + .81109 = \bar{7}.81109.$$

Had the characteristic of the above logarithm been 0 instead of $\bar{3}$, the process would have been exactly the same. Thus, .55145 = $\bar{1}$ + 1.55145; hence,

$$\bar{1} + 1.55145$$
$$3 + .74036$$
$$\text{difference} = \bar{4} + .81109 = \bar{4}.81109.$$

EXAMPLE.—Divide .02742 by 67.842.

SOLUTION.—
$$\text{Log } .02742 = \bar{2}.43807 = \bar{3} + 1.43807$$
$$\text{Log } 67.842 = 1.83150 = 1 + .83150$$
$$\text{difference} = \bar{4} + .60657 = \bar{4}.60657.$$

Number corresponding to $\bar{4}$.60657 = .00040417. Hence, .02742 ÷ 67.842 = .00040417. Ans.

EXAMPLE.—What is the reciprocal of 3.1416?

SOLUTION.—Reciprocal of $3.1416 = \dfrac{1}{3.1416}$, and $\log \dfrac{1}{3.1416} = \log 1 - \log 3.1416 = 0 - .49715$. Since $0 = -1 + 1$,

$$\bar{1} + 1.00000$$
$$\phantom{\bar{1} + 1}.49715$$
$$\text{difference} = \bar{1} + .50285 = \bar{1}.50285.$$

Number whose logarithm is $\bar{1}$.50285 = .31831. Ans.

38. Find the quotients of the following by the use of logarithms:

1.	$564.35 \div 34.96.$	Ans. 16.143.
2.	$9.643 \div 200.04.$	Ans. .048204.
3.	$.16071 \div 76.8.$	Ans. .0020926.
4.	$.00624 \div 3.096.$	Ans. .0020155.
5.	$.000119 \div .0719.$	Ans. .0016551.
6.	$1.19 \div 719.$	Ans. .0016551.
7.	$1 \div 1,728.$	Ans. .00057870.

INVOLUTION BY LOGARITHMS

39. If X represents a number whose logarithm is x, we have, from the definition of a logarithm,

$$10^x = X.$$

Raising both numbers to some power, as the nth, the equation becomes, by *Elementary Algebra* Art. **135,**

$$10^{xn} = X^n.$$

But X^n is the required power of X, and xn is its logarithm, from which it follows that the logarithm of a number, multiplied by the exponent of the power to which it is raised, is equal to the logarithm of the power. Hence,

40. To raise a number to any power by the use of logarithms:

Rule.—*Multiply the logarithm of the number by the exponent that denotes the power to which the number is to be raised, and the result will be the logarithm of the required power.*

EXAMPLE.—What is (a) the square of 7.92? (b) the cube of 94.7? (c) the 1.6 power of 512; that is, $512^{1.6}$?

SOLUTION.—(a) Log $7.92 = .89873$; the exponent of the power is 2. Hence, $.89873 \times 2 = 1.79746 = \log 7.92^2$. Number corresponding to $1.79746 = 62.727$. Hence, $7.92^2 = 62.727$, nearly. Ans.

(b) Log $94.7 = 1.97635$; $1.97635 \times 3 = 5.92905 = \log 94.7^3$. Number corresponding to $5.92905 = 849,280$. Hence, $94.7^3 = 849,280$, nearly. Ans.

(c)   Log $512^{1.6}$ = 1.6 × log 512 = 1.6 × 2.70927 = 4.334832, or 4.33483 (when using five-place logarithms) = log 21,619. Hence, $512^{1.6}$ = 21,619, nearly.   Ans.

41.   If the number is wholly decimal, so that the characteristic is negative, *multiply the two parts of the logarithm separately by the exponent of the number. If, after multiplying the mantissa, the product has a characteristic, add it, algebraically, to the negative characteristic, multiplied by the exponent, and the result will be the negative characteristic of the required power.*

EXAMPLE.—Raise .0751 to the fourth power.

SOLUTION.—Log $.0751^4$ = 4 × log .0751 = 4 × $\overline{2}$.87564.   Multiplying the parts separately, 4 × $\overline{2}$ = $\overline{8}$ and 4 × .87564 = 3.50256.   Adding the 3 and $\overline{8}$, 3 + (− 8) = − 5; therefore, log $.0751^4$ = $\overline{5}$.50256.   Number corresponding to this = .00003181.   Hence, $.0751^4$ = .00003181.   Ans.

42.   A decimal may be raised to a power whose exponent contains a decimal, as follows:

EXAMPLE.—Raise .8 to the 1.21 power.

SOLUTION.—Log $.8^{1.21}$ = 1.21 × $\overline{1}$.90309.   There are several ways of performing the multiplication.

First Method.—Adding the characteristic and mantissa algebraically, the result is − .09691.   Multiplying this by 1.21 gives − .1172611, or .11726, when using five-place logarithms.   To obtain a positive mantissa, add + 1 and − 1; whence, log $.8^{1.21}$ = − 1 + 1 − .11726 = $\overline{1}$.88274.

Second Method.—Multiplying the characteristic and mantissa separately gives − 1.21 + 1.09274.   Adding characteristic and mantissa algebraically gives − .11726; then, adding + 1 and − 1, log $.8^{1.21}$ = $\overline{1}$.88274.

Third Method.—Multiplying the characteristic and mantissa separately gives − 1.21 + 1.09274.   Adding the decimal part of the characteristic to the mantissa gives − 1 + (− .21 + 1.09274) = $\overline{1}$.88274 = log $.8^{1.21}$. The number corresponding to the logarithm $\overline{1}$.88274 = .76338.   Ans.

Any one of the above three methods may be used, but we recommend the first or the third.   The third is the most elegant, and saves figures, but requires the exercise of more caution than the first method does.   Following will be found the entire work of multiplication for both $.8^{1.21}$ and $.8^{.21}$.

$$
\begin{array}{r}
\overline{1}.9\,0\,3\,0\,9 \\
1.2\,1 \\
\hline
9\,0\,3\,0\,9 \\
1\,8\,0\,6\,1\,8 \\
9\,0\,3\,0\,9 \\
\hline
1.0\,9\,2\,7\,3\,8\,9 \\
-1.2\,1 \\
\hline
\overline{1}.8\,8\,2\,7\,3\,8\,9 \text{ or } \overline{1}.88274
\end{array}
$$

$$
\begin{array}{r}
\overline{1}.9\,0\,3\,0\,9 \\
.2\,1 \\
\hline
9\,0\,3\,0\,9 \\
1\,8\,0\,6\,1\,8 \\
+1.1\,8\,9\,6\,4\,8\,9 \\
-1-.2\,1 \\
\hline
\overline{1}.9\,7\,9\,6\,4\,8\,9 \text{ or } \overline{1}.97965
\end{array}
$$

In the second case, the negative decimal obtained by multiplying -1 and .21 was greater than the positive decimal obtained by multiplying .90309 and .21; hence, $+1$ and -1 were added as shown.

EXAMPLES FOR PRACTICE

43.   Find the values of the following by logarithms:

1.	$1,728^2$.	Ans. 2,985,900.
2.	$2.49^{1.24}$.	Ans. 3.0995.
3.	$32.16^{.42}$.	Ans. 4.2961.
4.	$.64^4$.	Ans. .16777.
5.	$.64^{.4}$.	Ans. .8365.
6.	$.0241^{2.8}$.	Ans. .000029489.

EVOLUTION BY LOGARITHMS

44.   If X represents a number whose logarithm is x, we have, from the definition of a logarithm,

$$10^x = X.$$

Extracting some root of both members, as the nth, the equation becomes, by Art. **136,** *Elementary Algebra,*

$$10^{\frac{x}{n}} = \sqrt[n]{X}.$$

But $\sqrt[n]{X}$ is the required root of X, and $\frac{x}{n}$ is its logarithm, from which it follows that the logarithm of a number divided by the index of the root to be extracted is equal to the logarithm of the root. Hence,

45. To extract any root of a number by means of logarithms:

Rule.—*Divide the logarithm of the number by the index of the root; the result will be the logarithm of the root.*

EXAMPLE.—Extract (*a*) the square root of 77,851; (*b*) the cube root of 698,970; (*c*) the 2.4 root of 8,964,300.

SOLUTION.—(*a*) Log 77,851 = 4.89127; the index of the root is 2; hence, log $\sqrt{77,851}$ = 4.89127 ÷ 2 = 2.44564; number corresponding to this = 279.02. Hence, $\sqrt{77,851}$ = 279.02, nearly. Ans.

(*b*) Log $\sqrt[3]{698,970}$ = 5.84446 ÷ 3 = 1.94815 = log 88.746; or, $\sqrt[3]{698,970}$ = 88.747, nearly. Ans.

(*c*) Log $\sqrt[2.4]{8,964,300}$ = 6.95251 ÷ 2.4 = 2.89688 = log 788.64; or, $\sqrt[2.4]{8,964,300}$ = 788.64, nearly. Ans.

46. If it is required to extract a root of a number wholly decimal, and the negative characteristic will not exactly contain the index of the root, without a remainder, proceed as follows:

Separate the two parts of the logarithm; add as many units (or parts of a unit) to the negative characteristic as will make it exactly contain the index of the root. Add the same number to the mantissa, and divide both parts by the index. The result will be the characteristic and mantissa of the root.

EXAMPLE 1.—Extract the cube root of .0003181.

SOLUTION.— $\sqrt[3]{.0003181} = \dfrac{\log .0003181}{3} = \dfrac{\overline{4}.50256}{3}$.

$$(\overline{4} + \overline{2} = \overline{6}) + (2 + .50256 = 2.50256).$$
$$(\overline{6} \div 3 = \overline{2}) + (2.50256 \div 3 = .83419);$$

or,   log $\sqrt[3]{.0003181} = \overline{2}.83419$ = log .068263.

Hence, $\sqrt[3]{.0003181}$ = .068263. Ans.

EXAMPLE 2.—Find the value of $\sqrt[1.4]{.0003181}$.

SOLUTION.—Log $\sqrt[1.4]{.0003181} = \dfrac{\log .0003181}{1.41} = \dfrac{\overline{4}.50256}{1.41}$.

If − .23 be added to the characteristic, it will contain 1.41 **exactly** 3 times. Hence,

$$[- 4 + (- .23) = - 4.23] + [.23 + .50256 = .73256].$$
$$(- 4.23 \div 1.41 = \overline{3}) + (.73256 \div 1.41 = .51955);$$

or,   log $\sqrt[1.4]{.0003181} = \overline{3}.51955$ = log .0033079.

Hence, $\sqrt[1.4]{.0003181}$ = .0033079. Ans.

EXAMPLES FOR PRACTICE

47. Find the values of the following by logarithms:

1. $\sqrt[4]{906.8}$.   Ans. 5.4876.
2. $\sqrt[5]{11}$.   Ans. 1.6154.
3. $.0497^{\frac{1}{3}}$.   Ans. .36766.
4. $.128^{\frac{1}{6}}$.   Ans. .7099.
5. $\sqrt[2.5]{.0227}$.   Ans. .21999.
6. $\sqrt[6]{.756}$.   Ans. .62738.

48. EXAMPLE 1.—Solve this expression by logarithms:

$$\frac{497 \times .0181 \times 762}{3,300 \times .6517} = ?$$

SOLUTION.—

Log   497 $= 2.69636$
Log   .0181 $= \bar{2}.25768$
Log   762 $= 2.88195$

Log product $= 3.83599$

Log   3,300 $= 3.51851$
Log   .6517 $= \bar{1}.81405$

Log product $= 3.33256$

$$3.83599 - 3.33256 = .50343 = \log 3.1874.$$

Hence, $\dfrac{497 \times .0181 \times 762}{3,300 \times .6517} = 3.1874.$ Ans.

EXAMPLE 2.—Solve $\sqrt[3]{\dfrac{504,203 \times 507}{1.75 \times 71.4 \times 87}}$ by logarithms.

SOLUTION.—

Log   504,203 $= 5.70260$
Log   507 $= 2.70501$

Log product $= 8.40761$

Log   1.75 $= .24304$
Log   71.4 $= 1.85370$
Log   87 $= 1.93952$

Log product $= 4.03626$

$$\frac{8.40761 - 4.03626}{3} = 1.45712 = \log 28.65.$$

Hence, $\sqrt[3]{\dfrac{504,203 \times 507}{1.75 \times 71.4 \times 87}} = 28.65.$ Ans.

49. Logarithms can often be applied to the solution of equations.

EXAMPLE.—Solve the equation $2.43x^5 = \sqrt[6]{.0648}$.

SOLUTION.— $2.43x^5 = \sqrt[6]{.0648}$.

Dividing by 2.43, $x^5 = \dfrac{\sqrt[6]{.0648}}{2.43}$.

Taking the logarithm of both numbers,
$$5 \times \log x = \frac{\log .0648}{6} - \log 2.43;$$

or, $5 \log x = \dfrac{\overline{2}.81158}{6} - .38561$

$$= \overline{1}.80193 - .38561$$

$$= \overline{1}.41632.$$

Dividing by 5, $\log x = \overline{1}.88326;$
whence, $x = .7643.$ Ans.

EXAMPLES FOR PRACTICE

50.   Find the values of the following:

1. $\dfrac{89 \times 753 \times .0097}{36,709 \times .08497}$.   Ans. .20840.

2. $\sqrt[3]{\dfrac{7,932 \times .00657 \times .80464}{.03274 \times .6428}}$.   Ans. 12.583.

3. $\sqrt[7]{\dfrac{.03271^2 \times 53.429 \times .77542^3}{32.769 \times .000371^4}}$.   Ans. 33.035.

Find the value of x in the following:

4. $5x^7 = \dfrac{129.4 \times .71}{30}$.   Ans. $x = .93237$.

5. $38x^{-4.2} = \dfrac{129.4 \times .71^2}{\sqrt{30}}$.   Ans. $x = .063133$.

Geometry and Trigonometry

GEOMETRY

1. **Geometry** is that branch of mathematics which treats of the properties of lines, angles, surfaces, and volumes.

LINES AND ANGLES

2. A **point** indicates position only. It has neither length, breadth, nor thickness.

3. A **line** has only one dimension: length.

4. A **straight line,** Fig. 1, is one that does not change its direction throughout its whole length. A straight line is also frequently called a **right line.**

FIG. 1

5. A **curved line,** Fig. 2, changes its direction at every point.

FIG. 2

6. A **broken line,** Fig. 3, is one made up wholly of straight lines lying in different directions.

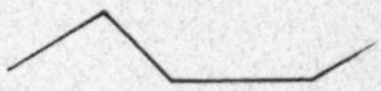

FIG. 3

7. **Parallel lines,** Fig. 4, are those which are equally distant from each other throughout their whole length, both lines being considered indefinite in extent. When every point of a line is the same distance from another line (or surface), it is said to be *parallel to the line* (or surface).

FIG. 4

§ 6

40—19

8. A line is **perpendicular** to another when it meets that line so as not to incline towards it on either side, Fig. 5.

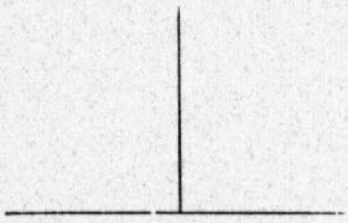

FIG. 5

9. A **horizontal line** is a line parallel to the horizon, or water level, Fig. 6.

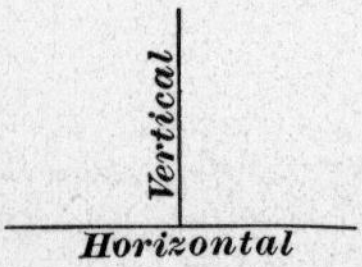

10. A **vertical line,** Fig. 6, is a line perpendicular to a horizontal line; consequently, it has the direction of a plumb-line.

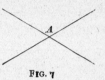

Horizontal

FIG. 6

11. When two lines cross or cut each other, as in Fig. 7, they are said to **intersect,** and the point at which they intersect is called the **point of intersection,** as at A.

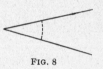

FIG. 7

12. An **angle,** Fig. 8, is the opening between two lines that intersect or meet; the point of meeting is called the **vertex** of the angle.

FIG. 8

13. In order to distinguish one line from another, two of its points are given if it is a straight line, and as many more as are considered necessary if it is a broken or curved line. Thus, in Fig. 9, the line A B would mean the straight line included between the points A and B. Similarly, the straight line between C and D would be called the line C D.

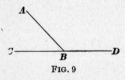

FIG. 9

The broken line made up of the lines A B and B D would be called the broken line A B D or D B A, according to the point started from. The line C D may be regarded as a single line or as made up of two lines C B and B D. B D may be regarded as C B extended, in which case it would be called C B *produced to* D, or simply C B **produced.** Similarly, C B is D B produced. One line, however, cannot be said to be another line produced, unless it is an extension of the line in a constant direction; i. e., *A B* cannot be referred to as *C B* produced or as *D B* produced.

14. To distinguish angles, name a point on each line, and the point of their intersection, or vertex of the angle. Thus, in Fig. 9, the angle formed by the lines *A B* and *C B* is called the angle *A B C* or the angle *C B A*, the letter at the vertex being placed between the other two.   The angle formed by the lines *A B* and *B D* is called the angle *A B D* or the angle *D B A*.

When an angle stands alone so that it cannot be mistaken for any other angle, only the vertex letter need be given; thus, the angle *E*, Fig. 20, the angle *B*, Fig. 21, etc.

15. Two angles having the same vertex and a common side are called **adjacent angles**.   Angles *A B C* and *A B D*, Fig. 9, are adjacent angles.

16. When one line meets another so that the adjacent angles formed are equal, as *A B C* and *A B D*, Fig. 10, the angles are called **right angles.**

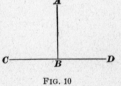

FIG. 10

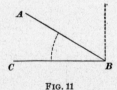

FIG. 11

17. An **acute angle** is less than a right angle.   *A B C*, Fig. 11, is an acute angle.

18. An **obtuse angle** is greater than a right angle.   *A B D*, Fig. 12, is an obtuse angle.

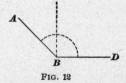

FIG. 12

19. When two straight lines intersect they form four angles about the point of intersection.   Thus, in Fig. 13, the

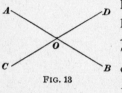

FIG. 13

lines A B and C D, intersecting at the point O, form four angles BOD, DOA, AOC, and COB about the point O. The angles that lie on the *same* side of one straight line, as DOB and DOA, are adjacent angles.   The angles that lie *opposite* each other are called **opposite angles.**   Thus, AOC and DOB, also DOA and BOC, are opposite angles.

20. When one straight line intersects another straight line, as in Fig. 13, the opposite angles are equal.   Thus, $DOB = AOC$, and $DOA = BOC$.

21. When one straight line meets another straight line at a point between its ends, the sum of the two adjacent angles ABD and ABC, Fig. 14, equals two right angles.

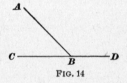

FIG. 14

22. If a number of straight lines on the same side of a

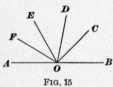

FIG. 15

given straight line meet at the same point, the sum of all the angles formed is equal to two right angles.   Thus, in Fig. 15, $COB + DOC + EOD + FOE + AOF =$ two right angles.

23. If a straight line intersects another straight line, so that the adjacent angles are equal, the lines are said to be *perpendicular to each other*.   In such a case, four right angles are formed about the point of intersection.   Thus, in Fig. 16, $BOC = COA$; hence, BOC, COA, AOD, and DOB are right angles.   From this it is seen that *four right angles* are all that can be formed about a given point.

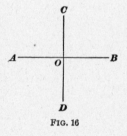

FIG. 16

24. Through a given point any number of straight lines may be drawn; and the sum of all the angles formed about the point of intersection equals four right angles. Thus, in Fig. 17, $HOF + FOC + COA + AOG + GOE + EOD + DOB + BOH =$ four right angles.

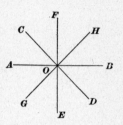

FIG. 17

EXAMPLE.—In a flywheel with 12 arms, what part of a right angle is included between the center lines of any two adjacent arms, the arms being spaced equally?

SOLUTION.—Since there are 12 arms, there are 12 angles. The sum of all the angles equals four right angles. Hence, one angle equals $\frac{1}{12}$ of 4 right angles, or $\frac{1}{12} \times 4 = \frac{4}{12} = \frac{1}{3}$ of 1 right angle. Ans.

25. A perpendicular drawn from a point over or under a given straight line is the shortest distance from the point to the line, or to the line produced. Thus, if A, Fig. 18, is the given point and CD the given line, then the perpendicular AB is the shortest distance from A to CD.

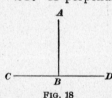

FIG. 18

26. An angle is said to be the **complement** of another when the sum of the two angles is *one* right angle. In Fig. 17, if FE is perpendicular to AB, FOH is the complement of BOH, and BOH is the complement of FOH. When referring to both angles, they are said to be **complementary.** Thus, BOH and FOH are complementary angles.

27. When the sum of two angles is equal to *two* right angles, the angles are said to be **supplementary,** and each is the **supplement** of the other. In Fig. 14, ABC is the supplement of ABD, and ABD is the supplement of ABC. The adjacent angles formed by two intersecting lines, as in Fig. 13, are supplementary. If one side of an angle, as BD, Fig. 14, be produced through the vertex, the angle between the side produced and the other side, i. e., the angle CBA, is the supplement of the original angle, DBA.

28. If two angles have their sides parallel and both the corresponding sides lie in the same or in opposite directions, they are equal. Thus, if the side AB, Fig. 19, is parallel to the side DE, and if the side BC is parallel to the side EF, then the angle $E =$ the angle B. But if one of the sides of one angle lies in the same direction and

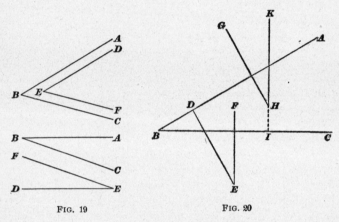

Fig. 19   Fig. 20

the other in the opposite direction to the corresponding sides of the other angle, the angles are supplementary. Thus, in Fig. 20, GH is parallel to and lies in the same direction as DE, and HI is parallel to but lies in the opposite direction to EF; hence, angle GHI is the supplement of DEF.

29. If two sides of an angle are perpendicular to two sides of another angle, the two angles are equal or supplementary. Thus, if DE and GH, Fig. 20, are perpendicular to BA, and EF and HK are perpendicular to BC, then will angle $E =$ angle $B =$ angle H; also GHI is the supplement of ABC.

EXAMPLES FOR PRACTICE

1. In a pulley with five arms, what part of a right angle is included between the center lines of any two•arms?   Ans. $\frac{4}{5}$ of a right angle.

2. If one straight line meets another straight line so as to form an angle equal to $1\frac{2}{3}$ right angles, what part of a right angle does its adjacent angle equal?   Ans. $\frac{1}{3}$ of a right angle.

3. If a number of straight lines meet a given straight line at a given point, all being on the same side of the given line, so as to form six equal angles, what part of a right angle is contained in each angle?
Ans. ⅓ of a right angle.

PLANE FIGURES

30. A **surface** has only two dimensions: *length* and *breadth*. A **plane surface,** usually called a **plane,** is a flat surface. If a straightedge be laid on a plane surface, every point along the edge of the straightedge will touch the surface, no matter in what direction it is laid.

31. A **plane figure** is any part of a plane surface bounded by straight or curved lines.

32. When a plane figure is bounded by **straight** lines only, it is called a **polygon.** The bounding lines are called the **sides,** and the broken line that bounds it (or the whole distance around it) is called the **perimeter** of the polygon.

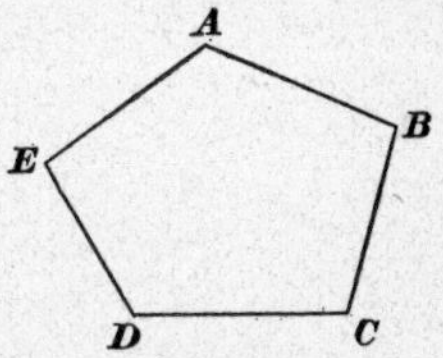

The angles formed by the sides are called the angles of the polygon. Thus, $ABCDE$, Fig. 21, is a polygon. AB, BC, etc. are the sides; EAB, ABC, etc. are the angles; and the broken line $ABCDEA$ is the perimeter.

FIG. 21

33. Polygons are classified according to the number of their sides: One of three sides is called a **triangle;** one of four sides, a **quadrilateral;** one of five sides, a **pentagon;** one of six sides, a **hexagon;** one of seven sides, a **heptagon;** one of eight sides, an **octagon;** one of ten sides, a **decagon;** one of twelve sides, a **dodecagon;** etc.

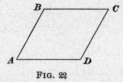

FIG. 22

34. Equilateral polygons are those in which the sides are all equal. Thus, in Fig. 22, $AB = BC = CD = DA$; hence, $ABCD$ is an equilateral polygon.

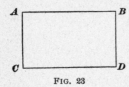

FIG. 23

35. An **equiangular polygon** is one in which all the angles are equal. Thus, in Fig. 23, angle A = angle B = angle D = angle C; hence, $A B D C$ is an equiangular polygon.

36. A **regular polygon** is one in which all the sides and all the angles are equal. Thus, in Fig. 24, $A B = B D = D C = C A$, and angle A = angle B = angle D = angle C; hence, $A B D C$ is a regular polygon.

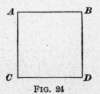

FIG. 24

37. Some regular polygons are shown in Fig. 25.

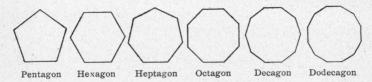

Pentagon   Hexagon   Heptagon   Octagon   Decagon   Dodecagon

FIG. 25

38. The sum of all the interior angles of any polygon equals two right angles, multiplied by a number which is two less than the number of sides of the polygon. Thus, $A B C D E F$, Fig. 26, is a polygon of six sides (hexagon), and the sum of all the interior angles $A + B + C + D + E + F = 2$ right angles $\times 4$ ($= 6 - 2$), or 8 right angles.

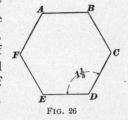

FIG. 26

EXAMPLE.—If the above figure is a regular hexagon (has equal sides and equal angles), how many right angles are there in each interior angle?

SOLUTION.— $6 - 2 = 4$. Two right angles $\times 4 = 8$ right angles = the total number of right angles in the polygon; and as there are 6 equal angles, we have $8 \div 6 = 1\frac{1}{3}$ right angles = the number of right angles in each interior angle. Ans.

THE TRIANGLE

39. Triangles are named according to their sides as *isosceles*, *equilateral*, and *scalene* triangles, and according to their angles as *right-angled* and *oblique-angled* triangles.

40. An **isosceles** triangle, Fig. 27, is one having two of its sides equal.

FIG. 27

41. When the three sides are equal, as in Fig. 28, it is called an **equilateral** triangle. An equilateral triangle is also isosceles.

FIG. 28

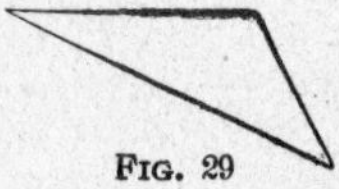

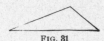

FIG. 29

42. A **scalene** triangle, Fig. 29, is one having no two of its sides equal.

43. A **right-angled** triangle, Fig. 30, is any triangle having one right angle. The side opposite the right angle is called the **hypotenuse.** For brevity, a right-angled triangle is now termed a **right triangle.**

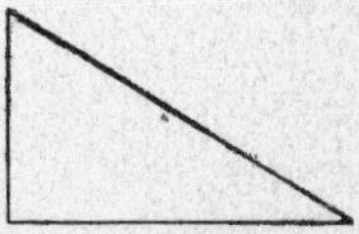

FIG. 30

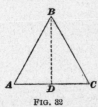

FIG. 31

44. An **oblique** triangle, Fig. 31, is one that has no right angle.

45. The **base** of any triangle is the side upon which the triangle is supposed to stand; any side may be considered to be the base. In Figs. 32, 33, and 34, *A-C* is the base.

46. The **altitude** of any triangle is a line drawn from the vertex of the angle opposite the base perpendicular to the base or to the base produced. Thus, in Figs. 32 and 33, *B D* is the *altitude* of the triangles *A B C.*

FIG. 32

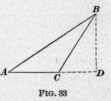

FIG. 33

47. In an isosceles triangle, the angles opposite the equal sides are equal. Thus, in Fig. 34, $AB = BC$; hence, angle $C =$ angle A. Therefore, if two angles of any triangle are equal, the triangle is isosceles.

FIG. 34

In any isosceles triangle, if a perpendicular be drawn from the vertex opposite the unequal side to that side, it bisects (cuts in halves) the side. Thus, AC, Fig. 34, is the unequal side in the isosceles triangle ABC; hence, the perpendicular BD from the vertex opposite AC bisects AC, or $AD = DC$.

48. In any triangle, the sum of the three angles equals two right angles. Thus, in Fig. 35, the sum of the angles at A, B, and $C =$ two right angles; that is, $A + B + C$ = two right angles. Hence, if any two angles of a triangle are given, the third may be found by subtracting the sum of the two from two right angles. Suppose that $A + B = 1\frac{7}{10}$ right

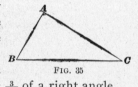

FIG. 35

angles; then, C must equal $2 - 1\frac{7}{10} = \frac{3}{10}$ of a right angle.

49. In any *right* triangle there can be but one right angle, and since the sum of all the angles equals two right angles, it is evident that the sum of the two acute angles must equal one right angle. Therefore, if in any right triangle one acute angle is known, the other can be found by subtracting the known angle from a right angle. Thus, in Fig. 36, ABC is a right triangle,

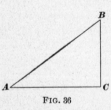

FIG. 36

right-angled at C. Then, the angles $A + B =$ one right angle. If $A = \frac{3}{7}$ of a right angle, $B = 1 - \frac{3}{7} = \frac{4}{7}$ of a right angle. The two acute angles of a right triangle are therefore complementary.

50. In any right triangle, the square described upon the hypotenuse is equal to the sum of the squares described upon the other two sides. If ABC, Fig. 37, is a right triangle, right-angled at B, then the square described upon the hypotenuse AC is equal to the sum of the squares described upon the sides AB and BC; consequently, if the lengths of the sides AB and BC are known, the length of the hypotenuse can be found by adding the squares of the lengths of the sides AB and BC and then extracting the square root of the sum.

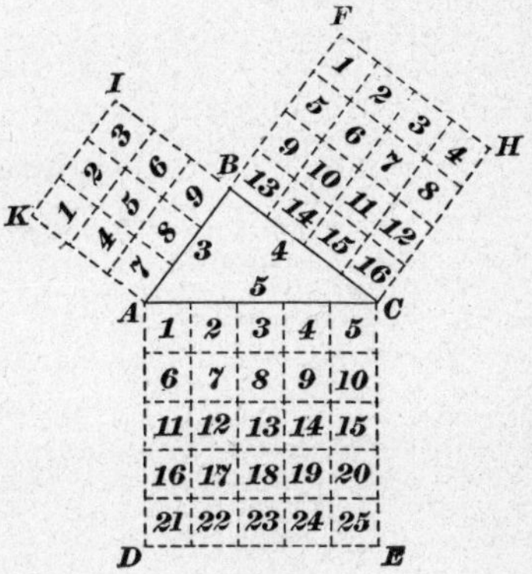

FIG. 37

EXAMPLE.—If $AB = 3$ inches and $BC = 4$ inches, what is the length of the hypotenuse AC?

SOLUTION.— $3^2 = 9; \ 4^2 = 16.$

Adding, $9 + 16 = 25.$

$$\sqrt{25} = 5.$$

Therefore, $AC = 5$ in.   Ans.

51. If the hypotenuse and one side are given, the other side can be found by subtracting the square of the given side from the square of the hypotenuse, and then extracting the square root of the remainder.

EXAMPLE 1.—The side given is 3 inches, the hypotenuse is 5 inches; what is the length of the other side?

SOLUTION.— $3^2 = 9; \ 5^2 = 25.$ $25 - 9 = 16$, and $\sqrt{16} = 4$ in. Ans.

EXAMPLE 2.—If, from a church steeple which is 150 feet high a rope is to be attached at the top and to a stake in the ground 85 feet from its foot (the ground being supposed to be level), what must be the length of the rope?

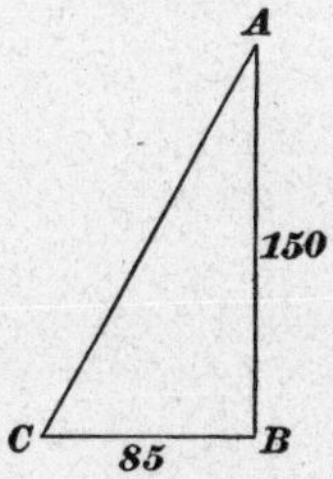

FIG. 38

SOLUTION.—In Fig. 38, AB represents the steeple, 150 feet high; C, a stake 85 feet from the foot of the steeple; and AC, the rope. Here we have a right triangle, right-angled at B, and AC is the hypotenuse.

The square of $AC = 85^2 + 150^2 = 7,225 + 22,500 = 29,725.$

Therefore, $AC = \sqrt{29,725} = 172.4$ ft., nearly.   Ans.

52. Two triangles are **equal** when the *sides* of one are equal to the sides of the other.

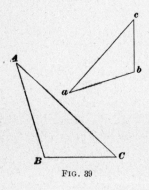

FIG. 39

53. Two triangles are **similar** when the *angles* of one are equal to the angles of the other. *The corresponding sides of similar triangles are proportional.*

For example, in the triangles ABC and abc, Fig. 39, side ac is perpendicular to AC, side ab is perpendicular to AB, and side bc is perpendicular to BC. Hence, angle $A =$ angle a, since the sides of one are perpendicular to the sides of the other. In like manner, angle $B =$ angle b, and angle $C =$ angle c. The two triangles are therefore similar and their corresponding sides are proportional. That is, any two sides of one triangle are to each other as the two corresponding sides of the other triangle; or, one side of one triangle is to the corresponding side of the other as another side of the first triangle is to the corresponding side of the second. The following are examples of the many proportions that may be written. In this case, the corresponding sides of the two triangles are the ones that are perpendicular to each other:

$$AB : BC = ab : bc,$$
$$AB : AC = ab : ac,$$
$$BC : bc = AB : ab,$$
$$AC : ac = BC : bc, \text{ etc.}$$

EXAMPLE.—The sides of a triangle are 18 inches and 21 inches and the base is 24 inches long; what are the lengths of the sides of a similar triangle whose base is 8 inches long?

SOLUTION.—Since the sides are proportional, we have the proportions $24 : 8 = 21 : x$, and $24 : 8 = 18 : x$. From the first, $x = 7$ in., and from the second, $x = 6$ in.   Ans.

54. If a straight line is drawn through two sides of a triangle parallel to the third side, it divides those sides proportionally. Thus, in Fig. 40, let the line $D E$ be drawn parallel to the side $B C$ in the tri-angle $A B C$. Then,

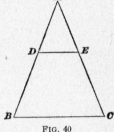

$$A D : D B = A E : E C.$$

It is to be noticed, also, that the tri-angles $A D E$ and $A B C$ are similar and their sides are proportional. The proportion $A D : D E = A B : B C$ is a useful one.

FIG. 40

EXAMPLE 1.—In the last figure, if $A E = 14$, $A D = 12$, and $E C = 9$, what does $D B$ equal ?

SOLUTION.—From the proportion $A D : D B = A E : E C$, we have $12 : D B = 14 : 9$, whence $D B = 7\frac{5}{7}$. Ans.

EXAMPLE 2.—The base of a right triangle is 12 inches and its altitude 40 inches. How wide is the triangle 24 inches from the base ?

SOLUTION.—Since the triangle is right-angled, the length of the perpendicular side equals the altitude, or 40 inches. By drawing a line parallel to the base and 24 inches above it, a second and similar triangle will be found whose corresponding side $= 40 - 24$, or 16 inches, and the length of whose base is the required width. Hence, $40 : 12 = 16 : x$, or $x = 4.8$ in. Ans.

EXAMPLES FOR PRACTICE

1. How many right angles are there in one of the interior angles of a regular heptagon ?   Ans. $1\frac{3}{7}$ right angles.

2. The angle at the vertex of an isosceles triangle equals $\frac{1}{2}$ of a right angle. What do the other angles equal ?   Ans. $\frac{3}{4}$ of a right angle.

3. One of the acute angles of a right triangle equals $\frac{5}{9}$ of a right angle. What is the size of the other acute angle ? Ans. $\frac{4}{9}$ of a right angle.

4. If the two sides about the right angle in a right triangle are 52 and 39 feet long, how long is the hypotenuse ?   Ans. 65 ft.

5. A ladder 65 feet long reaches to the top of a house when its foot is 25 feet from the house. How high is the house, supposing the ground to be level ?   Ans. 60 ft.

6. In a triangle $A B C$, side $A B = 32$ feet, $B C = 34$ feet, and $A C = 48$ feet. If side $A B$ of a similar triangle is 72 feet long, what are the lengths of the other two sides ?   Ans. $A C = 108$ ft. ; $B C = 76.5$ ft.

7. The base of a right triangle is 24 inches and its altitude 72 inches. At what distance from the top is the triangle 16 inches wide ?   Ans. 48 in.

THE CIRCLE

FIG. 41

55. A **circle**, Fig. 41, is a plane figure bounded by a curved line, called the **circumference**, every point of which is equally distant from a point within, called the **center**.

56. The **diameter** of a circle $A B$, Fig. 42, is a straight line passing through the center and terminated at both ends by the **circumference**.

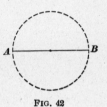

FIG. 42

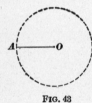

FIG. 43

57. The **radius** of a circle, $O A$, Fig. 43, is a straight line drawn from the center to the circumference. It is equal in length to one-half the diameter. The plural of radius is **radii**. All radii of any circle are equal in length.

58. An **arc** of a circle, as $a\,e\,b$, Fig. 44, is any part of its circumference.

FIG. 44

FIG. 45

59. A **chord** is a straight line joining any two points in a circumference; or, it is a straight line joining the extremities of an arc.

Thus, in Fig. 45, $a\,b$ is the chord of the arc $a\,e\,b$.

60. A **segment** of a circle is the space included between an arc and its chord.

Thus, in Fig. 45, the portion of the circle included between the chord *a b* and arc *a e b* is a segment.

61. A **sector** of a circle is the space included between an arc and two radii drawn to the extremities of the arc.

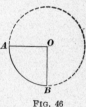

Thus, in Fig. 46, the space included between the arc *A B* and the radii *O A* and *O B* is a sector of the circle.

Fig. 46

62. Two circles are equal when the radius or diameter of one equals the radius or diameter of the other.

Two arcs are equal when the radius and chord of one equal the radius and chord of the other.

63. If *A D B C*, Fig. 47, is a circle in which two diameters *A B* and *C D* are drawn at right angles to each other, then, *A O D*, *D O B*, *B O C*, and *C O A* are right angles. The circumference is thus divided into four equal parts; each of these parts is called a **quadrant.**

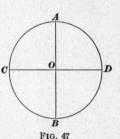

Fig. 47

64. In geometry, angles are measured by the number of right angles, or parts of a right angle, which they contain; since in the circle, a right angle intercepts a quadrant, an angle is also measured by the number of quadrants, or parts of a quadrant, that it intercepts. The word " intercept" as here used means the arc cut off by the sides of the angle.

65. An angle at the center is measured by its intercepted arc.

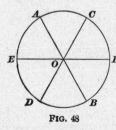

Fig. 48

EXAMPLE.—If a circle is divided into six equal sectors, how many quadrants, or parts of a quadrant, are contained in the angle of each sector ?

SOLUTION.—In Fig. 48, *A C F B D E* is a circle divided into six equal sectors. The sum of all the quadrants in the circle is 4. Hence, $4 \div 6 = \frac{2}{3}$ of a quadrant in each sector. Ans.

66. An **inscribed** angle is one whose vertex lies on the circumference of a circle and whose sides are chords. It is measured by *one-half* the intercepted arc. Thus, in Fig. 49, *A B C* is an inscribed angle and it is measured by one-half the arc *A D C*.

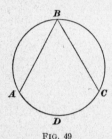

FIG. 49

EXAMPLE.—If in the figure the arc *A D C* = $\frac{2}{5}$ of the circumference, what is the measure of the inscribed angle *A B C*?

SOLUTION.—Since the angle is an inscribed angle, it is measured by one-half the intercepted arc, or $\frac{2}{5} \times \frac{1}{2} = \frac{1}{5}$ of the circumference. The whole circumference contains four quadrants; hence, $4 \times \frac{1}{5} = \frac{4}{5}$ of a quadrant, or $\frac{4}{5}$ of a right angle. Therefore, the measure of the angle *A B C* is $\frac{4}{5}$ of a quadrant. Ans.

67. If a circle is divided into halves, each half is called a **semicircle** and each half circumference is called a **semi-circumference.**

68. Any angle that is inscribed in a semicircle and intercepts a semi-circumference, as *A B C*, or *A D C*, Fig. 50, is a right angle, since it is measured by one-half a semi-circumference, that is, by a quadrant.

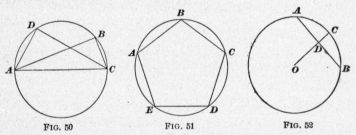

FIG. 50   FIG. 51   FIG. 52

69. An **inscribed** polygon is one whose vertexes lie on the circumference of a circle, and whose sides are chords, as *A B C D E*, Fig. 51.

70. If, in any circle, a radius be drawn perpendicular to any chord, it bisects (cuts in halves) the chord. Thus, if the radius *O C*, Fig. 52, is perpendicular to the chord *A B*, *A D = D B*.

EXAMPLE.—If a regular pentagon is inscribed in a circle and a radius is drawn perpendicular to one of the sides, what are the lengths of the two parts of the side, the perimeter of the pentagon being 27 inches?

SOLUTION. — A pentagon has five sides, and since it is a regular pentagon, all the sides are of equal length; the perimeter of the pentagon, which is the distance around it, equals the sum of all the sides, or 27 inches. Therefore, the length of one side $= 27 \div 5 = 5\frac{2}{5}$ inches. Since the pentagon is an inscribed pentagon, its sides are chords, and as a radius perpendicular to a chord bisects it, we have $5\frac{2}{5} \div 2$ $= 2\frac{7}{10}$ inches for the length of each of the parts of the side, cut by a radius perpendicular to it.   Ans.

71. If a straight line be drawn perpendicular to any chord at its middle point, it must pass through the center of the circle.

Through any three points not in the same straight line, a circumference can be drawn.   Let A, B, and C, Fig. 53, be any three points.   Join A and B, and B and C, by straight lines.   At the middle point of $A B$ draw $H K$ perpendicular to $A B$; at the middle point of $B C$ draw $E F$ perpendicular to $B C$.   These two perpendiculars intersect at O.   All points on $H K$ are equally distant from A and B, and all points on $E F$ are equally

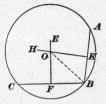

FIG. 53

distant from B and C; their intersection O is equally distant from A, B, and C.   Then, with O as a center and $O B$ as a radius, describe a circle; it will pass through A, B, and C.

72. A **tangent** to a circle is a straight line that touches the circle at one point only; it is always perpendicular to a radius drawn to that point. Thus, in Fig. 54, $A B$ drawn perpendicular to the radius $O E$ at its extremity E is a *tangent* to the circle.

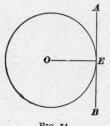

FIG. 54

40—20

If a straight line is perpendicular to a radius at its extremity, it is tangent to the circle.   Thus, in Fig. 54, if $A B$ is perpendicular to the radius $O E$ at E, $A B$ is tangent to the circle.

73. If two circles intersect each other, the line joining their centers bisects at right angles the line joining the two points of intersection. If the two circles, whose centers are O and P, Fig. 55, intersect at A and B, the line $O P$ bisects at right angles the line $A B$; or $A C = B C$. $A B$ is thus perpendicular to $O P$.

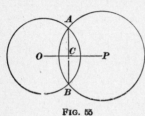

FIG. 55

74. One circle is said to be **tangent** to another circle when they touch each other at one point only, as in Fig. 56. This point is called the **point of tangency,** or the **point of contact.**

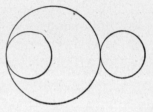

FIG. 56

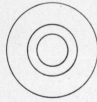

FIG. 57

75. When two or more circles are described from the same center, as in Fig. 57, they are called **concentric** circles.

76. If, from any point on the circumference of a circle, a perpendicular be let fall upon a given diameter, this perpendicular will be a mean proportional between the two parts into which it divides the diameter.

If $A B$, Fig. 58, is the given diameter and C any point on the circumference, then is the perpendicular $C D$ a mean proportional between $A D$ and $D B$, or

$$A D : C D = C D : D B.$$

Therefore, $\overline{C D}^2 = A D \times D B,$

and $C D = \sqrt{A D \times D B}.$

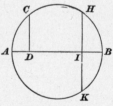

FIG. 58

EXAMPLE 1.—If $HK = 30$ feet and $IB = 8$ feet, what is the diameter of the circle, HK being perpendicular to AB?

SOLUTION.— $30 \text{ feet} \div 2 = 15 \text{ feet} = IH.$

$$BI : IH = IH : IA, \text{ or } 8 : 15 = 15 : IA.$$

Therefore, $IA = \dfrac{15^2}{8} = \dfrac{225}{8} = 28\tfrac{1}{8}$ feet,

and $IA + IB = 28\tfrac{1}{8} + 8 = 36\tfrac{1}{8}$ ft. $= AB$, diameter of circle.   Ans.

EXAMPLE 2.—The diameter of the circle AB is $36\tfrac{1}{8}$ feet and the distance BI is 8 feet; what is the length of the line HK?

SOLUTION.—As the diameter of the circle is $36\tfrac{1}{8}$ feet and as BI is 8 feet, IA is equal to $36\tfrac{1}{8} - 8 = 28\tfrac{1}{8}$ feet.   Hence, $BI : IH = IH : IA$, or $8 : IH = IH : 28\tfrac{1}{8}$.   Therefore, $IH = \sqrt{8 \times 28\tfrac{1}{8}} = 15$ feet, and as $HK = IH + IK$, or $2\,IH$, $HK = 15 \times 2 = 30$ ft.   Ans.

EXAMPLES FOR PRACTICE

1. If a circle is divided into ten equal sectors, what part of a quadrant is contained in the angle of each sector?   Ans. $\tfrac{2}{5}$ of a quadrant.

2. An angle inscribed in a circle intercepts one-fourth of the circumference.   What is the size of the angle?   Ans. $\tfrac{1}{2}$ of a right angle.

3. The perimeter of a regular inscribed octagon is 100 inches long. If a radius is drawn perpendicular to one of the sides, what are the lengths of the two parts of the side?   Ans. $6\tfrac{1}{4}$ in.

4. If, in Fig. 58, the diameter $AB = 32\tfrac{1}{2}$ feet and the distance $IB = 8$ feet, what is the length of the chord HK?   Ans. 28 ft.

5. In Fig. 58, if the distance BI is 6 inches and HK 18 inches, what is the diameter of the circle?   Ans. 19.5 in.

TRIGONOMETRY

77.   Trigonometry is that branch of mathematics which treats of the solution of triangles.

Every triangle has six parts — three **sides** and three **angles**.   If any three of the parts are given, one of them being a side, the other three can be found.   The process of finding the unknown parts from the given parts is called the **solution** of the triangle.

78.   In trigonometry, the circumference of every circle is supposed to be divided into 360 equal parts, called **degrees;**

every degree is subdivided into 60 equal parts, called **minutes**; and every minute is again divided into 60 equal parts, called **seconds**. Degrees, minutes, and seconds are denoted

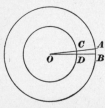

by the symbols °, ′, ″. Thus, the expression 37° 14′ 44″, is read 37 degrees 14 minutes 44 seconds.

Since one degree is $\frac{1}{360}$ of any circumference, it follows that the length of an arc of one degree will be different in circles of different diameters, but the proportion of the length of an arc of one

FIG. 59

degree to the whole circumference will always be the same, viz., $\frac{1}{360}$ of the circumference.

Hence, in two given circles the length of an arc of 1° will be proportional to the two radii. Thus, if $A\,O\,B$, Fig. 59, is an angle of 1° on the larger circle, it is also 1° on the smaller concentric circle, and the length of the arc $A\,B$ is to the length of the arc $C\,D$ as the radius $O\,B$ is to the radius $O\,D$; or,   arc $A\,B$: arc $C\,D = O\,B : O\,D.$

EXAMPLE.—If the arc $C\,D = 2$ inches, radius $O\,D = 5$ inches, and radius $O\,B = 9$ inches, what is the length of the arc $A\,B$?

SOLUTION.— $A\,B : 2 = 9 : 5$, or $A\,B = \dfrac{9 \times 2}{5} = 3\frac{3}{5}$ in.   Ans.

79. In trigonometry, the arcs of circles are used to measure angles. All angles are supposed to have their vertexes at the center O of the circle (see Fig. 60), one side of the angle lying to the right of O, and coinciding with the horizontal diameter, as $O\,B$.

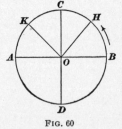

FIG. 60

The point B on the arc is the starting point in measuring an angle; the angle is supposed to increase by moving around the circumference in the direction indicated by the arrow until the number of degrees, minutes, and seconds in the angle have been measured off on the arc. Suppose that it stops at the point H; draw $O\,H$, and $H\,O\,B$ will be the angle. If K had been the stopping point, $K\,O\,B$ would have been the angle.

In practice, angles are most conveniently laid off by using a protractor (see *Geometrical Drawing*), which is usually graduated to degrees and half degrees, minutes being estimated by the eye.

80. Since a quadrant is a fourth part of a circle, the number of degrees in a quadrant is one-fourth of 360°, or 90°. Hence, a right angle always contains 90°.

EXAMPLE.—The earth turns completely around on its axis once every day; through how many degrees does it turn in 1 hour?

SOLUTION.—In 1 day there are 24 hours, and since the earth turns through 360° in 24 hours, in 1 hour it will turn through 360° ÷ 24 = 15°. Ans.

81. In adding two angles together, seconds are added to seconds, minutes to minutes, and degrees to degrees; so, also, in subtracting two angles, seconds are subtracted from seconds, minutes from minutes, and degrees from degrees.

EXAMPLE 1.—Add 75° 46′ 17″ and 14° 27′ 34″.

SOLUTION.—
$$75° \ 46′ \ 17″$$
$$14° \ 27′ \ 34″$$
$$\overline{89° \ 73′ \ 51″}$$

Since 73′ = 1° 13′, the 1° is added to the 89°, and the sum is then written 90° 13′ 51″. Ans.

EXAMPLE 2.—What is the difference between 126° 14′ 20″ and 45° 28′ 13″?

SOLUTION.—
$$126° \ 14′ \ 20″$$
$$45° \ 28′ \ 13″$$
$$\overline{7″}$$

Since 28′ cannot be taken from 14′, 1° (= 60′) is taken from 126° and added to the 14′, and the above is written:

$$125° \ 74′ \ 20″$$
$$45° \ 28′ \ 13″$$
$$\overline{80° \ 46′ \ 7″}. \ \text{Ans.}$$

EXAMPLE 3.—Subtract 49° 36′ 14″ from 90°.

SOLUTION.—Since 1° = 60′ and 1′ = 60″, we can write 90° = 89° 59′ 60″, and
$$89° \ 59′ \ 60″$$
$$49° \ 36′ \ 14″$$
$$\overline{40° \ 23′ \ 46″}. \ \text{Ans.}$$

EXAMPLE 4.—Add 83° 15′ 39″ and 96° 44′ 21″.

SOLUTION.—   83° 15′ 39″
                                    96° 44′ 21″
                                   ―――――――――――
                                   179° 59′ 60″

Since 60″ = 1′, add 1′ to 59′, making it 60′; since 60′ = 1°, add 1 to 179° making it 180°.

Therefore,   83° 15′ 39″ + 96° 44′ 21″ = 180°.   **Ans.**

EXAMPLES FOR PRACTICE

1. Add 43° 0′ 59″ and 10° 59′ 40″.   Ans. 54° 0′ 39″.
2. From 180° 12′ 20″ subtract 3° 12′ 56″.   Ans. 176° 59′ 24″.
3. From 84° take 83° 14′ 10″, and to the result add 14′ 10″. Ans. 1°.

THE TRIGONOMETRIC FUNCTIONS

82. A **function** of a quantity is another quantity depending on the first one for its value. The circumference of a circle, for example, is a function of the diameter, because the length of the circumference depends on the length of the diameter.

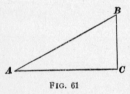

FIG. 61

83. In the right triangle ACB, Fig. 61, right-angled at C, the size of the angle A (and consequently, also, of angle B) depends on the relative lengths of the sides AC, AB, and BC. No one of the sides can be changed without altering the length of at least one other side, and consequently changing the angles A and B, the angle C remaining a right angle. For this reason the sides are functions of the angles.

84. In Fig. 62, ACB is a right triangle, right-angled at C. The sides AB and AC have been produced to B' and C', respectively, $B'C'$ being perpendicular to AC' and therefore parallel to BC. The two triangles ACB and $AC'B'$ are

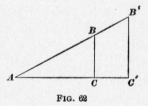

FIG. 62

similar, since their corresponding angles are equal; hence, their corresponding sides are proportional, and we have the proportions

$$\frac{BC}{AB} = \frac{B'C'}{AB'}; \qquad\qquad \frac{BC}{AC} = \frac{B'C'}{AC'}.$$

It is evident that, no matter what the lengths of the sides of these similar triangles may be, the ratios $\dfrac{BC}{AB}, \dfrac{B'C'}{AB'}, \dfrac{BC}{AC},$ $\dfrac{B'C'}{AC'}$ will always have the same value so long as the angles remain the same. Therefore, if we knew what the values were for all angles, we could lay off any angle whatever. For, suppose that the ratio $\dfrac{BC}{AB}$ was known to be $\dfrac{1}{3}$; then, $\dfrac{BC}{AB} = \dfrac{1}{3}$ or $BC = \frac{1}{3} AB$. If we call AB, 1, then $BC = \frac{1}{3}$ and the angle can be constructed as shown in Fig. 63. Take AB as a radius and describe a circle; draw the two diameters DH and EF at right angles to each other. Lay off $AG = \frac{1}{3}$ (AB being 1), and draw GB parallel to DC, intersecting the circle in B. Then draw AB, and BAC is the required angle, since $BC = AG = \frac{1}{3} AB$.

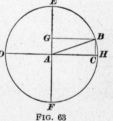

FIG. 63

In a similar manner we can construct an angle when the ratio $\dfrac{BC}{AC}$ or $\dfrac{B'C'}{AC'}$ is known. Suppose this ratio is $\frac{2}{5}$ and that AC be taken equal to 1. With AC, Fig. 64, as a radius describe a circle and erect a perpendicular at C. Make $CB = \frac{2}{5}$ (AC being 1) and draw AB. Then, BAC is the required angle.

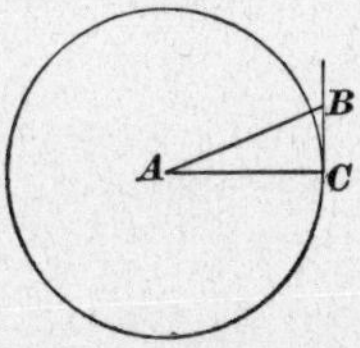

FIG. 64

85. Suppose, in Fig. 62, the distances AC' and $B'C'$ were known, but that they were so great that it was impossible to lay them off on a drawing so that AB' could be drawn and measured; also, that it was necessary to know the direction of the line AB'.

i. e., the angle A.   Of course, a drawing could be made to a
reduced scale; the angle A could be measured with a protractor; and the length of $A B'$ could be measured with a
scale.   The results obtained in this manner would not, in
general, be accurate; the method would be long and very
inconvenient, and facilities for doing this might not be at
hand.   If, however, we had a table giving the values of the
ratio $\dfrac{B C}{A C}$ for all angles, we could find the value of the
ratio $\dfrac{B' C'}{A C'}$ $\left(\text{which equals the value of the ratio } \dfrac{B C}{A C}\right)$, and
then by looking in the table, find what angle had this value;
this angle would be the angle A.   The length of $A B'$ could
be found by adding the squares of $A C'$ and $B' C'$ and
extracting the square root (see Art. **50**); an easier way
would be to look in a table giving the values of the
ratios $\dfrac{B C}{A B}$ and divide $B' C'$ by the ratio corresponding to
angle A.   For representing the value of the ratio $\dfrac{B C}{A B}$ by R,
we have

$$\frac{B C}{A B} = \frac{B' C'}{A B'} = R, \text{ or } A B' = \frac{B' C'}{R}.$$

From the foregoing, it will be perceived that the ratios
mentioned are extremely important—they constitute, in fact,
the foundations of trigonometry.   These ratios, together
with several others not yet described, are called the **trigonometric functions.**

86.   There are eight trigonometric functions, the four
principal ones being the *sine, cosine, tangent,* and *cotangent.*
The remaining four are the *secant, cosecant, versedsine,* and
coversedsine.

In some works on trigonometry and engineering, the trigonometric functions are treated as lines, while in others they
are treated as ratios.   We shall therefore define them both
ways, so the student will have no difficulty in understanding
either method.   These functions will now be defined.

87. In any right triangle, as $O\,C\,A$, Fig. 65, right-angled at C, considering the angle O, the side $A\,C$ is called the **side opposite** and the side $O\,C$ the **side adjacent**; $O\,A$ is, of course, the *hypotenuse.* Similarly, $O\,C$ is the side opposite and $A\,C$ the side adjacent for the angle A. The ratio of the side opposite to the hypotenuse is called the **sine;** that is, for the angle $A\,O\,C$,

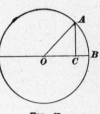

Fig. 65

$$\text{Sine} = \frac{\text{side opposite}}{\text{hypotenuse}} = \frac{A\,C}{O\,A},$$

which is equal to $A\,C$, when $O\,A$ is taken as equal to 1. In other words, if a circle whose center is O is described *with a radius of unit length*, the perpendicular dropped from the point where one side of the angle (whose vertex is at the center of the circle) cuts the circle to the other side is the *sine.*

88. The **cosine** of an angle, as O, Fig. 65, is the ratio of the side adjacent to the hypotenuse; therefore,

$$\text{Cosine} = \frac{\text{side adjacent}}{\text{hypotenuse}} = \frac{O\,C}{O\,A},$$

which is equal to $O\,C$, when the radius $O\,A = 1$. In other words, the *cosine* is the distance from the foot of the sine to the center of the circle, when the radius is unity.

89. The **tangent** of an angle, as $A\,O\,B$, Fig. 66, is the ratio of the side opposite to the side adjacent; therefore,

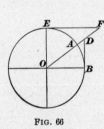

Fig. 66

$$\text{Tangent} = \frac{\text{side opposite}}{\text{side adjacent}} = \frac{D\,B}{O\,B},$$

which is equal to $D\,B$, when the radius $O\,B = 1$. In other words, if a tangent is drawn at the right extremity of the horizontal diameter of a circle (described with a unit radius), which forms one side of an angle, and the other side of the angle is prolonged to meet it, the distance intercepted by the two sides of the angle is called the *tangent* of that angle.

90. The **cotangent** of an angle, as $A\ O\ B$, Fig. 66, is the ratio of the side adjacent to the side opposite; therefore,

$$\text{Cotangent} = \frac{\text{side adjacent}}{\text{side opposite}} = \frac{O\ B}{D\ B}.$$

The cotangent is represented by the line $E\ F$, which is tangent to the circle at E, for the triangles $F\ E\ O$ and $D\ B\ O$ are similar, since they both have a right angle; the angles $E\ F\ O$ and $D\ O\ B$ are equal (see Art. **28**), and the angles $F\ O\ E$ and $O\ D\ B$ are also equal, being complements of the same angle $D\ O\ B$ (see Arts. **26** and **49**). Therefore, $\dfrac{O\ B}{D\ B} = \dfrac{E\ F}{E\ O}$. But $E\ O$ is the radius, which we assumed to be 1, and $\dfrac{O\ B}{D\ B}$ is the cotangent of $D\ O\ B$; hence,

$$\text{Cotangent} = \frac{O\ B}{D\ B} = \frac{E\ F}{E\ O} = EF,$$

when the radius $O\ E = 1$. In other words, if a tangent is drawn from the upper extremity of a vertical diameter of a circle, whose horizontal diameter forms one side of an angle, and the other side of the angle is produced until it meets this tangent, the distance intercepted on this tangent between the extremity of the vertical diameter and the produced line is called the *cotangent* of that angle, when the radius $= 1$.

91. The **secant** of an angle is the ratio of the hypotenuse to the side adjacent; therefore, referring to Fig. 67,

$$\text{Secant} = \frac{\text{hypotenuse}}{\text{side adjacent}} = \frac{O\ A}{O\ C} = \frac{O\ D}{O\ B} = O\ D,$$

when the radius $O\ B = 1$. In other words, the *secant* is the line included between the point of intersection of the tangent with the inclined side of the angle and the center of a circle, when the radius $= 1$. $O\ D$ is also the secant in Fig. 66.

92. The **cosecant** is the ratio of the hypotenuse to the side opposite. Therefore, referring to Fig. 67,

$$\text{Cosecant} = \frac{\text{hypotenuse}}{\text{side opposite}} = \frac{OA}{AC}.$$

But, since $O R N$ and $O C A$ are similar right triangles, the side $O R$ corresponding to side $A C$,

$$\text{Cosecant} = \frac{OA}{AC} = \frac{ON}{OR} = ON,$$

when the radius $O B = 1$.   In other words, the *cosecant* is the line included between the point of intersection of the cotangent with the inclined side of the angle and the center of a circle, when the radius $= 1$.   In Fig. 66, $O F$ is the cosecant.

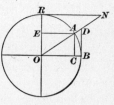

FIG. 67

93.   The versedsine and coversedsine are not generally treated as ratios. The **versedsine** is defined as 1 minus the cosine.   In Fig. 67,

$$\text{Versedsine} = 1 - \text{cosine} = 1 - \frac{OC}{OA} = 1 - OC = CB,$$

when radius $O A = 1$.

The versedsine might be defined as the ratio of $C B$ to $O A$ (Fig. 67), $C B$ being in all cases the distance from the foot C of the sine to the right extremity B of the horizontal diameter.

The **coversedsine** is equal to 1 minus the sine.   In Fig. 67, $A E$ is parallel to $O B$; hence, $E O = A C =$ sine of angle $A O C$, when radius $O A = 1$.   Therefore,

$$\text{Coversedsine} = 1 - \text{sine} = 1 - \frac{AC}{OA}$$

$$= 1 - A C = 1 - E O = E R,$$

when radius $O A = 1$.

94.   The four functions last defined are but little used except for special purposes; if required, they can be readily found from a table giving the values of sines, cosines, tangents, and cotangents; hence, we shall here treat only of the four functions first named.

In Art. **87,** the sine was defined as $\dfrac{\text{side opposite}}{\text{hypotenuse}}$, or as equal to $\dfrac{A\,C}{O\,A}$; in Art. **92,** the cosecant was defined as $\dfrac{\text{hypotenuse}}{\text{side opposite}}$, or as equal to $\dfrac{O\,A}{A\,C}$. It will be noticed that these two ratios are reciprocals* of each other, $\dfrac{A\,C}{O\,A} = \dfrac{1}{\frac{O\,A}{A\,C}} = \dfrac{A\,C}{O\,A}$.

In other words, the cosecant $= \dfrac{1}{\text{sine}}$, and, hence, to find the cosecant of an angle, all that is necessary is to divide 1 by the sine of the angle. From this it follows that dividing by the sine is the same as multiplying by the cosecant.

Similarly, the secant is the reciprocal of the cosine; that is, secant $= \dfrac{1}{\text{cosine}}$. Hence, if it is required to find the secant of some angle, the secant may be found by dividing 1 by the cosine of the angle. Therefore, dividing by the cosine is equivalent to multiplying by the secant.

To find the versedsine of angle, find its cosine and subtract it from 1; to find the coversedsine, find the sine of the angle and subtract it from 1.

By comparing the ratios of the tangent and cotangent, it will be noticed that the cotangent is the reciprocal of the tangent; likewise, the tangent is the reciprocal of the cotangent.

It may be readily shown that, by dividing the ratio for the sine by that for the cosine, the tangent is equal to $\dfrac{\text{sine}}{\text{cosine}}$.

Similarly, the cotangent is equal to $\dfrac{\text{cosine}}{\text{sine}}$. Hence, having given the sine and cosine of any angle, its tangent and cotangent are easily found.

---

*The *reciprocal* of a number is 1 divided by the number. The reciprocal of 4 is ¼, and 4 and ¼ are said to be reciprocals of each other. The reciprocal of a fraction is the fraction inverted; thus, the reciprocal of ⅞ is ⁸⁄₇.

95. The words cosine, cotangent, cosecant, and coversed‑sine are abbreviations for complement sine, complement tangent, etc., which in turn are abbreviations for the expressions "sine of complement," "tangent of comple‑ment," etc. In other words, the cosine of an angle is equal to the sine of the complement of that angle; the cotangent of an angle is equal to the tangent of its complement, etc.

That the cosine is equal to the sine of the complement is readily seen by referring to Fig. 67. Here, AOB is the given angle and AOR is its complement (see Art. **26**); AC is its sine and OC is its cosine. It is evident, from the definition of the sine, that EA is the sine of the angle AOR. But EA is equal to OC, since $EACO$ is a rectangle; therefore, the cosine of AOB is equal to the sine of its complement AOR.

Similarly, RN is the tangent of AOR and the cotangent of AOB, and ON is the secant of AOR and the cosecant of AOB. The cosine of AOR is OE, which is equal to AC, the sine of AOB. Therefore, the versedsine of AOR is ER, the coversedsine of AOB. In other words, the coversedsine of AOB is equal to the versedsine of AOR, the complement of AOB.

96. In order to save time and space in writing, the names of the functions are abbreviated as follows: **Sin** for sine; **cos** for cosine; **tan** for tangent; **cot** for cotangent; **sec** for secant; **csc** or **cosec** for cosecant; **vers** for versedsine; and **cvs** or **covers** for coversedsine. These abbreviations are used only when referring directly to angles; when the names are used in a general sense, they are written out in full. Let A represent some angle; then, if it were desired to refer to the sine, tangent, etc. of this angle, it would be written sin A, tan A, etc., and these expressions would be read "sine A," "tangent A," etc.

These abbreviations must always be pronounced in full. Thus, cos $14°\ 22'\ 46''$ is pronounced *cosine fourteen degrees twenty-two minutes forty-six seconds;* tan $45°$ is pronounced *tangent forty-five degrees.*

97. To facilitate calculations, tables of the trigonometric functions are employed. These tables give the sine, cosine, tangent, and cotangent of the degrees and minutes in a circle whose radius is 1. There are two kinds of tables giving the trigonometric functions; viz., the table of *natural functions* and the table of *logarithmic functions.* The table of **natural functions** gives the actual values of the ratios, while the table of **logarithmic functions** gives the logarithms of the natural functions. Only the table of natural functions is described in the present text.

98. From the definitions of the various trigonometric functions we derive the following very useful rules for right triangles:

$$Sine = \frac{side\ opposite}{hypotenuse}; \text{ therefore,}$$

Rule 1.—*Side opposite = hypotenuse × sine.**

Rule 2.—*Hypotenuse* $= \dfrac{side\ opposite}{sine}.$

$$Cosine = \frac{side\ adjacent}{hypotenuse}; \text{ therefore,}$$

Rule 3.—*Side adjacent = hypotenuse × cosine.*

Rule 4.—*Hypotenuse* $= \dfrac{side\ adjacent}{cosine}.$

$$Tangent = \frac{side\ opposite}{side\ adjacent}; \text{ therefore,}$$

Rule 5.—*Side opposite = side adjacent × tangent.*

$$Cotangent = \frac{side\ adjacent}{side\ opposite}; \text{ therefore,}$$

Rule 6.—*Side adjacent = side opposite × cotangent.*

---

* Since the quotient equals the dividend divided by the divisor, the dividend equals the product of the divisor and quotient.

TRIGONOMETRIC TABLES

99. We shall now explain how to find the sine, cosine, tangent, and cotangent of an angle by means of the table of natural trigonometric functions that accompanies this text. It may here be remarked that the values of the functions are never calculated directly (except in making a table), because the process is so long and laborious that it would require considerable time to calculate even the value of one function of a single angle, and there is no simple method of determining the angle corresponding to a given function, except by aid of a table. As they are not necessary, the secants, cosecants, versedsines, and coversedsines are omitted entirely.

100. Given an angle, to find its sine, cosine, tangent, and cotangent :

EXAMPLE 1.—Let it be required to find the sine, cosine, tangent, and cotangent of an angle of 37° 24′.

SOLUTION.—Look in the table of *natural sines* along the tops of the pages and find 37°. The left-hand column is marked (′), meaning that the minutes are to be sought in that column, and begin with 0, 1, 2, 3, etc., to 60. Glancing *down* this column until 24′ is found, find opposite this 24′ in the column marked *sine*, and headed 37°, the number .60738; then, .60738 = sin 37° 24′. In exactly the same manner, find opposite 24′ in the column marked *cosine*, and headed 37°, the number .79441, which corresponds to cos 37° 24′; or cos 37° 24′ = .79441. So, also, find in the column marked *tangent*, and headed 37°, and opposite 24′, the number .76456; whence, tan 37° 24′ = .76456. Finally, find in the column marked *cotangent*, and headed 37°, and opposite 24′, the number 1.30795; whence, cot 37° 24′ = 1.30795.

In most of the tables published, the angles run only from 0° to 45°, at the heads of the columns; to find an angle greater than 45°, *look at the bottom of the page and glance upwards*, **using the extreme right-hand column to find minutes,** which begin with 0 at the *bottom* and run upwards, 1, 2, 3, etc., to 60.

EXAMPLE 2. — Find the sine, cosine, tangent, and cotangent of 77° 43′.

SOLUTION.—Since this angle is greater than 45°, look along the bottom of the tables, until the column marked *sine* at the bottom, and having 77° under it, is found. Glancing *up* the column of minutes on the *right*, until 43' is found, find opposite 43' in the column marked *sine* at the bottom, and having 77° under it, the number .97711; this is the sine of 77° 43', or s*i*n 77° 43' = .97711. Similarly, in the column marked *cosine*, and having 77° under it, find opposite 43', in the right-hand column, the number .21275; this is the cosine of 77° 43', or cos 77° 43' = .21275. So, also, find that 4.59283 is the tangent of 77° 43', or tan 77° 43' = 4.59283. Finally, in the same manner, find that the cotangent of 77° 43' or cot 77° 43' = .21773.

101. Let it be required to find the sine of 14° 22' 26",

EXPLANATION.—The sine of 14° 22' 26" lies between the sine of 14° 22' and the sine of 14° 23'. For a difference of 1 minute or less between two or more angles, it is correct to assume that the differences in the values of the sine, cosine, etc. of the angles are proportional to the differences in the number of seconds in these angles. The difference in the number of seconds between 14° 22' and 14° 22' 26" is 26", and between 14° 22' and 14° 23' is 60". The sine of 14° 22' is .24813 ; sine of 14° 23' is .24841. The difference between the value of the sine of 14° 22' and the sine of 14° 22' 26" is not known; hence, represent it by x. The difference between the value of the sine of 14° 22' and the sine of 14° 23' is .24841 − .24813 = .00028, or 28 parts. Therefore, we have the proportion

$$26'' : 60'' = x \text{ parts} : 28 \text{ parts, or } \frac{26''}{60''} = \frac{x \text{ parts}}{28 \text{ parts}},$$

from which $x \text{ parts} = \dfrac{26}{60} \times 28 = 12.1 \text{ parts}.$

Neglecting the .1, since .1 is less than .5, we must add 12 parts, or .00012, to .24813 to obtain the sine of 14° 22' 26". Hence, sin 14° 22' 26" = .24813 + .00012 = .24825.

102. By referring to the table of sines, cosines, tangents, and cotangents, it will be observed that, as the angles increase in size, the sines and tangents increase, while the *cosines and cotangents decrease.* In the above example, there-fore, had it been required to find the *cosine* or the *cotangent* of 14° 22' 26", the correction for the 26" would have been *subtracted* from the cosine or the cotangent of 14° 22' instead of added to it.   The reason for this will be made apparent on referring to Fig. 67.   Here it will be seen that as the sine and tangent increase, the cosine and cotangent decrease, and vice versa.   From the foregoing we have, to find the sine, cosine, tangent, or cotangent of an angle containing seconds, the following rule :

Rule 7.—*Find in the table the sine, cosine, tangent, or cotangent corresponding to the degrees and minutes of the angle.*

For the seconds, find the difference between this value and the value of the sine, cosine, tangent, or cotangent of an angle 1 minute greater; multiply this difference by a fraction whose numerator is the number of seconds in the given angle and whose denominator is 60.

If the sine or tangent is sought, add this correction to the value first found; if the cosine or cotangent is sought, subtract the correction.

EXAMPLE.—Find the sine, cosine, tangent, and cotangent of 56°43′17″.

SOLUTION.—Sin 56° 43′ = .83597. Sin 56° 44′ = .83613. Since 56° 43′ 17″ is greater than 56° 43′ and less than 56° 44′, the value of the sine of the angle lies between .83597 and .83613; the difference = .83613 − .83597 = .00016. Multiplying this by the fraction $\frac{17}{60}$, .00016 × $\frac{17}{60}$ = .00005, nearly, which is to be *added* to .83597, the value first found, or .83597 + .00005 = .83602. Hence, sin 56° 43′ 17″ = .83602. Ans.

Cos 56° 43′ = .54878; cos 56° 44′ = .54854 ; the difference = .54878 − .54854 = .00024, and .00024 × $\frac{17}{60}$ = .00007, nearly. Now, since the *cosine* is sought, we must *subtract* this correction from cos 56° 43′ or .54878; subtracting, .54878 − .00007 = .54871. Hence, cos 56° 43′ 17″ = .54871. Ans.

Tan 56° 43′ = 1.52332; tan 56° 44′ = 1.52429; the difference = .00097, and .00097 × $\frac{17}{60}$ = .00027, nearly. Since the tangent is sought, we must *add*, giving 1.52332 + .00027 = 1.52359. Hence, tan 56° 43′ 17″ = 1.52359. Ans.

Cot 56° 43′ = .65646; cot 56° 44′ = .65604; the difference = .00042, and .00042 × $\frac{17}{60}$ = .00012, nearly. Since the cotangent is sought, we must *subtract*, giving .65646 − .00012 = .65634. Hence, cot 56° 43′ 17″ = .65634. Ans.

103. Given the sine, cosine, tangent, or cotangent, to find the angle corresponding :

EXAMPLE 1.—The sine of an angle is .47486; what is the angle?

SOLUTION.—Consulting the table of natural sines, glance down the columns marked *sine* until .47486 is found opposite 21', in the left-hand column, and under the column headed 28°. Therefore, the angle whose sine = .47486 is 28° 21', or sin 28° 21' = .47486. Ans.

EXAMPLE 2.—Find the angle whose cosine is .27032.

SOLUTION.—Looking in the columns marked *cosine*, at the top of the page, it is not found; hence, the angle is greater than 45°. Consequently, looking in the columns marked *cosine* at the bottom of the page, it is found opposite 19', in the *right-hand* column of minutes, and in the column having 74° at the bottom. Therefore, the angle whose cosine is .27032 is 74° 19', or cos 74° 19' = .27032. Ans.

EXAMPLE 3.—Find the angle whose tangent is 2.15925.

SOLUTION.—On searching the table of natural tangents, the given tangent is found to belong to an angle greater than 45°, so it must be looked for in the column marked *tangent* at the bottom. It is found opposite 9', in the right-hand column of minutes and in the column having 65° at the bottom. Therefore, tan 65° 9' = 2.15925. Ans.

EXAMPLE 4.—Find the angle whose cotangent is .43412.

SOLUTION.—From the table of natural cotangents, it is found that this value is less than the cotangent of 45°, so it must be found in the column marked *cotangent* at the bottom. Looking there, it is found in the column having 66° at the bottom, and opposite 32', in the right-hand column of minutes. Therefore, the angle whose cotangent is .43412 is 66° 32', or cot 66° 32' = .43412. Ans.

104. Let it be required to find the angle whose sine is .42531.

EXPLANATION.—Referring to the table of sines, this number is found to lie between .42525, the sine of 25° 10', and .42552, the sine of 25° 11'. The difference between these two numbers is .42552 − .42525 = .00027, or 27 parts; the difference between .42525, the sine of 25° 10', and .42531, the sine of the given angle, is .42531 − .42525 = .00006, or 6 parts. Representing by x the number of seconds that the angle whose sine is .42531 exceeds 25° 10', we have the proportion $x'' : 60'' = 6$ parts : 27 parts,

or
$$\frac{x''}{60''} = \frac{6 \text{ parts}}{27 \text{ parts}}$$

from which $x = 60 \times \dfrac{6}{27} = 13.3''$. Hence, the angle whose sine is .42531 is 25° 10' 13.3''.

The angle is found from the cosine, tangent, and cotangent in exactly the same manner.

105. To find the angle corresponding to a given sine, cosine, tangent, or cotangent, whose exact value is not contained in the table:

Rule 8.—*Find the difference of the two numbers in the table between which the given sine, cosine, tangent, or cotangent falls, and use the number of parts in this difference as the denominator of a fraction.*

Find the difference between the number belonging to the **smaller angle** *and the given sine, cosine, tangent, or cotangent, and use the number of parts in the difference just found as the numerator of the fraction mentioned above. Multiply this fraction by 60, and the result will be the number of seconds to be added to the* **smaller angle.**

EXAMPLE 1.—Find the angle whose sine is .57698.

SOLUTION.—Looking in the table of natural sines, in the columns marked *sine*, it is found between .57691 = sin 35° 14' and .57715 = sin 35° 15'. The difference between them is .57715 − .57691 = .00024, or 24 parts. The difference between the sine of the smaller angle, or sin 35° 14' = .57691, and the given sine, or .57698, is .57698 − .57691 = .00007, or 7 parts. Then, $\frac{7}{24} \times 60 = 17.5''$, and the required angle is 35° 14' 17.5'', or sin 35° 14' 17.5'' = .57698. Ans.

EXAMPLE 2.—Find the angle whose cosine is .27052.

SOLUTION.—Looking in the table of cosines, it is found to belong to a greater angle than 45° and, hence, must be sought for in the columns marked *cosine*, at the bottom of the page. It is found between the numbers .27060 = cos 74° 18' and .27032 = cos 74° 19'. The difference between the two numbers is .27060 − .27032 = .00028, or 28 parts. The cosine of the *smaller angle*, or 74° 18', is .27060, and the difference between this and the given cosine is .27060 − .27052 = .00008, or 8 parts. Hence, $\frac{8}{28} \times 60 = 17.1''$, nearly, and the angle whose cosine is .27052 = 74° 18' 17.1'', or cos 74° 18' 17.1'' = .27052. Ans.

EXAMPLE 3.—Find the angle whose tangent is 2.15841.

SOLUTION.— 2.15841 falls between 2.15760 = tan 65° 8' and 2.15925 = tan 65° 9'. The difference between these numbers is 2.15925 − 2.15760

= .00165, or 165 parts. 2.15841 − 2.15760 = .00081, or 81 parts. Hence, $\frac{81}{165} \times 60 = 29.5''$, nearly, and the angle whose tangent is 2.15841 = 65° 8′ 29.5″, or tan 65° 8′ 29.5″ = 2.15841. Ans.

EXAMPLE 4.—Find the angle whose cotangent is 1.26342.

SOLUTION.— 1.26342 falls between 1.26395 = cot 38° 21′ and 1.26319 = cot 38° 22′. The difference between these numbers is 1.26395 − 1.26319 = .00076. 1.26395 − 1.26342 = .00053. $\frac{53}{76} \times 60 = 41.9$, nearly, and the angle whose cotangent is 1.26342 = 38° 21′ 41.9″, or cot 38° 21′ 41.9″ = 1.26342. Ans.

EXAMPLES FOR PRACTICE

1. Find the (a) sine, (b) cosine, and (c) tangent of 48° 17′.

Ans. $\begin{cases} (a) & .74644. \\ (b) & .66545. \\ (c) & 1.12172. \end{cases}$

2. Find the (a) sine, (b) cosine, and (c) tangent of 13° 11′ 6″.

Ans. $\begin{cases} (a) & .22810. \\ (b) & .97364. \\ (c) & .23427. \end{cases}$

3. Find the (a) sine, (b) cosine, and (c) tangent of 72° 0′ 1.8″.

Ans. $\begin{cases} (a) & .95106. \\ (b) & .30901. \\ (c) & 3.07777. \end{cases}$

4. (a) Of what angle is .26489 the sine? (b) Of what is it the cosine?

Ans. $\begin{cases} (a) & 15° 21′ 37.2″. \\ (b) & 74° 38′ 22.8″. \end{cases}$

5. (a) Of what angle is .68800 the sine? (b) Of what the cosine? (c) Of what the tangent?

Ans. $\begin{cases} (a) & 43° 28′ 20″. \\ (b) & 46° 31′ 40″. \\ (c) & 34° 31′ 40.5″. \end{cases}$

THE SOLUTION OF TRIANGLES

RIGHT TRIANGLES

106. As previously stated, every triangle has **six parts,** three sides and three angles, and if any three parts are given, one of them being a side, the other three may be found.

In right triangles, it is only necessary to know *two* parts in addition to the right angle, one of which must be a side.

Rules **1** to **8** and the definitions of sine, cosine, tangent, and cotangent are sufficient for solving all cases of right triangles. The method is best illustrated by examples. There are two cases.

107. **Case I.**—*When the two given parts are a side and an angle:*

EXAMPLE 1.—In Fig. 68, the length of the hypotenuse $A B$ of the right triangle $A C B$, right-angled at C, is 24 feet, and the angle A is 29° 31'; find the sides $A C$ and $B C$ and the angle B.

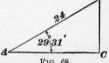

FIG. 68

NOTE.—When working examples of this kind, construct the figure and mark the known parts. This is a great help in solving the example. Hence, in the figure, draw the angle A to represent an angle of 29° 31' and complete the right triangle $A C B$, right-angled at C, as shown. Mark the angle A and the hypotenuse, as is done in the figure.

SOLUTION.—Referring to Art. **49**, angle $B = 90° - 29° 31' = 60° 29'$. To find $A C$, use rule **3**; viz., $A C$, or side adjacent = hypotenuse $\times$ cosine $= 24 \times \cos 29° 31' = 24 \times .87021 = 20.89$ feet, nearly.

To find $B C$, use the same rule; thus, $B C = 24 \times \cos 60° 29' = 24' \times .49268 = 11.82$ feet, nearly. To find $B C$, rule **1** could also have been used, viz., side opposite = hypotenuse $\times$ sine, or $B C = 24 \times \sin 29° 31' = 24 \times .49268 = 11.82$ feet, nearly.

Ans. $\begin{cases} \text{Angle } B = 60° 29'. \\ \text{Side } A C = 20.89 \text{ ft.} \\ \text{Side } B C = 11.82 \text{ ft.} \end{cases}$

EXAMPLE 2.—One side of a right triangle $A C B$, right-angled at C, Fig. 69, is 37 feet 7 inches long; the angle opposite is 25° 33' 7''. What are the lengths of the hypotenuse and the side adjacent, and what is the other angle?

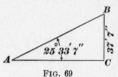

FIG. 69

SOLUTION. — Angle $B = 90° - 25° 33' 7'' = 64° 26' 53''$.

To find the hypotenuse, use rule **2**,

$$\text{Hypotenuse} = \frac{\text{side opposite}}{\text{sine}}.$$

Since the side opposite is given in feet and inches, both must be reduced to feet or both to inches.

7 inches $= \frac{7}{12}$ foot $= .583+$ foot; hence, $B C = 37.583$ feet.

Therefore, the hypotenuse is equal to

$$\frac{37.583}{\sin 25° 33' 7''} = \frac{37.583}{.43133} = 87.133 \text{ feet} = 87 \text{ feet 2 inches, nearly.}$$

To find the side $A\,C$, use rule **3**; side adjacent = hypotenuse × cosine = 87.133 × cos 25° 33′ 7″ = 87.133 × .90219 = 78.61 feet = 78 feet 7¼ inches, nearly.

$$\text{Ans.} \begin{cases} \text{Angle } B = 64°\ 26'\ 53''. \\ A\ C = 78 \text{ ft. } 7\tfrac{1}{4} \text{ in.} \\ A\ B = 87 \text{ ft. } 2 \text{ in.} \end{cases}$$

The work involved in finding the sine and cosine of 25° 33′ 7″, in the above example, is as follows: Sin 25° 33′ = .43130; sin 25° 34′ = .43156; difference = .00026; .00026 × $\tfrac{7}{60}$ = .00003. Hence, sin 25° 33′ 7″ = .43130 + .00003 = .43133.

Cos 25° 33′ = .90221; cos 25° 34′ = .90208; difference = .00013; .00013 × $\tfrac{7}{60}$ = .00002, nearly. Hence, cos 25° 33′ 7″ = .90221 − .00002 = .90219.

108. **Case II.**—*When two sides are given:*

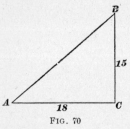

FIG. 70

EXAMPLE 1.—In the right triangle $A\,C\,B$, Fig. 70, right-angled at C, $A\,C = 18$ and $B\,C = 15$; find $A\,B$ and the angles A and B.

SOLUTION.—As neither of the two acute angles is given, one of the angles must be found by making use of the definition of one of the functions of the angle. Considering the angle A, we have: side opposite equals 15 and the side adjacent equals 18; hence, we may use the definition of either the tangent or cotangent. Using the definition of the tangent,

$$\tan A = \frac{\text{side opposite}}{\text{side adjacent}} = \frac{15}{18} = .83333.$$

To find the angle whose tangent is .83333, we have: Tangent of next less angle is .83317 = tan 39° 48′; tangent of the next greater angle is .83366; difference is .00049. The difference between .83317, the tangent of the smaller angle, and .83333, the given tangent, is .83333 − .83317 = .00016. Hence, $\tfrac{16}{49}$ × 60 = 19.6″, and the angle whose tangent is .83333 = 39° 48′ 19.6″ = angle A.

Angle $B = 90° − 39° 48′ 19.6″ = 50° 11′ 40.4″$.

To find the hypotenuse $A\,B$, use rule **2** or **4**; using rule **2**,

$$\text{Hypotenuse} = \frac{\text{side opposite}}{\text{sine}} = \frac{15}{\sin 39°\ 48'\ 19.6''} = \frac{15}{.64018} = 23.43.$$

$$\text{Ans.} \begin{cases} \text{Angle } A = 39°\ 48'\ 19.6''. \\ \text{Angle } B = 50°\ 11'\ 40.4''. \\ A\ B = 23.43. \end{cases}$$

EXAMPLE 2.—In the right triangle $A\,C\,B$, Fig. 71, right-angled at C, $A\,C = .024967$ mile and $A\,B = .04792$ mile; find the other parts.

SOLUTION.—Here the hypotenuse and the side adjacent are given; hence, using the definition of the cosine,

$$\cos A = \frac{\text{side adjacent}}{\text{hypotenuse}} = \frac{.024967}{.04792} = .52101.$$

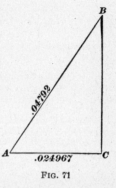

The angle whose cosine is .52101 = 58° 36′ = angle A. Angle $B = 90° - 58° 36′ = 31° 24′$.
To find side BC, use rule **5**.
Side opposite A = side adjacent × tan A, or $BC = .024967 × 1.63826 = .0409$ mile.

Ans. $\begin{cases} \text{Angle } A = 58° \ 36′. \\ \text{Angle } B = 31° \ 24′. \\ BC = .0409 \text{ mi.} \end{cases}$

FIG. 71

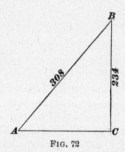

EXAMPLE 3.—In the right triangle ACB, Fig. 72, right-angled at C, $AB = 308$ feet and $BC = 234$ feet; find the other parts.

SOLUTION.—Here the hypotenuse and the side opposite are given; hence, using the definition of sine,

$$\sin A = \frac{\text{side opposite}}{\text{hypotenuse}} = \frac{234}{308} = .75974.$$

The angle whose sine is .75974 = 49° 26′ 28″, nearly, = angle A. Angle $B = 90° - 49° 26′ 28″ = 40° 33′ 32″$.

FIG. 72

To find AC, rule **1, 3, 5,** or **6** may be used. Using rule **6,**
side adjacent angle A = side opposite × cot A, or $AC = 234 × .85586 = 200.27$ feet.

Ans. $\begin{cases} \text{Angle } A = 49° \ 26′ \ 28″. \\ \text{Angle } B = 40° \ 33′ \ 32″. \\ AC = 200.27 \text{ ft.} \end{cases}$

EXAMPLES FOR PRACTICE

1. In the right triangle ACB, right-angled at C, the hypotenuse $AB = 40$ inches and angle $A = 28° 14′ 14″$. Solve the triangle.

Ans. $\begin{cases} \text{Angle } B = 61° \ 45′ \ 46″. \\ AC = 35.24 \text{ in.} \\ BC = 18.92 \text{ in.} \end{cases}$

2. In a right triangle ACB, right-angled at C, the side BC = 10 feet 4 inches. If angle $A = 26° 59′ 6″$, what do the other parts equal?

Ans. $\begin{cases} \text{Angle } B = 63° \ 0′ \ 54″. \\ AB = 22 \text{ ft. } 9\frac{1}{4} \text{ in., nearly.} \\ AC = 20 \text{ ft. } 3\frac{1}{2} \text{ in., nearly.} \end{cases}$

3. In a right triangle $A C B$, the hypotenuse $A B = 60$ feet and the side $A C = 22$ feet. Solve the triangle.

Ans. $\begin{cases} \text{Angle } A = 68° \ 29' \ 22.2''. \\ \text{Angle } B = 21° \ 30' \ 37.8''. \\ B C = 55.82 \text{ ft.} \end{cases}$

4. In a right triangle $A C B$, right-angled at C, side $A C = .364$ foot and side $B C = .216$ foot. Solve the triangle.

Ans. $\begin{cases} \text{Angle } A = 30° \ 41' \ 7.5''. \\ \text{Angle } B = 59° \ 18' \ 52.5''. \\ A B = .423 \text{ ft.} \end{cases}$

OBLIQUE TRIANGLES

109. When three parts of *any* triangle are given, one being a side, the remaining parts can be found by drawing a perpendicular from one angle to the opposite side, thus forming two right triangles. The parts of these right triangles can then be computed, and from them the parts of the required triangle can be found.

110. CAUTION.—*When dividing the triangle into two right triangles, care must be taken that the perpendicular be so drawn that one of the right triangles will have two known parts besides the right angle; otherwise the triangle cannot be solved.*

111. Case I.—*When the three known parts are a side and two angles, or two sides and the included angle:*

EXAMPLE 1.—In Fig. 73, the angle $A = 46° \ 14'$, the angle $B = 88° \ 24' \ 11''$, and the side $A B = 21$ inches; find $A C$, $B C$, and the angle C.

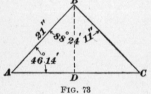

FIG. 73

SOLUTION.—Since the sum of all the angles of any triangle is 2 right angles, or 180° (Art. **48**), we can find the angle C by adding the two known angles and subtracting their sum from 180°.

$$88° \ 24' \ 11'' + 46° \ 14' = 134° \ 38' \ 11''.$$

$$180° - 134° \ 38' \ 11'' = 45° \ 21' \ 49'' = \text{angle } C.$$

From the vertex B, draw $B D$ perpendicular to $A C$. The triangle $A B C$ is now divided into two right triangles $A D B$ and $B D C$, both right-angled at D.

In the right triangle $A\,D\,B$, the angle A, the right angle D, and the hypotenuse $A\,B$ are known; find $B\,D$ and $A\,D$. Using rule **1,** side opposite, or $B\,D$, $= 21 \times \sin 46° 14' = 21 \times .72216 = 15.17$ inches, nearly.

Using rule **3,** side adjacent, or $A\,D$, $= 21 \times \cos 46° 14' = 21 \times .69172$, or $A\,D = 14.53$ inches, nearly.

In the right triangle $B\,D\,C$, the angle C and the side opposite, or $B\,D$, are known; find $B\,C$ and $D\,C$.

Using rule **2,** hypotenuse, or

$$B\,C = \frac{B\,D}{\sin 45° 21' 49''} = \frac{15.17}{.71158} = 21.32 \text{ inches, nearly.}$$

Using rule **3,** side adjacent, or $C\,D$, $= 21.32 \times \cos 45° 21' 49'' = 21.32 \times .70261 = 14.98$ inches.

Since $A\,D + D\,C = A\,C$, we have $14.53 + 14.98 = 29.51$ inches $= A\,C$

Ans. $\begin{cases} A\,C = 29.51 \text{ in.} \\ B\,C = 21.32 \text{ in.} \\ \text{Angle } C = 45° 21' 49''. \end{cases}$

If, in the above example, the angle C had been given instead of the angle A, the dividing line should have been drawn from the angle A to the side $B\,C$, as in the following example:

EXAMPLE 2.—In the triangle $A\,B\,C$, Fig. 74, given $A\,B = 18$ inches, angle $B = 60°$, and angle $C = 38° 42'$; find the other three parts.

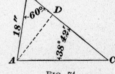

FIG. 74

SOLUTION.—In the triangle $A\,B\,C$, we have angle $A = 180° - (60° + 38° 42') = 81° 18'$.

From the vertex A, draw the line $A\,D$ perpendicular to $B\,C$, thus forming the right triangles $A\,D\,B$ and $A\,D\,C$.

In the triangle $A\,D\,B$, two parts (the side $A\,B$ and angle B) are known besides the right angle. To find $B\,D$, use rule **3.** $B\,D = 18 \times \cos 60° = 18 \times .5 = 9$ inches. To find $A\,D$, use rule **1.** $A\,D = 18 \times \sin 60° = 18 \times .86603 = 15.59$ inches.

In the right triangle $A\,D\,C$, $A\,D$ and the angle C are known. To find $A\,C$, use rule **2.**

$$A\,C = \frac{A\,D}{\sin C} = \frac{15.59}{.62524} = 24.93 \text{ inches.}$$

To obtain $D\,C$, use rule **3.**

$$D\,C = A\,C \times \cos C = 24.93 \times .78043 = 19.46 \text{ inches.}$$

Since $B\,C = B\,D + D\,C$, $B\,C = 9 + 19.46 = 28.46$ inches.

Ans. $\begin{cases} A\,C = 24.93 \text{ in.} \\ B\,C = 28.46 \text{ in.} \\ \text{Angle } A = 81° 18'. \end{cases}$

EXAMPLE 3.—In Fig. 75, $A\,B = 19$ inches, $A\,C = 23$ inches, and the
included angle $A = 36°\ 3'\ 29''$; find the
other two angles and the side $B\,C$.

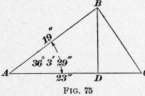

FIG. 75

SOLUTION.—From the vertex B, draw
$B\,D$ perpendicular to $A\,C$, forming the
two right triangles $A\,D\,B$ and $B\,D\,C$.
In the right triangle $A\,D\,B$, $A\,B$ is
known and also the angle A. Hence,
by rule **1**,

$B\,D = 19 \times \sin 36°\ 3'\ 29'' = 19 \times .58861 = 11.18$ inches, nearly.

By rule **3**, $A\,D = 19 \times \cos 36°\ 3'\ 29'' = 19 \times .80842 = 15.36$ inches.

$A\,C - A\,D = 23 - 15.36 = 7.64$ inches $= D\,C$.

In the right triangle $B\,D\,C$, the two sides $B\,D$ and $D\,C$, about the
right angle, are known; hence, from the definition of tangent,

$$\tan C = \frac{B\,D}{D\,C} = \frac{11.18}{7.64} = 1.46335, \text{ and angle } C = 55°\ 39'\ 10''.$$

Applying rule **2**,

$$B\,C = \frac{B\,D}{\sin 55°\ 39'\ 10''} = \frac{11.18}{.82564} = 13.54 \text{ inches.}$$

Angle $B = 180° - (36°3'\,29'' + 55°39'10'') = 180° - 91°42'39'' = 88°\ 17'\ 21''.$

Ans. $\begin{cases} \text{Angle } C = 55°\ 39'\ 10''. \\ \text{Angle } B = 38°\ 17'\ 21''. \\ \text{Side } B\,C = 13.54 \text{ in.} \end{cases}$

112. **Case II.**—*When the three known parts are two
sides and an angle opposite one of them:*

For this case there are, in general, two solutions. This
is readily seen by referring to Fig. 76. Suppose the given
parts are the sides $A\,B$ and
$B\,C$ and the angle A opposite
the side $B\,C$. We construct
the triangle by first drawing the lines $A\,E$ and $A\,F$ in
such a manner that the angle
A shall be of the required
size, and then lay off the distance $A\,B$ along $A\,E$ to rep-

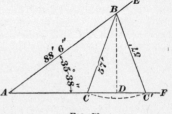

FIG. 76

resent the length of the side $A\,B$. To draw the side $B\,C$,
we take the point B as a center, and with a radius equal to
the length of $B\,C$, we describe the arc $C\,C'$ and draw $B\,C$
and $B\,C'$. The required triangle may be either $A\,B\,C$ or

$A\,B\,C'$. In practice, the conditions will indicate to us which triangle to select; but when the two sides and the angle opposite one of them only are given and no other condition is stated, it is necessary to solve both triangles, which is readily done as follows:

First solve the triangle $A\,B\,C$. To do this, find the length of the perpendicular $B\,D$ by applying rule **1** to angle A ($B\,D = A\,B \times \sin A$); find angle $B\,C\,D$ by applying definition of sine to angle $B\,C\,D$ $\left(\sin B\,C\,D = \dfrac{B\,D}{C\,B}\right)$; find $C\,D$ by applying rule **3** ($C\,D = C\,B \times \cos B\,C\,D$); find $A\,D$ by applying rule **3** ($A\,D = A\,B \times \cos A$). We now know all that is necessary to determine the unknown parts of both triangles. For, the angle $A\,C\,B$ is the supplement (see Art. **27**) of the angle $B\,C\,D$, and is therefore equal to $180° -$ angle $B\,C\,D$; the angle $A\,B\,C = 180° -$ (angle $B\,A\,C +$ angle $A\,C\,B$); the side $A\,C = A\,D - C\,D$; since $C\,B\,C'$ is an isosceles triangle, angle $B\,C\,D = B\,C'\,D$ and $C'\,D = C\,D$; $A\,C' = A\,D + C'\,D$; and, finally, angle $A\,B\,C' = 180° -$ (angle $A +$ angle C').

113. While, in general, there are two solutions to examples falling under Case II, there may be no solution or only one solution, depending on the length of the side $B\,C$.

a. If $B\,C$ is less than the perpendicular $B\,D$, the arc $C\,C'$ will not touch the side $A\,F$ of the angle, and no triangle can be formed; hence, in this instance there is no solution.

b. If $B\,C$ is just equal to $B\,D$, the arc $C\,C'$ will touch $A\,F$ at only one point; only one triangle can be formed—a right triangle—and there is one solution.

c. If $B\,C$ is greater than $B\,D$ and less than $A\,B$, the arc $C\,C'$ will cut $A\,F$ between A and D, and also to the right of D; this gives two triangles and two solutions.

d. If $B\,C$ is just equal to $A\,B$, the arc $C\,C'$ will cut $A\,F$ at A and at a point at a distance $A\,D$ to the right of D; this gives one triangle and one solution.

e. If $B\,C$ is greater than $A\,B$, the arc $C\,C'$ will not cut $A\,F$ between A and D, but will cut $A\,F$ at a point to the right of D; hence, but one triangle can be formed and there is but one solution.

EXAMPLE.—In Fig. 76, $A B = 88$ feet 6 inches, $B C = 57$ feet, and angle $A = 35° \ 0' \ 38''$; find the other parts.

SOLUTION.—Applying the various steps in the order given in Art. **112**, we have by rule **1**, $B D = 88$ feet 6 inches $\times \sin 35° \ 0' \ 38'' = 88.5 \times .57373 = 50.78$ feet.

$\text{Sin } B C D = \dfrac{B D}{B C} = \dfrac{50.78}{57} = .89088$; whence, angle $B C D = 62° \ 59' \ 4.3''$.

By rule **3**, $C D = 57 \times \cos 62° \ 59' \ 4.3'' = 57 \times .45423 = 25.89$ feet.

By rule **3**, $A D = 88.5 \times \cos 35° \ 0' \ 38'' = 88.5 \times .81905 = 72.49$ feet.

We now have the data necessary for obtaining the required parts of the triangle $A B C$. Since the angle $B C D = 62° \ 59' \ 4.3''$, the adjacent angle $A C B = 180° - 62° \ 59' \ 4.3'' = 117° \ 0' \ 55.7''$. Also, angle $A B C = 180° - (35° \ 0' \ 38'' + 117° \ 0' \ 55.7'') = 180° - 152° \ 1' \ 33.7'' = 27° \ 58' \ 26.3''$. Since $A D = 72.49$ feet and $C D = 25.89$ feet, $A C = 72.49 - 25.89 = 46.6$ feet.

For the triangle $A B C'$, angle $C' = 62° \ 59' \ 4.3''$ and angle $A B C' = 180° - (35° \ 0' \ 38'' + 62° \ 59' \ 4.3'') = 82° \ 0' \ 17.7''$. $A C' = 72.49 + 25.89 = 98.38$ feet.

Ans. $\begin{cases} \text{Angle } C = 117° \ 0' \ 55.7''. \\ \text{Angle } B = 27° \ 58' \ 26.3''. \\ \text{Side } A C = 46.6 \text{ ft.} \\ \text{Angle } A B C' = 82° \ 0' \ 17.7''. \\ \text{Angle } C' = 62° \ 59' \ 4.3''. \\ \text{Side } A C' = 98.38 \text{ ft.} \end{cases}$

114. Case III.—*When the three sides are given, to find the angles:*

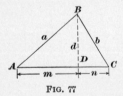

FIG. 77

This case is solved by drawing a line from the vertex of the angle opposite the longest side, perpendicular to that side, as $B D$ in Fig. 77. The parts m and n of the side $A C$ are then deter- mined from the following proportion:

$$m + n \ (\text{or } A C) : a + b = a - b : m - n.$$

This gives the value of $m - n$. The value of $m + n = A C$ is already known, and from the two, m and n may be deter- mined by the principles of arithmetic, as explained below. Having m and n, therefore, the right triangles $A B D$ and $C B D$ may be solved.

Having found the value of $m - n$ and knowing the value of $m + n$, the values of m and n may be determined as follows: It is a principle of arithmetic that if the sum of two numbers and their difference be given, *the greater of the two numbers is equal to one-half the sum of their sum and their difference, and the less of two numbers is equal to one-half the difference between their sum and their difference.* For example, suppose that the sum of two numbers is 22 and their difference is 8. Then, the greater number is $(22 + 8) \div 2 = 15$, and the less number is $(22 - 8) \div 2 = 7$. Therefore, letting m be the greater number and n the less number, $m + n$ represents their sum and $m - n$ their difference; whence,

$$m = \frac{(m + n) + (m - n)}{2},$$

$$n = \frac{(m + n) - (m - n)}{2}.$$

EXAMPLE.—Given, a triangle whose sides are 17 feet 3 inches, 21 feet, and 32 feet long. Find the angles.

SOLUTION.— $m + n$, the longest side, = 32 feet.
$a + b$, the sum of the two shorter sides, $= 21 + 17.25 = 38.25$ feet.
$a - b$, the difference of the two shorter sides, $= 3.75$ feet. Hence,

$$32 : 38.25 = 3.75 : m - n, \text{ or } m - n = \frac{38.25 \times 3.75}{32} = 4.48 \text{ feet.}$$

Then, $m = \dfrac{(m + n) + (m - n)}{2} = \dfrac{32 + 4.48}{2} = 18.24$ feet;

and $n = \dfrac{(m + n) - (m - n)}{2} = \dfrac{32 - 4.48}{2} = 13.76$ feet.

Now, referring to the last figure, we have, in the triangle $A D B$, side $a = 21$ feet and $m = 18.24$ feet; whence, by definition of cosine,

$$\cos A = \frac{18.24}{21} = .86857, \text{ or } A = 29° \ 42' \ 25.7''.$$

In triangle $C B D$, side $b = 17.25$ feet and $n = 13.76$ feet; whence,

$$\cos C = \frac{13.76}{17.25} = .79768, \text{ or } C = 37° \ 5' \ 26.7''.$$

Angle $A B C = 180° - (29° \ 42' \ 25.7'' + 37° \ 5' \ 26.7'') = 113° \ 12' \ 7.6''$.

Ans. $\begin{cases} \text{Angle } A = 29° \ 42' \ 25.7''. \\ \text{Angle } B = 113° \ 12' \ 7.6''. \\ \text{Angle } C = 37° \ 5' \ 26.7''. \end{cases}$

EXAMPLES FOR PRACTICE

1. Given, an oblique triangle $A B C$, in which side $A B = 21$ feet, angle $A = 22° 10' 16''$, and angle $B = 78° 24' 24''$. Find the other parts.

Ans. $\begin{cases} \text{Angle } C = 79° 25' 20''. \\ A C = 20.93 \text{ ft.} \\ B C = 8.06 \text{ ft.} \end{cases}$

2. Given, a triangle $A B C$, in which $A B = 32$ inches, angle $B = 54° 16'$, and angle $C = 58° 18' 9''$. Find the other parts.

Ans. $\begin{cases} \text{Angle } A = 67° 25' 51''. \\ A C = 30.53 \text{ in.} \\ B C = 34.73 \text{ in.} \end{cases}$

3. In a triangle $A B C$, $A B = 20$ feet 6 inches, $B C = 16$ feet, and angle $B = 46° 40' 42''$. Find the values of the other parts.

Ans. $\begin{cases} \text{Angle } A = 50° 42' 51''. \\ \text{Angle } C = 82° 36' 27''. \\ A C = 15.04 \text{ ft.} \end{cases}$

4. In a triangle $A B C$, $A C = 100$ feet, $B C = 60$ feet, and angle $A = 20°$. Solve the triangle.

Ans. $\begin{cases} \text{Angle } B = 34° 45' 7.5'', \text{ or} \\ \text{angle } B = 145° 14' 52.5''. \\ \text{Angle } C = 125° 14' 52.5''. \\ A B = 143.268 \text{ ft., or } A B \\ \quad = 44.67 \text{ ft.} \end{cases}$

5. In a triangle $A B C$, $A B = 98$ inches, $B C = 140$ inches, and $A C = 210$ inches. Compute the angles A, B, and C.

Ans. $\begin{cases} A = 34° 2' 52.5''. \\ B = 122° 52' 40.2''. \\ C = 23° 4' 27.3''. \end{cases}$

MENSURATION

115. **Mensuration** is that part of geometry which treats of the measurement of lines, surfaces, and solids.

MENSURATION OF PLANE SURFACES

116. The **area** of a surface is expressed by the number of unit squares it will contain.

117. A **unit square** is the square whose side is equal in length to the unit. For example, if the unit is 1 inch, the unit square is the square whose sides measure 1 inch in length, and the area would be expressed by the number of square inches that the surface contains. If the unit were

1 foot, the unit square would measure 1 foot on each side, and the area would be the number of square feet that the surface contains, etc.   The square that measures 1 inch on a side is called a **square inch** and the one that measures 1 foot on a side is called a **square foot.**   Square inch and square foot are abbreviated to sq. in. and sq. ft., or are indicated by □ '' and □ '.

_____

THE TRIANGLE

118. **Rule.**—*The area of any triangle equals one-half the product of the base and the altitude.*

Letting b be the base, h the altitude, and A the area,

$$A = \frac{b\,h}{2}.$$

If the triangle is a right triangle, one of the short sides may be taken as the base, and the other short side as the altitude; hence, *the area of a right triangle is equal to one-half the product of the two short sides.*

EXAMPLE.—What is the area of a triangle whose base is 18 feet and altitude 7 feet 9 inches?

SOLUTION.— 9 inches = $\frac{9}{12}$ foot = $\frac{3}{4}$ foot; hence

$$A = \frac{b\,h}{2} = \frac{18 \times 7\frac{3}{4}}{2} = 69\frac{3}{4} \text{ sq. ft.   Ans.}$$

119. The area of any triangle may be found, when the length of each side is known, by means of the following formula, in which a, b, and c represent the lengths of the sides, s half the sum of the lengths, and A the area of the triangle:

$$A = \sqrt{s\,(s-a)\,(s-b)\,(s-c)}, \text{ where } s = \frac{a+b+c}{2}.$$

EXAMPLE.—What is the area of a triangle having two sides 19.8 feet long and one side 28 feet long?

SOLUTION.—It is immaterial which side is called a, b, or c. Applying the formula, $s = \dfrac{a+b+c}{2} = \dfrac{28 + 19.8 + 19.8}{2} = 33.8$, the half sum; taking b and c as the short sides, $s - a = 33.8 - 28 = 5.8$ and $s - b$ and $s - c$ are each $33.8 - 19.8 = 14$.   Then,

$$A = \sqrt{s\,(s-a)\,(s-b)\,(s-c)} = \sqrt{33.8 \times 5.8 \times 14 \times 14}$$
$$= 196+ \text{ sq. ft.   Ans.}$$

THE QUADRILATERAL

120. A **parallelogram** is a quadrilateral whose oppo-site sides are parallel. There are four kinds of parallelo-grams: the *square*, the *rectangle*, the *rhombus*, and the *rhomboid*.

FIG. 78

121. A **rectangle**, Fig. 78, is a paral-lelogram whose angles are all right angles.

122. A **square**, Fig. 79, is a rectangle, all of whose sides are equal.

FIG. 79

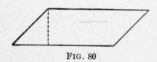

FIG. 80

123. A **rhomboid**, Fig. 80, is a parallelogram whose opposite sides only are equal and whose angles are not right angles.

124. A **rhombus**, Fig. 81, is a parallelogram having equal sides and whose angles are not right angles.

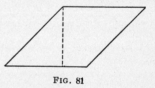

FIG. 81

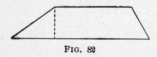

FIG. 82

125. A **trapezoid**, Fig. 82, is a quadrilateral which has only two of its sides parallel.

126. A **trapezium**, Fig. 83, is a quadrilateral having no two sides parallel.

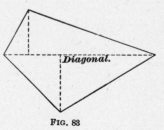

FIG. 83

127. The **altitude** of a parallelogram, or of a trapezoid, is the perpendicular distance between the parallel sides. See dotted line in Figs. 80, 81, and 82.

128. A **diagonal** is a straight line drawn from the vertex of any angle of a quadrilateral to the vertex of the angle opposite; a diagonal divides a quadrilateral into two triangles. See Figs. 78 and 83.

A diagonal divides a parallelogram into two *equal* and *similar* triangles.

129. To find the area of a parallelogram :

Rule.—*The area of any parallelogram equals the product of the base and the altitude.*

Let b be the base, h the altitude, and A the area; then,

$$A = b\,h.$$

EXAMPLE.—What is the area of a parallelogram whose base is 12 feet and altitude $7\frac{1}{2}$ feet ?

SOLUTION.—Applying the formula, $A = bh = 12 \times 7\frac{1}{2} = 90$ sq. ft. Ans.

If the area and one dimension are given, the other may be found by dividing the area by the known dimension. If the parallelogram is a square, and its area is given, the length of a side is found by extracting the square root of the area ; that is, $b = \sqrt{A}$.

130. To find the area of a trapezoid :

Rule.—*The area of a trapezoid equals one-half the sum of the parallel sides multiplied by the altitude.*

Let a and b represent the lengths of the parallel sides and h the altitude; then,

$$A = \left(\frac{a + b}{2}\right) h.$$

EXAMPLE.—What is the area of a trapezoid whose parallel sides are 9 feet and 15 feet and whose altitude is 6 feet 7 inches ?

SOLUTION.— 6 feet 7 inches $= 6\frac{7}{12}$ feet. Using the formula,

$$A = \left(\frac{a + b}{2}\right) h = \frac{9 + 15}{2} \times 6\frac{7}{12} = 79 \text{ sq. ft.} \text{Ans.}$$

40–22

THE CIRCLE

131. To find the circumference, diameter, or radius of a circle:

Rule.—*The circumference of a circle equals the diameter multiplied by 3.1416.*

Rule.—*The diameter of a circle equals the circumference divided by 3.1416; the radius equals the circumference divided by 2 × 3.1416.*

Let d be the diameter, r the radius, and c the circumference, $$c = \pi d = 2\,\pi\,r;$$

and $$d = \frac{c}{\pi}; \text{ or } r = \frac{c}{2\,\pi}.$$

EXAMPLE 1.—What is the circumference of a circle whose diameter is 15 inches?

SOLUTION.—Using the formula, $c = \pi d = 3.1416 \times 15 = 47.12$ in.
Ans.

EXAMPLE 2.—What is the diameter of a circle whose circumference is 65.973 inches?

SOLUTION.—Using the formula, $d = \dfrac{c}{\pi} = \dfrac{65.973}{3.1416} = 21$ in.   Ans.

The number 3.1416 is the ratio of the circumference of a circle to its diameter; it is represented very frequently by the Greek letter π, pronounced "pi." Its value has been calculated to over 700 decimal places, but the value here given is the one most generally used, four decimal places being sufficient for all practical purposes. The values $\frac{1}{4}\pi$, or .7854, and $\frac{1}{6}\pi$, or .5236, are frequently used farther on.

132. To find the length of an arc of a circle:

Rule.—*The length of an arc of a circle equals the circumference of the circle of which the arc is a part multiplied by the number of degrees in the arc and the product divided by 360.*

Let l be the length of arc, c the circumference, d the diameter of the circle, and n the number of degrees in the arc ; then,

$$l = \frac{\pi\,d\,n}{360}.$$

EXAMPLE.—What is the length of an arc of 24°, the radius of the circle being 18 inches ?

SOLUTION.— $18 \times 2 = 36$ inches, the diameter of the circle. Using the formula, $l = \dfrac{\pi\, d\, n}{360} = \dfrac{3.1416 \times 36 \times 24}{360} = 7.54$ in., length of arc. Ans.

133. When only the chord of the arc and the height of segment (that is, $A\,B$ and $C\,D$, Fig. 84) are given, the following closely approximate formula may be used :

Let c be the length of chord, h the height of segment, and l the length of arc ; then,

$$l = \frac{4\sqrt{c^2 + 4\,h^2} - c}{3}.$$

EXAMPLE.—If $A\,B$, Fig. 84, is 5 feet and $C\,D$ is 1 foot, what is the length of arc $A\,D\,B$?

SOLUTION.—Applying the formula,

$$l = \frac{4\sqrt{c^2 + 4\,h^2} - c}{3} = \frac{4\sqrt{25 + 4} - 5}{3} = 5.51 \text{ ft.} \quad \text{Ans.}$$

When the quotient obtained by dividing the chord by the height is less than 4.8, that is, when $\dfrac{c}{h}$ is less than 4.8, the formula does not work well, the results not being sufficiently exact. In such a case, bisect the arc and then apply the formula.

134. To find the area of a circle :

Rule.—*Square the diameter and multiply by .7854 ; or, square the radius and multiply by 3.1416.*

Let A be the area ; then,

$$A = \tfrac{1}{4}\,\pi\, d^2 = .7854\, d^2 ; \text{ or, } A = \pi\, r^2 = 3.1416\, r^2.$$

EXAMPLE.—What is the area of a circle whose diameter is 15 inches ?

SOLUTION.— $15^2 = 225$. Using the formula, $A = .7854\, d^2 = .7854 \times 225 = 176.72$ sq. in. Ans.

135. Given the area of a circle, to find its diameter:

Rule.—*Divide the area by .7854 and extract the square root of the quotient.*

Expressed as a formula, the rule is

$$d = \sqrt{\frac{A}{.7854}} = 1.1284 \sqrt{A} = \sqrt{\frac{4A}{\pi}}.$$

EXAMPLE.—The area of a circle = 17,671.5 square inches. What is its diameter in feet ?

SOLUTION.—Using the formula,

$$d = \sqrt{\frac{A}{.7854}} = \sqrt{\frac{17,671.5}{.7854}} = 1.1284 \sqrt{17,671.5} = 150 \text{ inches.}$$

$$\frac{150}{12} = 12\tfrac{1}{2} \text{ ft. diameter.   Ans.}$$

136. To find the area of a flat circular ring:

Rule.—*Subtract the area of the smaller circle from that of the larger; the difference is the area of the ring.*

Let d equal the longer diameter, d_1 the shorter diameter, and A the area of ring; then,

$$A = .7854\, d^2 - .7854\, d_1^2 = .7854\, (d^2 - d_1^2).$$

EXAMPLE.—What is the area of a ring whose longer and shorter diameters are 6.5 feet and 4 feet, respectively ?

SOLUTION.—Applying the formula,

$$A = .7854\ (6.5^2 - 4^2) = .7854 \times 26.25 = 20.62 \text{ sq. ft.   Ans.}$$

If one diameter and the area of the ring are known, the other diameter may be found by adding to or subtracting from the area of the given circle that of the ring, and finding the diameter corresponding to the resulting area.

137. To find the area of a sector:

Rule.—*Divide the number of degrees in the arc of the sector by 360. Multiply the result by the area of the circle of which the sector is a part.*

Let n be the number of degrees in the arc, A the area of circle, d the diameter of circle, and A' the area of sector; then,

$$A' = \frac{nA}{360} = .0021817\, d^2 n.$$

EXAMPLE.—The number of degrees in the angle formed by drawing radii from the center of a circle to the extremities of the arc of the circle is 75. The diameter of the circle is 12 inches; what is the area of the sector?

SOLUTION.— $12^2 \times .7854 = 113.1$ square inches, nearly, area of circle. Applying the formula,

$$A' = \frac{n\,A}{360} = \frac{75 \times 113.1}{360} = 23.56 \text{ sq. in. Ans.}$$

138. If the length of arc and radius of a sector are given, the following rule may be used:

Rule.—*The area of a sector is equal to one-half the product of the radius and length of arc.*

Let l be the length of arc, r the radius, and A' the area; then,

$$A' = \frac{l\,r}{2}.$$

EXAMPLE.—If the radius of an arc is 5 feet and the length of arc is 4 feet, what is the area of the sector?

SOLUTION.—Applying the formula,

$$A' = \frac{l\,r}{2} = \frac{4 \times 5}{2} = 10 \text{ sq. ft. Ans.}$$

139. To find the area of a segment of a circle:

Rule.—*Draw radii from the center of the circle to the extremities of the arc of the segment; find the area of the sector thus formed, subtract from this the area of the triangle formed by the radii and the chord of the arc of the segment; the result is the area of the segment.*

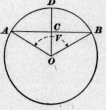

FIG. 84

In problems requiring the area of the segment, the chord $A\,B$, Fig. 84, may be given, or the height of the segment $C\,D$, or the angle V; if any one of these three is given and the radius of the circle is known, the area can be found.

Also, if any two are given, the radius can be found.

EXAMPLE 1.—If the diameter of the circle is 10 inches and the chord of the segment is 7 inches, what is the area of the segment?

SOLUTION.—In the above figure, suppose that the chord $A B$ = 7 inches and the diameter = 10 inches; draw $O A, O B$, and a radius perpendicular to the chord, thus dividing $A B$ into two equal parts (see Art. **70**). The triangle $A O B$ is now divided into two equal right triangles $A C O$ and $B C O$, in which the hypotenuse = radius = $\frac{10}{2}$ = 5 inches, and one side $A C = B C = \frac{7}{2}$, or $3\frac{1}{2}$ inches.

Sin $C O B = \dfrac{C B}{O B} = \dfrac{3\frac{1}{2}}{5} = .70000$, and angle $C O B = 44° 26'$, nearly.

Angle $A O B = 44° 26' \times 2 = 88° 52'$. $C O = O B \times \cos C O B = 5 \times .71407 = 3.57$ inches.

Area of sector $= 10^2 \times .7854 \times \dfrac{88\frac{52}{60}}{360} = 19.39$ sq. in., nearly.

Area of triangle $= \dfrac{7 \times 3.57}{2} = 12.5$ sq. in., nearly.

$19.39 - 12.5 = 6.89$ sq. in., the area of segment.   Ans.

EXAMPLE 2.—Given the chord of the arc of a segment = 7 inches and the height of the segment = 1.43 inches, to find the radius.

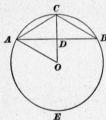

FIG. 85

SOLUTION.—Suppose that in Fig. 85, $A C B E$ is a circle struck with the required radius, that the chord $A B = 7$ inches, and that the height $C D$ of the segment = 1.43 inches. Join C with A and B, and the right triangle $A D C = B D C$.

Tan $C B D = \dfrac{C D}{B D} = \dfrac{1.43}{3.5} = .40857$.

Angle $C B D = 22° 13\frac{1}{2}'$, nearly.

Since $C B D$ or its equal $C B A$ is an inscribed angle (see Art. **66**) it is measured by one-half the intercepted arc $A C$; hence, the number of degrees in arc $A C = 22° 13\frac{1}{2}' \times 2 = 44° 27'$, or the number of degrees in the angle $A O C$.

In the right triangle $A D O$,

$$A O = \frac{\text{side opposite}}{\sin A O D} = \frac{A D}{\sin A O C} = \frac{3.5}{.70029} = 5 \text{ in., nearly.   Ans.}$$

NOTE.—The principles explained in the two preceding examples may be used in solving problems relating to length of radius, chord, sub-chord (chord, as $A C$, of half the arc $A B$), height of segment, etc. These all involve the principle of the right triangle.

REGULAR POLYGONS

140.   A **regular polygon** may be divided into as many equal isosceles triangles as there are sides, by drawing lines from the center to the angles.   Each of the angles formed at the center is equal to 360° divided by the number of sides.

To find the area of a regular polygon:

Rule.—*Multiply together the number of sides, the square of the length of a side, and the cotangent of* **one-half** *the central angle, and divide the product by 4.   The result will be the area of the regular polygon.*

Let A be the area, n the number of sides, l the length of a side, and x *one-half* the central angle included between two lines drawn from the center to the extremities of a side; then,

$$A = \frac{n\,l^2 \cot x}{4}.$$

EXAMPLE.—What is the area of a regular decagon having sides 5 feet long ?

SOLUTION.—Here n is 10; l is 5 feet; x is $\frac{360}{10} \div 2 = 18°$; cot 18° $= 3.07768$; whence,

$$A = \frac{n\,l^2 \cot x}{4} = \frac{10 \times 5 \times 5 \times 3.07768}{4} = 192.35 \text{ sq. ft.}\quad \text{Ans.}$$

141.   The area of a regular polygon whose sides are known may also be found in the following manner:

Rule.—*Square the length of a side and multiply by the proper multiplier in the subjoined table.*

Name.	No. Sides.	Multiplier.	Name.	No. Sides.	Multiplier.
Equilateral Triangle.....	3	0.4330	Octagon	8	4.8284
Square.........	4	1.0000	Nonagon......	9	6.1818
Pentagon	5	1.7205	Decagon......	10	7.6942
Hexagon.......	6	2.5981	Undecagon....	11	9.3656
Heptagon......	7	3.6339	Dodecagon....	12	11.1960

EXAMPLE.—What is the area of a regular octagon having sides 8 feet long?

SOLUTION.— $8^2 = 64$; multiplying 64 by the corresponding tabular number, 4.8284, the area is found to be $64 \times 4.8284 = 309.02$ sq. ft. Ans.

THE ELLIPSE

142. An **ellipse** is a plane figure bounded by a curved line, to any point of which the sum of the distances from two fixed points within, called the **foci,** is equal to the sum of the distances from the foci to any other point on the curve.

In Fig. 86, let A and B be the foci and let C and D

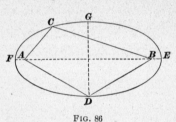

FIG. 86

be any two points on the perimeter. Then, according to the above definition, $A C + C B = A D + D B$, and both these sums are also equal to the long diameter $F E$.

The foci may be located from G or D as a center by striking arcs cutting $F E$ at A and B, using a radius equal to one-half of $F E$.

The long diameter of an ellipse, as $F E$, Fig. 86, is called the **major axis;** the short diameter, as $G D$, is called the **minor axis.**

143. To find the periphery (perimeter) of an ellipse: There is no exact method, but the following formula gives values very nearly exact.   In the formula,

$$\pi = 3.1416;$$
$$C = \text{periphery},$$
$$a = \text{half the major axis};$$
$$b = \text{half the minor axis};$$

$$D = \frac{a - b}{a + b}.$$
$$C = \pi \, (a + b) \frac{64 - 3 \, D^4}{64 - 16 \, D^2}.$$

EXAMPLE.—What is the periphery of an ellipse whose axes are 10 inches and 4 inches?

SOLUTION.—Applying the formula, $a = 5$, $b = 2$, $D = \dfrac{5-2}{5+2} = \dfrac{3}{7}$.

Then, $C = 3.1416\,(5+2)\,\dfrac{64 - 3(\frac{3}{7})^4}{64 - 16(\frac{3}{7})^2} = 23.013$ in.   Ans.

144.   To find the area of an ellipse:

Rule.—*The area of an ellipse is equal to the product of its two diameters multiplied by .7854.*

Let A be the longer diameter, or major axis; B the shorter diameter, or minor axis; and S the area; then,

$$S = \tfrac{1}{4}\pi A B = .7854\,A B.$$

EXAMPLE.—What is the area of an ellipse whose diameters are 10 inches and 6 inches?

SOLUTION.—Applying the formula, $S = .7854\,A B = .7854 \times 10 \times 6 = 47.12$ sq. in. area.   Ans.

EXAMPLES FOR PRACTICE

1.   What is the area in square feet of a rhombus whose base is 84 inches and whose altitude is 3 feet?   Ans. 21 sq. ft.

2.   One side of a room is 16 feet long. If the floor contains 240 square feet, what is the length of the other side?   Ans. 15 ft.

3.   How many square feet in a board 12 feet long, 18 inches wide at one end and 12 inches wide at the other end?   Ans. 15 sq. ft.

4.   How many square yards of plastering will be required for the ceiling and walls of a room 10 ft. × 15 ft. and 9 feet high? The room contains one door $3\frac{1}{2}$ ft. × 7 ft., three windows $3\frac{1}{2}$ × 6 ft., and a base-board 8 inches high.   Ans. 53.5 sq. yd.

5.   What is the area of a triangle whose base is 10 feet 6 inches long and whose altitude is 18 feet?   Ans. 94.5 sq. ft.

6.   The area of a triangle is 16 square inches. If the altitude is 4 inches, what does the base measure?   Ans. 8 in.

7.   The upper side of a trapezium is 16 inches long and the lower side 14 inches. If the figure be divided into two triangles by a diagonal whose altitudes, drawn from their vertexes to the two given sides as bases, are 17 inches and 3 inches, respectively, what is the area of the trapezium?   Ans. 157 sq. in.

8.   Find the area of a circle 2 feet 3 inches in diameter.
                    Ans. 3.976 sq. ft.

9.   A carriage wheel was observed to make $71\frac{2}{3}$ turns while going 300 yards. What was its diameter?   Ans. 4 ft., nearly.

10.   Required, the diameter of a circle whose area is 2,004 square inches.   Ans. 50.51 in.

11.   Required, the area of a regular pentagon inscribed in a circle whose diameter is 20 inches.   Ans. 237.77 sq. in.

12.   The number of degrees in the angle formed by drawing radii from the center of a circle to the extremities of the arc of the circle is 84.   The diameter of the circle is 17 inches; what is the area of the sector?   Ans. 52.96 sq. in.

13.   Given, the chord of the arc of a segment $= 24$ inches and the height of the segment $= 6.5$ inches, to find (a) the diameter of the circle, and (b) the area of the segment.   Ans. $\begin{cases} (a) & 28.654 \text{ in.} \\ (b) & 109.87 \text{ sq. in.} \end{cases}$

14.   (a) What is the perimeter of an ellipse whose axes are 15 inches and 9 inches, and (b) what is the area?   Ans. $\begin{cases} (a) & 38.29 \text{ in.} \\ (b) & 106.03 \text{ sq. in.} \end{cases}$

145.   To find the area of any plane figure bounded by straight or curved lines:

Rule.—*The area of any plane figure may be found by dividing it into triangles, quadrilaterals, circles or parts of circles, and ellipses, finding the area of each part separately and adding them together.*

EXAMPLE 1.—The diagonal of a trapezium is 15 feet.   The altitudes drawn from the vertexes of the two triangles to this diagonal as a base are 6 feet 8 inches and 4 feet 9 inches, respectively.   What is the area of the trapezium?

SOLUTION.—   8 inches $= \frac{8}{12}$ foot $= \frac{2}{3}$ foot. $\dfrac{15 \times 6\frac{2}{3}}{2} = 50$ square feet $=$ the area of one triangle.

9 inches $= \frac{9}{12}$ foot $= \frac{3}{4}$ foot. $\dfrac{15 \times 4\frac{3}{4}}{2} = 35.63$ square feet $=$ the area of the other triangle.

The area of the trapezium equals $50 + 35.63 = 85.63$ sq. ft.   Ans.

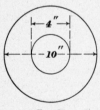

FIG. 87

EXAMPLE 2.—What is the area of a flat circular ring, Fig. 87, whose outside diameter equals 10 inches and whose inside diameter equals 4 inches?

SOLUTION.—The area of the large circle $= 10^2 \times .7854 = 78.54$ square inches; the area of the small circle $= 4^2 \times .7854 = 12.57$ square inches.

$78.54 - 12.57 = 65.97$ sq. in., or the area.   Ans

EXAMPLE 3.—What is the exact area in square inches of Fig. 88 ?

SOLUTION. — Divide the figure into rectangles, triangles, and parts of a circle, as shown by the dotted lines, then the total area equals 8-inch circle − 4-inch circle − segment $A B$ + rectangle $A B G F$ + 2 times the triangle $C D E$ + 2 times the triangle $R S T$ + 2 times the rectangle $D E S R$ + the rectangle $H I K L$ + 2 times the rectangle $L M N P$ + 2 times the triangle $M O N$.

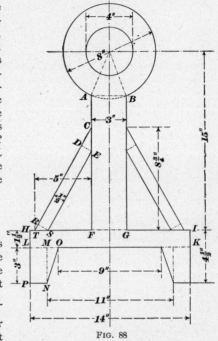

FIG. 88

$8^2 \times .7854 = 50.27 \, \square'''$·
$4^2 \times .7854 = 12.57 \, \square''$.

The chord $A B = 3$ inches and the radius of the circle $= 4$ inches; hence, the sine of one-half the angle at center $= \dfrac{1.5}{4} = .375$, and one-half the angle at center $= 22° \ 1' \ 27''$, or angle at center $= 44° \ 2' \ 54'' = 44.05°$.   Area of sector $= 50.27 \times \dfrac{44.05}{360} = 6.15 \, \square''$.

The altitude of the triangle $= 4 \times \cos 22° \ 1' \ 27'' = 3.71$ inches.

The area of the triangle $= \dfrac{3.71 \times 3}{2} = 5.56 \, \square''$.

The area of the segment $= 6.15 - 5.56 = 0.59 \, \square''$.
The area of the rectangle $A B G F = (15 - 3.71) \times 3 = 33.87 \, \square''$.
In the triangle $C D E$,

$$\tan C = \frac{5}{8\frac{3}{4}} = .57143 = \frac{D E}{C D} = \frac{.5}{C D}.$$

Hence, $C D = \dfrac{.5}{.57143} = .875$ inch.

The area of the triangle $C D E = \dfrac{.875 \times .5}{2} = .22 \, \square''$, nearly.

$.22 \times 2 = .44 \, \square'' =$ twice the area of the triangle $C D E$. Since, in the triangle $R S T$, $R S$ is perpendicular to $C R$ and $T S$ is perpendicular to $C F$, the angle $S =$ angle C; hence, $\tan S = .57143$ $= \dfrac{R\,T}{S\,R} = \dfrac{R\,T}{.5}$; therefore, $R\,T = .57143 \times .5 = .29$ inch, nearly.

Area $R\,S\,T = \dfrac{.29 \times .5}{2} = .07\,\square\,''$, nearly.

Twice the area of the triangle $R\,S\,T = .07 \times 2 = .14\,\square\,''$.

Since $\tan C = .57143$, $C = 29° 44' 42''$.

In the rectangle $D\,E\,S\,R$, $D\,R = C\,T - (C\,D + R\,T)$.   But $C\,T$ $= \dfrac{5}{\sin 29° 44' 42''} = \dfrac{5}{.49614} = 10.08$ inches.

$C\,D + R\,T = .875 + .29 = 1.16$. $D\,R = 10.08 - 1.16 = 8.92$.   8.92 $\div 2 = 4.46\,\square\,'' =$ the area of $D\,E\,S\,R$.

Twice the area of the rectangle $D\,E\,S\,R = 4.46 \times 2 = 8.92\,\square\,''$.

The area of the rectangle $H\,I\,K\,L = 14 \times 1\frac{1}{2} = 21\,\square\,''$.

The area of the rectangle $L\,M\,N\,P = \left(\dfrac{14 - 11}{2}\right) \times 3 = 1\frac{1}{2} \times 3 = 4\frac{1}{2}\,\square\,''$; and $4\frac{1}{2} \times 2 = 9\,\square\,''$.

The area of the triangle $M\,O\,N = \left(\dfrac{11 - 9}{2} \times 3\right) \div 2 = 1.5\,\square\,''$.

Twice the area of the triangle $M\,O\,N = 1.5$ inches $\times 2 = 3\,\square\,''$.

Then, $50.27 + 33.87 + 0.44 + 0.14 + 8.92 + 21 + 9 + 3 = 126.64\,\square\,''$. $12.57 + 0.59 = 13.16\,\square\,''$. $126.64 - 13.16 = 113.48\,\square\,''$.

Therefore, the area of the figure $= 113.48\,\square\,''$.   Ans.

THE MENSURATION OF SOLIDS

146. A **solid,** or body, has three dimensions: length, breadth, and thickness. The sides which enclose it are called the **faces** and their intersections are called **edges.**

147. The **entire surface** of a solid is the area of the whole outside of the solid, including the ends.

148. The **convex surface** of a solid is the same as the entire surface, except that the areas of the ends are not included.

149. The **volume** of a solid is expressed by the number of times it will contain another volume, called the unit of volume. Instead of the word *volume*, the expression **cubical contents** is frequently used.

THE PRISM AND CYLINDER

150. A **prism** is a solid whose ends are equal polygons and parallel to each other and whose sides are parallelograms.

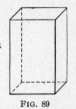

151. A **parallelopipedon,** Fig. 89, is a prism whose bases (ends) are parallelograms.

FIG. 89

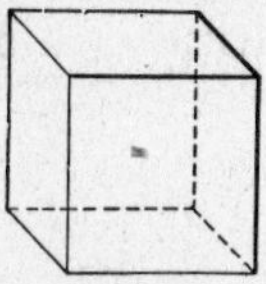

152. A **cube,** Fig. 90, is a parallelopipedon whose faces and ends are squares.

FIG. 90

153. The cube, whose edges are equal to the unit of length, is taken as the unit of volume when finding the volume of a solid.

Thus, if the unit of length is 1 inch, the unit of volume will be the cube each of whose edges measures 1 inch, or 1 *cubic inch;* and the number of cubic inches the solid contains will be its volume.   If the unit of length is 1 foot, the unit of volume will be 1 *cubic foot,* etc.   Cubic inch, cubic foot, and cubic yard are abbreviated to cu. in., cu. ft., and cu. yd., respectively.

154. Prisms take their names from their bases.   Thus, a *triangular prism* is one whose bases are triangles; a *pentagonal prism* is one whose bases are pentagons, etc.

155. A **cylinder,** Fig. 91, is a round body of uniform diameter with circles for its ends.

FIG. 91

156. A **right prism,** or **right cylinder,** is one whose center line (axis) is perpendicular to its base. In this section all of the solids will be considered as having their center lines perpendicular to their bases.

157. The **altitude** of a prism or cylinder is the perpendicular distance between its two ends.

158. To find the area of the convex surface of any right prism, or right cylinder:

Rule.—*Multiply the perimeter of the base by the altitude.*

Let p be the perimeter of the base, h the altitude, and S the convex surface; then,

$$S = p\,h.$$

EXAMPLE 1.—In a right prism whose base is a square, one side of which is 9 inches and whose altitude is 16 inches, what is its convex area ?

SOLUTION.— $9 \times 4 = 36 =$ the perimeter of the base. Applying the formula,

$$S = p\,h = 36 \times 16 = 576 \,\square\,'', \text{ the convex area. Ans.}$$

To find the entire area, add the areas of the two ends to the convex area:

EXAMPLE 2.—What is the entire area of the parallelopipedon mentioned in the last question ?

SOLUTION.—The area of one end $= 9^2 = 81 \,\square\,''$. $81 \times 2 = 162 \,\square\,''$, or the area of both ends. $576 + 162 = 738 \,\square\,''$, the entire area of the parallelopipedon. Ans.

EXAMPLE 3.—What is the entire area of a right cylinder whose base is 16 inches in diameter and whose altitude is 24 inches ?

SOLUTION.— $16 \times 3.1416 = 50.27$ inches, or the perimeter (circumference) of the base. $50.27 \times 24 = 1,206.48 \,\square\,''$, the convex area.
$16^2 \times .7854 \times 2 = 402.12 \,\square\,''$, the area of the ends.
$1,206.48 + 402.12 = 1,608.6 \,\square\,''$, the entire area. Ans.

159. To find the volume of a right prism, or cylinder:

Rule.—*The volume of any right prism or cylinder equals the area of the base multiplied by the altitude.*

Let A be the area of the base, h the altitude, and V the volume; then,

$$V = A\,h.$$

If the given prism is a cube, the three dimensions are all equal and the volume equals the cube of one of the edges. Hence, if the volume is given, the length of an edge is found by extracting the cube root.

If the volume and area are given, the altitude $= \dfrac{V}{A}$. If the cylinder or prism is hollow, the volume is equal to the area of the ring or base multiplied by the altitude.

EXAMPLE 1.—What is the volume of a rectangular prism whose base is 6 in. $\times$ 4 in. and whose altitude is 12 inches ?

SOLUTION.—The base of a rectangular prism is a rectangle. Hence, $6 \times 4 = 24 \square''$, the area of the base. Applying the formula $V = A\,h$ $= 24 \times 12 = 288$ cu. in., or the volume. Ans.

EXAMPLE 2.—What is the volume of a cube whose edge is 9 inches ?

SOLUTION.— $9^3 = 9 \times 9 \times 9 = 729$ cu. in., the volume. Ans.

EXAMPLE 3.—What is the volume of a cylinder whose base is 7 inches in diameter and whose altitude is 11 inches ?

SOLUTION.— $7^2 \times .7854 = 38.48 \square''$, the area of the base. Applying the formula, $V = A\,h = 38.48 \times 11 = 423.28$ cu. in., the volume. Ans.

THE PYRAMID AND CONE

160. A **pyramid,** Fig. 92, is a solid whose base is a polygon and whose sides are triangles uniting at a common point called the **vertex.**

FIG. 92

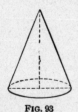

FIG. 93

161. A **cone,** Fig. 93, is a solid whose base is a circle and whose convex surface tapers uniformly to a point called the **vertex.**

162.   The **altitude** of a pyramid or cone is the perpendicular distance from the vertex to the base.

163.   The **slant height** of a *pyramid* is a line drawn from the vertex perpendicular to one of the sides of the base.   The slant height of a *cone* is any straight line drawn from the vertex to the circumference of the base.

164.   To find the area of a right pyramid or right cone:

Rule.—*The convex area of a right pyramid or cone equals the perimeter of the base multiplied by one-half the slant height.*

Let p be the perimeter, s the slant height, and C the convex area; then,

$$C = \frac{p\,s}{2}.$$

EXAMPLE 1.—What is the convex area of a pentagonal pyramid, if each side of the base measures 6 inches and the slant height equals 14 inches?

SOLUTION.—The base of the pentagonal pyramid is a pentagon, and, consequently, it has five sides.

$6 \times 5 = 30$ inches, or the perimeter of the base.

Applying the formula,

$$C = \frac{p\,s}{2} = \frac{30 \times 14}{2} = 210\,\square\,'', \text{ the convex area.   Ans.}$$

EXAMPLE 2.—What is the entire area of a right cone whose slant height is 17 inches and whose base is 8 inches in diameter?

SOLUTION.— $8 \times 3.1416 = 25.1328$ inches, the perimeter.

$25.1328 \times \frac{17}{2} = 213.63\,\square\,''$, the convex area.
$8^2 \times .7854 = 50.27\,\square\,''$, the area of base.

$Sum = \overline{263.90\,\square\,''}$, the entire area.   Ans.

165.   To find the volume of a right pyramid or cone:

Rule.—*The volume of a right pyramid or cone equals the area of the base multiplied by one-third of the altitude.*

Let A be the area of the base, h the altitude, and V the volume; then,

$$V = \frac{A\,h}{3}.$$

If the base of the pyramid is a regular polygon, its area may be found by the rules in Arts. **140** and **141.**

EXAMPLE 1.—What is the volume of a triangular pyramid, the edges of whose base each measure 6 inches and whose altitude is 8 inches?

SOLUTION.—The base is an equilateral triangle, hence, applying the rule in Art. **141,** the area is $6^2 \times .433 = 15.59 \,\square\,''$. Applying the formula,

$$V = \frac{A\,h}{3} = \frac{15.59 \times 8}{3} = 41.57 \text{ cu. in.}\quad \text{Ans.}$$

EXAMPLE 2.—What is the volume of a cone whose altitude is 18 inches and whose base is 14 inches in diameter?

SOLUTION.— $14^2 \times .7854 = 153.94 \,\square\,''$, the area of the base. Applying the formula,

$$V = \frac{A\,h}{3} = \frac{153.94 \times 18}{3} = 923.64 \text{ cu. in., the volume.}\quad \text{Ans.}$$

THE FRUSTUM OF A PYRAMID OR CONE

166. If a pyramid be cut by a plane parallel to the base, as in Fig. 94, so as to form two parts, the lower part is called the **frustum** of the pyramid.

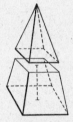

FIG. 94

167. If a cone be cut in a similar manner, as in Fig. 95, the lower part is called the **frustum** of the cone.

FIG. 95

40—23

168. The upper end of the frustum of a pyramid or cone is called the **upper base,** and the lower end the **lower base.** The **altitude** of a frustum is the perpendicular distance between the bases.

169. To find the convex area of a frustum of a right pyramid or right cone:

Rule.—*The convex area of a frustum of a right pyramid or right cone equals one-half the sum of the perimeters of its· bases multiplied by the slant height of the frustum.*

Let p be the perimeter of the lower base, p' that of the upper base, s the slant height, and C the convex area; then,

$$C = \left(\frac{p + p'}{2}\right)s.$$

EXAMPLE 1.—Given, the frustum of a triangular pyramid, in which each side of the lower base measures 10 inches, each side of the upper base measures 6 inches, and whose slant height is 9 inches; find the convex area.

SOLUTION.— 10 inches × 3 = 30 inches, the perimeter of the lower base.

6 inches × 3 = 18 inches, the perimeter of the upper base.

Applying the formula,

$$C = \left(\frac{p + p'}{2}\right)s = \frac{30 + 18}{2} \times 9 = 216 \,\square\,'', \text{ the convex area. Ans.}$$

EXAMPLE 2.—If the diameters of the two bases of a frustum of a cone are 12 inches and 8 inches, respectively, and the slant height is 12 inches, what is the entire area of the frustum ?

SOLUTION.— $\dfrac{(12 \times 3.1416) + (8 \times 3.1416)}{2} \times 12 = 376.99 \,\square\,''$, the area of the convex surface.

$$8^2 \times .7854 = 50.27 \,\square\,''.$$
$$12^2 \times .7854 = 113.1 \,\square\,''.$$
$$113.1 + 50.27 = 163.37 \,\square\,'', \text{ the area of the two ends.}$$
$$376.99 + 163.37 = 540.36 \,\square\,'', \text{ the entire area of the frustum. Ans.}$$

170. To find the volume of the frustum of a pyramid or cone:

Rule.—*Add the areas of the upper base, the lower base, and the square root of the product of the areas of the two bases; multiply this sum by one-third of the altitude.*

Let A be the area of lower base, a the area of upper base, h the altitude, and V the volume; then,

$$V = (A + a + \sqrt{Aa})\frac{h}{3}.$$

If the base is a regular polygon, the area may be found by the rules in Arts. **140** and **141.**

EXAMPLE 1.—Given, a frustum of a hexagonal pyramid, each edge of the lower base measuring 8 inches and each edge of the upper base 5 inches, and whose altitude is 14 inches, what is its volume?

SOLUTION.—A hexagonal pyramid is one whose base is a regular hexagon, as shown in Fig. 96. Hence, using the formula in Art. **140**,

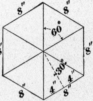

FIG. 96

$$A = \frac{n\,l^2 \cot x}{4} = \frac{6 \times 8 \times 8 \times 1.73205}{4} = 166.28 \,\square\,''.$$

In a similar way, find the area of the upper base to be 64.95 $\square$ ''. Then, applying the formula,

$$166.28 + 64.95 + \sqrt{166.28 \times 64.95} = 166.28 + 64.95 + 103.92 = 335.15.$$
$$335.15 \times \tfrac{14}{3} = 1,564.03 \text{ cu. in.} = \text{the volume.}\quad \text{Ans.}$$

EXAMPLE 2.—What is the volume of a frustum of a cone whose upper base is 8 inches, the lower base is 12 inches in diameter, and whose altitude is 15 inches?

SOLUTION.—The area of the upper base is $8^2 \times .7854 = 50.27\,\square\,''$. The area of the lower base is $12^2 \times .7854 = 113.1\,\square\,''$, nearly. The square root of their product is $\sqrt{50.27 \times 113.1} = 75.4$.

$$50.27 + 113.1 + 75.4 = 238.77.$$
$$238.77 \times \tfrac{15}{3} = 1,193.85 \text{ cu. in., the volume.}\quad \text{Ans.}$$

THE SPHERE

FIG. 97

171. A **sphere,** Fig. 97, is a solid bounded by a uniformly curved surface, every point of which is equally distant from a point within, called the center.

The word **ball** is commonly used instead of sphere.

172. To find the area of the surface of a sphere:

Rule.—*The area of the surface of a sphere equals the square of the diameter multiplied by 3.1416.*

Let S be the surface and d the diameter; then,

$$S = \pi d^2.$$

EXAMPLE.—What is the area of the surface of a sphere whose diameter is 14 inches?

SOLUTION.—Applying the formula, $S = \pi d^2 = 3.1416 \times 14^2 = 3.1416 \times 14 \times 14 = 615.75 \,\square\,''$, the area.   Ans.

173. To find the volume of a sphere:

Rule.—*The volume of a sphere equals the cube of the diameter multiplied by .5236.*

Let V be the volume and d the diameter; then,

$$V = \tfrac{1}{6} \pi d^3 = .5236\, d^3.$$

EXAMPLE.—What is the weight of a lead cannon ball 12 inches in diameter, a cubic inch of lead weighing .41 pound?

SOLUTION.—Applying the formula, $V = .5236\, d^3 = .5236 \times 12 \times 12 \times 12 = 904.78$ cubic inches, the volume of the ball. $904.78 \times .41 = 370.96$ lb.   Ans.

The volume of a spherical shell or hollow sphere is equal to the difference in volume between two spheres having the outer and inner diameters of the shell.

174. To find the diameter of a sphere of known volume:

Rule.—*Divide the volume by .5236 and extract the cube root of the quotient. The result is the diameter.*

$$d = \sqrt[3]{\frac{V}{.5236}} = 1.2407 \sqrt[3]{V}.$$

EXAMPLE.—The volume of a sphere is 96.1 cubic inches. What is its diameter?

SOLUTION.—Applying the formula,

$$d = \sqrt[3]{\frac{V}{.5236}} = \sqrt[3]{\frac{96.1}{.5236}} = 1.2407 \sqrt[3]{96.1} = 5.68 + \text{in.}   \text{Ans.}$$

THE CYLINDRICAL RING

175.   If any solid be sliced in pieces whose adjacent surfaces are flat, any piece is called a **plane section** of the solid.

Plane sections are divided into three classes : Longitudinal sections, cross-sections, and right sections.   A **longitudinal section** is any plane section taken lengthwise
through the solid.   Any other plane section is called a
cross-section.   If the surface exposed by taking a plane
section of a solid is perpendicular to the center line of the
solid, the section is called a **right section.**   The surface
exposed by any longitudinal section of a cylinder is a rectangle.   The surface exposed by a right section of a cube is
a square; of a cylinder or cone, a circle; an oblique cross-
section of a cylinder is an ellipse.   The lower half of a right
section of a cone or pyramid is called a frustum of the cone
or pyramid.

176.   To find the convex area of a
cylindrical ring:

A **cylindrical ring** is a cylinder
bent to a circle.   The **altitude** of the
cylinder before bending is the same as
the length of the dotted center line *D*,
Fig. 98.

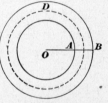

FIG. 98

177.   The **base** will correspond to a cross-section on
the line *A B* drawn from the center *O*.   Hence, to find
the convex area, multiply the circumference of an imaginary cross-section on the line *A B* by the length of the
center line *D*.

EXAMPLE.—A piece of round-iron rod is bent into circular form to
make a ring for a chain; if the outside diameter of the ring is 12 inches
and the inside diameter is 8 inches, what is its convex area ?

SOLUTION.—The diameter of the center circle equals one-half the
sum of the inside and outside diameters $= \dfrac{12 + 8}{2} = 10$, and 10×3.1416

$= 31.416$ inches, the length of the center line.   The radius of the inside
circle is 4 inches, of the outside circle 6 inches; therefore, the diameter
of the cross-section on the line *A B* is 2 inches.   Then, 2×3.1416
$= 6.2832$ inches, and $6.2832 \times 31.416 = 197.4 \square''$, or the convex area.   Ans.

178. To find the volume of a cylindrical ring:

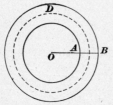

FIG. 99

The volume will be the same as that of a cylinder whose altitude equals the length of the dotted center line D, Fig. 99, and whose base is the same as a cross-section of the ring on the line A B, drawn from the center O. Hence, to find the volume of a cylindrical ring, multiply the area of an imaginary cross-section on a line A B by the length of the center line D.

EXAMPLE.—What is the volume of a cylindrical ring whose outside diameter is 12 inches and whose inside diameter is 8 inches?

SOLUTION.—The diameter of the center circle equals one-half the sum of the inside and outside diameters $= \dfrac{12+8}{2} = 10$.

$10 \times 3.1416 = 31.416$ inches, the length of the center line.

The radius of the outside circle $= 6$ inches, of the inside circle $= 4$ inches; therefore, the diameter of the cross-section on the line $A\ B$ $= 2$ inches.

Then, $2^2 \times .7854 = 3.1416\ \square''$, the area of the imaginary cross-section.

And $3.1416 \times 31.416 = 98.7$ cu. in., the volume. Ans.

EXAMPLES FOR PRACTICE

1. Find the weight of an iron bar 16 feet long and 2 inches in diameter, the weight of iron being taken at .28 pound per cubic inch.

Ans. 168.89 lb.

2. What is the area of the entire surface of a hexagonal prism 12 inches long, each edge of the base being 1 inch long?

Ans. 77.196 sq. in.

3. What is the volume of a triangular pyramid, one edge of whose base measures 3 inches and whose altitude is 4 inches? Ans. 5.2 cu. in.

4. Find the volume of a cone whose altitude is 12 inches and the circumference of whose base is 31.416 inches.   Ans. 314.16 cu. in.

5. A round tank is 8 feet in diameter at the top (inside) and 10 feet at the bottom. If the tank is 12 feet deep, how many gallons will it hold, there being 231 cubic inches in a gallon?   Ans. 5,734.2 gal.

6. Required, the area of the convex surface of the frustum of a square pyramid whose altitude is 16 inches, one side of the lower base being 28 inches long and of the upper base 10 inches. Ans. 1,395.18 sq. in.

7. What is the volume of a sphere 30 inches in diameter?

Ans. 14,137.2 cu. in.

8. How many square inches in the surface of the sphere of example 7 ? Ans. 2,827.44 sq. in.

9. Required, the area of the convex surface of a circular ring, the outside diameter of the ring being 10 inches and the inside diameter 7¼ inches. Ans. 107.95 sq. in.

10. Find the cubical contents of the ring in the last example.
Ans. 33.734 cu. in.

11. The volume of a sphere is 606.132 cubic inches; required, the area of the convex surface of a cone whose slant height is 10 inches and the diameter of whose base is the same as the diameter of the sphere.
Ans. 164.934 sq. in.

12. What is the volume of the frustum of example 6 ?
Ans. 6,208 cu. in.

PROJECTIONS

179. If perpendiculars be drawn from the extremities of a line, as *A B*, Fig. 100, or Fig. 102, to another line, as *H K*, as shown in the figures, that portion of *H K* included between the foot of each perpendicular is called the **projection** of *A B* upon *H K*. Thus, *C D* is the projection of *A B* upon *H K*, the point *C* is the projection of the point *A* upon *H K*, and the point *D* is the projection of the point *B* upon *H K*.

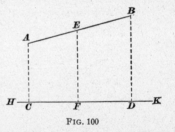

FIG. 100

The projection of any point of *A B*, as *E*, can be found by drawing a perpendicular from *E* to *H K*, and the point where this perpendicular intersects *H K* is its projection; in this case the point *F* is the projection of the point *E* upon *H K*.

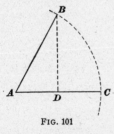

FIG. 101

From the foregoing it is evident that the projection of any straight line upon another line is found by considering the inclined line as the hypotenuse of a right triangle, as *A B*, Fig. 101, so that the projected length may be found by multiplying the hypotenuse by the cosine of the angle that it makes with the other line; thus, AD is the projection of AB upon the horizontal line AC and BD is its projection on a vertical line.

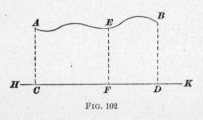

FIG. 102

It makes no difference whether a line is straight or curved, the method of finding the projection is exactly the same.

In a similar way, a surface is projected upon a flat surface.

Thus, it is desired to project the irregular surface $abdc$, Fig. 103, upon the flat surface $ABDC$. Draw the lines aa', bb' perpendicular to the flat surface; join the points a' and b' where these perpendiculars intersect the flat surface $ABDC$ by a straight line $a'b'$, and $a'b'$ is the projection of ab upon

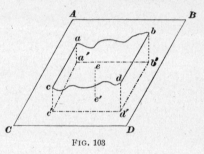

FIG. 103

$ABDC$. The projection of the surface $abdc$ upon the plane $ABDC$ is in this case the quadrilateral $a'b'd'c'$.

SYMMETRICAL AND SIMILAR FIGURES

180. An **axis of symmetry** is any line so drawn that, if the part of the figure on one side of the line be folded on this line, it will coincide exactly with the other part, point for point and line for line. Thus, in Fig. 104, if the upper half be folded over on the diameter CD, it will coincide exactly with the lower half; also, if the part on the right of the diameter AB be folded over on AB, it will coincide exactly with the part on the left of this line.

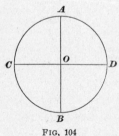

FIG. 104

It is evident from the above that a circle may have any number of axes of symmetry. In certain cases, however, a figure may be symmetrical with regard to only one axis. Thus, the isosceles triangle $A B C$, Fig. 105, is symmetrical with regard to the axis $B D$, because the part $B C D$ would coincide with the part $B A D$ if folded over on the line $B D$; but no other axis of symmetry could be drawn. A rectangle has two axes of symmetry at right angles to each other. A hexagon has six axes of symmetry.

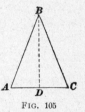

FIG. 105

181. Similar figures are those which are alike in form. As in the case of triangles, which have been considered, two figures, to be similar, must have their corresponding sides in proportion, and the angles of one equal to the corresponding angles of the other. Any two circles or any two regular polygons of the same number of sides are similar.

182. The areas of two similar figures are to each other as the squares of any one dimension. Thus, a parallelogram 10 inches long and 4 inches wide contains 40 square inches. A similar parallelogram 20 inches long would be 8 inches wide and would contain 160 square inches, while the two areas would be to each other as the squares of the corresponding sides of the parallelograms. That is,

$$40 : 160 = 10^2 : 20^2,$$

or
$$40 : 160 = 4^2 : 8^2.$$

EXAMPLE.—A circle 10 inches in diameter contains 78.54 square inches; what is the area of one 12 inches in diameter?

SOLUTION.—Let $x =$ the area of the larger circle. Then,

$$78.54 : x = 10^2 : 12^2, \text{ or } x = \frac{78.54 \times 144}{100} = 113.0976 \text{ sq. in.} \quad \text{Ans.}$$

183. The cubical contents (and weights) of **similar solids** are to each other as the *cubes* of any one dimension.

EXAMPLE 1.—If a cast-iron ball 9 inches in diameter weighs 100 pounds, what would one 15 inches in diameter weigh?

SOLUTION.— $100 : x = 9^3 : 15^3,$

or $x = \dfrac{100 \times 3,375}{729} = 462.96$ lb., the weight of larger ball.   Ans.

EXAMPLE 2.—A regular hexagon has sides 5 inches long; how much greater will the area of another regular hexagon be whose sides are 30 inches long?

SOLUTION.— $30 \div 5 = 6,$ or the length of a side of a 30-inch hexagon is 6 times as great as the length of a side of a 5-inch hexagon; the area will be $6^2 = 36$ times as great.   Ans.

This example may also be solved by letting 1 represent the area of the 5-inch hexagon.   Then,

$$1 : x = 5^2 : 30^2, \text{ or } x = \frac{900}{25} = 36.$$

184. The principles given in Arts. **182** and **183** are extremely useful and find many applications in practice, especially in drafting-room practice.   Draftsmen almost invariably make their drawings to scale, as it is termed; that is, the size of the paper they are using prevents them from drawing the machine or other object full size, and they are obliged to draw them one-half size, one-quarter size, one-twelfth size, etc.; in other words, each line or dimension on the drawing is $\frac{1}{2}, \frac{1}{4}, \frac{1}{12}$, etc. the length of the corresponding line or dimension on the object.   For example, the object represented in Fig. 88 is only $\frac{1}{8}$ the actual size, i. e., the length of each line or dimension in the cut is only $\frac{1}{8}$ as long as it would be were the drawing made full size.   Suppose there were no dimensions given, but we knew that the drawing was $\frac{1}{8}$ the actual size, and we wanted to know the actual area of the figure.   We could measure such lines and dimensions as were necessary and calculate the area of the figure as represented on the drawing.   Then, knowing that this figure is *similar* in outline to the object itself, and that any line or dimension on the object is 8 times as long as the corresponding line or dimension on the drawing, we could find the area of the object by multiplying the area of figure by 8^2, or 64.   The multiplier 8^2 is obtained from the proportion (see Art. **182**),

area of figure : actual area of object $= 1^2 : 8^2$,

or   actual area of object $= 64 \times$ area of figure.

From the foregoing, it will be readily seen that if we know the area of any figure, no matter what its shape, the area of any similar figure may be found by finding the ratio of any two lines or dimensions similarly placed and *squaring the ratio.* Also, if the volume of any solid is known, the volume of a similar solid may be found by finding the ratio of any two lines or dimensions similarly placed and *cubing the ratio.* For example, suppose the area of a certain figure is known to be 1,024 square inches and it is desired to find the area of a similar figure, the ratio of any two corresponding dimensions being 5 : 4 or $1\frac{1}{4}$: 1. The area desired is obtained by multiplying the known area by $(1\frac{1}{4})^2$, or by squaring the ratio 5 : 4, obtaining 25 : 16; putting this in the fractional form $\frac{25}{16}$, and multiplying 1,024 by this fraction, we get $1,024 \times \frac{25}{16} = 1,600$ square inches.

Again, if the volume of a certain solid is known, the volume of a similar solid that is, say, with dimensions $\frac{1}{3}$ as large, may be readily found by multiplying the known volume by $(\frac{1}{3})^3 = \frac{1}{27}$.

A SERIES OF QUESTIONS
AND EXAMPLES

Relating to the Subjects
Treated of in This Volume

It will be noticed that the pages of the Examination Questions that follow have been given the same section numbers as the Instruction Papers to which they refer. No attempt should be made to answer any of the questions or to solve any of the examples until the Instruction Paper having the same section number has been carefully studied.

ARITHMETIC.

(SECTION 1.)

EXAMINATION QUESTIONS.

(1)   What is arithmetic?

(2)   What is a number?

(3)   What is the difference between a concrete number and an abstract number?

(4)   Define notation and numeration.

(5)   Write each of the following numbers in words:
(*a*) 980 ;   (*b*) 605 ;   (*c*) 28,284 ;   (*d*) 9,006,042 ;   (*e*) 850,- 317,002;   (*f*) 700,004.

(6)   Represent in figures the following expressions:
(*a*) Seven thousand six hundred.   (*b*) Eighty-one thousand four hundred two.   (*c*) Five million four thousand seven. (*d*) One hundred eight million ten thousand one.   (*e*) Eighteen million six.   (*f*) Thirty thousand ten.

(7)   What is the sum of $3,290 + 504 + 865,403 + 2,074 + 81 + 7$?   Ans. 871,359.

(8) $709 + 8,304,725 + 391 + 100,302 + 300 + 909 =$ what?
                              Ans. 8,407,336.

(9)   Find the difference between the following:
(*a*) 50,962 and 3,338;   (*b*) 10,001 and 15,339.
                    Ans. $\begin{cases} (a) & 47,624 \\ (b) & 5,338. \end{cases}$

(10)   (a) $70,968 - 32,975 = ?$ (b) $100,000 - 98,735 = ?$

$$\text{Ans.} \begin{cases} (a) & 37,993. \\ (b) & 1,265. \end{cases}$$

(11)   The greater of two numbers is 1,004 and their difference is 49; what is their sum?   Ans. 1,959.

(12)   From $5,962 + 8,471 + 9,023$ take $3,874 + 2,039.$
Ans. 17,543.

(13)   A man willed $125,000 to his wife and two children;
to his son he gave $44,675, to his daughter $26,380, and to
his wife the remainder.   What was his wife's share?
Ans. $53,945.

(14)   Find the products of the following:
   (a) $526,387 \times 7$;   (b) $700,298 \times 17$;   (c) $217 \times 103 \times 67.$

$$\text{Ans.} \begin{cases} (a) & 3,684,709. \\ (b) & 11,905,066. \\ (c) & 1,497,517. \end{cases}$$

(15)   If your watch ticks once every second, how many
times will it tick in one week?   Ans. 604,800 times.

(16)   If a monthly publication contains 24 pages in each
issue, how many pages will there be in 8 yearly volumes?
Ans. 2,304.

(17)   An engine and boiler in a manufactory are worth
$3,246.   The building is worth three times as much, plus
$1,200, and the tools are worth twice as much as the build-
ing, plus $1,875.   (a) What is the value of the building and
tools?   (b) What is the value of the whole plant?

$$\text{Ans.} \begin{cases} (a) & \$34,689. \\ (b) & \$37,935. \end{cases}$$

(18)   Solve the following by cancelation:

   (a) $\dfrac{72 \times 48 \times 28 \times 5}{96 \times 15 \times 7 \times 6} = ?$ (b) $\dfrac{80 \times 60 \times 50 \times 16 \times 14}{70 \times 50 \times 24 \times 20} = ?$

$$\text{Ans.} \begin{cases} (a) & 8. \\ (b) & 32. \end{cases}$$

(19) If a mechanic earns $1,500 a year for his labor, and his expenses are $968 per year, in what time can he save enough to buy 28 acres of land at $133 an acre?

Ans. 7 yr.

(20) A freight train ran 365 miles in one week, and 3 times as far, lacking 246 miles, the next week; how far did it run the second week?   Ans. 849 mi.

(21) If the driving wheel of a locomotive is 16 feet in circumference, how many revolutions will it make in going from Philadelphia to Pittsburg, the distance between which is 354 miles, there being 5,280 feet in one mile?

Ans. 116,820 rev.

(22) What is the quotient of:

(a) 589,824 ÷ 576? (b) 369,730,620 ÷ 43,911? (c) 2,527,-525 ÷ 505? (d) 4,961,794,302 ÷ 1,234?

$$\text{Ans.} \begin{cases} (a) & 1,024. \\ (b) & 8,420. \\ (c) & 5,005. \\ (d) & 4,020,903. \end{cases}$$

(23) A man paid $444 for a horse, wagon, and harness. If the horse cost $264 and the wagon $153, how much did the harness cost?   Ans. $27.

(24) What is the product of:

(a) 1,024 × 576? (b) 5,005 × 505? (c) 43,911 × 8,420?

$$\text{Ans.} \begin{cases} (a) & 589,824. \\ (b) & 2,527,525. \\ (c) & 369,730,620. \end{cases}$$

(25) If a man receives 30 cents an hour for his wages, how much will he earn in a year, working 10 hours a day and averaging 25 days per month?   Ans. $900.

ARITHMETIC.

(SECTION 2.)

EXAMINATION QUESTIONS.

(26) What is a fraction?

(27) What are the terms of a fraction?

(28) What does the denominator show?

(29) What does the numerator show?

(30) How do you find the value of a fraction?

(31) Is $\frac{13}{8}$ a proper or an improper fraction, and why?

(32) Write three mixed numbers.

(33) Reduce the following fractions to their lowest terms: $\frac{4}{8}, \frac{4}{16}, \frac{8}{32}, \frac{32}{64}$.   Ans. $\frac{1}{2}, \frac{1}{4}, \frac{1}{4}, \frac{1}{2}$.

(34) Reduce 6 to an improper fraction whose denominator is 4.   Ans. $\frac{24}{4}$.

(35) Reduce $7\frac{7}{8}$, $13\frac{5}{16}$, and $10\frac{3}{4}$ to improper fractions.   Ans. $\frac{63}{8}, \frac{213}{16}, \frac{43}{4}$.

(36) What is the value of each of the following: $\frac{13}{2}, \frac{17}{4}, \frac{69}{16}, \frac{16}{8}, \frac{67}{64}$?   Ans. $6\frac{1}{2}, 4\frac{1}{4}, 4\frac{5}{16}, 2, 1\frac{3}{64}$.

(37) Solve the following:

(a) $35 \div \frac{5}{16}$; (b) $\frac{9}{16} \div 3$; (c) $\frac{17}{2} \div 9$; (d) $\frac{113}{64} \div \frac{7}{16}$; (e) $15\frac{3}{4} \div 4\frac{3}{8}$.

Ans. $\left\{ \begin{array}{ll} (a) & 112. \\ (b) & \frac{3}{16}. \\ (c) & \frac{17}{18}. \\ (d) & 4\frac{1}{28}. \\ (e) & 3\frac{3}{5}. \end{array} \right.$

(38) $\frac{1}{8}+\frac{2}{8}+\frac{5}{8} = ?$ Ans. 1.

(39) $\frac{1}{4}+\frac{3}{8}+\frac{5}{16} = ?$ Ans. $\frac{15}{16}$.

(40) $42+31\frac{5}{8}+9\frac{7}{16} = ?$ Ans. $83\frac{1}{16}$.

(41) An iron plate is divided into four sections: the first contains $29\frac{3}{4}$ square inches; the second, $50\frac{5}{8}$ square inches; the third, 41 square inches; and the fourth, $69\frac{3}{16}$ square inches. How many square inches are in the plate?

Ans. $190\frac{9}{16}$ sq. in.

(42) Find the value of each of the following:

$$(a)\ \frac{\frac{7}{3}}{16};\quad (b)\ \frac{\frac{15}{32}}{\frac{5}{8}};\quad (c)\ \frac{\frac{4+3}{2+6}}{5}.$$

Ans. $\begin{cases}(a) & 37\frac{1}{3}. \\ (b) & \frac{3}{4}. \\ (c) & \frac{7}{40}.\end{cases}$

(43) The numerator of a fraction is 28, and the value of the fraction $\frac{7}{8}$; what is the denominator?   Ans. 32.

(44) What is the difference between (a) $\frac{7}{8}$ and $\frac{7}{16}$? (b) 13 and $7\frac{7}{16}$? (c) $312\frac{9}{16}$ and $229\frac{5}{32}$?

Ans. $\begin{cases}(a) & \frac{7}{16}. \\ (b) & 5\frac{9}{16}. \\ (c) & 83\frac{13}{32}.\end{cases}$

(45) If a man travels $85\frac{5}{12}$ miles in one day, $78\frac{9}{15}$ miles in another day, and $125\frac{17}{35}$ miles in another day, how far did he travel in the three days?   Ans. $289\frac{211}{420}$ mi.

(46) From $573\frac{4}{5}$ tons take $216\frac{5}{8}$ tons.   Ans. $357\frac{7}{40}$ T.

(47) At $\frac{3}{8}$ of a dollar a yard, what will be the cost of $9\frac{1}{4}$ yards of cloth?   Ans. $3\frac{15}{32}$ dollars.

(48) Multiply $\frac{2}{3}$ of $\frac{3}{4}$ of $\frac{7}{11}$ of $\frac{13}{20}$ of 11 by $\frac{7}{8}$ of $\frac{5}{6}$ of 45.

Ans. $109\frac{13}{128}$.

(49) How many times is $\frac{2}{3}$ contained in $\frac{3}{4}$ of 16?

Ans. 18 times.

(50) Bought $211\frac{1}{4}$ pounds of old lead for $1\frac{7}{8}$ cents per pound. Sold a part of it for $2\frac{1}{2}$ cents per pound, receiving for it the same amount as I paid for the whole. How many pounds did I have left?   Ans. $52\frac{13}{16}$ lb.

ARITHMETIC.

(SECTION 3.)

EXAMINATION QUESTIONS.

(51) Write out in words the following numbers: .08, .131, .0001, .000027, .0108, and 93.0101.

(52) How do you place decimals for addition and subtraction?

(53) Give a rule for multiplication of decimals.

(54) Give a rule for division of decimals.

(55) State the difference between a fraction and a decimal.

(56) State how to reduce a fraction to a decimal.

(57) Reduce the following fractions to equivalent decimals: $\frac{1}{2}$, $\frac{7}{8}$, $\frac{5}{32}$, $\frac{65}{100}$, and $\frac{125}{1000}$.

$$\text{Ans.} \begin{cases} .5. \\ .875. \\ .15625. \\ .65. \\ .125. \end{cases}$$

(58) Solve the following:

(a) $\dfrac{32.5 + .29 + 1.5}{4.7 + 9}$;

(b) $\dfrac{1.283 \times \overline{8 + 5}}{2.63}$;

(c) $\dfrac{\overline{589 + 27} \times \overline{163 - 8}}{25 + 39}$;

(d) $\dfrac{\overline{40.6 + 7.1} \times (3.029 - 1.874)}{6.27 + 8.53 - 8.01}$.

$$\text{Ans.} \begin{cases} (a) & 2.5029. \\ (b) & 6.3418. \\ (c) & 1,491.875. \\ (d) & 8.1139. \end{cases}$$

(59) How many inches in .875 of a foot?   Ans. $10\frac{1}{2}$ in.

(60)　What decimal part of a foot is $\frac{3}{16}$ of an inch?

Ans. .015625.

(61)　A cubic inch of water weighs .03617 of a pound. What is the weight of a body of water whose volume is 1,500 cubic inches?　　　　Ans. 54.255 lb.

(62)　If by selling a carload of coal for \$82.50, at a profit of \$1.65 per ton, I make enough to pay for 72.6 feet of fencing at \$.50 a foot, how many tons of coal were in the car?　　　　Ans. 22 T.

(63)　Divide 17,892 by 231, and carry the result to four decimal places.　　　　Ans. 77.4545+.

(64)　What is the value of the following expression carried to three decimal places:

$$\frac{74.26 \times 24 \times 3.1416 \times 19 \times 19 \times 350}{33,000 \times 12 \times 4} = ?$$　　Ans. 446.619—.

(65)　Express: (a) .7928 in 64ths; (b) .1416 in 32ds; (c) .47915 in 16ths.

Ans. $\begin{cases} (a) & \frac{51}{64}. \\ (b) & \frac{5}{32}. \\ (c) & \frac{8}{16}. \end{cases}$

(66)　Work out the following examples:

(a) 709.63 − .8514; (b) 81.963 − 1.7; (c) 18 − .18; (d) 1 − .001; (e) 872.1 − (.8721 + .008); (f) (5.028 + .0073) − (6.704 − 2.38).

Ans. $\begin{cases} (a) & 708.7786. \\ (b) & 80.263. \\ (c) & 17.82. \\ (d) & .999. \\ (e) & 871.2199. \\ (f) & .7113. \end{cases}$

(67)　Work out the following:

(a) $\frac{7}{8} - .807$; (b) $.875 - \frac{3}{8}$; (c) $(\frac{5}{32} + .435) - (\frac{21}{100} - .07)$; (d) What is the difference between the sum of 33 millionths and 17 thousandths, and the sum of 53 hundredths and 274 thousandths?

Ans. $\begin{cases} (a) & .068. \\ (b) & .5. \\ (c) & .45125. \\ (d) & .786967. \end{cases}$

(68) What is the sum of .125, .7, .089, .4005, .9, and .000027 ?   Ans. 2.214527.

(69) $927.416 + 8.274 + 372.6 + 62.07938 = ?$

         Ans. 1,370.36938.

(70) Add 17 thousandths, 2 tenths, and 47 millionths.

         Ans. .217047.

(71) Find the products of the following expressions:

(a) $.013 \times .107$; (b) $203 \times 2.03 \times .203$; (c) $2.7 \times 31.85 \times (3.16 - .316)$; (d) $(107.8 + 6.541 - 31.96) \times 1.742$.

$$\text{Ans.} \begin{cases} (a) & .001391. \\ (b) & 83.65427. \\ (c) & 244.56978. \\ (d) & 143.507702. \end{cases}$$

(72) Solve the following:

(a) $(\frac{7}{16} - .13) \times \overline{.625 + \frac{5}{8}}$; (b) $(\frac{19}{32} \times .21) - (.02 \times \frac{3}{16})$; (c) $(\frac{13}{4} + .013 - 2.17) \times \overline{13\frac{1}{4} - 7\frac{5}{16}}$.

$$\text{Ans.} \begin{cases} (a) & .384375. \\ (b) & .1209375. \\ (c) & 6.4896875. \end{cases}$$

(73) Solve the following:

(a) $.875 \div \frac{1}{2}$; (b) $\frac{7}{8} \div .5$; (c) $\dfrac{.375 \times \frac{1}{4}}{\frac{5}{16} - .125}$.

$$\text{Ans.} \begin{cases} (a) & 1.75. \\ (b) & 1.75. \\ (c) & .5. \end{cases}$$

(74) Find the value of the following expression:

$$\frac{\dfrac{1.25 \times 20 \times 3}{87 + (11 \times 8)}}{459 + 32}$$

         Ans. $210\frac{3}{7}$.

(75) From 1 plus .001 take .01 plus .000001.

         Ans. .990999.

ARITHMETIC.

(SECTION 4.)

EXAMINATION QUESTIONS.

(1) What is 25 per cent. of 8,428 lb.?   Ans. 2,107 lb.

(2) What is 1 per cent. of $100?   Ans. $1.

(3) What is $\frac{1}{2}$ per cent. of $35,000?   Ans. $175.

(4) What per cent. of 50 is 2?   Ans. 4%.

(5) What per cent. of 10 is 10?   Ans. 100%.

(6) Solve the following:

(a) Base = $2,522 and percentage = $176.54. What is the rate? (b) Percentage = 16.96 and rate = 8 per cent. What is the base? (c) Amount = 216.7025 and base = 213.5. What is the rate? (d) Difference = 201.825 and base = 207. What is the rate?

$$\text{Ans.} \begin{cases} (a) & 7\%. \\ (b) & 212. \\ (c) & 1\frac{1}{2}\%. \\ (d) & 2\frac{1}{2}\%. \end{cases}$$

(7) A farmer gained 15% on his farm by selling it for $5,500. What did it cost him?   Ans. $4,782.61.

(8) A man receives a salary of $950. He pays 24% of it for board, 12$\frac{1}{2}$% of it for clothing, and 17% of it for other expenses. How much does he save in a year? Ans. $441.75.

(9) If 37$\frac{1}{2}$ per cent. of a number is 961.38, what is the number?   Ans. 2,563.68.

(10) A man owns ¾ of a property. 30% of his share is worth $1,125. What is the whole property worth?

Ans. $5,000.

(11) What sum diminished by 35% of itself equals $4,810?

Ans. $7,400.

(12) A merchant's sales amounted to $197.55 on Monday, and this sum was 12½% of his sales for the week. How much were his sales for the week?   Ans. $1,580.40.

(13) The distance between two stations on a certain railroad is 16.5 miles, which is 12½% of the entire length of the road. What is the length of the road?   Ans. 132 mi.

(14) After paying 60% of my debts I find that I still owe $35. What was my whole indebtedness?   Ans. $87.50.

(15) Reduce 28 rd. 4 yd. 2 ft. 10 in. to inches.

Ans. 5,722 in.

(16) Reduce 5,722 in. to higher denominations.

Ans. 28 rd. 4 yd. 2 ft. 10 in.

(17) How many seconds in 5 weeks and 3.5 days?

Ans. 3,326,400 sec.

(18) How many pounds, ounces, pennyweights, and grains are contained in 13,750 gr.?

Ans. 2 lb. 4 oz. 12 pwt. 22 gr.

(19) Reduce 4,763,254 links to miles.

Ans. 595 mi. 32 ch. 54 li.

(20) Reduce 764,325 cu.in. to cu.yd.

Ans. 16 cu.yd. 10 cu.ft. 549 cu.in.

(21) What is the sum of 2 rd. 2 yd. 2 ft. 3 in.; 4 yd. 1 ft. 9 in.; 2 ft. 7 in.?   Ans. 3 rd. 2 yd. 2 ft. 1 in.

(22) What is the sum of 3 gal. 3 qt. 1 pt. 3 gi.; 6 gal. 1 pt. 2 gi.; 4 gal. 1 gi.; 8 qt. 5 pt.? Ans. 16 gal. 3 qt. 2 gi.

(23) What is the sum of 240 gr. 125 pwt. 50 oz. and 3 lb.?

Ans. 7 lb. 8 oz. 15 pwt.

(24) What is the sum of 11° 16′ 12″; 13° 19′ 30″; 20° 25″; 26′ 29″; 10° 17′ 11″?   Ans. 55° 19′ 47″.

(25) What is the sum of 130 rd. 5 yd. 1 ft. 6 in.; 215 rd. 2 ft. 8 in.; 304 rd. 4 yd. 11 in.?   Ans. 2 mi. 10 rd. 5 yd. 7 in.

(26) What is the sum of 21 A. 67 sq.ch. 3 sq.rd. 21 sq.li.; 28 A. 78 sq.ch. 2 sq.rd. 23 sq.li.; 47 A. 6 sq.ch. 2 sq.rd. 18 sq.li.; 56 A. 59 sq.ch. 2 sq.rd. 16 sq.li.; 25 A. 38 sq.ch. 3 sq.rd. 23 sq.li.; 46 A. 75 sq.ch. 2 sq.rd. 21 sq.li.?
        Ans. 255 A. 3 sq.ch. 14 sq.rd. 122 sq.li.

(27) From 20 rd. 2 yd. 2 ft. 9 in. take 300 ft.
        Ans. 2 rd. 1 yd. 2 ft. 9 in.

(28) From a farm containing 114 A. 80 sq.rd. 25 sq.yd., 75 A. 70 sq.rd. 30 sq.yd. are sold. How much remains?
        Ans. 39 A. 9 sq.rd. 25¼ sq.yd.

(29) From a hogshead of molasses, 10 gal. 2 qt. 1 pt. are sold at one time, and 26 gal. 3 qt. at another time. How much remains?   Ans. 25 gal. 2 qt. 1 pt.

(30) If a person were born June 19, 1850, how old would he be August 3, 1892?   Ans. 42 yr. 1 mo. 14 da.

(31) A note was given August 5, 1890, and was paid June 3, 1892. What length of time did it run?
        Ans. 1 yr. 9 mo. 28 da.

(32) What length of time elapsed from 16 min. past 10 o'clock A. M., July 4, 1883, to 22 min. before 8 o'clock P. M., Dec. 12, 1888?   Ans. 5 yr. 5 mo. 8 da. 9 hr. 22 min.

(33) If 1 iron rail is 17 ft. 3 in. long, how long would 51 rails be, if placed end to end?   Ans. 53 rd. 1½ yd. 9 in.

(34) Multiply 3 qt. 1 pt. 3 gi. by 4.7.
        Ans. 4 gal. 2 qt. 1.7 gi.

(35) Multiply 3 lb. 10 oz. 13 pwt. 12 gr. by 1.5.
        Ans. 5 lb. 10 oz. 6 gr.

(36) How many bushels of apples are contained in 9 bbl., if each barrel contains 2 bu. 3 pk. 6 qt.?

Ans. 26 bu. 1 pk. 6 qt.

(37) Multiply 7 T. 15 cwt. 10.5 lb. by 1.7.

Ans. 13 T. 3 cwt. 67.85 lb.

(38) Divide 358 A. 57 sq.rd. 6 sq.yd. 2 sq.ft. by 7.

Ans. 51 A. 31 sq.rd. 8 sq.ft.

(39) Divide 282 bu. 3 pk. 1 qt. 1 pt. by 12.

Ans. 23 bu. 2 pk. 2 qt. $\frac{1}{4}$ pt.

(40) How many iron rails, each 30 ft. long, are required to lay a railroad track 23 mi. long?   Ans. 8,096 rails.

(41) How many boxes, each holding 1 bu. 1 pk. 7 qt., can be filled from 356 bu. 3 pk. 5 qt. of cranberries?

Ans. 243 boxes.

(42) If 16 square miles are equally divided into 62 farms, how much land will each contain?

Ans. 165 A. 25 sq.rd. 24 sq.yd. 3 sq.ft. 80+ sq.in.

ARITHMETIC.

(SECTION 5.)

EXAMINATION QUESTIONS.

(43) What is the square of 108? Ans. 11,664.

(44) Find the fifth power of 9. Ans. 59,049.

(45) What is the value of .0133³? Ans. .000002352637.

(46) Extract the square root of 90. Ans. 9.4868.

(47) Find the value of $(3\frac{3}{4})^3$. Ans. $52\frac{47}{64}$, or 52.734375.

(48) What is the cube root of 92,416? Ans. 45.211.

(49) Find the value of $\sqrt{502,681}$. Ans. 709.

(50) What is the value of $\sqrt[3]{\frac{27}{64}}$? Ans. $\frac{3}{4}$.

(51) What is the value of $\sqrt[3]{\frac{3}{8}}$? Ans. .72112.

(52) Find the square root of .7854. Ans. .88623.

(53) What number multiplied by itself equals 114.9184? Ans. 10.72.

(54) Extract the square root of 3,486,784. Ans. 1,867.3.

(55) Find the square root of .00041209. Ans. .0203.

(56) Find the fourth root of 2,490.31. Ans. 7.0642.

(57) Find the fifth root of 6,039,065,434. Ans. 90.405.

(58) Find the fifth root of .127. Ans. .66185.

ARITHMETIC.

(SECTION 6.)

EXAMINATION QUESTIONS.

Find the value of x in the following:

(59) $11.7 : 13 :: 20 : x.$ Ans. $22.22+$.

(60) (a) $20 + 7 : 10 + 8 :: 3 : x$; (b) $12^2 : 100^2 :: 4 : x.$

$$\text{Ans.} \begin{cases} (a) & 2. \\ (b) & 277.7+. \end{cases}$$

(61) $(a) \dfrac{4}{x} = \dfrac{7}{21}$; $(b) \dfrac{x}{24} = \dfrac{8}{16}$; $(c) \dfrac{2}{10} = \dfrac{x}{100}$; $(d) \dfrac{15}{45} = \dfrac{60}{x}$;

$(e) \dfrac{10}{150} = \dfrac{x}{600}.$

$$\text{Ans.} \begin{cases} (a) & x = 12. \\ (b) & x = 12. \\ (c) & x = 20. \\ (d) & x = 180. \\ (e) & x = 40. \end{cases}$$

(62) $x : 5 :: 27 : 12.5.$ Ans. $10\frac{4}{5}$.

(63) $45 : 60 :: x : 24.$ Ans. $18.$

(64) $x : 35 :: 4 : 7.$ Ans. $20.$

(65) $9 : x :: 6 : 24.$ Ans. $36.$

(66) $\sqrt[3]{1,000} : \sqrt[3]{1,331} = 27 : x.$ Ans. $29.7.$

(67) $64 : 81 = 21^2 : x^2.$ Ans. $23.625.$

(68) $7 + 8 : 7 = 30 : x.$ Ans. $14.$

(69)   A man whose steps measure 2 ft. 5 in. takes 2,480 steps in walking a certain distance.   How many steps of 2 ft. 7 in. will be required for the same distance?

Ans. 2,320 steps.

(70)   If a horse travels 12 mi. in 1 hr. 36 min., how far will he travel at the same rate in 15 hr.?   Ans. 112.5 mi.

(71)   If a column of mercury 27.63 in. high weighs .76 of a pound, what will be the weight of a column of mercury having the same diameter, 29.4 in. high?   Ans. .808+ lb.

(72)   If 2 gal. 3 qt. 1 pt. of water will last a man 5 da., how long will 5 gal. 3 qt. last him, if he drinks at the same rate?   Ans. 10 da.

(73)   Heat from a burning body varies inversely as the square of the distance from it.   If a thermometer held 6 ft. from a stove shows a rise in temperature of 24°, how many degrees rise in temperature would it indicate if held 12 ft. from the stove?   Ans. 6°.

(74)   If a pile of wood 12 ft. long, 4 ft. wide, and 3 ft. high is worth $12, what is the value of a pile of wood 15 ft. long, 5 ft. wide, and 6 ft. high?   Ans. $37.50.

(75)   If 100 gal. of water run over a dam in 2 hr., how many gallons will run over the dam in 14 hr. 28 min.?

Ans. 723⅓ gal.

(76)   If a cistern 28 ft. long, 12 ft. wide, 10 ft. deep holds 798 bbl. of water, how many barrels of water will a cistern hold that is 20 ft. long, 17 ft. wide, and 6 ft. deep?

Ans. 484½ bbl.

(77)   If a railway train runs 444 mi. in 8 hr. 40 min., in what time can it run 1,060 mi. at the same rate of speed?

Ans. 20 hr. 41.44 min.

(78)   If sound travels at the rate of 6,160 ft. in 5½ sec., how far does it travel in 1 min.?   Ans. 67,200 ft.

(79) If 5 men by working 8 hours a day can do a certain amount of work, how many men by working 10 hours a day can do the same work?
Ans. 4 men.

(80) If a man travels 540 miles in 20 days of 10 hours each, how many hours a day must he travel to cover 630 miles in 25 days?
Ans. $9\frac{1}{3}$ hr.

ELEMENTS OF ALGEBRA

(PART 1)

EXAMINATION QUESTIONS

(1) Divide $3a^3 + 2 - 4a^5 + 7a + 2a^6 - 5a^4 + 10a^2$ by $a^3 - 1 - a^2 - 2a$. $\qquad$ Ans. $2a^3 - 2a^2 - 3a - 2$

(2) Multiply: (a) $2 + 4a - 5a^2 - 6a^3$ by $7a^3$; (b) $4x^2 - 4y^2 + 6z^2$ by $3x^2y$; (c) $3b + 5c - 2d$ by $6a$.

$$\text{Ans.} \begin{cases} (a) & 14a^3 + 28a^4 - 35a^5 - 42a^6 \\ (b) & 12x^4y - 12x^2y^3 + 18x^2yz^2 \\ (c) & 18ab + 30ac - 12ad \end{cases}$$

(3) Translate the following algebraic expressions into ordinary language: $\sqrt{\dfrac{a+b+c}{n}} + \sqrt{a} + \dfrac{b+c}{n} + \sqrt{a+b} + \dfrac{c}{n} + (a+b)c + a + bc$.

(4) From $a^4 - b^4$ take $5a^3b - 7a^2b^2 + 5ab^3$, and from the result take $3a^4 - 4a^3b + 6a^2b^2 + 5ab^3 - 3b^4$.

$\qquad$ Ans. $- 2a^4 - a^3b + a^2b^2 - 10ab^3 + 2b^4$

(5) (a) Give an illustration, not contained in the text, that will explain the difference between positive and negative quantities. (b) In what respects are addition and subtraction different in algebra from addition and subtraction in arithmetic?

(6) (a) What is the value of a^0? (b) What does $a^0 \div a^{-1}$ equal?

(7) (*a*) What is the reciprocal of $\frac{24}{49}$? (*b*) Of what number is 700 the reciprocal?

(8) (*a*) From $3a - 2b + 3c$ take $2a - 7b - c - b$. (*b*) Subtract $x^3 + y^3 - xy^2$ from $2x^3 - 3x^2y + 2xy^3$. (*c*) From $14a + 4b - 6c - 3d$ take $11a - 2b + 4c - 4d$.

$$\text{Ans.} \begin{cases} (a) & a + 6b + 4c \\ (b) & x^3 - 3x^2y + xy^2 + 2xy^3 - y^3 \\ (c) & 3a + 6b - 10c + d \end{cases}$$

(9) Find the numerical values of the following expressions when $a = 16$, $b = 10$, and $x = 5$: (*a*) $(ab^2x + 2abx)4a$; (*b*) $2\sqrt{4a} - \dfrac{2bx}{a-b} + \dfrac{b-x}{x}$; (*c*) $(b - \sqrt{a})(x^3 - b^2)(a^2 - b^2)$.

$$\text{Ans.} \begin{cases} (a) & 614,400 \\ (b) & \frac{1}{3} \\ (c) & 23,400 \end{cases}$$

(10) Find the sum of the following: (*a*) $4xyz - 3xyz - 5xyz$, $6xyz - 9xyz + 3xyz$; (*b*) $3a^2 + 2ab + 4b^2$, $5a^2 - 8ab + b^2$, $-a^2 + 5ab - b^2$, $18a^2 - 20ab - 19b^2$, and $14a^2 - 3ab + 20b^2$; (*c*) $4mn + 3ab - 4c$, $3x - 4ab + 2mn$, and $3m^2 - 4p$.

$$\text{Ans.} \begin{cases} (a) & -4xyz \\ (b) & 39a^2 - 24ab + 5b^2 \\ (c) & 6mn - ab - 4c + 3x + 3m^2 - 4p \end{cases}$$

(11) (*a*) Explain in your own words the difference between a coefficient and an exponent. (*b*) How are coefficients and exponents treated in multiplication, and how in division? (*c*) What is the law of signs in multiplication?

(12) State how you would read the following expressions: (*a*) $a^2x^2 + 2a^3b^5 - (a + b)$; (*b*) $\sqrt[3]{x} + y(a - n^2)^{\frac{2}{3}}$; (*c*) $(m + n)(m - n)^2\left(m - \dfrac{n}{2}\right)$.

(13) (*a*) Write a monomial; a binomial; a polynomial. (*b*) In the expression $a + 2ab - b^2$, why cannot the indicated addition and subtraction be performed? (*c*) What operation is indicated between the quantities in $4ac^2d$?

(14) Remove the symbols of aggregation from the following:

(a) $2a - \{3b + [4c - 4a - (2a + 2b)] + [3a - \overline{b + c}]\};$
(b) $7a - \{3a - [(2a - 5a) + 4a]\};$
(c) $a - \{2b + [3c - 3a - (a + b)] + [2a - (b + c)]\}.$

$$\text{Ans.} \begin{cases} (a) & 5a - 3c \\ (b) & 5a \\ (c) & 3a - 2c \end{cases}$$

(15) (a) Arrange $a^3b^2 + 2abc + 3 - 7a^2b^3 + 6a^4b^4$ according to the decreasing powers of a; (b) according to the increasing powers of b. (c) With $a^2 + 1 + 2a^3 + ax$ arranged according to the increasing powers of a, should the 1 be placed first or last, and why?

(16) Multiply: (a) $2x^3 + 2x^2 + 2x - 2$ by $x - 1$; (b) $x^2 - 4ax + c$ by $2x + a$; and (c) $- a^3 + 3a^2b - 2b^3$ by $5a^2 + 9ab$.

$$\text{Ans.} \begin{cases} (a) & 2x^4 - 4x + 2 \\ (b) & 2x^3 - 7ax^2 + 2cx - 4a^2x + ac \\ (c) & - 5a^5 + 6a^4b + 27a^3b^2 - 10a^2b^3 - 18ab^4 \end{cases}$$

(17) Divide: (a) $3x^2 + x + 9x^3 - 1$ by $3x - 1$; (b) $a^3 - 2ab^2 + b^3$ by $a - b$; (c) $7x^3 + 58x - 24x^2 - 21$ by $7x - 3$.

$$\text{Ans.} \begin{cases} (a) & 3x^2 + 2x + 1 \\ (b) & a^2 + ab - b^2 \\ (c) & x^2 - 3x + 7 \end{cases}$$

(18) Why are letters used in algebra, and in what ways do they differ from figures?

ELEMENTS OF ALGEBRA

(PART 2)

EXAMINATION QUESTIONS

(1) How may the signs of all the terms of the denominator of a fraction be changed from $+$ to $-$ or from $-$ to $+$ without altering the value of the fraction?

(2) Find the products of:

(a) $\dfrac{9m^2n^2}{8p^3q^3}$, $\dfrac{5p^2q}{2xy}$, and $\dfrac{24x^2y^2}{90mn}$;

(b) $3ax + 4$ and $\dfrac{a^2}{9a^3x^2 + 24a^2x + 16a}$.

Ans. $\begin{cases} (a) \quad \dfrac{3mnxy}{4pq^2} \\[2ex] (b) \quad \dfrac{a}{3ax + 4} \end{cases}$

(3) Reduce $\dfrac{c(a + b) + cd}{(a + b)c}$ to its simplest form.

(4) Simplify $\dfrac{3 + 2x}{2 - x} - \dfrac{2 - 3x}{2 + x} + \dfrac{16x - x^2}{x^2 - 4}$. Ans. $\dfrac{1}{x + 2}$

(5) Multiply $\dfrac{a^2 + c^2 + ac}{a^2 + b^2 - c^2 - 2ab}$ by $\dfrac{a^2 + c^2 - b^2 - 2ac}{a^3c + a^2c^2 + ac^3}$.

Ans. $\dfrac{a + b - c}{ac(a - b + c)}$

SUGGESTION.—Factor the numerators and denominators before multiplying.

(6) Change the fraction $-\dfrac{c - (a - b)}{c + (a + b)}$ so that the sign before the dividing line will be $+$.

§ 4

(7) Resolve into their factors: (a) $45x^7y^{10} - 90x^5y^7 - 360x^4y^9$; (b) $a^2b^2 + 2abcd + c^2d^2$; (c) $(a+b)^2 - (c-d)^2$.

Ans. (c) $(a+b+c-d)(a+b-c+d)$

(8) Perform the indicated additions:

(a) $\dfrac{x}{x-y} + \dfrac{x-y}{y-x}$; (b) $\dfrac{x^2}{x^2-1} + \dfrac{x}{x+1} - \dfrac{x}{1-x}$;

(c) $\dfrac{3a-4b}{7} - \dfrac{2a-b+c}{3} + \dfrac{13a-4c}{12}$.

$$\text{Ans.} \begin{cases} (a) & \dfrac{y}{x-y} \\[2mm] (b) & \dfrac{3x^2}{x^2-1} \\[2mm] (c) & \dfrac{71a-20b-56c}{84} \end{cases}$$

(9) Factor the following: (a) $9x^4 + 12x^2y^2 + 4y^4$; (b) $49a^4 - 154a^2b^2 + 121b^4$; (c) $64x^2y^2 + 64xy + 16$.

(10) (a) Reduce $1 + 2x - \dfrac{4x-4}{5x}$ to a fractional form.

(b) Change $\dfrac{3x^2+2x+1}{x+4}$ to a mixed quantity.

$$\text{Ans.} \begin{cases} (a) & \dfrac{10x^2+x+4}{5x} \\[2mm] (b) & 3x - 10 + \dfrac{41}{x+4} \end{cases}$$

(11) What are the factors of: (a) $x^3 + 8$? (b) $x^3 - 27y^3$? and (c) $xm - nm + xy - ny$? Ans. (c) $(x-n)(m+y)$

(12) Factor: (a) $x^8y^2 - 64x^2y^2$; (b) $a^2 - b^2 - c^2 + 1 - 2a + 2bc$; (c) $1 - 16a^2 + 8ac - c^2$.

$$\text{Ans.} \begin{cases} (a) & x^2y^2(x+2)(x-2)(x^2+2x+4)(x^2-2x+4) \\ (b) & (a-1+b-c)(a-1-b+c) \\ (c) & (1+4a-c)(1-4a+c) \end{cases}$$

(13) Raise to their indicated powers:

$$(2a^2bc^3)^4, \quad (-3a^2b^2c)^5 \text{ and } (-7m^3nx^2y^4)^2$$

(14) Find the values of the following:

$$\left(c^{-\frac{2}{3}}\right)^{-\frac{1}{2}}; \quad \left(m\sqrt{n^{3}}\right)^{-\frac{1}{2}}; \quad \left(cd^{-2}\right)^{\frac{1}{a}}$$

(15) (*a*) Express with radical signs: $x^{\frac{3}{4}}; \; 3x^{\frac{1}{2}}y^{-\frac{3}{2}}; \; 3x^{\frac{1}{2}}y^{-\frac{2}{3}}z^{\frac{1}{3}}.$

(*b*) Clear $a^{-1}b^{\frac{1}{2}} + \dfrac{c^{-2}}{a+b} + (m-n)^{-1} - \dfrac{a^{2}b^{-2}c}{c^{-3}}$ of negative exponents.   (*c*) Express with fractional exponents: $\sqrt[7]{x^{6}};$ $\sqrt[3]{x^{-4}}; \; \left(\sqrt[4]{b^{5}x^{9}}\right)^{3}.$

ELEMENTS OF ALGEBRA

(PART 3)

EXAMINATION QUESTIONS

(1) A man performed a journey of 48 miles in a certain number of hours, but if he had traveled 4 miles more each hour, he would have performed the journey in 6 hours less time. How many miles did he travel per hour ?

$$\text{Ans. 4 miles}$$

(2) Solve: (a) $\sqrt{3x - 2} = 2(x - 4)$;

$$(b) \quad \sqrt{x - 4ab} = \frac{(a + b)\,(a - b)}{\sqrt{x}}.$$

Ans. $\begin{cases} (a) & x = 6 \text{ or } 2\frac{3}{4} \\ (b) & x = (a + b)^2 \text{ or } - (a - b)^2 \end{cases}$

(3) Solve:

(a) $\sqrt{3x - 5} = \dfrac{\sqrt{7x^2 + 36x}}{x}$;

(b) $(x - 2)\,(x - 4) - 2(x - 1)\,(x - 3) = 0.$

Ans. $\begin{cases} (a) & x = 6 \text{ or } - 2 \\ (b) & x = 1 \pm \sqrt{3} \end{cases}$

(4) Solve by substitution:

$$\left. \begin{array}{l} 5x - 2y = 51. \\ 19x - 3y = 180. \end{array} \right\}$$

Ans. $\begin{cases} x = 9 \\ y = -3 \end{cases}$

§ 5

(5) Solve the following equations: (a) $2x^2 - 27x = 14$;
(b) $x^2 - \dfrac{2x}{3} + \dfrac{1}{12} = 0$; (c) $x^2 + ax = bx + ab$.

$$\text{Ans.} \begin{cases} (a) & x = 14 \text{ or } -\tfrac{1}{2} \\ (b) & x = \tfrac{1}{2} \text{ or } \tfrac{1}{6} \\ (c) & x = b \text{ or } -a \end{cases}$$

(6) A crew that can pull at the rate of 12 miles an hour down the stream finds that it takes twice as long to row a given distance up stream as it does down stream. What is the rate of the current?   Ans. 3 miles per hour

(7) Solve the following equations, eliminating by addition or subtraction:

$$\begin{aligned} 11x + 3y &= 100. \\ 4x - 7y &= 4. \end{aligned} \quad\quad \text{Ans.} \begin{cases} x = 8 \\ y = 4 \end{cases}$$

(8) Solve the following equations:

$$\begin{aligned} x + y &= 13. \\ xy &= 36. \end{aligned} \quad\quad \text{Ans.} \begin{cases} x = 9, y = 4 \\ x = 4, y = 9 \end{cases}$$

(9) Find the values of x in the following:

(a) $5x^2 - 9 = 2x^2 + 24$;   (b) $\dfrac{3}{4x^2} - \dfrac{1}{6x^2} = \dfrac{7}{3}$;

(c) $\dfrac{x^2}{5} - \dfrac{x^2 - 10}{15} = 7 - \dfrac{50 + x^2}{25}$.

$$\text{Ans.} \begin{cases} (a) & x = \pm\sqrt{11} \\ (b) & x = \pm\tfrac{1}{2} \\ (c) & x = \pm 5 \end{cases}$$

(10) Solve by comparison:

$$\begin{aligned} 4x + 3y &= 48. \\ 5y - 3x &= 22. \end{aligned} \quad\quad \text{Ans.} \begin{cases} x = 6 \\ y = 8 \end{cases}$$

(11) Solve:

$$2x - \dfrac{y-3}{5} - 4 = 0.$$

$$3y + \dfrac{x-2}{3} - 9 = 0.$$

$$\text{Ans.} \begin{cases} x = 2 \\ y = 3 \end{cases}$$

(12) A person has two horses, and a saddle worth $10. If the saddle be put on the first horse, his value becomes double that of the second; but if the saddle be put on the second horse, his value will not amount to that of the first horse by $13.   What is the value of each horse ?

Ans. $56 and $33

(13) If A should give B $5 he would then have $6 less than B; but if he received $5 from B, three times his money would be $20 more than four times B's.   How much money did each have ?

Ans. $\begin{cases} \text{A, } \$31 \\ \text{B, } \$27 \end{cases}$

(14) Solve the following equations :

(a) $x^2 - 6x = 16$; (b) $x^2 - 7x = 8$; (c) $9x^2 - 12x = 21$.

Ans. $\begin{cases} (a) & x = 8 \text{ or } -2 \\ (b) & x = 8 \text{ or } -1 \\ (c) & x = 2\frac{1}{3} \text{ or } -1 \end{cases}$

(15) A wine merchant has two kinds of wine, one worth 90 cents a quart, and the other 50 cents a quart.   How much of each must be put in a mixture of 60 quarts, that the mixture may be worth 75 cents a quart ?

Ans. $\begin{cases} 37\frac{1}{2} \text{ qt. of 90-cent wine} \\ 22\frac{1}{2} \text{ qt. of 50-cent wine} \end{cases}$

(16) What fraction is that whose numerator being doubled, and denominator being increased by 7, the value becomes $\frac{2}{3}$; but the denominator being doubled, and the numerator increased by 2, the value becomes $\frac{3}{5}$?   Ans. $\frac{4}{5}$

(17) When 4 is added to the greater of two numbers, the greater number is $3\frac{1}{4}$ times the less; but when 8 is added to the less, the less is one-half the greater.   What are the two numbers ?   Ans. 48 and 16

LOGARITHMS

EXAMINATION QUESTIONS

(1)   Solve, using logarithms,
$$x = 351.36 \times 100 \times 24[1 - (\tfrac{200}{100})^{.29078}].$$

NOTE.—In logarithmic work, negative quantities are used as though they were positive, the sign of the result being determined independently.

Ans. $x = -188{,}300.$

(2)   What are the logarithms of the following numbers: (a) 2,376?   (b) .6413?   (c) .0002507?

(3)   Divide the following by using logarithms: (a) 755.4 ÷ .00324;   (b) .05555 ÷ .0008601;   (c) 4.62 ÷ .6448.

Ans. $\begin{cases}(a) & 233{,}150. \\ (b) & 64.584. \\ (c) & 7.1648.\end{cases}$

(4)   Find the value of x, by using logarithms, in
$$x^{.74} = \frac{238 \times 1{,}000}{.0042^{.6602}}.$$
Ans. $x = 2{,}432{,}700{,}000.$

(5)   Divide $\sqrt[4]{.00743}$ by $\sqrt[6]{.006}$.   Ans. 1,893.6.

(6)   Multiply together the following by using logarithms: 1,728, .00024, .7462, 302.1, and 7.6094.   Ans. 711.40.

(7)   Calculate the value of $\dfrac{\sqrt{5.954} \times \sqrt[3]{61.19}}{\sqrt[5]{298.54}}$.

Ans. 3.0759.

(8)   Calculate the value of $\sqrt[7]{.0532864}$.   Ans. .65780.

(9)   Obtain the values of: (a) $32^{4.8}$; (b) $.76^{3.62}$; (c) $.84^{.38}$.

Ans. $\begin{cases}(a) & 16{,}777{,}000. \\ (b) & .37028. \\ (c) & .93590.\end{cases}$

§ 5

(10)   Calculate the value of $\sqrt[6]{\dfrac{1}{249}} \div \sqrt[5]{\dfrac{23}{71}}.$ .Ans. .49950.

(11)   Find the numbers corresponding to the following logarithms: .81293, 2.52460, 1.27631.

(12)   Find the value of v_1 in $p v^{1.41} = p_1 v_1^{1.41}$, when $p = 134.7$, $v = 1.495$, and $p_1 = 16.421$.   Ans. 6.6504.

(13)   What is the value of

$$\sqrt[5]{\dfrac{7.1895 \times 4,764.2^2 \times .00326^5}{.000489 \times 457^3 \times .576^2}}?$$ Ans. .020786.

(14)   In the formula $p = 960,000 \dfrac{t^{2.18}}{l\,d}$, find the value of p, when $t = \frac{3}{16}$, $l = 120$, and $d = 2\frac{1}{4}$.   Ans. 92.480.

(15)   Referring to example 14, what is the value of t, when $p = 160$, $l = 132$, and $d = 2$?   Ans. .23863.

Geometry and Trigonometry

EXAMINATION QUESTIONS

NOTE.—In solving the following examples, the student will find that he will understand them much better if he draws a diagram for each, showing the given conditions and results sought.

(1) ' If one of the angles formed by one straight line meeting another straight line equals $\frac{4}{5}$ of a right angle, what is the other angle equal to ?   Ans. $1\frac{1}{5}$ right angles.

(2) If a triangle has two equal angles, what kind of a triangle is it ?

(3) The perimeter of a regular decagon is 40 inches; what is the length of a side ?   Ans. 4. in.

(4) What is one angle of a regular dodecagon equal to ?   Ans. $1\frac{2}{3}$ right angles.

(5) A triangle has three equal angles; what is it called ?

(6) A certain triangle has two equal angles. If, from the vertex of the other angle, a perpendicular is drawn to the side opposite, which is 7 inches long, what are the lengths of the two parts of the side thus divided by the perpendicular ?

(7) The shortest distance from a given point to a given line is 9 inches; the distances from this point to the two extremities of the line are 12 inches and 15 inches; what is the length of the line ?   Ans. 19.94 in.

(8) What is one of the angles of an equiangular octagon equal to ?   Ans. $1\frac{1}{2}$ right angles.

§ 6

(9) Given three points A, B, and C, and the distance from A to B equal to $1\frac{1}{2}$ inches, from B to C $1\frac{1}{2}$ inches, and from C to A 2 inches; pass a circle through these three points.

(10) The chord of an arc in a circle whose radius is 6 inches is 4 inches long; what is the length of the chord of half the arc?   Ans. 2.03 in.

(11) The length of a perpendicular from the center of a circle to a chord is $5\frac{3}{4}$ inches; if the diameter of the circle is 17 inches, what is the length of the chord?   Ans. 12.52 in.

(12) The sides of an inscribed angle intercept three-fourths of the circumference; how many quadrants are there in the angle?   Ans. $1\frac{1}{2}$ quadrants.

(13) How many equal sectors are there in a circle, if each sector measures $\frac{2}{7}$ of a right angle?   Ans. 14 sectors.

(14) If the perimeter of a regular inscribed octagon is 24 inches and the length of the perpendicular from the center to one of the sides is 3.62 inches, what is the diameter of the circle in which the octagon is inscribed?
                                                        Ans. 7.84 in.

(15) What part of a circle is an arc of 19° 19′ and 19″? Express it decimally.   Ans. .053672 of a circle.

(16) In a triangle $A B C$, $A B = 26$ feet 7 inches, $A C = 40$ feet, and the included angle $A = 36° 20′ 43″$; find the remaining parts.
Ans. $\begin{cases} C = 40° 16′ 52″. \\ B = 103° 22′ 25″. \\ B C = 24 \text{ ft. } 4.4 \text{ in.} \end{cases}$

(17) In a triangle $A B C$, the side $A B = 16$ feet 5 inches, the side $B C = 13$ feet $6\frac{1}{2}$ inches, and the angle $A = 54°$ 54′ 54″; find the remaining parts.
Ans. $\begin{cases} B = 42° 19′ 36″, \text{ or} \\ \qquad 27° 50′ 36″. \\ C = 82° 45′ 30″, \text{ or} \\ \qquad 97° 14′ 30″. \\ A C = 11 \text{ ft. } 1\frac{3}{4} \text{ in.,} \\ \qquad \text{or } 7 \text{ ft. } 8\frac{3}{4} \text{ in.} \end{cases}$

(18) If one-third of an angle of a certain triangle = 14° 47′ 10″, what are the angles, one of the other two being two and one-half times the given angle?

$$\text{Ans.} \begin{cases} 24° 44′ 45″. \\ 44° 21′ 30″. \\ 110° 53′ 45″. \end{cases}$$

(19) In a right triangle $A B C$, the two sides are 437 feet and 792 feet in length; find the hypotenuse and the two acute angles?

$$\text{Ans.} \begin{cases} 28° 53′ 19″. \\ 61° 6′ 41″. \\ 904 \text{ ft. } 6\tfrac{3}{4} \text{ in.} \end{cases}$$

(20) In a triangle $A B C$, angle $A = 29° 21′$, angle $C = 76° 44′ 18″$, and the side $A C = 31$ feet 10 inches; find the other three parts.

$$\text{Ans.} \begin{cases} B C = 16 \text{ ft. } 3 \text{ in.} \\ A B = 32 \text{ ft. } 3 \text{ in.} \\ B = 73° 54′ 42″. \end{cases}$$

(21) (a) The area of a circle is 89.42 square inches; what is its diameter and circumference? (b) What is the length of a side of the largest regular hexagon that could be inscribed in it? Ans. (b) 5.335 in.

(22) The distance between two parallel sides of a wrought-iron octagon bar is 2 inches; what is the weight of a bar 10 feet long, a cubic inch of wrought iron weighing .282 pound? Ans. 112 lb. 2 oz.

(23) The outside and inside diameters of a cast-iron spherical shell are 16 inches and 12 inches; what is its weight, a cubic inch of cast iron weighing .261 pound?

Ans. 323.61 lb.

(24) The length of an arc of a circle is $5\tfrac{13}{32}$ inches by measurement. If the number of degrees in the arc is 27, what is the diameter of the circle? Ans. 22.95 in.

(25) (a) What is the area of a circle whose diameter is $17\tfrac{1}{64}$ inches? (b) What is the length of an arc of 16° 7′ 21″ in the above circle? Ans. (b) 2.394 in.

(26) (a) What is the area of an ellipse whose axes are 12 inches and 8 inches? (b) What is its perimeter?

$$\text{Ans.} \begin{cases} (a) & 75.4 \text{ sq. in.} \\ (b) & 31.731 \text{ in.} \end{cases}$$

(27)   What is the entire surface of a cone whose base is 7 inches in diameter and whose altitude is 11 inches?
Ans. 165.41 sq. in.

(28)   What is the height of a cone having the same volume and diameter as a 10-inch sphere?   Ans. 20 in.

(29)   What is the height of a cylinder having the same volume and diameter as a 12-inch sphere?   Ans. 8 in.

(30)   (a) What is the area of a triangle whose base is $9\frac{1}{2}$ inches and whose altitude is 12 inches?   (b) If the angle which one side forms with the base is 79° 22', what is the perimeter of the triangle?   Ans. (b) 35.73 in.

(31)   The diagonal of a trapezium is 11 inches; the lengths of the perpendiculars from the opposite vertexes upon this diagonal are $4\frac{1}{4}$ inches and 7 inches; what is the area of the trapezium?

(32)   The length of a chord of a segment in a circle whose diameter is 10 inches is $6\frac{3}{4}$ inches; what is the area of the segment and the number of degrees in its arc?
Ans. $\begin{cases} 6.074 \text{ sq. in.} \\ 84° \ 54' \ 28.6''. \end{cases}$

(33)   What is the volume and entire area of a frustum of a cone whose upper base is 12 inches and lower base is 18 inches in diameter and whose altitude is 14 inches?
Ans. $\begin{cases} 2,506.997 \text{ cu. in.} \\ 1,042.38 \text{ sq. in.} \end{cases}$

(34)   What is the area of the surface of a sphere 27 inches in diameter?   Ans. 2,290.2 sq. in.

(35)   What is the volume of an engine cylinder, in cubic feet, whose diameter is 19 inches and whose stroke is 24 inches?   Ans. 3.938 cu. ft.

(36)   The chord of the arc of a segment is 14 inches long and the height of the segment is 2 inches; what is the radius?   Ans. $13\frac{1}{4}$ in.

(37)   (a) What is the volume of a cylindrical ring whose outside diameter is 16 inches and inside diameter 13 inches? (b) If made of cast iron, what is its weight?
Ans. (b) 21 lb.

(38) The altitude of a parallelopipedon is 18 inches; its base is a square, one edge measuring 5¼ inches; what is its convex area, entire area, and volume ?

$$\text{Ans.} \begin{cases} 378 \text{ sq. in.} \\ 433.125 \text{ sq. in.} \\ 496.125 \text{ cu. in.} \end{cases}$$

(39) What is the convex area and entire area of a hexagonal pyramid, the slant height being 37 feet and one edge of the base measuring 12 feet ?

$$\text{Ans.} \begin{cases} 1,332 \text{ sq. ft.} \\ 1,706.112 \text{ sq. ft.} \end{cases}$$

(40) If the altitude of the pyramid in the last problem had been 37 feet, what would have been its volume ?

Ans. 4,614 cu. ft.

(41) What is the area of a sector if the chord of the arc is 6⅞ inches long and the diameter of the circle is 10 inches ?

Ans. 18.95 sq. in.

(42) What is the area in square feet of a parallelogram whose base is 129 inches long, if the shortest distance between the base and side opposite is 7 feet ?

(43) The parallel sides of a trapezoid are 15 feet 7 inches and 21 feet 11 inches long; the altitude is 7 feet 8 inches. What is the area of the trapezoid ?   Ans. 143.75 sq. ft.

.(44) What would be (*a*) the length of a side of a square having the same area as the trapezoid in the last problem ? (*b*) the diameter of a circle ?   (*c*) How much shorter is the circumference of the circle than the perimeter of the square ?

$$\text{Ans.} \begin{cases} (a) \quad 11.99 \text{ ft.} \\ (b) \quad 13\tfrac{1}{2} \text{ ft.} \\ (c) \quad 5 \text{ ft. } 6.6 \text{ in.} \end{cases}$$

(45) In a triangle ABC, $AB = 24$ feet, $BC = 11$ feet 3 inches, and $AC = 18$ feet; required, the three angles.

$$\text{Ans.} \begin{cases} A = 26° \ 28' \ 5''. \\ B = 45° \ 29' \ 23''. \\ C = 108° \ 2' \ 32''. \end{cases}$$

A KEY

TO ALL THE QUESTIONS AND EXAMPLES
INCLUDED IN THE EXAMINATION QUESTIONS.

It will be noticed that the Keys have been given the same section numbers as occur on the headlines of Examination Questions to which they refer. All article references refer to the Instruction Paper bearing the same section number as the Key in which it occurs, unless the title of some other Instruction Paper is given in connection with the article number.

To be of the greatest benefit, the Keys should be used sparingly. They should be used much in the same manner as a pupil would go to a teacher for instruction with regard to answering some example he was unable to solve. If used in this manner, the Keys will be of great help and assistance to the student, and will be a source of encouragement to him in studying the various papers composing the Course.

ARITHMETIC.

(QUESTIONS 1–75. SEC. 1–3.)

(1)   See Art. **1.**

(2)   See Art. **3.**

(3)   See Arts. **5** and **6.**

(4)   See Arts. **10** and **11.**

(5)   980 = Nine hundred eighty.

605 = Six hundred five.

28,284. = Twenty-eight thousand two hundred eighty-four.

9,006,042 = Nine million six thousand forty-two.

850,317,002 = Eight hundred fifty million three hundred seventeen thousand two.

700,004 = Seven hundred thousand four.

(6)   Seven thousand six hundred = 7,600.

Eighty-one thousand four hundred two = 81,402.

Five million four thousand seven = 5,004,007.

One hundred eight million ten thousand one = 108,-010,001.

Eighteen million six = 18,000,006.

Thirty thousand ten = 30,010.

(7)   In adding whole numbers, place the numbers to be added directly under each other so that the extreme right-hand figures will stand in the same column, regardless of the position of those at the left.   Add the first column of figures at the extreme right, which equals 19 units, or 1 ten and 9 units.   We place

$$
\begin{array}{r}
3\,2\,9\,0 \\
5\,0\,4 \\
8\,6\,5\,4\,0\,3 \\
2\,0\,7\,4 \\
8\,1 \\
7 \\
\hline
8\,7\,1\,3\,5\,9 \quad \text{Ans.}
\end{array}
$$

9 units under the units column, and reserve 1 ten for the column of tens. $1+8+7+9 = 25$ tens, or 2 hundreds and 5 tens. Place 5 tens under the tens column, and reserve 2 hundreds for the hundreds column. $2+4+5+2 = 13$ hundreds, or 1 thousand and 3 hundreds. Place 3 hundreds under the hundreds column, and reserve the 1 thousand for the thousands column. $1+2+5+3 = 11$ thousands, or 1 ten thousand and 1 thousand. Place the 1 thousand in the column of thousands, and reserve the 1 ten thousand for the column of ten thousands. $1+6 = 7$ ten thousands. Place this 7 ten thousands in the ten thousands column. There is but one figure, 8, in the hundreds of thousands place in the numbers to be added, so it is placed in the hundreds of thousands column of the sum.

A simple (though less scientific) explanation of the same problem is the following: $7+1+4+3+4+0 = 19$; write the 9 and reserve the 1. $1+8+7+0+0+9 = 25$; write the 5 and reserve the 2. $2+0+4+5+2 = 13$; write the 3 and reserve the 1. $1+2+5+3 = 11$; write the 1 and reserve 1. $1+6 = 7$; write the 7. Bring down the 8 to its place in the sum.

```
(8)                    7 0 9
                 8 3 0 4 7 2 5
                       3 9 1
               1 0 0 3 0 2
                     3 0 0
                     9 0 9
              ─────────────
               8 4 0 7 3 3 6   Ans.
```

(9) (a) In subtracting whole numbers, place the subtrahend, or smaller number, under the minuend, or larger number, so that the right-hand figures stand directly under each other. Begin at the *right* to subtract. We cannot subtract 8 units from 2 units, so we take 1 ten from the 6 tens and add it to the 2 units. 1 ten = 10 units, so we have 10 units + 2 units = 12 units. Then 8 units from 12 units leaves 4 units. We took 1 ten from 6 tens, so only 5

tens remain. 3 tens from 5 tens leaves 2
tens. In the hundreds column we have 3   5 0 9 6 2
hundreds from 9 hundreds leaves 6 hun-   3 3 3 8
dreds. We cannot subtract 3 thousands   4 7 6 2 4   Ans.
from 0 thousands, so we take 1 ten thou-
sand from 5 ten thousands and add it to the 0 thousands.
1 ten thousand = 10 thousands, and 10 thousands + 0 thousands = 10 thousands. Subtracting, we have 3 thousands
from 10 thousands leaves 7 thousands. We took 1 ten thousand from 5 ten thousands and have 4 ten thousands
remaining. Since there are no ten thousands in the subtrahend, the 4 in the ten thousands column in the minuend is
brought down into the same column in the remainder,
because 0 from 4 leaves 4.

$$(b) \quad 1\,5\,3\,3\,9$$
$$1\,0\,0\,0\,1$$
$$\overline{\quad 5\,3\,3\,8 \quad} \text{ Ans.}$$

(10)   (a)   7 0 9 6 8   (b)   1 0 0 0 0 0
          3 2 9 7 5   9 8 7 3 5
      3 7 9 9 3   Ans.   1 2 6 5   Ans.

(11) We have given the minuend or greater number
(1,004) and the difference or remainder (49). Placing these
in the usual form of subtraction, we have $\dfrac{1\,0\,0\,4}{\quad\quad}$ in which
$\quad\quad 4\,9$
the dash (——) represents the number sought. This number is evidently *less* than 1,004 by the difference 49, hence,
1,004 — 49 = 955, the smaller number. For the sum of the
two numbers we then have
$$1\,0\,0\,4 \; larger$$
$$9\,5\,5 \; smaller$$
$$\overline{1\,9\,5\,9 \; sum.} \quad \text{Ans.}$$

Or, this problem may be solved as follows: If the greater
of two numbers is 1,004, and the difference between them
is 49, then it is evident that the smaller number must be
equal to the difference between the greater number (1,004)
and the difference (49); or, 1,004 — 49 = 955, the smaller

number. Since the greater number equals 1,004 and the smaller number equals 955, their sum equals 1,004 + 955 = 1,959. Ans.

(12) The numbers connected by the plus (+) sign must first be added. Performing these operations we have

$$
\begin{array}{r}
5\ 9\ 6\ 2 \\
8\ 4\ 7\ 1 \\
9\ 0\ 2\ 3 \\
\hline
2\ 3\ 4\ 5\ 6\ \textit{sum.}
\end{array}
\qquad
\begin{array}{r}
3\ 8\ 7\ 4 \\
2\ 0\ 3\ 9 \\
\hline
5\ 9\ 1\ 3\ \textit{sum.}
\end{array}
$$

Subtracting the smaller number (5,913) from the greater (23,456), we have

$$
\begin{array}{r}
2\ 3\ 4\ 5\ 6 \\
5\ 9\ 1\ 3 \\
\hline
1\ 7\ 5\ 4\ 3\ \textit{difference.} \quad \text{Ans.}
\end{array}
$$

(13) $\$\ 4\ 4\ 6\ 7\ 5$ = amount willed to his son.
  $2\ 6\ 3\ 8\ 0$ = amount willed to his daughter.
  $\$\ 7\ 1\ 0\ 5\ 5$ = amount willed to his two children.
  $\$\ 1\ 2\ 5\ 0\ 0\ 0$ = amount willed to his wife and two children.
  $7\ 1\ 0\ 5\ 5$ = amount willed to his two children.
  $\$\ 5\ 3\ 9\ 4\ 5$ = amount willed to his wife. Ans.

(14) In the multiplication of whole numbers, place the multiplier under the multiplicand, and multiply each term of the multiplicand by each term of the multiplier, writing the right-hand figure of each product obtained under the term of the multiplier which produces it.

(a) $5\ 2\ 6\ 3\ 8\ 7$
  7
  $\overline{3\ 6\ 8\ 4\ 7\ 0\ 9}$ Ans.

7 times 7 units = 49 units, or 4 tens and 9 units. We write the 9 units and reserve the 4 tens. 7 times 8 tens = 56 tens; 56 + 4 tens reserved = 60 tens, or 6 hundreds and 0 tens. Write the 0 tens and reserve the 6 hundreds. 7 × 3 hundreds = 21 hundreds; 21 + 6 hundreds reserved = 27 hundreds, or 2 thousands and 7 hundreds. Write the 7 hundreds and reserve the 2 thousands. 7 × 6 thousands = 42 thousands;

42 + 2 thousands reserved = 44 thousands, or 4 ten thousands and 4 thousands.   Write the 4 thousands and reserve
the 4 ten thousands.   7 × 2 ten thousands = 14 ten thousands; 14 + 4 ten thousands reserved = 18 ten thousands,
or 1 hundred thousand and 8 ten thousands.   Write the 8
ten thousands and reserve the 1 hundred thousand.   7 × 5
hundred thousands = 35 hundred thousands; 35 + 1 hundred thousand reserved = 36 hundred thousands.   Since
there are no more figures in the multiplicand to be multiplied, we write the 36 hundred thousands in the product.
This completes the multiplication.

A simpler (though less scientific) explanation of the same
problem is the following:

7 times 7 = 49; write the 9 and reserve the 4.   7 times
8 = 56; 56 + 4 reserved = 60; write the 0 and reserve the 6.
7 times 3 = 21; 21 + 6 reserved = 27; write the 7 and
reserve the 2.   7 × 6 = 42; 42 + 2 reserved = 44; write the
4 and reserve 4.   7 × 2 = 14; 14 + 4 reserved = 18; write
the 8 and reserve the 1.   7 × 5 = 35; 35 + 1 reserved = 36;
write the 36.

In this case the multiplier is
17 *units*, or 1 ten and 7 units, so
that the product is obtained by
adding two partial products,
namely, 7 × 700,298 and 10
× 700,298.   The actual operation is performed as follows:

$$(b) \qquad 700298$$
$$\underline{17}$$
$$4902086$$
$$\underline{700298}$$
$$11905066 \text{ Ans.}$$

7 times 8 = 56; write the 6 and reserve the 5.   7 times 9
= 63; 63 + 5 reserved = 68; write the 8 and reserve the 6.
7 times 2 = 14; 14 + 6 reserved = 20; write the 0 and
reserve the 2.   7 times 0 = 0; 0 + 2 reserved = 2; write
the 2.   7 times 0 = 0; 0 + 0 reserved = 0; write the 0.
7 times 7 = 49; 49 + 0 reserved = 49; write the 49.

To multiply by the 1 ten we say 1 times 700,298 = 700,-
298, and write 700,298 under the first partial product, as
shown, with the right-hand figure 8 under the multiplier 1.
Add the two partial products; their sum equals the entire
product.

(c)

```
    2 1 7
    1 0 3
    6 5 1
  2 1 7 0
  2 2 3 5 1
        6 7
  1 5 6 4 5 7
1 3 4 1 0 6
1 4 9 7 5 1 7   Ans.
```

Multiply any two of the numbers together and multiply their product by the third number.

(15) If your watch ticks every second, then to find how many times it ticks in 1 week, it is necessary to find the number of seconds in one week.

```
    6 0  seconds = 1 minute.
    6 0  minutes = 1 hour.
  3 6 0 0  seconds = 1 hour.
      2 4  hours = 1 day.
  1 4 4 0 0
  7 2 0 0
  8 6 4 0 0  seconds = 1 day.
        7  days = 1 week.
6 0 4 8 0 0  seconds in 1 week, or the number of times that
            your watch ticks in 1 week.  Ans.
```

(16) If a monthly publication contains 24 pages, a yearly volume will contain 12×24, or 288 pages, since there are 12 months in one year; and eight yearly volumes will contain 8×288, or 2,304 pages.

```
    2 4
    1 2
    2 8 8
        8
  2 3 0 4   Ans.
```

(17) If an engine and boiler are worth $3,246, and the building is worth 3 times as much, plus $1,200, then the building is worth

```
      $ 3 2 4 6
    ×       3
      9 7 3 8
    +   1 2 0 0
    $ 1 0 9 3 8  = value of building.
```

If the tools are worth twice as much as the building, plus $1,875, then the tools are worth

$$
\begin{array}{r}
\$1\,09\,3\,8 \\
\times \qquad 2 \\
\hline
2\,1\,8\,7\,6 \\
+\quad 1\,8\,7\,5 \\
\hline
\$2\,3\,7\,5\,1
\end{array}
= \text{value of tools.}
$$

$$
\begin{array}{ll}
\text{Value of building} = & \$1\,0\,9\,3\,8 \\
\text{Value of tools} \quad\;\; = & \underline{2\,3\,7\,5\,1} \\
& \$3\,4\,6\,8\,9
\end{array}
= \begin{array}{l}\text{value of the building} \\ \text{and tools.} \quad (a)\ \text{Ans.}\end{array}
$$

$$
\begin{array}{ll}
\text{Value of engine and} \\
\quad \text{boiler} \qquad\qquad\;\; = & \$\quad 3\,2\,4\,6 \\
\text{Value of building and} \\
\quad \text{tools} \qquad\qquad\;\; = & \underline{\;\;3\,4\,6\,8\,9} \\
& \$3\,7\,9\,3\,5
\end{array}
= \begin{array}{l}\text{value of the whole} \\ \text{plant.} \quad (b)\ \text{Ans.}\end{array}
$$

(18) (a) $(72 \times 48 \times 28 \times 5) \div (96 \times 15 \times 7 \times 6)$.

Placing the numerator over the denominator the problem becomes

$$
\frac{72 \times 48 \times 28 \times 5}{96 \times 15 \times 7 \times 6} = ?
$$

The 5 in the dividend and 15 in the divisor are both divisible by 5, since 5 divided by 5 equals 1, and 15 divided by 5 equals 3. Cross off the 5 and write the 1 over it; also, cross off the 15 and write the 3 under it. Thus,

$$
\frac{72 \times 48 \times 28 \times \overset{1}{\cancel{5}}}{96 \times \underset{3}{\cancel{15}} \times 7 \times 6} =
$$

The 5 and 15 are not to be considered any longer, and, in fact, may be erased entirely and the 1 and 3 placed in their stead, and treated as if the 5 and the 15 never existed. Thus,

$$
\frac{72 \times 48 \times 28 \times 1}{96 \times 3 \times 7 \times 6} =
$$

72 in the dividend and 96 in the divisor are divisible by 12, since 72 divided by 12 equals 6, and 96 divided by 12 equals 8. Cross off the 72 and write the 6 over it; also, cross off the 96 and write the 8 under it. Thus,

$$\frac{\overset{6}{\cancel{72}}\times 48\times 28\times 1}{\underset{8}{\cancel{96}}\times 3\times 7\times 6} =$$

The 72 and 96 are not to be considered any longer, and, in fact, may be erased entirely and the 6 and 8 placed in their stead, and treated as if the 72 and 96 never existed. Thus,

$$\frac{6\times 48\times 28\times 1}{8\times 3\times 7\times 6} =$$

Again, 28 in the dividend and 7 in the divisor are divisible by 7, since 28 divided by 7 equals 4, and 7 divided by 7 equals 1. Cross off the 28 and write the 4 over it; also, cross off the 7 and write the 1 under it. Thus,

$$\frac{6\times 48\times \overset{4}{\cancel{28}}\times 1}{8\times 3\times \underset{1}{\cancel{7}}\times 6} =$$

The 28 and 7 are not to be considered any longer, and, in fact, may be erased entirely and the 4 and 1 placed in their stead, and treated as if the 28 and 7 never existed. Thus,

$$\frac{6\times 48\times 4\times 1}{8\times 3\times 1\times 6} =$$

Again, 48 in the dividend and 6 in the divisor are divisible by 6, since 48 divided by 6 equals 8, and 6 divided by 6 equals 1. Cross off the 48 and write the 8 over it; also, cross off the 6 and write the 1 under it. Thus,

$$\frac{6\times \overset{8}{\cancel{48}}\times 4\times 1}{8\times 3\times 1\times \underset{1}{\cancel{6}}} =$$

The **48** and **6** are not to be considered any longer, and, in fact, may be erased entirely and the 8 and 1 placed in their stead, and treated as if the 48 and 6 never existed. Thus,

$$\frac{6\times8\times4\times1}{8\times3\times1\times1} =$$

Again, 6 in the dividend and 3 in the divisor are divisible by 3, since 6 divided by 3 equals 2, and 3 divided by 3 equals **1**.   Cross off the 6 and write the 2 over it; also, cross off the **3** and write the 1 under it.   Thus,

$$\frac{\overset{2}{\cancel{6}}\times8\times4\times1}{8\times\cancel{3}\times1\times1} =$$
$$\underset{1}{}$$

The 6 and 3 are not to be considered any longer, and, in fact, may be erased entirely and the 2 and 1 placed in their stead, and treated as if the 6 and 3 never existed. Thus,

$$\frac{2\times8\times4\times1}{8\times1\times1\times1} =$$

Canceling the 8 in the dividend and the 8 in the divisor, the result is

$$\frac{2\times\overset{1}{\cancel{8}}\times4\times1}{\underset{1}{\cancel{8}}\times1\times1\times1} = \frac{2\times1\times4\times1}{1\times1\times1\times1}.$$

Since there are no two remaining numbers (one in the dividend and one in the divisor) divisible by any number except 1, without a remainder, it is impossible to cancel further.

Multiply all the uncanceled numbers in the dividend together, and divide their product by the product of all the uncanceled numbers in the divisor. The result will be the quotient. The product of all the uncanceled numbers in the dividend equals $2\times1\times4\times1 = 8$; the

product of all the uncanceled numbers in the divisor
equals $1 \times 1 \times 1 \times 1 = 1$.

Hence, $\dfrac{2 \times 1 \times 4 \times 1}{1 \times 1 \times 1 \times 1} = \dfrac{8}{1} = 8$. Ans.

Or, $\dfrac{72 \times 48 \times 28 \times 5}{96 \times 15 \times 7 \times 6} = \dfrac{8}{1} = 8$. Ans.

(b) $(80 \times 60 \times 50 \times 16 \times 14) \div (70 \times 50 \times 24 \times 20)$.

Placing the numerator over the denominator, the problem
becomes

$$\frac{80 \times 60 \times 50 \times 16 \times 14}{70 \times 50 \times 24 \times 20} = ?$$

The 50 in the dividend and 70 in the divisor are both divisible by 10, since 50 divided by 10 equals 5, and 70 divided by
10 equals 7. Cross off the 50 and write the 5 over it; also,
cross off the 70 and write the 7 under it. Thus,

$$\frac{80 \times 60 \times \overset{5}{50} \times 16 \times 14}{\underset{7}{70} \times 50 \times 24 \times 20} =$$

The 50 and 70 are not to be considered any longer, and, in
fact, may be erased entirely and the 5 and 7 placed in their
stead, and treated as if the 50 and 70 never existed. Thus,

$$\frac{80 \times 60 \times 5 \times 16 \times 14}{7 \times 50 \times 24 \times 20} =$$

Also, 80 in the dividend and 20 in the divisor are divisible
by 20, since 80 divided by 20 equals 4, and 20 divided by 20
equals 1. Cross off the 80 and write the 4 over it; also, cross
off the 20 and write the 1 under it. Thus,

$$\frac{\overset{4}{80} \times 60 \times 5 \times 16 \times 14}{7 \times 50 \times 24 \times \underset{1}{20}} =$$

The 80 and 20 are not to be considered any longer, and, in fact, may be erased entirely and the 4 and 1 placed in their stead, and treated as if the 80 and 20 never existed. Thus,

$$\frac{4 \times 60 \times 5 \times 16 \times 14}{7 \times 50 \times 24 \times 1} =$$

Again, 16 in the dividend and 24 in the divisor are divisible by 8, since 16 divided by 8 equals 2, and 24 divided by 8 equals 3. Cross off the 16 and write the 2 over it; also, cross off the 24 and write the 3 under it. Thus,

$$\frac{4 \times 60 \times 5 \times \overset{2}{\cancel{16}} \times 14}{7 \times 50 \times \underset{3}{\cancel{24}} \times 1} =$$

The 16 and 24 are not to be considered any longer, and, in fact, may be erased entirely and the 2 and 3 placed in their stead, and treated as if the 16 and 24 never existed. Thus,

$$\frac{4 \times 60 \times 5 \times 2 \times 14}{7 \times 50 \times 3 \times 1} =$$

Again, 60 in the dividend and 50 in the divisor are divisible by 10, since 60 divided by 10 equals 6, and 50 divided by 10 equals 5. Cross off the 60 and write the 6 over it; also, cross off the 50 and write the 5 under it. Thus,

$$\frac{4 \times \overset{6}{\cancel{60}} \times 5 \times 2 \times 14}{7 \times \underset{5}{\cancel{50}} \times 3 \times 1} =$$

The 60 and 50 are not to be considered any longer, and, in fact, may be erased entirely and the 6 and 5 placed in their stead, and treated as if the 60 and 50 never existed. Thus,

$$\frac{4 \times 6 \times 5 \times 2 \times 14}{7 \times 5 \times 3 \times 1} =$$

The 14 in the dividend and 7 in the divisor are divisible by 7, since 14 divided by 7 equals 2, and 7 divided by 7 equals 1.

Cross off the 14 and write the 2 over it: also, cross off the 7 and write the 1 under it.　Thus,

$$\frac{4\times6\times5\times2\times\overset{2}{\cancel{14}}}{\underset{1}{\cancel{7}}\times5\times3\times1} =$$

The 14 and 7 are not to be considered any longer, and, in fact, may be erased entirely and the 2 and 1 placed in their stead, and treated as if the 14 and 7 never existed.　Thus,

$$\frac{4\times6\times5\times2\times2}{1\times5\times3\times1} =$$

The 5 in the dividend and the 5 in the divisor are divisible by 5, since 5 divided by 5 equals 1.　Cross off the 5 of the dividend and write the 1 over it; also, cross off the 5 of the divisor and write the 1 under it.　Thus

$$\frac{4\times6\times\overset{1}{\cancel{5}}\times2\times2}{1\times\underset{1}{\cancel{5}}\times3\times1} =$$

The 5 in the dividend and 5 in the divisor are not to be considered any longer, and, in fact, may be erased entirely and 1 and 1 placed in their stead, and treated as if the 5 and 5 never existed.　Thus,

$$\frac{4\times6\times1\times2\times2}{1\times1\times3\times1} =$$

The 6 in the dividend and 3 in the divisor are divisible by 3, since 6 divided by 3 equals 2, and 3 divided by 3 equals 1. Cross off the 6 and place the 2 over it; also, cross off the 3 and place the 1 under it.　Thus,

$$\frac{4\times\overset{2}{\cancel{6}}\times1\times2\times2}{1\times1\times\underset{1}{\cancel{3}}\times1} =$$

The 6 and 3 are not to be considered any longer, and, in fact, may be erased entirely and 2 and 1 placed in

their stead, and treated as if the 6 and 3 never existed.
Thus,

$$\frac{4\times 2\times 1\times 2\times 2}{1\times 1\times 1\times 1} = \frac{32}{1} = 32. \quad \textbf{Ans.}$$

Hence,

$$\frac{\overset{2}{\cancel{8}\cancel{0}}\times\overset{1}{\cancel{6}\cancel{0}}\times\cancel{5}\cancel{0}\times\overset{2}{\cancel{1}\cancel{6}}\times\overset{2}{\cancel{1}\cancel{4}}}{\underset{\underset{1}{7}}{\cancel{7}\cancel{0}}\times\underset{\underset{1}{5}}{\cancel{5}\cancel{0}}\times\underset{\underset{1}{3}}{\cancel{2}\cancel{4}}\times\underset{1}{\cancel{2}\cancel{0}}} = \frac{4\times 2\times 1\times 2\times 2}{1\times 1\times 1\times 1} = \frac{32}{1} = 32. \quad \text{Ans.}$$

(19) 28 acres of land at $133 an acre would cost

$$28\times \$1\ 3\ 3 = \$3,724$$

$$\begin{array}{r} 2\ 8 \\ \hline 1\ 0\ 6\ 4 \\ 2\ 6\ 6 \\ \hline \$3\ 7\ 2\ 4 \end{array}$$

If a mechanic earns $1,500 a year and his expenses are $968
per year, then he would save $ 1 5 0 0 — $968, or $532 per year.

$$\begin{array}{r} 9\ 6\ 8 \\ \hline \$5\ 3\ 2 \end{array}$$

If he saves $532 in 1 year, to save $3,724 it would take as
many years as $532 is contained times in $3,724, or 7 years.

$$5\ 3\ 2\ )\ 3\ 7\ 2\ 4\ (\ 7 \text{ years.   Ans.}$$
$$\underline{3\ 7\ 2\ 4}$$

(20) If the freight train ran 365 miles in one week, and
3 times as far lacking 246 miles the next week, then it ran
(3 × 365 miles) — 246 miles, or 849 miles the second week.
Thus,

$$\begin{array}{r} 3\ 6\ 5 \\ 3 \\ \hline 1\ 0\ 9\ 5 \\ 2\ 4\ 6 \\ \hline \textit{difference}\quad 8\ 4\ 9 \text{ miles.   Ans.} \end{array}$$

(21) The distance from Philadelphia to Pittsburg is 354 miles. Since there are 5,280 feet in 1 mile, in 354 miles there are 354 × 5,280 feet, or 1,869,120 feet. If the driving wheel of the locomotive is 16 feet in circumference, then in going from Philadelphia to Pittsburg, a distance of 1,869,120 feet, it will make 1,869,120 ÷ 16, or 116,820 revolutions.

```
16 ) 1 8 6 9 1 2 0 ( 1 1 6 8 2 0 rev.   Ans.
     1 6
       2 6
       1 6
       1 0 9
         9 6
         1 3 1
         1 2 8
             3 2
             3 2
```

(22) (a)   5 7 6) 5 8 9 8 2 4 (1 0 2 4   Ans.
```
                 5 7 6
                 1 3 8 2
                 1 1 5 2
                   2 3 0 4
                   2 3 0 4
```

(b) 4 3 9 1 1) 3 6 9 7 3 0 6 2 0 (8 4 2 0   Ans.
```
                 3 5 1 2 8 8
                 1 8 4 4 2 6
                 1 7 5 6 4 4
                     8 7 8 2 2
                     8 7 8 2 2
```

(c)   5 0 5) 2 5 2 7 5 2 5 (5 0 0 5   Ans.
```
                 2 5 2 5
                   2 5 2 5
                   2 5 2 5
```

(*d*)   1 2 3 4) 4 9 6 1 7 9 4 3 0 2 (4 0 2 0 9 0 3   Ans.
$$\underline{4\ 9\ 3\ 6}$$
$$2\ 5\ 7\ 9$$
$$\underline{2\ 4\ 6\ 8}$$
$$1\ 1\ 1\ 4\ 3$$
$$\underline{1\ 1\ 1\ 0\ 6}$$
$$3\ 7\ 0\ 2$$
$$\underline{3\ 7\ 0\ 2}$$

(23)   The harness evidently cost the difference between
$444 and the amount which he paid for the horse and wagon.
Since $264 + $153 = $417, the amount paid for the horse and
wagon, $444 − $417 = $27, the cost of the harness.

$$\begin{array}{r} \$2\ 6\ 4 \\ 1\ 5\ 3 \\ \hline \$4\ 1\ 7 \end{array} \qquad\qquad \begin{array}{r} \$4\ 4\ 4 \\ 4\ 1\ 7 \\ \hline \$2\ 7 \end{array} \text{ Ans.}$$

(24)   (*a*)   (*b*)   (*c*)

$$\begin{array}{r} 1\ 0\ 2\ 4 \\ 5\ 7\ 6 \\ \hline 6\ 1\ 4\ 4 \\ 7\ 1\ 6\ 8 \\ 5\ 1\ 2\ 0 \\ \hline 5\ 8\ 9\ 8\ 2\ 4 \end{array} \text{ Ans.}$$

$$\begin{array}{r} 5\ 0\ 0\ 5 \\ 5\ 0\ 5 \\ \hline 2\ 5\ 0\ 2\ 5 \\ 2\ 5\ 0\ 2\ 5\ 0 \\ \hline 2\ 5\ 2\ 7\ 5\ 2\ 5 \end{array} \text{ Ans.}$$

$$\begin{array}{r} 4\ 3\ 9\ 1\ 1 \\ 8\ 4\ 2\ 0 \\ \hline 8\ 7\ 8\ 2\ 2\ 0 \\ 1\ 7\ 5\ 6\ 4\ 4 \\ 3\ 5\ 1\ 2\ 8\ 8 \\ \hline 3\ 6\ 9\ 7\ 3\ 0\ 6\ 2\ 0 \end{array} \text{ Ans.}$$

(25)   Since there are 12 months in a year, the number of
days the man works is 25 × 12 = 300 days. As he works 10
hours each day, the number of hours that he works in one
year is 300 × 10 = 3,000 hours.   Hence, he receives for his
work 3,000 × 30 = 90,000 cents, or 90,000 ÷ 100 = $900. Ans.

(26)   See Art. **71.**

(27)   See Art. **77.**

(28)   See Art. **73.**

(29)   See Art. **73.**

(30)   See Art. **75.**

(31) $\frac{13}{8}$ is an improper fraction, since its numerator, 13, is
greater than its denominator, 8.

(32) $4\frac{1}{2}$; $14\frac{3}{10}$; $85\frac{4}{19}$.

(33) To reduce a fraction to its lowest terms means to change its form without changing its value. In order to do this, we must divide both numerator and denominator by the same number until we can no longer find any number (except 1) which will divide both of these terms without a remainder.

To reduce the fraction $\frac{4}{8}$ to its lowest terms, we divide both numerator and denominator by 4, and obtain as a result the fraction $\frac{1}{2}$. Thus, $\frac{4 \div 4}{8 \div 4} = \frac{1}{2}$; similarly, $\frac{4 \div 4}{16 \div 4} = \frac{1}{4}$;

$\frac{8 \div 4}{32 \div 4} = \frac{2 \div 2}{8 \div 2} = \frac{1}{4}$; $\frac{32 \div 8}{64 \div 8} = \frac{4 \div 4}{8 \div 4} = \frac{1}{2}$. Ans.

(34) When the denominator of any number is not expressed, it is understood to be 1, so that $\frac{6}{1}$ is the same as $6 \div 1$, or 6. To reduce $\frac{6}{1}$ to an improper fraction whose denominator is 4, we must multiply both numerator and denominator by some number which will make the denominator of 6 equal to 4. Since this denominator is 1, by multiplying both terms of $\frac{6}{1}$ by 4 we shall have $\frac{6 \times 4}{1 \times 4} = \frac{24}{4}$, which has the *same value* as 6, but has a *different form*. Ans.

(35) In order to reduce a mixed number to an improper fraction, we must multiply the whole number by the denominator of the fraction and add the numerator of the fraction to that product. This *result* is the numerator of the improper fraction, of which the denominator is the denominator of the fractional part of the mixed number.

$7\frac{7}{8}$ means the same as $7 + \frac{7}{8}$. In 1 there are $\frac{8}{8}$, hence in 7 there are $7 \times \frac{8}{8} = \frac{56}{8}$; $\frac{56}{8}$ plus the $\frac{7}{8}$ of the mixed number $= \frac{56}{8} + \frac{7}{8} = \frac{63}{8}$, which is the required improper fraction.

$$13\frac{5}{16} = \frac{(13 \times 16) + 5}{16} = \frac{213}{16}; \quad 10\frac{3}{4} = \frac{(10 \times 4) + 3}{4} = \frac{43}{4}.$$

(36) The value of a fraction is obtained by dividing the numerator by the denominator.

To obtain the value of the fraction $\frac{13}{2}$ we divide the numerator, 13, by the denominator, 2. 2 is contained in 13, 6 times, with 1 remaining. This 1 remaining is written over the denominator, 2, thereby making the fraction $\frac{1}{2}$, which is annexed to the whole number, 6, and we obtain $6\frac{1}{2}$ as the mixed number. The reason for performing this operation is the following: In 1 there are $\frac{2}{2}$ (two halves), and in $\frac{13}{2}$ (thirteen halves) there are as many ones (1) as 2 is contained times in 13, which is 6, and $\frac{1}{2}$ (one-half) remaining. Hence, $\frac{13}{2} = 6 + \frac{1}{2} = 6\frac{1}{2}$, the required mixed number.

$\frac{17}{4} = 4\frac{1}{4}$; $\frac{69}{16} = 4\frac{5}{16}$; $\frac{16}{8} = 2$; $\frac{67}{64} = 1\frac{3}{64}$.   Ans.

(37) In division of fractions, invert the divisor (or, in other words, turn it upside down) and then proceed as in multiplication.

(a) $35 \div \frac{5}{16} = \frac{35}{1} \times \frac{16}{5} = \frac{35 \times 16}{1 \times 5} = \frac{560}{5} = 112.$ Ans.

(b) $\frac{9}{16} \div 3 = \frac{9}{16} \div \frac{3}{1} = \frac{9}{16} \times \frac{1}{3} = \frac{9 \times 1}{16 \times 3} = \frac{9}{48} = \frac{3}{16}.$ Ans.

(c) $\frac{17}{2} \div 9 = \frac{17}{2} \div \frac{9}{1} = \frac{17}{2} \times \frac{1}{9} = \frac{17 \times 1}{2 \times 9} = \frac{17}{18}.$ Ans.

(d) $\frac{113}{64} \div \frac{7}{16} = \frac{113}{64} \times \frac{16}{7} = \frac{113 \times 16}{64 \times 7} = \frac{1808}{448} = \frac{452}{112} = \frac{113}{28}.$

$$28 \overline{)113} \; (\; 4\frac{1}{28}. \quad \text{Ans.}$$
$$\underline{112}$$
$$1$$

(e) $15\frac{3}{4} \div 4\frac{3}{8} = ?$ Before proceeding with the division, reduce both of the mixed numbers to improper fractions. Thus, $15\frac{3}{4} = \frac{(15 \times 4) + 3}{4} = \frac{60 + 3}{4} = \frac{63}{4}$, and $4\frac{3}{8} = \frac{(4 \times 8) + 3}{8}$
$= \frac{32 + 3}{8} = \frac{35}{8}.$ The problem is now $\frac{63}{4} \div \frac{35}{8} = ?$ As before, invert the divisor and multiply; $\frac{63}{4} \div \frac{35}{8} = \frac{63}{4} \times \frac{8}{35}$
$= \frac{63 \times 8}{4 \times 35} = \frac{504}{140} = \frac{252}{70} = \frac{126}{35} = \frac{18}{5}.$

$$5 \overline{)18} \; (\; 3\frac{3}{5}. \quad \text{Ans.}$$
$$\underline{15}$$
$$3$$

(38) $\frac{1}{8} + \frac{2}{8} + \frac{5}{8} = \frac{1 + 2 + 5}{8} = \frac{8}{8} = 1.$ Ans.

When the denominators of the fractions to be added are alike, we know that the units are divided into the same number of parts (in this case eighths); we, therefore, add the numerators of the fractions to find the number of parts (eighths) taken or considered, thereby obtaining $\frac{8}{8}$ or 1 as the sum.

(39) When the denominators are *not* alike we know that the units are divided into unequal parts, so before adding them we must find a common denominator for the denominators of all the fractions. Reduce the fractions to fractions having this common denominator, add the numerators, and write the sum over the common denominator.

In this case, the least common denominator, or the least number that will contain all the denominators, is 16; hence, we must reduce all these fractions to 16ths and then add their numerators.

$\frac{1}{4} + \frac{3}{8} + \frac{5}{16} = ?$ To reduce the fraction $\frac{1}{4}$ to a fraction having 16 for a denominator, we must multiply both terms of the fraction by some number which will make the denominator 16. This number evidently is 4; hence, $\frac{1 \times 4}{4 \times 4} = \frac{4}{16}$.

Similarly, both terms of the fraction $\frac{3}{8}$ must be multiplied by 2 to make the denominator 16, and we have $\frac{3 \times 2}{8 \times 2} = \frac{6}{16}$.

The fractions now have a common denominator, 16; hence, we find their sum by adding the numerators and placing their sum over the common denominator, thus: $\frac{4}{16} + \frac{6}{16} + \frac{5}{16} = \frac{4+6+5}{16} = \frac{15}{16}$. Ans.

(40) When mixed numbers and whole numbers are to be added, add the fractional parts of the mixed numbers separately, and if the resulting fraction is an improper fraction, reduce it to a whole or mixed number. Next, add all the whole numbers, including the one obtained from the addition of the fractional parts, and annex to their sum the fraction of the mixed number obtained from reducing the improper fraction.

$42 + 31\frac{5}{8} + 9\frac{7}{16} = ?$ Reducing $\frac{5}{8}$ to a fraction having a denominator of 16, we have $\frac{5 \times 2}{8 \times 2} = \frac{10}{16}$. Adding the two fractional parts of the mixed numbers, we have $\frac{10}{16} + \frac{7}{16}$

$= \frac{10 + 7}{16} = \frac{17}{16} = 1\frac{1}{16}.$

The problem now becomes $42 + 31 + 9 + 1\frac{1}{16} = ?$

4 2   Adding all the whole numbers and the number
3 1   obtained from adding the fractional parts of the
9   mixed numbers, we obtain $83\frac{1}{16}$ as their sum.

$1\frac{1}{16}$

——————

8 3$\frac{1}{16}$ Ans.

(41) $29\frac{3}{4} + 50\frac{5}{8} + 41 + 69\frac{3}{16} = ?$ $\frac{3}{4} = \frac{3 \times 4}{4 \times 4} = \frac{12}{16}.$

$\frac{5}{8} = \frac{5 \times 2}{8 \times 2} = \frac{10}{16}.$ $\frac{12}{16} + \frac{10}{16} + \frac{3}{16} = \frac{12 + 10 + 3}{16} = \frac{25}{16} = 1\frac{9}{16}.$

The problem now becomes $29 + 50 + 41 + 69 + 1\frac{9}{16} = ?$

2 9   square inches.
5 0   square inches.
4 1   square inches.
6 9   square inches.
1$\frac{9}{16}$ square inches.

——————

1 9 0$\frac{9}{16}$ square inches.   Ans.

(42)   (a) $\dfrac{7}{\frac{3}{16}} = 7 \div \frac{3}{16} = 7 \times \frac{16}{3} = \frac{7 \times 16}{3} = \frac{112}{3} = 37\frac{1}{3}.$ Ans.

The line between 7 and $\frac{3}{16}$ means that the 7 is to be divided
by $\frac{3}{16}.$

(b) $\dfrac{\frac{15}{32}}{\frac{5}{8}} = \frac{15}{32} \div \frac{5}{8} = \frac{15}{32} \times \frac{8}{5} = \frac{\overset{3}{15} \times \overset{}{8}}{\underset{4}{32} \times \underset{}{5}} = \frac{3}{4}.$ Ans.

(c) $\dfrac{\frac{4+3}{2+6}}{5} = \frac{\frac{7}{8}}{5} = \frac{7}{8 \times 5} = \frac{7}{40}.$ (See Art. **131**.)   Ans.

(43) $\frac{7}{8}$ = value of the fraction, and 28 = the numerator.
We find that 4 multiplied by $7 = 28$, so multiplying 8, the
denominator of the fraction, by 4, we have 32 for the required
denominator, and $\frac{28}{32} = \frac{7}{8}.$ Hence, 32 is the required denominator.   Ans.

(44) (*a*) $\frac{7}{8} - \frac{7}{16} = ?$ When the denominators of fractions are not alike, it is evident that the units are divided into unequal parts; therefore, before subtracting, reduce the fractions to fractions having a common denominator. Then, subtract the numerators and place the remainder over the common denominator.

$$\frac{7 \times 2}{8 \times 2} = \frac{14}{16}. \quad \frac{14}{16} - \frac{7}{16} = \frac{14 - 7}{16} = \frac{7}{16}. \quad \text{Ans.}$$

(*b*) $13 - 7\frac{7}{16} = ?$ This problem may be solved in two ways:

First : $13 = 12\frac{16}{16}$, since $\frac{16}{16} = 1$, and $12\frac{16}{16} = 12 + \frac{16}{16} = 12 + 1 = 13$.

$\begin{array}{l} 1\ 2\frac{16}{16} \\ \underline{7\frac{7}{16}} \\ 5\frac{9}{16} \end{array}$ We can now subtract the whole numbers separately, and the fractions separately, and obtain $12 - 7 = 5$, and $\frac{16}{16} - \frac{7}{16} = \frac{16 - 7}{16} = \frac{9}{16}. \quad 5 + \frac{9}{16} = 5\frac{9}{16}. \quad \text{Ans.}$

Second : By reducing both numbers to improper fractions having a denominator of 16.

$$13 = \frac{13}{1} = \frac{13 \times 16}{1 \times 16} = \frac{208}{16}. \quad 7\frac{7}{16} = \frac{(7 \times 16) + 7}{16} = \frac{112 + 7}{16} = \frac{119}{16}.$$

Subtracting, we have $\frac{208}{16} - \frac{119}{16} = \frac{208 - 119}{16} = \frac{89}{16}$ and $\frac{89}{16}$,

$\begin{array}{l} = 1\,6\,)\,8\,9\,(\,5\frac{9}{16} \\ \underline{8\,0} \\ 9 \end{array}$ the same result that was obtained by the first method. Ans.

(*c*) $312\frac{9}{16} - 229\frac{5}{32} = ?$ We first reduce the fractions of the two mixed numbers to fractions having a common denominator. Doing this, we have $\frac{9}{16} = \frac{9 \times 2}{16 \times 2} = \frac{18}{32}$. We can now subtract the whole numbers and fractions separately, and have $312 - 229 = 83$, and $\frac{18}{32} - \frac{5}{32} = \frac{18 - 5}{32} = \frac{13}{32}$.

$\begin{array}{l} 3\,1\,2\frac{18}{32} \\ \underline{2\,2\,9\frac{5}{32}} \\ 8\,3\frac{13}{32} \end{array}$ $83 + \frac{13}{32} = 83\frac{13}{32}. \quad \text{Ans.}$

(45) The man evidently traveled $85\frac{5}{12} + 78\frac{9}{15} + 125\frac{17}{35}$ miles. Adding the fractions separately in this case,

$$\frac{5}{12} + \frac{9}{15} + \frac{17}{35} = \frac{5}{12} + \frac{3}{5} + \frac{17}{35} = \frac{175 + 252 + 204}{420} = \frac{631}{420} = 1\frac{211}{420}.$$

Adding the whole numbers and the mixed number representing the sum of the fractions, the sum is $289\frac{211}{420}$ miles. Ans.

$$\begin{array}{r} 8\ 5 \\ 7\ 8 \\ 1\ 2\ 5 \\ 1\frac{211}{420} \\ \hline 2\ 8\ 9\frac{211}{420} \end{array}$$

To find the least common denominator, we have

$$\begin{array}{r} 5\ )\ 12,\quad 5,\quad 35 \\ 7\ )\ 12,\quad 1,\quad 7 \\ \hline 12,\quad 1,\quad 1,\ \text{or}\ 5\times7\times12 = 420. \end{array}$$

(46)

$$\begin{array}{ll} 5\ 7\ 3\frac{4}{5}\ \text{tons.} & \frac{4}{5} = \frac{32}{40} \\ 2\ 1\ 6\frac{5}{8}\ \text{tons.} & \frac{5}{8} = \frac{25}{40} \\ \hline \textit{difference}\ \ 3\ 5\ 7\frac{7}{40}\ \text{tons. Ans.} & \frac{7}{40} = \textit{difference.} \end{array}$$

(47) Reducing $9\frac{1}{4}$ to an improper fraction, it becomes $\frac{37}{4}$. Multiplying $\frac{37}{4}$ by $\frac{3}{8}$, $\frac{37}{4} \times \frac{3}{8} = \frac{111}{32} = 3\frac{15}{32}$ dollars. Ans.

(48) Referring to Arts. **114** and **116**,

$\frac{2}{3}$ of $\frac{3}{4}$ of $\frac{7}{11}$ of $\frac{19}{20}$ of 11 multiplied by $\frac{7}{8}$ of $\frac{5}{6}$ of 45

$$= \frac{2\times3\times7\times19\times\cancel{11}\times7\times5\times\overset{3}{\cancel{\overset{15}{45}}}}{\underset{4}{\cancel{3}}\times4\times\cancel{11}\times\cancel{20}\times1\times8\times\underset{\cancel{6}}{\cancel{6}}\times1} = \frac{7\times19\times7\times5\times3}{4\times4\times8} = \frac{13,965}{128}$$

$$= 109\frac{13}{128}. \text{ Ans.}$$

(49) $\frac{3}{4}$ of $16 = \frac{3}{4} \times \frac{\overset{4}{\cancel{16}}}{1} = 12.$ $12 \div \frac{2}{3} = \frac{\overset{6}{\cancel{12}}}{1} \times \frac{3}{\cancel{2}} = 18.$ Ans.

(50) $211\frac{1}{4} \times 1\frac{7}{8} = \frac{845}{4} \times \frac{15}{8}$, reducing the mixed numbers to improper fractions. $\frac{845}{4} \times \frac{15}{8} = \frac{12,675}{32}$ cents = amount paid for the lead. The number of pounds sold is evidently

$$\frac{12,675}{32} \div 2\frac{1}{2} = \frac{\overset{2,535}{\cancel{12,675}}}{\underset{16}{\cancel{32}}} \times \frac{2}{\cancel{5}} = \frac{2,535}{16} = 158\frac{7}{16} \text{ pounds.} \quad \text{The}$$

amount remaining is $211\frac{1}{4} - 158\frac{7}{16} = \dfrac{845}{4} - \dfrac{2,535}{16} = \dfrac{3,380}{16}$ $- \dfrac{2,535}{16} = \dfrac{845}{16} = 52\frac{13}{16}$ pounds. **Ans.**

(51)   .0 8 = *Eight* **hundredths.**

     .1 3 1 = *One hundred thirty-one* **thousandths.**

     .0 0 0 1 = *One* **ten-thousandth.**

     .0 0 0 0 2 7 = *Twenty-seven* **millionths.**

     .0 1 0 8 = *One hundred eight* **ten-thousandths.**

93.0 1 0 1 = Ninety-three, and *one hundred one* **ten-thousandths.**

In reading decimals, read the number just as you would if there were no ciphers before it.   Then count from the decimal point towards the right, beginning with tenths, to as many places as there are figures, and the *name* of the last figure must be annexed to the previous reading of the figures to give the decimal reading.   Thus, in the first example above, the simple reading of the figure is *eight*, and the name of its position in the decimal scale is **hundredths,** so that the decimal reading is *eight* **hundredths.**   Similarly, the figures in the fourth example are ordinarily read *twenty-seven ;* the name of the position of the figure 7 in the decimal scale is **millionths,** giving, therefore, the decimal reading as *twenty-seven* **millionths.**

If there should be a whole number before the decimal point, read it as you would read any whole number, and read the decimal as you would if the whole number were not there; or, read the whole number and then say, "and" so many hundredths, thousandths, or whatever it may be, as "ninety-three, and one hundred one ten-thousandths."

(52)   See Art. **139.**

(53)   See Art. **153.**

(54)   See Art. **160.**

(55)   A fraction is one or more of the equal parts of a unit, and is expressed by a numerator and a denominator, while a decimal fraction is a number of tenths, hundredths, thousandths, etc. of a unit, and is expressed by placing a period (.), called a decimal point, to the left of the figures of the number, and omitting the denominator.

(56)   See Art. **165.**

(57)   To reduce the fraction $\frac{1}{2}$ to a decimal, we annex one cipher to the numerator, which makes it 1.0.   Dividing 1.0, the numerator, by 2, the denominator, gives a quotient of .5, the decimal point being placed before the *one* figure of the

quotient, or .5, since only one cipher was annexed to the numerator.

$$\overset{7}{8\,)\,7.0\,0\,0}$$
$$\overline{\quad.8\,7\,5}$$

$$\overset{5}{32\,)\,5.0\,0\,0\,0\,0\,(\,.1\,5\,6\,2\,5\quad\text{Ans.}}$$

Since $.65 = \frac{65}{100}$, then, $\frac{65}{100}$ must equal .65. Or, when the denominator is 10, 100, 1,000, etc., point off as many places in the numerator as there are ciphers in the denominator. Doing so, $\frac{65}{100} = .65$. Ans.

$$\begin{array}{r} 3\,2 \\ \hline 1\,8\,0 \\ 1\,6\,0 \\ \hline 2\,0\,0 \\ 1\,9\,2 \\ \hline 8\,0 \\ 6\,4 \\ \hline 1\,6\,0 \\ 1\,6\,0 \\ \hline \end{array}$$

$\frac{125}{1000} = .125$. Ans.

(58) (*a*) This example, written in the form of a fraction, means that the numerator $(32.5+.29+1.5)$ is to be divided by the denominator $(4.7+9)$. The operation is as follows:

$$\frac{32.5+.29+1.5}{4.7+9} = ?$$

$$\begin{array}{r} 3\,2.5 \\ +\quad.2\,9 \\ +\quad1.5 \\ \hline \end{array}$$

$$13.7\,)\,3\,4.2\,9\,0\,0\,0\,(\,2.5\,0\,2\,9\quad\text{Ans}$$

$$\begin{array}{r} 4.7 \\ +\quad9.0 \\ \hline 1\,3.7 \end{array}$$

$$\begin{array}{r} 2\,7\,4 \\ \hline 6\,8\,9 \\ 6\,8\,5 \\ \hline 4\,0\,0 \\ 2\,7\,4 \\ \hline 1\,2\,6\,0 \\ 1\,2\,3\,3 \\ \hline 2\,7 \end{array}$$

Since there are 5 decimal places in the dividend, and 1 in the divisor, there are $5-1$ or 4 places to be pointed off in the quotient. The fifth figure of the decimal is evidently less than 5.

(*b*) Here again the problem is to divide the numerator, which is $(1.283 \times \overline{8+5})$, by the denominator, which is 2.63. The operation is as follows:

$$\frac{1.283 \times \overline{8+5}}{2.63} = ? \qquad \overline{8+5} = 13.$$

$$
\begin{array}{r}
1.2\,8.3 \\
\times \quad 1\,3 \\
\hline
3\,8\,4\,9 \\
1\,2\,8\,3 \\
\end{array}
$$

$$
\begin{array}{r}
2.6\,3\,)\,1\,6.6\,7\,9\,0\,0\,0\,(\,6.3\,4\,1\,8 \quad \textbf{Ans.} \\
1\,5\,7\,8 \\
\hline
8\,9\,9 \\
7\,8\,9 \\
\hline
1\,1\,0\,0 \\
1\,0\,5\,2 \\
\hline
4\,8\,0 \\
2\,6\,3 \\
\hline
2\,1\,7\,0 \\
2\,1\,0\,4 \\
\hline
6\,6 \\
\end{array}
$$

(*c*) $\dfrac{\overline{589+27} \times \overline{163-8}}{25+39} = ?$

$$
\begin{array}{r}
1\,6\,3 \\
-\quad 8 \\
\hline
1\,5\,5 \\
\end{array}
$$

$$
\begin{array}{r}
5\,8\,9 \\
+\quad 2\,7 \\
\hline
6\,1\,6 \\
\end{array}
\qquad
\begin{array}{r}
1\,5\,5 \\
\times 6\,1\,6 \\
\hline
9\,3\,0 \\
1\,5\,5 \\
9\,3\,0 \\
\hline
9\,5\,4\,8\,0 \\
\end{array}
$$

64)95480.000(1491.875
    64
            314
25   256
+39   588
64   576
        120
There are three decimal   64
places in the quotient, since   560
three ciphers were annexed   512
to the dividend.   480
        448
        320
        320

(d) $\dfrac{40.6+7.1\times(3.029-1.874)}{6.27+8.53-8.01}=?$

                3.029
40.6   −1.874
+ 7.1   1.155
47.7   × 47.7
                8085
6.27   8085
+ 8.53   4620
14.80   6.79)55.093500(8.1139 Ans.
− 8.01   5432
6.79   773
6 decimal places in the   679
dividend − 2 decimal places   945
in the divisor = 4 decimal   679
places to be pointed off in   2660
the quotient.   2037
                6230
                6111
                119

(59) $.875 = \frac{875}{1000} = \frac{175}{200} = \frac{7}{8}$ of a foot.

1 foot = 12 inches.

$\frac{7}{8}$ of 1 foot $= \dfrac{7}{\overset{}{\underset{2}{8}}} \times \dfrac{\overset{3}{12}}{1} = \frac{21}{2} = 10\frac{1}{2}$ inches.   **Ans.**

(60)   12 inches = 1 foot.

$\frac{3}{16}$ of an inch $= \frac{3}{16} \div 12 = \dfrac{3}{16} \times \dfrac{1}{\overset{}{\underset{4}{12}}} = \frac{1}{64}$ of a foot.

$\frac{1}{64}$) 1.0 0 0 0 0 0 (0 1 5 6 2 5   **Ans.**

    6 4
    ———
    3 6 0   Point off 6 decimal places in
    3 2 0   the quotient, since we annexed
    ———   six ciphers to the dividend, the
     4 0 0   divisor containing no decimal
     3 8 4   places; hence, $6 - 0 = 6$ places
     ———   to be pointed off.
      1 6 0
      1 2 8
      ———
       3 2 0
       3 2 0

(61)   If 1 cubic inch of water weighs .03617 of a pound, the weight of 1,500 cubic inches will be .03617 × 1,500 = 54.255 lb.

        .0 3 6 1 7 lb.
          1 5 0 0
        ———————
       1 8 0 8 5 0 0
       3 6 1 7
       ———————
      5 4.2 5 5 0 0 lb.   **Ans.**

(62)   72.6 feet of fencing at $.50 a foot would cost

         7 2.6 × .50, or $36.30.
            .5 0
        ——————
       $ 3 6.3 0 0

If, by selling a carload of coal at a profit of $1.65 per ton, I make $36.30, then there must be as many tons of coal in the car as 1.65 is contained times in 36.30, or 22 tons.

$$1.6\,5\,)\,3\,6.3\,0\,(\,2\,2 \text{ tons. Ans.}$$
$$\underline{3\,3\,0}$$
$$3\,3\,0$$
$$\underline{3\,3\,0}$$

(63) $2\,3\,1\,)\,1\,7\,8\,9\,2.0\,0\,0\,0\,0\,(\,7\,7.4\,5\,4\,5\,4$, or 77.4545
$$\underline{1\,6\,1\,7}\qquad\qquad\text{to four decimal}$$
$$1\,7\,2\,2\qquad\qquad\text{places. Ans.}$$
$$\underline{1\,6\,1\,7}$$
$$1\,0\,5\,0$$
$$\underline{9\,2\,4}$$
$$1\,2\,6\,0$$
$$\underline{1\,1\,5\,5}$$
$$1\,0\,5\,0$$
$$\underline{9\,2\,4}$$
$$1\,2\,6\,0$$
$$\underline{1\,1\,5\,5}$$
$$1\,0\,5\,0$$

(64) $37.13\quad 2\quad .0952$
$$\frac{74.26 \times 24 \times 3.1416 \times 19 \times 19 \times 350}{33,000 \times 12 \times 4}$$
$$1,000\qquad\qquad 2$$

$$=\frac{37.13 \times .0952 \times 19 \times 19 \times 350}{1,000}=\frac{446,618.947600}{1,000}$$

$$= 446.619 \text{ to three decimal places.   Ans.}$$

3 7.1 3	1 9	3 6 1	3.5 3 4 7 7 6
.0 9 5 2	1 9	3 5 0	1 2 6 3 5 0
7 4 2 6	1 7 1	1 8 0 5 0	1 7 6 7 3 8 8 0 0
1 8 5 6 5	1 9	1 0 8 3	1 0 6 0 4 3 2 8
3 3 4 1 7	3 6 1	1 2 6 3 5 0	2 1 2 0 8 6 5 6
3.5 3 4 7 7 6			7 0 6 9 5 5 2
			3 5 3 4 7 7 6
			4 4 6 6 1 8.9 4 7 6 0 0

(65) See Art. **174.** Applying rule in Art. **175,**

(a)　$.7928 \times \frac{64}{64} = \dfrac{50.7392}{64} = \frac{51}{64}.$　Ans.

(b)　$.1416 \times \frac{32}{32} = \dfrac{4.5312}{32} = \frac{5}{32}.$　Ans.

(c)　$.47915 \times \frac{16}{16} = \dfrac{7.6664}{16} = \frac{8}{16} = \frac{1}{2}.$　Ans.

(66) In subtraction of decimals, place the decimal points **directly** under each other, and proceed as in the subtraction of whole numbers, placing the decimal point in the remainder directly under the decimal points above.

(a)　$\begin{array}{r} 7\,0\,9.6\,3\,0\,0 \\ .8\,5\,1\,4 \\ \hline 7\,0\,8.7\,7\,8\,6 \end{array}$　Ans.

In the above example we proceed as follows: We cannot subtract 4 ten-thousandths from 0 ten-thousandths, and as there are no thousandths, we take 1 hundredth from the 3 hundredths. 1 hundredth = 10 thousandths = 100 ten-thousandths. 4 ten-thousandths from 100 ten-thousandths leaves 96 ten-thousandths. 96 ten-thousandths = 9 thousandths + 6 ten-thousandths. Write the 6 ten-thousandths in the ten-thousandths place in the remainder. The next figure in the subtrahend is 1 thousandth. This must be subtracted from the 9 thousandths, which is a part of the 1 hundredth taken previously from the 3 hundredths. Subtracting, we have 1 thousandth from 9 thousandths leaves 8 thousandths, the 8 being written in its place in the remainder. Next we have to subtract 5 hundredths from 2 hundredths (1 hundredth having been taken from the 3 hundredths makes it but 2 hundredths now). Since we cannot do this, we take 1 tenth from 6 tenths. 1 tenth (= 10 hundredths) + 2 hundredths = 12 hundredths. 5 hundredths from 12 hundredths leaves 7 hundredths. Write the 7 in the hundredths place in the remainder. Next we have to subtract 8 tenths from 5 tenths (5 tenths now, because 1 tenth was taken from the 6 tenths). Since this cannot be done, we take 1 unit from the 9 units. 1 unit = 10 tenths; 10 tenths + 5 tenths = 15 tenths, and 8 tenths from 15 tenths leaves 7 tenths. Write the 7 in the tenths place in the remainder. In the minuend we now have 708 units (1 unit having been taken away) and 0 units in the subtrahend. 0 units from 708 units leaves 708 units; hence, we write 708 in the remainder.

(b)　8 1.9 6 3　　(c)　1 8.0 0　　(d)　1.0 0 0
　　　1.7 0 0　　　　　.1 8　　　　　.0 0 1
　　8 0.2 6 3 Ans.　　1 7.8 2 Ans.　　.9 9 9 Ans.

(e)　$872.1 - (.8721 + .008) = ?$　In this problem we are to subtract $(.8721 + .008)$ from 872.1. First perform the operation as indicated by the sign between the decimals enclosed by the parenthesis.

.8 7 2 1
.0 0 8 0
———
.8 8 0 1 *sum.*

Subtracting the sum (obtained by adding the decimals enclosed within the parenthesis) from the number 872.1 (as required by the minus sign before the parenthesis), we obtain the required remainder.

8 7 2.1 0 0 0
　　.8 8 0 1
———————
8 7 1.2 1 9 9 Ans.

(f)　$(5.028 + .0073) - (6.704 - 2.38) = ?$　First perform the operations as indicated by the signs between the numbers enclosed by the parentheses. The first parenthesis shows that 5.028 and .0073 are to be added. This gives 5.0353 as their sum.

5.0 2 8 0
.0 0 7 3
———
5.0 3 5 3 *sum.*

The second parenthesis shows that 2.38 is to be subtracted from 6.704 The difference is found to be 4.324.

6.7 0 4
2.3 8 0
———
4.3 2 4 *difference.*

The sign between the parentheses indicates that the quantities obtained by performing the above operations are to be subtracted, namely, that 4.324 is to be subtracted from 5.0353. Performing this operation, we obtain .7113 as the final result.

5.0 3 5 3
4.3 2 4 0
———
.7 1 1 3 Ans.

(67)　In subtracting a decimal from a fraction, or in subtracting a fraction from a decimal, either reduce the fraction to a decimal before subtracting or reduce the decimal to a fraction and then subtract.

(*a*) $\frac{7}{8} - .807 = ?$ $\frac{7}{8}$ reduced to a decimal becomes $\frac{7}{8}$) $\overline{7.0\ 0\ 0}$
.8 7 5

$$.8\ 7\ 5$$
$$.8\ 0\ 7$$
$$\overline{.0\ 6\ 8} \quad \text{Ans.}$$

Subtracting .807 from .875, the remainder is .068, as shown.

(*b*) $.875 - \frac{3}{8} = ?$ Reducing .875 to a fraction, we have

$.875 = \frac{875}{1000} = \frac{175}{200} = \frac{35}{40} = \frac{7}{8}$;   hence, $\frac{7}{8} - \frac{3}{8} = \frac{7-3}{8} = \frac{4}{8}$

$= \frac{1}{2}$, or, .5.   Ans.

Or, by reducing $\frac{3}{8}$ to a decimal, $\frac{3}{8}$) $\overline{3.0\ 0\ 0}$ and then sub-
.3 7 5

$$.8\ 7\ 7$$
$$.3\ 7\ 5$$
$$\overline{.5\ 0\ 0} \quad \text{Ans.}$$

tracting, we obtain $.875 - .375 = .5 = \frac{5}{10}$ $= \frac{1}{2}$, the same answer as above.

(*c*) $(\frac{5}{32} + .435) - (\frac{21}{100} - .07) = ?$ We first perform the operations as indicated by the signs between the numbers enclosed by the parentheses. Reduce $\frac{5}{32}$ to a decimal and we obtain $\frac{5}{32} = .15625$ (see example 60).

Adding .15625 and .435,

$$.1\ 5\ 6\ 2\ 5 \qquad \frac{21}{100} = .21; \text{ subtracting, } \qquad .2\ 1$$
$$.4\ 3\ 5 \qquad\qquad\qquad\qquad\qquad\qquad .0\ 7$$
$$sum\ \overline{.5\ 9\ 1\ 2\ 5} \qquad\qquad\qquad\qquad difference\ \overline{.1\ 4}$$

We are now prepared to perform the   .5 9 1 2 5
operation indicated by the minus sign   .1 4
between the parentheses, which is, $\overline{.4\ 5\ 1\ 2\ 5}$ Ans.

(*d*)   This problem means that 33 millionths and 17 thousandths are to be added. Also, that 53 hundredths and 274 thousandths are to be added, and the smaller of these sums is to be subtracted from the larger sum. Thus $(.53 + .274) - (.000033 + .017) = ?$

$$
\begin{array}{ll}
.8\ 0\ 4 & \textit{larger sum.} \\
.0\ 1\ 7\ 0\ 3\ 3 & \textit{smaller sum.} \\
\textit{difference } .7\ 8\ 6\ 9\ 6\ 7 & \text{Ans.}
\end{array}
$$

tenths.
hundredths.
thousandths.
ten-thousandths.
hundred-thousandths.
millionths.

tenths.
hundredths.
thousandths.

.0 0 0 0 3 3   .5 3

.0 1 7   .2 7 4

.0 1 7 0 3 3 *sum.*   .8 0 4 *sum.*

(68) In addition of decimals the decimal points must be placed directly under each other, so that tenths will come under tenths, hundredths under hundredths, thousandths under thousandths, etc. The addition is then performed as in whole numbers, the decimal point of the sum being placed directly under the decimal points above.

.1 2 5
.7
.0 8 9
.4 0 0 5
.9
.0 0 0 0 2 7
2.2 1 4 5 2 7   Ans

(69)   9 2 7.4 1 6
           8.2 7 4
         3 7 2.6
          6 2.0 7 9 3 8
        1 3 7 0.3 6 9 3 8   Ans.

(70)

tenths.
hundredths.
thousandths.
ten-thousandths.
hundred-thousandths.
millionths.

.0 1 7,
.2
0 0 0 0 4 7
.2 1 7 0 4 7   Ans.

(71) (*a*) There are 3 decimal places in the multiplicand and 3 in the multiplier; hence, there are $3+3$ or 6 decimal places in the product. Since the product contains but four figures, we prefix two ciphers in order to obtain the necessary six decimal places.

.1 0 7
.0 1 3
3 2 1
1 0 7
.0 0 1 3 9 1   Ans.

(*b*)

```
      2 0 3
      2.0 3
     ───────
      6 0 9
    4 0 6 0
   ─────────
    4 1 2.0 9
       .2 0 3
   ─────────
    1 2 3 6 2 7
    8 2 4 1 8 0
   ─────────────
    8 3.6 5 4 2 7   Ans.
```

There are 2 decimal places in the multiplier and none in the multiplicand; hence, there are $2+0$ or 2 decimal places in the first product.

Since there are 2 decimal places in the multiplicand and 3 decimal places in the multiplier, there are $3+2$ or 5 decimal places in the second product.

(*c*) First perform the operations indicated by the signs between the numbers enclosed by the parenthesis, and then perform whatever may be required by the sign before the parenthesis.

Multiply together the numbers 2.7 and 31.85.

The parenthesis shows that .316 is to be taken from 3.16.

```
    3.1 6 0
     .3 1 6
   ─────────
    2.8 4 4
```

```
      3 1.8 5
         2.7
     ─────────
      2 2 2 9 5
      6 3 7 0
     ─────────
      8 5.9 9 5
```

The product obtained by the first operation is now multiplied by the remainder obtained by performing the operation indicated by the signs within the parenthesis.

```
      8 5.9 9 5
        2.8 4 4
     ───────────
      3 4 3 9 8 0
      3 4 3 9 8 0
      6 8 7 9 6 0
    1 7 1 9 9 0
   ─────────────────
    2 4 4.5 6 9 7 8 0   Ans.
```

(*d*) $(107.8 + 6.541 - 31.96) \times 1.742 = ?$

```
      1 0 7.8
   +    6.5 4 1
   ───────────
    1 1 4.3 4 1
   −   3 1.9 6
   ───────────
      8 2.3 8 1
```

```
        8 2.3 8 1
     ×    1.7 4 2
     ─────────────
      1 6 4 7 6 2
      3 2 9 5 2 4
      5 7 6 6 6 7
      8 2 3 8 1
     ───────────────
    1 4 3.5 0 7 7 0 2   Ans.
```

(72) (a) $(\frac{7}{16} - .13) \times \overline{.625 + \frac{5}{8}} = ?$

First perform the operation indicated by the parenthesis.

$\frac{7}{16} = \frac{7}{16}$) 7.0 0 0 0 (.4 3 7 5   We point off four decimal places, since we annex four ciphers.

```
        6 4
        ────
        6 0
        4 8
        ────
        1 2 0
        1 1 2
        ──────
            8 0
            8 0
            ──
```

    .4 3 7 5
    .1 3
    ────────

Subtracting, we obtain .3 0 7 5

The vinculum·has the same meaning as the parenthesis;

$\frac{5}{8} = \frac{5}{8}$) 5.0 0 0   hence, we perform the operation indicated by it. We point off three decimal places, since three ciphers were annexed to the 5.
    .6 2 5

Adding the terms in-   .6 2 5
cluded by the vinculum,   .6 2 5
we obtain   1.2 5 0

The final operation is to perform the work indicated by the sign between the parenthesis and the vinculum, thus,

```
            .3 0 7 5
             1.2 5
            ────────
            1 5 3 7 5
            6 1 5 0
            3 0 7 5
            ──────────
            .3 8 4 3 7 5   Ans.
```

(b) $(\frac{19}{32} \times .21) - (.02 \times \frac{3}{16}) = ?$

$.21 = \frac{21}{100}.$ $\frac{19}{32} \times \frac{21}{100} = \frac{399}{3200}.$ $.02 = \frac{2}{100}.$ $\frac{2}{100} \times \frac{3}{16} = \frac{6}{1600}$

$= \frac{3}{800}.$ $\frac{3}{800} = \frac{3 \times 4}{800 \times 4} = \frac{12}{3200}.$ $\frac{399}{3200} - \frac{12}{3200}$

$$= \frac{399 - 12}{3,200} = \frac{387}{3200}.$$

Reducing $\frac{387}{3200}$ to a decimal, we obtain

$$387$$

$$3{,}200 \,)\, 3\,8\,7.0\,0\,0\,0\,0\,0\,0\,(.1\,2\,0\,9\,3\,7\,5 \quad \textbf{Ans.}$$

$$
\begin{array}{l}
3\,2\,0\,0 \\ \hline
6\,7\,0\,0 \\
6\,4\,0\,0 \\ \hline
3\,0\,0\,0\,0 \\
2\,8\,8\,0\,0 \\ \hline
1\,2\,0\,0\,0 \\
9\,6\,0\,0 \\ \hline
2\,4\,0\,0\,0 \\
2\,2\,4\,0\,0 \\ \hline
1\,6\,0\,0\,0 \\
1\,6\,0\,0\,0 \\ \hline
\end{array}
$$

Point off seven decimal places, since seven ciphers were annexed to the dividend.

(c) $\left(\frac{13}{4}+.013-2.17\right)\times\overline{13\frac{1}{4}-7\frac{5}{16}} =?$

$\frac{13}{4} =$
$$
\begin{array}{l}
13 \\ \hline
4\,)\,1\,3.0\,0 \\ \hline
3.2\,5
\end{array}
$$
Point off two decimal places, since two ciphers were annexed to the dividend.

$$
\begin{array}{r}
3.2\,5 \\
+\ \ .0\,1\,3 \\ \hline
3.2\,6\,3 \\
-2.1\,7 \\ \hline
1.0\,9\,3
\end{array}
$$

$\frac{5}{16}$ reduced to a decimal is .3125, since

$$
\begin{array}{l}
5 \\ \hline
16\,)\,5.0\,0\,0\,0\,(.3\,1\,2\,5 \\
4\,8 \\ \hline
2\,0 \\
1\,6 \\ \hline
4\,0 \\
3\,2 \\ \hline
8\,0 \\
8\,0 \\ \hline
\end{array}
$$

Point off four decimal places, since four ciphers were annexed to the dividend.

Then, $7\frac{5}{16} = 7.3125$, and $13\frac{1}{4} = 13.25$, since $\frac{1}{4} = $
$$
\begin{array}{l}
1 \\ \hline
4\,)\,1.0\,0 \\ \hline
.2\,5
\end{array}
$$

$$
\begin{array}{r}
1\,3.2\,5 \\
-\ \ 7.3\,1\,2\,5 \\ \hline
5.9\,3\,7\,5
\end{array}
$$

$$
\begin{array}{r}
5.9\,3\,7\,5 \\
\times\ \ 1.0\,9\,3 \\ \hline
1\,7\,8\,1\,2\,5 \\
5\,3\,4\,3\,7\,5 \\
5\,9\,3\,7\,5\,0 \\ \hline
6.4\,8\,9\,6\,8\,7\,5 \quad \text{Ans.}
\end{array}
$$

(73) (*a*) $.875 \div \frac{1}{2} = .875 \div .5$ (since $\frac{1}{2} = .5$) $= 1.75$. Ans.
Another way of solving this is to reduce .875 to its equivalent common fraction and then divide.

$.875 = \frac{7}{8}$, since $.875 = \frac{875}{1000} = \frac{175}{200} = \frac{35}{40} = \frac{7}{8}$; then,

$$\frac{7}{8} \div \frac{1}{2} = \frac{7}{\underset{4}{8}} \times \frac{\overset{2}{2}}{1} = \frac{7}{4} = 1\frac{3}{4}.$$

Since $\frac{3}{4} = \quad \frac{3}{4}\,)\,3.0\,0\,(.7\,5, \quad 1\frac{3}{4} = 1.75$, the same answer as
$\qquad \underline{2\,8} \qquad\qquad\qquad\qquad$ above.
$\qquad \quad 2\,0$
$\qquad \quad \underline{2\,0}$

(*b*) $\frac{7}{8} \div .5 = \frac{7}{8} \div \frac{1}{2}$ (since $.5 = \frac{1}{2}$) $= \frac{7}{\underset{4}{8}} \times \frac{\overset{2}{2}}{1} = \frac{7}{4} = 1\frac{3}{4}$, or
1.75. Ans.

This can also be solved by reducing $\frac{7}{8}$ to its equivalent decimal and dividing by .5; $\frac{7}{8} = .875$; $.875 \div .5 = 1.75$. Since there are 3 decimal places in the dividend and 1 in the divisor, there are $3 - 1$ or 2 decimal places in the quotient.

(*c*) $\dfrac{.375 \times \frac{1}{4}}{\frac{5}{16} - .125} = ?$ We shall solve this problem by first reducing the decimals to their equivalent common fractions.

$.375 = \frac{375}{1000} = \frac{75}{200} = \frac{15}{40} = \frac{3}{8}$. $\frac{3}{8} \times \frac{1}{4} = \frac{3}{32}$, or the value of the numerator of the fraction.

$.125 = \frac{125}{1000} = \frac{25}{200} = \frac{1}{8}$. Reducing $\frac{1}{8}$ to 16ths, we have $\frac{1 \times 2}{8 \times 2} = \frac{2}{16}$. Then, $\frac{5}{16} - \frac{2}{16} = \frac{3}{16}$, or the value of the denominator of the fraction. The problem is now reduced to

$\dfrac{\frac{3}{32}}{\frac{3}{16}} = ?$ $\dfrac{\frac{3}{32}}{\frac{3}{16}} = \frac{3}{32} \div \frac{3}{16} = \frac{\overset{}{\cancel{3}}}{\underset{2}{32}} \times \frac{\overset{16}{\cancel{16}}}{\cancel{3}} = \frac{1}{2}$ or .5. Ans.

(74) $\dfrac{1.25 \times 20 \times 3}{87 + (11 \times 8)} = ?$ In this problem $1.25 \times 20 \times 3$ constitutes the numerator of the
$\qquad \underline{459 + 32}$ complex fraction.

$\qquad 1.2\,5$ Multiplying the factors of the numerator
$\times \quad \underline{2\,0}$ together, we find their product to be 75.
$\qquad 2\,5.0\,0$
$\times \quad \underline{\quad 3}$
$\qquad 7\,5$

The fraction $\dfrac{87+(11\times 8)}{459+32}$ constitutes the denominator of the complex fraction. The value of the numerator of this fraction equals $87+88 = 175$.

The numerator is combined as though it were written $87+(11\times 8)$, and its result is

$$
\begin{array}{r}
1\,1 \\
\times\ \ 8 \\
\hline
8\,8 \\
+\ \ \ 8\,7 \\
\hline
1\,7\,5
\end{array}
$$

The value of the denominator of this fraction is equal to $459+32 = 491$. The problem then becomes

$$\frac{75}{\frac{175}{491}} = \frac{75}{1} \div \frac{175}{491} = \frac{75}{1} \times \frac{491}{175} = \frac{\overset{3}{\cancel{75}}\times 491}{\underset{7}{\cancel{175}}} = \frac{1473}{7} = 210\tfrac{3}{7}.$$

                                                                     Ans.

(75)   1 plus .001 $= 1.001$.   .01 plus .000001 $= .010001$. And $1.001 - .010001 = .990999$.   Ans.

ARITHMETIC.

---

(1) A certain per cent. of a number means so many hundredths of that number.

25% of 8,428 lb. means 25 hundredths of 8,428 lb. Hence, 25% of 8,428 lb. $= .25 \times 8,428$ lb. $= 2,107$ lb. Ans.

(2) Here $100 is the base and 1% $= .01$ is the rate. Then, $.01 \times \$100 = \$1$. Ans.

(3) $\frac{1}{2}$% means one-half of 1 per cent. Since 1% is .01, $\frac{1}{2}$% is .005, for 2)$\overline{.0\ 1\ 0}$. And $.005 \times \$35,000 = \$175$. Ans.
$$\overline{.0\ 0\ 5}$$

(4) Here 50 is the base, 2 is the percentage, and it is required to find the rate. Applying rule, Art. **12,**

rate $=$ percentage $\div$ base;

rate $= 2 \div 50 = .04$, or 4%. Ans.

(5) By Art. **12,** rate $=$ percentage $\div$ base.*

As percentage $= 10$ and base $= 10$, we have

rate $= 10 \div 10 = 1 = 100\%$.

Hence, 10 is 100% of 10. Ans.

---

* Remember that an expression of this form means that the **first** term is to be *divided by* the second term. Thus, as above, it means percentage *divided by* base.

(6) (*a*) Rate = percentage ÷ base. Art. **12.**

As percentage = \$176.54 and base = \$2,522, we have
$$\text{rate} = 176.54 \div 2,522 = .07 = 7\%. \quad \text{Ans.}$$

$$2\,5\,2\,2\,)\,1\,7\,6.5\,4$$
$$.0\,7$$

(*b*) Base = percentage ÷ rate. Art. **11.**

As percentage = 16.96 and rate = 8% = .08, we have
$$\text{base} = 16.96 \div .08 = 212. \quad \text{Ans.}$$

$$.0\,8\,)\,1\,6.9\,6$$
$$2\,1\,2$$

(*c*) Amount is the sum of the base and percentage; hence, the percentage = amount minus the base.

Amount = 216.7025 and base = 213.5; hence, percentage = 216.7025 − 213.5 = 3.2025.

Rate = percentage ÷ base. Art. **12.**

Therefore, rate = 3.2025 ÷ 213.5 = .015 = 1½%. Ans.
$$2\,1\,3.5\,)\,3.2\,0\,2\,5\,(.0\,1\,5 = 1\tfrac{1}{2}\%.$$

$$2\,1\,3\,5$$
$$\overline{1\,0\,6\,7\,5}$$
$$1\,0\,6\,7\,5$$

(*d*) The difference is the remainder found by subtracting the percentage from the base; hence, base minus the difference = the percentage. Base = 207 and difference = 201.825; hence, percentage = 207 − 201.825 = 5.175.

Rate = percentage ÷ base. Art. **12.**

Therefore, rate = 5.175 ÷ 207 = .025 = .02½ = 2½%. Ans.
$$2\,0\,7\,)\,5.1\,7\,5\,(.0\,2\,5 = 2\tfrac{1}{2}\%.$$

$$4\,1\,4$$
$$\overline{1\,0\,3\,5}$$
$$1\,0\,3\,5$$

(7) In this problem \$5,500 is the amount, since it equals what he paid for the farm plus what he gained; 15% is the rate, and the cost (to be found) is the base. Applying rule, Art. **16,**

base = amount ÷ (1 + rate); hence,
base = \$5,500 ÷ (1 + .15) = \$4,782.61. **Ans.**

$$1.1\,5\,)\,5\,5\,0\,0.0\,0\,0\,0\,(\,4\,7\,8\,2.6\,1-$$
$$\underline{4\,6\,0}$$
$$\underline{9\,0\,0}$$
$$8\,0\,5$$
$$\underline{9\,5\,0}$$
$$9\,2\,0$$
$$\underline{3\,0\,0}$$
$$2\,3\,0$$
$$\underline{7\,0\,0}$$
$$6\,9\,0$$
$$\underline{1\,0\,0}$$
$$1\,1\,5$$

The example can also be solved as follows: 100% = cost; if he gained 15%, then $100 + 15 = 115\% = \$5,500$, the selling price.

If $115\% = \$5,500$, $1\% = \frac{1}{115}$ of $\$5,500 = \$47.8261$, and 100%, or the cost $= 100 \times \$47.8261 = \$4,782.61$. Ans.

(8) $2\,4\ \%$ of $\$950 = 950 \times .24\ = \$2\,2\,8.0\,0$
$1\,2\frac{1}{2}\%$ of $\$950 = 950 \times .125 =\ 1\,1\,8.7\,5$
$\underline{1\,7\ \%\ \text{of}\ \$950 = 950 \times .17\ =\ 1\,6\,1.5\,0}$
$5\,3\frac{1}{2}\%$ of $\$950\qquad\qquad = \$5\,0\,8.2\,5$

The total amount of his yearly expenses, then, is \$508.25; hence, his savings are $\$950 - \$508.25 = \$441.75$. Ans.

Or, as above, $24\% + 12\frac{1}{2}\% + 17\% = 53\frac{1}{2}\%$, the total percentage of expenditures; hence, $100\% - 53\frac{1}{2}\% = 46\frac{1}{2}\% =$ per cent. saved.   And $\$950 \times .465 = \$441.75 =$ his yearly savings.

Ans.

(9) The percentage is 961.38, and the rate is $.37\frac{1}{2}$. By Art. **11,**

base = percentage ÷ rate
$= 961.38 ÷ .375 = 2,563.68$, the number. Ans.

```
.3 7 5 ) 9 6 1.3 8 0 0 0 ( 2 5 6 3.6 8
        7 5 0
        2 1 1 3
        1 8 7 5
          2 3 8 8
          2 2 5 0
            1 3 8 0
            1 1 2 5
              2 5 5 0
              2 2 5 0
                3 0 0 0
                3 0 0 0
```

Another method of solving is the following:

If $37\frac{1}{2}\%$ of a number is 961.38, then $.37\frac{1}{2}$ times the number = 961.38, and the number = $961.38 \div .37\frac{1}{2}$, which, as above = 2,563.68. Ans.

(10) Here $1,125 is 30% of some number; hence, $1,125 = the percentage, 30% = the rate, and the required number is the base. Applying rule, Art. **11**,

base = percentage ÷ rate = $1,125 ÷ .30 = $3,750.

Since $3,750 is $\frac{3}{4}$ of the property, one of the fourths is $\frac{1}{3}$ of $3,750 = $1,250, and 4 fourths, or the entire property, is $4 \times $1,250 = $5,000. Ans.

(11) Here $4,810 is the difference and 35% the rate. By Art. **17**,

base = difference ÷ (1 − rate)
     = $4,810 ÷ (1 − .35) = $4,810 ÷ .65 = $7,400. Ans.

```
.6 5 ) 4 8 1 0.0 0 ( 7 4 0 0       1.0 0
        4 5 5                        .3 5
          2 6 0                      .6 5
          2 6 0
```

Solution can also be effected as follows: 100% = the sum diminished by 35%, then (1 − .35) = .65, which is $4,810.

If 65% = $4,810, 1% = $\frac{1}{65}$ of $4,810 = $74, and 100% = 100 × $74 = $7,400. Ans.

(12) In this example the sales on Monday amounted to $197.55, which was $12\frac{1}{2}\%$ of the sales for the entire week; i.e., we have given the percentage, $197.55, and the rate, $12\frac{1}{2}\%$,

and the required number (or the amount of sales for the week)
equals the base.   By Art. **11,**

$$base = percentage \div rate = \$197.55 \div .125;$$

or,   .1 2 5) 1 9 7.5 5 0 0 (1 5 8 0.4
                        1 2 5
                        ――――――
                          7 2 5
                          6 2 5
                        ――――――
                        1 0 0 5
                        1 0 0 0
                        ――――――
                              5 0 0
                              5 0 0
                              ――――――

Therefore, base = $1,580.40, which also equals the sales
for the week.   Ans.

(13)   16.5 miles = $12\frac{1}{2}\%$ of the entire length of the road.
We wish to find the *entire* length.

16.5 miles is the percentage, $12\frac{1}{2}\%$ is the rate, and the
entire length will be the base.   By Art. **11,**

$$base = percentage \div rate = 16.5 \div .12\frac{1}{2}.$$

.1 2 5) 1 6.5 0 0 (1 3 2 miles.   Ans.
    1 2 5
    ――――――
      4 0·0
      3 7 5
    ――――――
        2 5 0
        2 5 0
        ――――――

(14)   Here we have given the difference, or $35, and the
rate, or 60%, to find the base.   We use the rule in Art. **17,**

$$base = difference \div (1 - rate)$$
$$= \$35 \div (1 - .60) = \$35 \div .40 = \$87.50.   Ans.$$

.4 0) 3 5.0 0 0 (8 7.5
    3 2 0
    ――――――
      3 0 0
      2 8 0·
    ――――――
        2 0 0
        2 0 0
        ――――――

Or, $100\% =$ whole debt; $100\% - 60\% = 40\% = \$35$.

If $40\% = \$35$, then $1\% = \frac{1}{40}$ of $\$35 = \dfrac{\$35}{40}$, and 100%

$= \dfrac{\$35}{40} \times 100 = \$87.50$.   Ans.

(15)   28 rd. 4 yd. 2 ft. 10 in. to inches.

$$
\begin{array}{r}
\times \quad 5\frac{1}{2} \\
\hline
1\ 5\ 4 \\
+ \quad 4 \\
\hline
1\ 5\ 8 \ \text{yards.} \\
\times \quad 3 \\
\hline
4\ 7\ 4 \\
+ \quad 2 \\
\hline
4\ 7\ 6 \ \text{feet.} \\
\times \quad 1\ 2 \\
\hline
5\ 7\ 1\ 2 \\
+ \quad 1\ 0 \\
\hline
5\ 7\ 2\ 2 \ \text{inches.}
\end{array}
$$

Since there are $5\frac{1}{2}$ yards in 1 rod, in 28 rods there are 28 $\times 5\frac{1}{2}$, or 154 yards; 154 yards $+4$ yards $= 158$ yards. There are 3 feet in 1 yard; therefore, in 158 yards there are 3×158, or 474 feet; 474 feet $+2$ feet $= 476$ feet. There are 12 inches in 1 foot, and in 476 feet there are 12 $\times 476$, or 5,712 inches; 5,712 inches $+ 10$ inches $= 5,722$ inches.   Ans.

(16) $1\ 2\ )\ 5\ 7\ 2\ 2\ $ inches.

                 $3\ )\ 4\ 7\ 6 + 10$ inches.

             $5\frac{1}{2}\ )\ 1\ 5\ 8 + 2$ feet.

                  $2\ 8 + 4$ yards.

28 rd. 4 yd. 2 ft. 10 in.   Ans.

EXPLANATION.—There are 12 inches in 1 foot; hence, in 5,722 inches there are as many feet as 12 is contained times in 5,722 inches, or 476 feet and 10 inches remaining. Write these 10 inches as a remainder. There are 3 feet in 1 yard; hence, in 476 feet there are as many yards as 3 is contained times in 476 feet, or 158 yards and 2 feet remaining. There are $5\frac{1}{2}$ yards in 1 rod; hence, in 158 yards there are 28 rods and 4 yards remaining. Then, in 5,722 inches, there are 28 rd. 4 yd. 2 ft. 10 in.

(17)   5   weeks 3.5 days.

$$
\begin{array}{r}
\times \quad 7 \\
\hline
3\ 5 \quad \text{days in 5 weeks.} \\
+ \quad 3.5 \\
\hline
3\ 8.5 \ \text{days.}
\end{array}
$$

Then, we find how many seconds there are in 38.5 days.

$$3\,8.5 \text{ days.}$$
$$\times\quad 2\,4 \text{ hours in 1 day.}$$
$$\overline{1\,5\,4\,0}$$
$$\underline{7\,7\,0}$$
$$9\,2\,4.0 \text{ hours in 38.5 days.}$$
$$\times\qquad 6\,0 \text{ minutes in 1 hour.}$$
$$\overline{5\,5\,4\,4\,0 \text{ minutes in 38.5 days.}}$$
$$\times\qquad\quad 6\,0 \text{ seconds in 1 minute.}$$
$$\overline{3\,3\,2\,6\,4\,0\,0 \text{ seconds in 38.5 days.}}\quad \text{Ans.}$$

(18) Since there are 24 gr. in 1 pwt., in 13,750 gr. there are as many pennyweights as 24 is contained times in 13,750, or 572 pwt. and 22 gr. remaining. Since there are 20 pwt. in 1 oz., in 572 pwt. there are as many ounces as 20 is contained times in 572, or 28 oz. and 12 pwt. remaining. Since there are 12 oz. in 1 lb. (Troy), in 28 oz. there are as many pounds as 12 is contained times in 28, or 2 lb. and 4 oz. remaining. We now have the pounds and ounces required by the problem; therefore, in 13,750 gr. there are 2 lb. 4 oz. 12 pwt. 22 gr.

$$2\,4\,)\,1\,3\,7\,5\,0 \text{ gr.}$$
$$2\,0\,)\,5\,7\,2 \text{ pwt.} + 22 \text{ gr.}$$
$$1\,2\,)\,2\,8 \text{ oz.} + 12 \text{ pwt.}$$
$$2 \text{ lb.} + 4 \text{ oz.}$$

2 lb. 4 oz. 12 pwt. 22 gr. Ans.

(19) $$1\,0\,0\,)\,4\,7\,6\,3\,2\,5\,4 \text{ li.}$$
$$8\,0\,)\,4\,7\,6\,3\,2 + 54 \text{ li.}$$
$$5\,9\,5 + 32 \text{ ch.}$$

595 mi. 32 ch. 54 li. Ans.

EXPLANATION.—There are 100 links in 1 chain; hence, in 4,763,254 li. there are as many chains as 100 is contained times in 4,763,254 li., or 47,632 ch. and 54 li. remaining. Write the 54 li. as a remainder. There are 80 ch. in 1 mile; hence, in 47,632 ch. there are as many miles as 80 is contained times in 47,632 ch., or 595 mi. and 32 ch. remaining.

Then, in 4,763,254 li. there are 595 mi. 32 ch. 54 li.

(20)   1 7 2 8) 7 6 4 3 2 5 cu. in.
             2 7) 4 4 2 + 549 cu. in.
                     1 6 cu. yd. + 10 cu. ft.

16 cu. yd. 10 cu. ft. 549 cu. in.   Ans.

EXPLANATION.—There are 1,728 cu. in. in 1 cubic foot; hence, in 764,325 cu. in. there are as many cubic feet as 1,728 is contained times in 764,325, or 442 cu. ft. and 549 cu. in. remaining. Write the 549 cu. in. as a remainder. There are 27 cu. ft. in 1 cubic yard; hence, in 442 cu. ft. there are as many cubic yards as 27 is contained times in 442 cu. ft., or 16 cu. yd. and 10 cu. ft. remaining. Then, in 764,325 cu. in. there are 16 cu. yd. 10 cu. ft. 549 cu. in.

(21) We must arrange the different terms in columns, taking care to have like denominations in the same column.

rd.	yd.	ft.	in.
2	2	2	3
	4	1	9
		2	7
3	2½	0	7

or, 3 rd. 2 yd. 2 ft. 1 in.   Ans.

EXPLANATION.—We begin to add at the right-hand column. $7 + 9 + 3 = 19$ in.; as 12 in. make 1 foot, 19 in. $= 1$ ft. and 7 in. Place the 7 in. in the inches column, and reserve the 1 ft. to add to the next column.

1 (reserved) $+ 2 + 1 + 2 = 6$ ft. Since 3 ft. make 1 yard, 6 ft. $= 2$ yd. and 0 ft. remaining. Place the cipher in the column of feet and reserve the 2 yd. for the next column.

2 (reserved) $+ 4 + 2 = 8$ yd. Since 5½ yd. $= 1$ rd., 8 yd. $= 1$ rd. and 2½ yd. Place 2½ yd. in the yards column and reserve 1 rd. for the next column; 1 (reserved) $+ 2 = 3$ rd.

Ans. $=$ 3 rd.   2½ yd.   0 ft.   7 in.,
   or 3 rd.   2 yd.   1 ft.   13 in.,
   or 3 rd.   2 yd.   2 ft.   1 in.

(22) We write the compound numbers so that the units of the same denomination shall stand in the same column.

gal.	qt.	pt.	gi.
3	3	1	3
6	0	1	2
4	0	0	1
	8	5	0

16 gal. 3 qt. 0 pt. 2 gi.

Beginning to add with the lowest denomination, we find that the sum of the gills is $1+2+3 = 6$. Since there are 4 gi. in 1 pint, in 6 gi. there are as many pints as 4 is contained times in 6, or 1 pt. and 2 gi. We place 2 gi. under the gills column and reserve the 1 pt. for the pints column; the sum of the pints is 1 (reserved) $+5+1+1 = 8$. Since there are 2 pt. in 1 quart, in 8 pt. there are as many quarts as 2 is contained times in 8, or 4 qt. and 0 pt. We place the cipher under the column of pints and reserve the 4 for the quarts column. The sum of the quarts is 4 (reserved) $+8+3 = 15$. Since there are 4 qt. in 1 gallon, in 15 qt. there are as many gallons as 4 is contained times in 15, or 3 gal. and 3 qt. remaining. We now place the 3 under the quarts column and reserve the 3 gal. for the gallons column. The sum of the gallons column is 3 (reserved) $+4+6+3 = 16$ gal. Since we cannot reduce 16 gal. to any higher denomination, we have 16 gal. 3 qt. 0 pt. and 2 gi. for the answer.

(23) Reduce the grains, pennyweights, and ounces to higher denominations.

2 4) 2 4 0 gr.   2 0) 1 2 5 pwt.   1 2) 5 0 oz.

     1 0 pwt.   6 oz. 5 pwt.   4 lb. 2 oz.

Then, 3 lb. $+$ 4 lb. 2 oz. $+$ 6 oz. 5 pwt. $+$ 10 pwt. $=$

1b.	oz.	pwt.
3		
4	2	
6		5
		10

7 lb.   8 oz.   15 pwt.   Ans.

(24) Since "seconds" is the lowest denomination in this problem, we find their sum first, which is $11+29+25+30$

+12, or 107 seconds. Since there are 60 seconds in 1 minute, in 107 seconds there are as many minutes as 60 is contained times in 107, or 1 minute and 47 seconds remaining. We place the 47 under the seconds column and reserve the 1 for the minutes column. The sum of the minutes is 1 (reserved)

deg.	min.	sec.
1 1	1 6	1 2
1 3	1 9	3 0
2 0	0	2 5
0	2 6	2 9
1 0	1 7	1 1
5 5°	1 9′	4 7″

+17+26+19+16, or 79. Since there are 60 minutes in 1 degree, in 79 minutes there are as many degrees as 60 is contained times in 79, or 1 degree and 19 minutes remaining. We place the 19 under the minutes column and reserve the 1 degree for the degrees column. The sum of the degrees is 1 (reserved) +10+20+13+11, or 55 degrees. Since we cannot reduce 55 degrees to any higher denomination, we have 55° 19′ 47″ for the answer.

(25) Since "inches" is the lowest denomination in this problem, we find their sum first, which is 11+8+6, or 25 inches. Since there are 12 inches in 1 foot, in 25 inches there are as many feet as 12 is contained times in 25, or 2 feet and 1 inch remaining. Place the 1 inch under the inches column, and reserve the 2 feet to add to the column of feet. The sum of the feet is 2 feet (reserved)

rd.	yd.	ft.	in.
1 3 0	5	1	6
2 1 5	0	2	8
3 0 4	4	0	1 1
6 5 0	4½	2	1
mi. rd.	yd.	ft.	in.
or, 2 10	5	0	7 Ans.

+2+1 = 5 feet. Since there are 3 feet in 1 yard, in 5 feet there are as many yards as 3 is contained times in 5 feet, or 1 yard and 2 feet remaining. Place the 2 feet under the column of feet, and reserve the 1 yard to add to the column of yards. The sum of the yards is 1 yard (reserved) +4 +5 = 10 yards. Since there are 5½ yards in 1 rod, in 10 yards there are as many rods as 5½ is contained times in 10, or 1 rod and 4½ yards remaining. Place the 4½ yards under the column of yards, and reserve the 1 rod for the column of rods. The sum of the rods is 1 (reserved) + 304 + 215 + 130 = 650 rods. Place 650 rods under the column of rods. Therefore, the sum is 650 rd. $4\frac{1}{2}$ yd. 2 ft. 1 in. Or, since $\frac{1}{2}$ a yard = 1 ft. 6 in., and since there are 320 rods in 1 mile, the sum may be expressed as 2 mi. 10 rd. 5 yd. 0 ft. 7 in. Ans.

(26) Since "square links" is the lowest denomination in this problem, we find their sum first, which is 21 + 23 + 16 + 18 + 23 + 21, or 122 square links. Place 122 square links under the column of square links. The sum of the square rods is 2 + 3 + 2 + 2 + 2 + 3, or 14 square rods. Place 14 square rods under the column of square rods. The sum of the square chains is 323 square chains. Since there are 10 square chains in 1 acre, in 323 square chains there are as many acres as 10 is contained times in 323 square chains, or 32 acres and 3 square chains remaining. Place 3 square chains under the column of square chains, and reserve the 32 acres to add to the column of acres. The sum of the acres is 32 acres (reserved) + 46 + 25 + 56 + 47 + 28 + 21, or 255 acres. Place 255 acres under the column of acres. Therefore, the sum is 255 A. 3 sq. ch. 14 sq. rd. 122 sq. li.

A.	sq. ch.	sq. rd.	sq. li.
2 1	6 7	3	2 1
2 8	7 8	2	2 3
4 7	6	2	1 8
5 6	5 9	2	1 6
2 5	3 8	3	2 3
4 6	7 5	2	2 1
2 5 5	3	1 4	1 2 2

Ans.

(27) Before we can subtract 300 ft. from 20 rd. 2 yd. 2 ft. and 9 in., we must reduce the 300 ft. to higher denominations.

Since there are 3 feet in 1 yard, in 300 feet there are as many yards as 3 is contained times in 300, or 100 yards. There are $5\frac{1}{2}$ yards in 1 rod, hence in 100 yards there are as many rods as $5\frac{1}{2}$, or $\frac{11}{2}$, is contained times in 100 = $18\frac{2}{11}$ rods.

$$100 \div \tfrac{11}{2} = 100 \times \tfrac{2}{11} = \frac{100 \times 2}{11} = \frac{200}{11}$$

$$11 \,)\, 2\,0\,0\, (\, 1\, 8\tfrac{2}{11}\ \text{rd.}$$
$$\underline{1\ 1}$$
$$9\ 0$$
$$\underline{8\ 8}$$
$$2$$

Since there are $5\tfrac{1}{2}$ or $\tfrac{11}{2}$ yards in 1 rod, in $\tfrac{2}{11}$ rod there are $\dfrac{2}{11} \times \dfrac{11}{2}$, or 1 yard, so we find that 300 feet equals 18 rods and 1 yard. The problem now is as follows: From 20 rd. 2 yd. 2 ft. and 9 in. take 18 rd. and 1 yd.

We place the smaller number under the larger one, so that the units of the same denomination fall in the same

rd.	yd.	ft.	in.
20	2	2	9
18	1	0	0
2	1	2	9

column. Beginning with the lowest denomination, we see that 0 inches from 9 inches leaves 9 inches. Going to the next higher denomination, we see that 0 feet from 2 feet leaves 2 feet. Subtracting 1 yard from 2 yards, we have 1 yard remaining, and 18 rods from 20 rods leaves 2 rods. Therefore, the difference is 2 rd. 1 yd. 2 ft. 9 in. Ans.

(28)

	A.	sq. rd.	sq. yd.
	1 1 4	8 0	2 5
	7 5	7 0	3 0
	3 9	9	2 5$\tfrac{1}{4}$ Ans.

EXPLANATION.—Place the subtrahend under the minuend so that like denominations are under each other. Then begin at the right with the lowest denomination. We cannot subtract 30 from 25, so we take 1 square rod ($= 30\tfrac{1}{4}$ square yards) from 80 square rods, leaving 79 square rods; adding $30\tfrac{1}{4}$ square yards to 25 square yards, we have $55\tfrac{1}{4}$ square yards; subtracting 30 from $55\tfrac{1}{4}$ square yards, leaves $25\tfrac{1}{4}$ yards; we now subtract 70 square rods from 79 square rods, which leaves 9 square rods; next, we subtract 75 acres from

114 acres, which leaves 39 acres, which we place under the column of acres.

(29) If 10 gal. 2 qt. and 1 pt. of molasses are sold from a hogshead at one time, and 26 gal. 3 qt. are sold at another time, then the total amount of molasses sold equals 10 gal. 2 qt. 1 pt. plus 26 gal. 3 qt.

Since the pint is the lowest denomination, we add the pints first, which equal $0 + 1$, or 1 pint. We cannot reduce 1 pint to any higher denomination, so we place it under the pints column. The number of quarts is $3 + 2$, or 5. Since there are 4 quarts in 1 gallon, in 5 quarts there are as many gallons as 4 is

gal.	qt.	pt.
1 0	2	1
2 6	3	0
3 7	1	1

contained times in 5, or 1 gallon and 1 quart remaining. We place the 1 quart under the quarts column, and reserve the 1 gallon to add to the column of gallons. The number of gallons equals 1 (reserved) $+ 26 + 10$, or 37 gallons.

If 37 gal. 1 qt. and 1 pt. are sold from a hogshead of molasses (63 gal.), there remains the difference between 63 gal. and 37 gal. 1 qt. 1 pt., or 25 gal. 2 qt. 1 pt.

63 gal. is the same as 62 gal. 3 qt. 2 pt., since 1 gal. equals 4 qt., and 1 qt. equals 2 pt.

Beginning with the lowest denomination, we subtract 1 pt. from the 2 pt. 1 pint from 2 pints leaves 1 pint, 1 quart from 3 quarts leaves 2 quarts, and 37 gallons from 62 gallons leaves 25 gallons. Therefore, there are 25 gal. 2 qt. and 1 pt. of molasses remaining in the hogshead. Ans.

gal.	qt.	pt.
6 2	3	2
3 7	1	1
2 5	2	1

(30) If a person were born June 19, 1850, in order to find how old he would be on Aug. 3, 1892, subtract the earlier date from the later date.

On Aug. 3, 7 mo. and 3 da. have elapsed from the beginning of the year, and on June 19, 5 mo. and 19 da.

Beginning with the lowest denomination, we find that 19

days cannot be taken from 3 days, so we take 1 month from
7 months. The 1 month which we took equals 30 days, for
in all cases 30 days are allowed to a

yr.	mo.	da.
1 8 9 2	7	3
1 8 5 0	5	1 9
4 2	1	1 4

month. Adding 30 days to the 3 days,
we have 33 days; subtracting 19 days
from 33 days, we have 14 days remaining. Since we borrowed 1 month from
the months column, we have 7 − 1, or
6 months remaining; subtracting 5 months from 6 months,
we have 1 month remaining. 1,850 from 1,892 leaves 42
years. Therefore, he would be 42 years, 1 month, and 14
days old. Ans.

(31) If a note given Aug. 5, 1890, were paid June 3, 1892,
in order to find the length of time it was due, subtract the
earlier date from the later date.

Beginning with the lowest denomination, we find that 5
cannot be subtracted from 3, so we

yr.	mo.	da.
1 8 9 2	5	3
1 8 9 0	7	5
1	9	2 8

take a unit from the next higher denomination, which is months. The 1
month which we take equals 30 days.
Adding the 30 days to the 3 days, we
have 33 days. 5 days from 33 days
leaves 28 days. Since we took 1
month from the months column, only 4 months remain.
7 months cannot be taken from 4 months, so we take 1 year
from the years column, which equals 12 months. 12 months
+4 months = 16 months. 7 months from 16 months = 9
months. Since we took 1 year from the years column, we
have 1,892 − 1, or 1,891 remaining. 1,890 from 1,891 leaves
1 year. Hence, the note ran 1 year, 9 months, and 28
days. Ans.

(32) Write the number of the year, month, day, hour,
and minute of the earlier date under the year, month, day,
hour, and minute of the later date, and subtract.

22 minutes before 8 o'clock is the same as 38 minutes after
7 o'clock. 7 o'clock P. M. is 19 hours from the beginning of
the day, as there are 12 hours in the morning and 7 in the

afternoon.   December is 11 months from the beginning of the year.

10 o'clock A. M. is 10 hours from the beginning of the day. July is 6 months from the beginning of the year.   The minuend would be the later date, or 1,888 years, 11 months, 11 days, 19 hours, and 38 minutes.

The subtrahend would be the earlier date or 1,883 years, 6 months, 3 days, 10 hours, and 16 minutes.

Subtracting, we have

yr.	mo.	da.	hr.	min.
1 8 8 8	1 1	1 1	1 9	3 8
1 8 8 3	6	3	1 0	1 6
5	5	8	9	2 2

or, 5 yr. 5 mo. 8 da. 9 hr. and 22 min.   Ans.

16 minutes subtracted from 38 minutes leaves 22 minutes; 10 hours from 19 hours leaves 9 hours; 3 days from 11 days leaves 8 days; 6 months subtracted from 11 months leaves 5 months; 1,883 from 1,888 leaves 5 years.

(33)   In multiplication of denominate numbers, we place the multiplier under the lowest denomination of the multiplicand, as

$$1\ 7 \text{ ft.}\quad 3 \text{ in.}$$
$$5\ 1$$
$$\overline{8\ 7\ 9 \text{ ft.}\quad 9 \text{ in.}}$$

and begin at the right to multiply. $51 \times 3 = 153$ in.   As there are 12 inches in 1 foot, in 153 in. there are as many feet as 12 is contained times in 153, or 12 feet and 9 inches remaining.   Place the 9 inches under the inches, and reserve the 12 feet. 51×17 ft. $= 867$ ft. 867 ft. $+ 12$ ft. (reserved) $= 879$ ft.

879 feet can be reduced to higher denominations by dividing by 3 feet to find the number of yards, and by $5\frac{1}{2}$ yards to find the number of rods.

$$3\,)\,8\,7\,9 \text{ ft. } 9 \text{ in.}$$
$$5.5\,)\,2\,9\,3 \text{ yd.}$$
$$5\,3 \text{ rd. } 1\tfrac{1}{2} \text{ yd}$$

Then, product = 53 rd. $1\frac{1}{2}$ yd. 0 ft. 9 in., or 53 rd. 1 yd. 2 ft. 3 in. Ans.

		qt.	pt.	gi.
(34)		3	1	3
				4.7
		1 8.2	0	.1
	or,	1 8 qt.	0 pt.	1.7 gi.
or,	4 gal.	2 qt.	0 pt.	1.7 gi. Ans.

Place the multiplier under the lowest denomination of the multiplicand, and proceed to multiply. 4.7×3 gi. $= 14.1$ gi. As 4 gi. = 1 pt., there are as many pints in 14.1 gi. as 4 is contained times in 14.1 = 3.5 pt. and .1 gi. over. Place .1 under gills and carry the 3.5 pt. forward. 4.7×1 pt. = 4.7 pt.; 4.7 + 3.5 pt. = 8.2 pt. As 2 pt. = 1 qt., there are as many quarts in 8.2 pt. as 2 is contained times in 8.2 = 4.1 qt. and no pints over. Place a cipher under the pints, and carry the 4.1 qt. to the next product. 4.7×3 qt. = 14.1; 14.1 + 4.1 qt. = 18.2 qt. The answer now is 18.2 qt. 0 pt. .1 gi. Reducing the fractional part of a quart, we have 18 qt. 0 pt. 1.7 gi. (.2 qt. = $.2 \times 8$ = 1.6 gi.; 1.6 + .1 gi. = 1.7 gi.). Then we can reduce 18 qt. to gallons $(18 \div 4 = 4$ gal. and 2 qt.) = 4 gal. 2 qt. 1.7 gi. Ans.

The answer may be obtained in another and much easier way by reducing all to gills, multiplying by 4.7, and then changing back to quarts and pints. Thus,

$$
\begin{array}{r}
3 \text{ qt.} \\
\times \ \underline{2} \text{ pt.} \\
6 \text{ pt.} \\
+ \ \underline{1} \text{ pt.} \\
7 \text{ pt.} \\
\times \ \underline{4} \text{ gi.} \\
2\,8 \text{ gi.} \\
+ \ \underline{3} \text{ gi.} \\
3\,1 \text{ gi.}
\end{array}
$$

3 qt. 1 pt. 3 gi. = 31 gi.
31 gi. $\times 4.7$ = 145.7 gi.

$$
\begin{array}{r}
4\,)\ \underline{1\,4\,5.7}\ \text{gi.} \\
2\,)\ \underline{3\,6}\quad \text{pt.} + 1.7\ \text{gi.} \\
1\,8\quad \text{qt.} + \quad 0\ \text{pt.}
\end{array}
$$

Ans. = 18 qt. 1.7 gi.;
or, 4 gal. 2 qt. 1.7 gi.

(35)   (3 lb. 10 oz. 13 pwt. 12 gr.) × 1.5 = ?

$$
\begin{array}{r}
\text{3 lb. 10 oz. 13 pwt. 12 gr.} \\
\times\ 12 \\
\hline
3\,6 \text{ oz.} \\
+\,1\,0 \\
\hline
4\,6 \text{ oz.} \\
\times\quad 2\,0 \\
\hline
9\,2\,0 \text{ pwt.} \\
+\quad 1\,3 \\
\hline
9\,3\,3 \text{ pwt.} \\
\times\qquad 2\,4 \\
\hline
2\,2\,3\,9\,2 \text{ gr.} \\
+\qquad 1\,2 \\
\hline
2\,2\,4\,0\,4 \text{ gr.}
\end{array}
$$

22,404 gr. × 1.5 = 33,606 gr.

$$
\begin{array}{l}
2\,4\,)\,3\,3\,6\,0\,6 \text{ gr.} \\
\ \ 2\,0\,)\,1\,4\,0\,0 \text{ pwt.} + 6 \text{ gr.} \\
\ \ \ \ 1\,2\,)\,7\,0 \text{ oz.} + 0 \text{ pwt.} \\
\ \ \ \ \ \ \ \ 5 \text{ lb.} + 10 \text{ oz.}
\end{array}
$$

Since there are 24 gr. in 1 pwt., in 33,606 gr. there are as many pennyweights as 24 is contained times in 33,606, or 1,400 pwt. and 6 gr. remaining. This gives us the number of grains in the answer. We now reduce 1,400 pwt. to higher denominations. Since there are 20 pwt. in 1 oz., in 1,400 pwt. there are as many ounces as 20 is contained times in 1,400, or 70 oz. and 0 pwt. remaining; therefore, there are 0 pwt. in the answer. We reduce 70 oz. to higher denominations. Since there are 12 oz. in 1 lb., in 70 oz. there are as many pounds as 12 is contained times in 70, or 5 lb. and 10 oz. remaining. We cannot reduce 5 lb. to any higher denominations. Therefore, our answer is 5 lb. 10 oz. 6 gr.

Another but more complicated way of working this problem is as follows:

lb.	oz.	pwt.	gr.
3	1 0	1 3	1 2
			1.5
4.5	1 5	1 9.5	1 8
or, 4	2 1	1 9	3 0
or, 5	1 0	0	6 Ans.

To get rid of the decimal in the pounds, reduce .5 of a pound to ounces. Since 1 lb. = 12 oz., .5 of a pound equals .5 lb. × 12 = 6 oz. 6 oz. + 15 oz. = 21 oz. We now have 4 lb. 21 oz. 19.5 pwt. and 18 gr.; but we still have a decimal in the column of pwt., so we reduce .5 pwt. to grains to get rid of it. Since 1 pwt. = 24 gr., .5 pwt. = .5 pwt. × 24 = 12 gr. 12 gr. + 18 gr. = 30 gr. We now have 4 lb. 21 oz. 19 pwt. and 30 gr. Since there are 24 gr. in 1 pwt., in 30 gr. there is 1 pwt. and 6 gr. remaining. Place 6 gr. under the column of grains and add 1 pwt. to the pwt. column. Adding 1 pwt., we have 19 + 1 = 20 pwt. Since there are 20 pwt. in 1 oz., we have 1 oz. and 0 pwt. remaining. Write the 0 pwt. under the pwt. column, and reserve the 1 oz. to the oz. column. 21 oz. + 1 oz. = 22 oz. Since there are 12 oz. in 1 lb., in 22 oz. there is 1 lb. and 10 oz. remaining. Write the 10 oz. under the ounce column, and reserve the 1 lb. to add to the pounds column. 4 lb. + 1 lb. (reserved) = 5 lb. Hence, the answer equals 5 lb. 10 oz. 6 gr.

(36) If each barrel of apples contains 2 bu. 3 pk. and 6 qt., then 9 bbl. will contain 9 × (2 bu. 3 pk. 6 qt.).

We write the multiplier under the lowest denomination of the multiplicand, which is quarts in this problem.

bu.	pk.	qt.
2	3	6
		9
1 8	2 7	5 4
or, 2 6	1	6

9 times 6 qt. equals 54 qt. There are 8 qt. in 1 pk., and in 54 qt. there are as many pecks as 8 is contained times in 54, or 6 pk. and 6 qt. We write the 6 qt. under the column of quarts, and reserve the 6 pk. to add to the product of the pecks. 9 times 3 pk. equals 27 pk.; 27 pk. plus the 6 pk. (reserved) equals 33 pk. Since there are 4 pk. in 1 bu., in 33 pk. there are as many bushels as 4 is contained times in 33, or 8 bu. and 1 pk. remaining. We write the 1 pk. under the column of pecks, and reserve the 8 bu.

for the product of the bushels. 9 times 2 bu. plus the 8 bu. (reserved) equals 26 bu. Therefore, we find that 9 bbl. contain 26 bu. 1 pk. 6 qt. of apples. Ans.

(37) (7 T. 15 cwt. 10.5 lb.) × 1.7 = ? When the multiplier is a decimal, instead of multiplying the denominate numbers as in the case when the multiplier is a whole number, it is much easier to reduce the denominate numbers to the lowest denomination given; then multiply that result by the decimal, and, lastly, reduce the product to higher denominations. Although the correct answer can be obtained by working examples involving decimals in the manner as in the last example, it is much more complicated than this method.

$$7 \text{ T. } 15 \text{ cwt. } 10.5 \text{ lb.}$$
$$\times \ 20$$
$$\overline{140 \text{ cwt.}}$$
$$+ \ 15$$
$$\overline{155 \text{ cwt.}}$$
$$\times \ \ \ 100$$
$$\overline{15500 \text{ lb.}}$$
$$+ \ \ \ \ \ 10.5$$
$$\overline{15510.5 \text{ lb.}}$$

15,510.5 lb. × 1.7 = 26,367.85 lb.

There are 100 lb. in 1 cwt., and in 26,367.85 lb. there are as many cwt. as 100 is contained times in 26,367.85, which

100) 26367.85 lb.

20) 263 cwt. + 67.85 lb.

13 T. + 3 cwt.

equals 263 cwt. and 67.85 lb. remaining. Since we have the number of pounds for our answer, we reduce 263 cwt. to higher denominations. There are 20 cwt. in 1 ton, and in 263 cwt. there are as many tons as 20 is contained times in 263, or 13 T. and 3 cwt. remaining. Since we cannot reduce 13 T. any higher, our answer is 13 T. 3 cwt. 67.85 lb. Or, since .85 lb. = .85 lb. × 16 = 13.6 oz., the answer may be written 13 T. 3 cwt. 67 lb. 13.6 oz.

(38) 7) 358 A.   57 sq. rd.   6 sq. yd.   2 sq. ft.

51 A.   31 sq. rd.   0 sq. yd.   8 sq. ft. Ans.

We begin with the highest denomination, and divide each term in succession by 7.

7 is contained in 358 A. 51 times and 1 A. remaining. We write the 51 A. under the 358 A. and reduce the remaining 1 A. to square rods = 160 sq. rd.; 160 sq. rd. + the 57 sq. rd. in the dividend = 217 sq. rd. 7 is contained in 217 sq. rd. 31 times and 0 sq. rd. remaining. 7 is not contained in 6 sq. yd., so we write 0 under the sq. yd. and reduce 6 sq. yd. to square feet. 9 sq. ft. × 6 = 54 sq. ft. 54 sq. ft. + 2 sq. ft. in the dividend = 56 sq. ft. 7 is contained in 56 sq. ft. 8 times. We write 8 under the 2 sq. ft. in the dividend.

(39) 12) 282 bu. 3 pk. 1 qt. 1 pt.

          23 bu. 2 pk. 2 qt. ¼ pt. Ans.

12 is contained in 282 bu. 23 times and 6 bu. remaining. We write 23 bu. under the 282 bu. in the dividend, and reduce the remaining 6 bu. to pecks = 24 pk. + the 3 pk. in the dividend = 27 pk. 12 is contained in 27 pk. 2 times and 3 pk. remaining. We write 2 pk. under the 3 pk. in the dividend, and reduce the remaining 3 pk. to quarts. 3 pk. = 24 qt.; 24 qt. + the 1 qt. in the dividend = 25 qt. 12 is contained in 25 qt. 2 times and 1 qt. remaining. We write 2 qt. under the 1 qt. in the dividend, and reduce 1 qt. to pints = 2 pt. + the 1 pt. in the dividend = 3 pt. $3 \div 12 = \frac{3}{12}$ or ¼ pt.

(40) We must first reduce 23 miles to feet before we can divide by 30 feet. 1 mile contains 5,280 ft.; hence 23 mi. contain $5,280 \times 23 = 121,440$ ft.

121,440 ft. ÷ 30 ft. = 4,048 rails for 1 side of the track.

The number of rails for 2 sides of the track = $2 \times 4,048$, or 8,096 rails. Ans.

(41) In this case, where both dividend and divisor are compound, reduce each to the lowest denomination mentioned in either, and then divide as in simple numbers.

$$
\begin{array}{ll}
\text{1 bu. 1 pk. 7 qt.} & \text{3 5 6 bu. 3 pk. 5 qt.} \\
\times 4 & \times \quad 4 \\
\hline
\text{4 pk.} & \text{1 4 2 4 pk.} \\
+1 & +\quad 3 \\
\hline
\text{5 pk.} & \text{1 4 2 7 pk.} \\
\times \quad 8 & \times \quad \quad 8 \\
\hline
\text{4 0 qt.} & \text{1 1 4 1 6 qt.} \\
+\quad 7 & +\quad \quad 5 \\
\hline
\text{4 7 qt.} & \text{1 1 4 2 1 qt.}
\end{array}
$$

4 7) 1 1 4 2 1 (2 4 3

     9 4

     2 0 2   11,421 qt. ÷ 47 qt. = 243 boxes. Ans.

     1 8 8

      1 4 1

      1 4 1

(42) We must first reduce 16 square miles to acres.

In 1 sq. mi. there are 640 A., and in 16 sq. mi. there are 16×640 A. = 10,240 A.

6 2) 1 0 2 4 0 A.

1 6 5 A. 25 sq. rd. 24 sq. yd. 3 sq. ft. 80+ sq. in. Ans.

62 is contained in 10,240 A. 165 times and 10 A. remaining. We write 165 A. under the 10,240 A. in the dividend and reduce 10 A. to sq. rd. In 1 A. there are 160 sq. rd., and in 10 A. there are $10 \times 160 = 1,600$ sq. rd. 62 is contained in 1,600 sq. rd. 25 times and 50 sq. rd. remaining. We write 25 sq. rd. in the quotient and reduce 50 sq. rd. to sq. yd. In 1 sq. rd. there are $30\frac{1}{4}$ sq. yd., and in 50 sq. rd. there are $50 \times 30\frac{1}{4}$ sq. yd. $= 1,512\frac{1}{2}$ sq. yd. 62 is contained in $1,512\frac{1}{2}$ sq. yd. 24 times and $24\frac{1}{2}$ sq. yd. remaining. We write 24 sq. yd. in the quotient and reduce $24\frac{1}{2}$ sq. yd. to sq. ft. In 1 sq. yd. there are 9 sq. ft., and in $24\frac{1}{2}$ sq. yd. there are $24\frac{1}{2} \times 9 = 220\frac{1}{2}$ sq. ft. 62 is contained in $220\frac{1}{2}$ sq. ft. 3 times and $34\frac{1}{2}$ sq. ft. remaining. We write 3 sq. ft. in the quotient and reduce $34\frac{1}{2}$ sq. ft. to sq. in. In 1 sq. ft. there are 144 sq. in., and in $34\frac{1}{2}$ sq. ft. there are $34\frac{1}{2} \times 144 = 4,968$ sq. in.

62 is contained in 4,968 sq. in. 80 times and 8 sq. in. remaining. We write 80+ sq. in. in the quotient.

(43) To square a number, we must multiply the number by itself once, that is, use the number twice as a factor. Thus, the second power of 108 is $108 \times 108 = 11,664$. Ans.

$$
\begin{array}{r}
1\,0\,8 \\
1\,0\,8 \\
\hline
8\,6\,4 \\
1\,0\,8\,0 \\
\hline
1\,1\,6\,6\,4
\end{array}
$$

(44) $9^5 = 9 \times 9 \times 9 \times 9 \times 9 = 59,049$.   Ans

$$
\begin{array}{r}
9 \\
9 \\
\hline
8\,1 \\
9 \\
\hline
7\,2\,9 \\
9 \\
\hline
6\,5\,6\,1 \\
9 \\
\hline
5\,9\,0\,4\,9
\end{array}
$$

(45) $.0133^3 = .0133 \times .0133 \times .0133 = .000002352637$.

Ans.

$$
\begin{array}{r}
.0\,1\,3\,3 \\
.0\,1\,3\,3 \\
\hline
3\,9\,9 \\
3\,9\,9 \\
1\,3\,3 \\
\hline
.0\,0\,0\,1\,7\,6\,8\,9 \\
.0\,1\,3\,3 \\
\hline
5\,3\,0\,6\,7 \\
5\,3\,0\,6\,7 \\
1\,7\,6\,8\,9 \\
\hline
.0\,0\,0\,0\,0\,2\,3\,5\,2\,6\,3\,7
\end{array}
$$

Since there are four decimal places in the multiplicand and four in the multiplier, we must point off $4 + 4 = 8$ decimal places in the product; but as there are only five figures in the product, we prefix three ciphers to form the eight necessary decimal places in the first product.

Since there are eight decimal places in the multiplicand and four in the multiplier, we must point off $8 + 4 = 12$ decimal places in the product; but as there are only seven figures in the product, we prefix five ciphers to make the twelve necessary decimal places in the final product.

(46) See page 9 of the table.

$9.49^{2} = 9\ 0.0\ 6\ 0\ 1$ *given number* $= 9\ 0.0\ 0\ 0\ 0$

$9.48^{2} = 8\ 9.8\ 7\ 0\ 4$ $9.48^{2} = 8\ 9.8\ 7\ 0\ 4$

first difference $=\ \overline{1\ 8\ 9\ 7}$ *second difference* $=\ \overline{1\ 2\ 9\ 6}$

$$1\ 8\ 9\ 7\ )\ 1\ 2\ 9\ 6.0\ 0\ 0\ (.6\ 8\ 3\ \text{or}\ .6\ 8$$
$$\underline{1\ 1\ 3\ 8\ 2}$$
$$1\ 5\ 7\ 8\ 0$$
$$\underline{1\ 5\ 1\ 7\ 6}$$
$$6\ 0\ 4\ 0$$
$$\underline{5\ 6\ 9\ 1}$$
$$3\ 4\ 9$$

Therefore, $\sqrt{90} = 9.4868$. Ans.

(47) To find any power of a mixed number, first reduce it to an improper fraction, and then multiply the numerators together for the numerator of the answer, and multiply the denominators together for the denominator of the answer.

$$\left(3\tfrac{3}{4}\right)^{3} = \frac{15}{4} \times \frac{15}{4} \times \frac{15}{4} = \frac{15 \times 15 \times 15}{4 \times 4 \times 4} = \frac{3.375}{64} = 52\tfrac{47}{64}$$

$= 52.734375$. Ans.

$$3\tfrac{3}{4} = \frac{3 \times 4 + 3}{4} = \frac{12 + 3}{4} = \frac{15}{4}.$$

1 5	$6\ 4\ )\ 3\ 3\ 7\ 5\ (\ 5\ 2\tfrac{47}{64}$
1 5	3 2 0
7 5	1 7 5
1 5	1 2 8
2 2 5	4 7
1 5	
1 1 2 5	
2 2 5	
3 3 7 5	

$$64)47.000000(.734375$$

$$
\begin{array}{r}
448 \\
\hline
220 \\
192 \\
\hline
280 \\
256 \\
\hline
240 \\
192 \\
\hline
480 \\
448 \\
\hline
320 \\
320 \\
\hline
\end{array}
$$

Since six ciphers were annexed to the dividend, six deci-mal places must be pointed off in the quotient.

(48)   Given number = 92,416 = 92′416.
Altered number = 92.416.
See page 4 of the table.

$4.53^3 =$	9 2.9 5 9 7	*altered number* =	9 2.4 1 6 0
$4.52^3 =$	9 2.3 4 5 4	$4.52^3 =$	9 2.3 4 5 4
first difference =	6 1 4 3	*second difference* =	7 0 6

$$6143)706.000(.114 \text{ or } .11$$

$$
\begin{array}{r}
6143 \\
\hline
9170 \\
6143 \\
\hline
30270 \\
24572 \\
\hline
5698 \\
\end{array}
$$

Therefore, $\sqrt[3]{92.416} = 4.5211$, and $\sqrt[3]{92,416} = 45.211$. Ans.

(49)   Given number = 502,681 = 50′26′81.
Altered number = 50.2681.

Referring to page 7 of the table, $7.09^2 = 50.2681$; hence, $\sqrt{50.2681} = 7.09$. Since there are three periods in the integral part of the given number, there are three figures in the integral part of the root; therefore, $\sqrt{502,681} = 709$.

Ans.

(50) $\sqrt[3]{\dfrac{27}{64}} = \dfrac{\sqrt[3]{27}}{\sqrt[3]{64}} = \dfrac{3}{4}.$ **Ans.**

(51)   Since $\frac{3}{8} = .375$, $\sqrt[3]{\frac{3}{8}} = \sqrt[3]{.375}$.
Given number $= .375$.
Altered number $= 375.000$.
See page 7 of the table.

$$7.22^3 = 3\ 7\ 6.3\ 6\ 7 \qquad altered\ number = 3\ 7\ 5.0\ 0\ 0$$
$$7.21^3 = 3\ 7\ 4.8\ 0\ 5 \qquad\qquad\quad 7.21^3 = 3\ 7\ 4.8\ 0\ 5$$

first difference $=$ 1 5 6 2   *second difference* $=$ 1 9 5

$$1\ 5\ 6\ 2\ )1\ 9\ 5.0\ 0\ 0(.1\ 2\ 4 \text{ or } .1\ 2$$
$$\underline{1\ 5\ 6\ 2}$$
$$\begin{array}{r} 3\ 8\ 8\ 0 \\ 3\ 1\ 2\ 4 \end{array}$$
$$\begin{array}{r} \overline{7\ 5\ 6\ 0} \\ 6\ 2\ 4\ 8 \end{array}$$
$$\overline{1\ 3\ 1\ 2}$$

Therefore, $\sqrt[3]{375} = 7.2112$, and $\sqrt[3]{.375} = \sqrt[3]{\frac{3}{8}} = .72112$. **Ans.**

(52)   Given number $= .7854 = .78'54$.
Altered number $= 78.5400$.
See page 8 of the table.

$$8.87^2 = 7\ 8.6\ 7\ 6\ 9 \qquad altered\ number = 7\ 8.5\ 4\ 0\ 0$$
$$8.86^2 = 7\ 8.4\ 9\ 9\ 6 \qquad\qquad\quad 8.86^2 = 7\ 8.4\ 9\ 9\ 6$$

first difference $=$ 1 7 7 3   *second difference* $=$ 4 0 4

$$1\ 7\ 7\ 3\ )4\ 0\ 4.0\ 0\ 0(.2\ 2\ 7 \text{ or } .2\ 3$$
$$\underline{3\ 5\ 4\ 6}$$
$$\begin{array}{r} 4\ 9\ 4\ 0 \\ 3\ 5\ 4\ 6 \end{array}$$
$$\begin{array}{r} \overline{1\ 3\ 9\ 4\ 0} \\ 1\ 2\ 4\ 1\ 1 \end{array}$$
$$\overline{1\ 5\ 2\ 9}$$

Therefore, $\sqrt{78.54} = 8.8623$, and $\sqrt{.7854} = .88623$.   **Ans.**

(53)   The number is evidently the square root of 114.9184.
Given number = 114.9184 = 1'14'.91'84.
Altered number = 1.149184 = 1.1492.
See page 1 of the table.

$$1.08^2 = 1.1\ 6\ 6\ 4 \qquad altered\ number = 1.1\ 4\ 9\ 2$$
$$1.07^2 = 1.1\ 4\ 4\ 9 \qquad\qquad 1.07^2 = 1.1\ 4\ 4\ 9$$

first difference =   2 1 5   second difference =   4 3

2 1 5) 4 3.0 (.2
4 3 0

Therefore, $\sqrt{1.1492} = 1.072$, and $\sqrt{114.9184} = 10.72$. Ans.

(54)   Given number = 3,486,784 = 3'48'67'84.
Altered number = 3.486784 = 3.4868.
See page 1 of the table.

$$1.87^2 = 3.4\ 9\ 6\ 9 \qquad altered\ number = 3.4\ 8\ 6\ 8$$
$$1.86^2 = 3.4\ 5\ 9\ 6 \qquad\qquad 1.86^2 = 3.4\ 5\ 9\ 6$$

first difference =   3 7 3   second difference =   2 7 2

3 7 3) 2 7 2.0 0 0 (.7 2 9 or .7 3
2 6 1 1
————
1 0 9 0
7 4 6
————
3 4 4 0
3 3 5 7
————
8 3

Therefore, $\sqrt{3.4868} = 1.8673$, and $\sqrt{3,486,784} = 1,867.3$.
Ans.

(55)   Given number = .00041209 = .00'04'12'09.
Altered number = 4.1209.
See page 2 of the table.

$2.03^2 = 4.1209$.   Therefore, $\sqrt{4.1209} = 2.03$, and $\sqrt{.00041209} = .0203$.   Ans.

(56)   Given number = 2,490.31 = 2490'.3100.
Altered number = given number = 2490.31.
See page 7 of the table.

$7.07^4 = 2\,4\,9\,8.4\,9$ *given number* $= 2\,4\,9\,0.3\,1$
$7.06^4 = \underline{2\,4\,8\,4.3\,8}$ $7.06^4 = \underline{2\,4\,8\,4.3\,8}$
first difference $= \quad 1\,4\,1\,1$ *second difference* $= \quad\quad 5\,9\,3$

$$1\,4\,1\,1\,)\,5\,9\,3.0\,0\,0\,(\,.4\,2\,0 \text{ or } .4\,2$$
$$\underline{5\,6\,4\,4}$$
$$2\,8\,6\,0$$
$$\underline{2\,8\,2\,2}$$
$$3\,8\,0$$

Therefore, $\sqrt[4]{2490.31} = 7.0642$. Ans.

(57) Given number $= 6{,}039{,}065{,}434 = 60390'65434$.
Altered number $= 60390.65434 = 60390.7$.
See page 9 of the table.

$9.05^5 = 6\,0\,7\,0\,7.6$ *altered number* $= 6\,0\,3\,9\,0.7$
$9.04^5 = \underline{6\,0\,3\,7\,2.9}$ $9.04^5 = \underline{6\,0\,3\,7\,2.9}$
first difference $= \quad 3\,3\,4\,7$ *second difference* $= \quad\quad 1\,7\,8$

$$3\,3\,4\,7\,)\,1\,7\,8.0\,0\,0\,(\,.0\,5\,3 \text{ or } .0\,5$$
$$\underline{1\,6\,7\,3\,5}$$
$$1\,0\,6\,5\,0$$
$$\underline{1\,0\,0\,4\,1}$$
$$6\,0\,9$$

Therefore, $\sqrt[5]{60390.7} = 9.0405$, and $\sqrt[5]{6{,}039{,}065{,}434} =$ 90.405. Ans.

(58) Given number $= .127 = .12700$.
Altered number $= 12700$.
See page 6 of the table.

$6.62^5 = 1\,2\,7\,1\,4.2$ *altered number* $= 1\,2\,7\,0\,0.0$
$6.61^5 = \underline{1\,2\,6\,1\,8.5}$ $6.61^5 = \underline{1\,2\,6\,1\,8.5}$
first difference $= \quad 9\,5\,7$ *second difference* $= \quad\quad 8\,1\,5$

$$9\,5\,7\,)\,8\,1\,5.0\,0\,0\,(\,.8\,5\,1 \text{ or } .8\,5$$
$$\underline{7\,6\,5\,6}$$
$$4\,9\,4\,0$$
$$\underline{4\,7\,8\,5}$$
$$1\,5\,5\,0$$
$$\underline{9\,5\,7}$$
$$5\,9\,3$$

Therefore, $\sqrt[5]{12700} = 6.6185$, and $\sqrt[5]{.127} = .66185$. Ans.

(59) $11.7 : 13 :: 20 : x.$ The product of the means

       $11.7x = 13 \times 20$ is equal to the product of the

       $11.7x = 260$ extremes.

$$x = \frac{260}{11.7}$$

```
11.7 ) 2 6 0.0 0 0 ( 22.22+.   Ans.
       2 3 4
       ─────
         2 6 0
         2 3 4
         ─────
           2 6 0
           2 3 4
           ─────
             2 6 0
             2 3 4
             ─────
               2 6
```

(60)   (a) $20 + 7 : 10 + 8 :: 3 : x.$

         $27 : 18 :: 3 : x.$

         $27x = 18 \times 3$

         $27x = 54$

         $x = \frac{54}{27} = 2.$ Ans.

   (b) $(12)^2 : (100)^2 :: 4 : x.$

         $144 : 10,000 :: 4 : x.$

         $144x = 10,000 \times 4$

         $144x = 40,000$

         $x = 277.7+.$ Ans.

$$x = \frac{40,000}{144}$$

```
144 ) 4 0 0 0 0.0 ( 277.7+.   Ans.
      2 8 8
      ─────
      1 1 2 0
      1 0 0 8
      ───────
        1 1 2 0
        1 0 0 8
        ───────
          1 1 2 0
          1 0 0 8
          ───────
            1 1 2
```

(61) (a) $\frac{4}{x} = \frac{7}{21}$ is equivalent to $4 : x :: 7 : 21$. The product of the means equals the product of the extremes. Hence, $7x = 4 \times 21$

$$7x = 84$$

$$x = \tfrac{84}{7} \text{ or } 12. \quad \text{Ans.}$$

(b) In like manner,

$$\frac{x}{24} = \tfrac{8}{16} \text{ is equivalent to } x : 24 :: 8 : 16.$$

$$16x = 24 \times 8$$

$$16x = 192$$

$$x = \tfrac{192}{16} = 12. \quad \text{Ans.}$$

(c) $\tfrac{2}{10} = \dfrac{x}{100}$ is equivalent to $2 : 10 :: x : 100$.

$$10x = 2 \times 100$$

$$10x = 200$$

$$x = \tfrac{200}{10} = 20. \quad \text{Ans.}$$

(d) $\tfrac{15}{45} = \dfrac{60}{x}$ is equivalent to   (e) $\tfrac{10}{150} = \dfrac{x}{600}$ is equivalent to

$15 : 45 :: 60 : x$. $10 : 150 :: x : 600$.

$15x = 45 \times 60$ $150x = 10 \times 600$

$15x = 2,700$ $150x = 6,000$

$$x = \frac{2,700}{15} = 180.$$ $$x = \frac{6,000}{150} = 40.$$

Ans.   Ans.

(62) $x : 5 :: 27 : 12.5$.

$$
\begin{array}{r}
5 \\
1\,2\,5\,)\,1\,3\,5.0\,(\,10\tfrac{4}{5}. \quad \text{Ans.} \\
1\,2\,5 \\ \hline
1\,0\,0 \\
1\,2\,5
\end{array}
= \tfrac{4}{5}.
$$

(63) $45 : 60 :: x : 24$.

$$60x = 45 \times 24$$

$$60x = 1,080$$

$$x = \frac{1,080}{60} = 18. \quad \text{Ans.}$$

(64) $x : 35 :: 4 : 7.$
  $7x = 35 \times 4$
  $7x = 140$
  $x = \frac{140}{7} = 20.$ Ans.

(65) $9 : x :: 6 : 24.$
  $6x = 9 \times 24$
  $6x = 216$
  $x = \frac{216}{6} = 36.$ Ans.

(66) $\sqrt[3]{1,000} : \sqrt[3]{1,331} :: 27 : x.$

Referring to the table, we find that the $\sqrt[3]{1,000} = 10$ and $\sqrt[3]{1,331} = 11.$

$$10 : 11 :: 27 : x.$$
$$10x = 297$$
$$x = \frac{297}{10} = 29.7.\quad \text{Ans.}$$

(67) $64 : 81 :: 21^2 : x^2.$

Extracting the square root of each term of any proportion does not change its value, so we find that $\sqrt{64} : \sqrt{81} :: \sqrt{21^2} : \sqrt{x^2}$ is the same as

$$8 : 9 :: 21 : x.$$
$$8x = 189$$
$$x = 23.625.\quad \text{Ans.}$$

(68) $7 + 8 : 7 :: 30 : x$ is equivalent to
$$15 : 7 :: 30 : x.$$
$$15x = 7 \times 30$$
$$15x = 210$$
$$x = \frac{210}{15} = 14.\quad \text{Ans.}$$

(69) 2 ft. 5 in. = 29 in.; 2 ft. 7 in. = 31 in. Stating as a direct proportion, $29 : 31 = 2,480 : x.$ Now, it is easy to see that x will be greater than 2,480. But x should be less than 2,480, since when a man lengthens his steps, the number of steps required for the same distance is less; hence, the proportion is an inverse one, and
$$29 : 31 = x : 2,480,$$
or $31x = 71,920;$
whence, $x = 71,920 \div 31 = 2,320$ steps. Ans.

(70) This is evidently a direct proportion. 1 hr. 36 min. = 96 min.; 15 hr. = 900 min. Hence,
$$96 : 900 = 12 : x.$$
or $96x = 10,800;$
whence, $x = 10,800 \div 96 = 112.5$ mi. **Ans.**

(71) This is also a direct proportion; hence,

$$27.63 : 29.4 = .76 : x,$$

or $\qquad 27.63x = 29.4 \times .76 = 22.344;$

whence, $\qquad x = 22.344 \div 27.63 = .808+$ lb.   Ans.

(72) 2 gal. 3 qt. 1 pt. $= 23$ pt.; 5 gal. 3 qt. $= 46$ pt.

Hence, $\qquad 23 : 46 = 5 : x,$

or $\qquad\qquad 23x = 46 \times 5 = 230;$

whence, $\qquad\qquad x = 230 \div 23 = 10$ days.   Ans.

(73) Stating as a direct proportion, and squaring the distances, as directed by the statement of the example, $6^2 : 12^2 = 24 : x$. Inverting the second couplet, since this is an inverse proportion,

$$6^2 : 12^2 = x : 24.$$

Dividing both terms of the first couplet (see Art. **129**) by 6,

$$1^2 : 2^2 = x : 24; \text{ or, } 1 : 4 = x : 24;$$

whence, $\qquad 4x = 24$, or $x = 6$ degrees.   Ans.

(74) Taking the dimensions as the causes,

$$\begin{array}{c|c} \cancel{12} & 15 \\ 4 & 5 \\ 2 & 2 \\ \cancel{3} & \cancel{6} \end{array} = \cancel{12} \; \bigg| \; x,$$ whence, $2x = 75$, or $x = \$37.50$.   Ans.

(75) 2 hr. $= 120$ min.; 14 hr. 28 min. $= 868$ min.   Hence,

$$120 : 868 = 100 : x,$$

or $\qquad\qquad 120x = 86,800;$

whence, $\qquad\qquad x = 723\frac{1}{3}$ gal.   Ans.

(76) Taking the dimensions as the causes,

$$\begin{array}{c|cc} 14 & \cancel{2} & \\ \cancel{28} & \cancel{20} & \\ \cancel{2} & & = \cancel{798} \\ \cancel{12} & 17 & 399 \\ \cancel{10} & \cancel{6} & \end{array} \; \bigg| \; x,$$ whence, $14x = 17 \times 399 = 6,783,$

$\qquad\qquad$ or $x = 484\frac{1}{2}$ bbl.   Ans.

(77) 8 hr. 40 min. $= 520$ min.   Hence,

$$444 : 1,060 = 520 : x,$$

or $x = \dfrac{1,060 \times \overset{130}{\cancel{520}}}{\underset{111}{\cancel{444}}} = \dfrac{137,800}{111} = 1,241.44+$ min. $= 20$ hr. 41.44$+$ min.   Ans.

(78) 1 min. = 60 sec. Hence,

$$5\tfrac{1}{2} : 60 = 6{,}160 : x,$$

or $$x = \frac{60 \times 6{,}160}{5.5} = 67{,}200 \text{ ft. Ans.}$$

(79) Writing the statement as a direct proportion, 8 : 10 = 5 : x, it is easy to see that x will be greater than 5; but, it should be smaller, since by working longer hours, fewer men will be required to do the same work. Hence, the proportion is inverse. Inverting the second couplet,

$$8 : 10 = x : 5,$$

or $$x = \frac{\overset{4}{\cancel{8}} \times \cancel{5}}{\underset{2}{\cancel{10}}} = 4 \text{ men. Ans.}$$

(80) Taking the times as the causes,

20	25		14
	5		70
		= 540	630; whence, $3x = 2 \times 14 = 28$,
10	x	27	or $x = 9\tfrac{1}{3}$ hr. Ans.
2		3	

ELEMENTS OF ALGEBRA

(PART 1)

(1)

$$2a^6 - 4a^5 - 5a^4 + 3a^3 + 10a^2 + 7a + 2(a^3 - a^2 - 2a - 1$$
$$2a^6 - 2a^5 - 4a^4 - 2a^3 \qquad\qquad (2a^3 - 2a^2 - 3a - 2$$
$$\underline{ - 2a^5 - a^4 + 5a^3 + 10a^2} \qquad\qquad \text{Ans.}$$
$$- 2a^5 + 2a^4 + 4a^3 + 2a^2$$
$$- 3a^4 + a^3 + 8a^2 + 7a$$
$$- 3a^4 + 3a^3 + 6a^2 + 3a$$
$$- 2a^3 + 2a^2 + 4a + 2$$
$$- 2a^3 + 2a^2 + 4a + 2$$

(2) **(a)** $2 + 4a - 5a^2 - 6a^3$
$$\underline{7a^3}$$
$$14a^3 + 28a^4 - 35a^5 - 42a^6 \quad \text{Ans.} \quad \text{(Art. 62.)}$$

(b) $4x^2 - 4y^2 + 6z^2$
$$\underline{3x^2y}$$
$$12x^4y - 12x^2y^3 + 18x^2yz^2 \quad \text{Ans.}$$

(c) $3b + 5c - 2d$
$$\underline{6a}$$
$$18ab + 30ac - 12ad \quad \text{Ans.}$$

(3) The square root of the fraction *a* plus *b* plus *c* over *n*, plus the square root of *a*, plus the fraction *b* plus *c* over *n*, plus the square root of the quantity *a* plus *b*, plus the fraction *c* over *n*, plus the parenthesis *a* plus *b*, times *c*, plus *a*, plus *bc*.

(4) If none of the terms are similar, the subtraction of one expression from another may be represented only by

§ 3

connecting the subtrahend with the minuend by means of the sign —.   Thus, if it is required to subtract $5a^3b - 7a^2b^2 + 5ab^3$ from $a^4 - b^4$, the result will be represented by $a^4 - b^4 - (5a^3b - 7a^2b^2 + 5ab^3)$, which, on removing the parenthesis (Art. **49**), becomes $a^4 - b^4 - 5a^3b + 7a^2b^2 - 5ab^3$.   From this result subtract $3a^4 - 4a^3b + 6a^2b^2 + 5ab^3 - 3b^4$.

$$
\begin{aligned}
a^4 - \quad b^4 - 5a^3b + 7a^2b^2 - \quad 5ab^3 \quad &\textit{minuend.} \\
- 3a^4 + 3b^4 + 4a^3b - 6a^2b^2 - \quad 5ab^3 \quad &\textit{subtrahend, with signs changed} \\
\hline
- 2a^4 + 2b^4 - \quad a^3b + \quad a^2b^2 - 10ab^3 \quad &\textit{remainder.} \qquad \text{(Art. \textbf{47}.)}
\end{aligned}
$$

Or, $-2a^4 - a^3b + a^2b^2 - 10ab^3 + 2b^4$, arranged according to the decreasing powers of a.   Ans.

(5)   (*a*) See Art. **29.**

(*b*) While in arithmetic only positive quantities can be added or subtracted, in algebra operations can be performed on both positive and negative quantities.

(6)   (*a*) The value of a^0 is 1.   (Art. **70**.)

(*b*) $\dfrac{a^0}{a^{-1}} = 1 \div \dfrac{1}{a} = a.$ Ans.   (Art. **72**.)

Or, $\dfrac{a^0}{a^{-1}} = a^{0-(-1)} = a^1 = a$

(7)   (*a*) By Art. **71,** the reciprocal of $\frac{24}{49} = 1 \div \frac{24}{49} = 1 \times \frac{49}{24} = \frac{49}{24}$.   Ans.

(*b*) Since, by Art. **71,** a number may be found from its reciprocal by dividing 1 by the reciprocal, the number $= 1 \div 700 = .0014\frac{2}{7}$.   Ans.

(8)   (*a*)
$$
\begin{array}{ll}
3a - 2b + 3c & \qquad 3a - 2b + 3c \\
\underline{2a - 8b - \quad c} \ \text{becomes} & \underline{-2a + 8b + \quad c} \\
& \qquad a + 6b + 4c
\end{array}
$$

when the signs of the subtrahend are changed.   Now, adding each term (with its sign changed) in the subtrahend to its corresponding term in the minuend, we have $(-2a) + (+3a) = a$; $(+8b) + (-2b) = +6b$; $(+c) + (3c) = +4c$.   Hence, $a + 6b + 4c$ equals the difference.   Ans.

(b)

$$2x^3 - 3x^2y + 2xy^3 \qquad\qquad 2x^3 - 3x^2y + 2xy^3$$
$$\underline{x^3 \qquad\qquad\quad +y^3 - xy^2} \text{ becomes } \underline{-x^3 \qquad\qquad -y^3 + xy^2}$$
$$x^3 - 3x^2y + 2xy^3 - y^3 + xy^2$$

when the signs of the subtrahend are changed. Adding each term in the subtrahend (with its sign changed) to its corresponding term in the minuend, we have $x^3 - 3x^2y + 2xy^3 - y^3 + xy^2$, which, arranged according to the decreasing powers of x, equals $x^3 - 3x^2y + xy^2 + 2xy^3 - y^3$.   Ans.

(c)
$$\begin{array}{l} 14a + 4b - 6c - 3d \\ \underline{11a - 2b + 4c - 4d} \end{array}$$

On changing the sign of each term in the subtrahend, the problem becomes

$$\begin{array}{l} 14a + 4b - 6c - 3d \\ \underline{-11a + 2b - 4c + 4d} \\ 3a + 6b - 10c + d \end{array}$$

Adding each term of the subtrahend (with the sign changed) to its corresponding term in the minuend, the difference, or result, is $3a + 6b - 10c + d$.   Ans.

(9)   The numerical values of the following, when $a = 16$, $b = 10$, and $x = 5$, are:

(a) $(ab^2x + 2abx)\, 4a = (16 \times 10^2 \times 5 + 2 \times 16 \times 10 \times 5) \times 4 \times 16$. It must be remembered that when no sign is expressed between symbols or quantities, the sign of multiplication is understood.

$(16 \times 100 \times 5 + 2 \times 16 \times 10 \times 5) \times 64 = (8{,}000 + 1{,}600) \times 64 = 9{,}600 \times 64 = 614{,}400$.   Ans.

(b)
$$2\sqrt{4a} - \frac{2bx}{a - b} + \frac{b - x}{x}$$

$$= 2\sqrt{64} - \frac{2 \times 10 \times 5}{16 - 10} + \frac{10 - 5}{5}$$

$$= 16 - \frac{100}{6} + 1 = \frac{96 - 100 + 6}{6} = \frac{2}{6} = \frac{1}{3} \quad \text{Ans.}$$

40—31

(c) $(b - \sqrt{a})\,(x^3 - b^2)\,(a^2 - b^2) = (10 - \sqrt{16}) \times (5^3 - 10^2)$
$\times\,(16^2 - 10^2) = (10 - 4)\,(125 - 100)\,(256 - 100) = 6 \times 25$
$\times\,156 = 23{,}400.$ Ans.

(10)   (a)

$\begin{aligned}&4xyz\\&-3xyz\\&-5xyz\\&6xyz\\&-9xyz\\&3xyz\\\hline&-4xyz\quad\text{Ans.}\end{aligned}$

The sum of the coefficients of the positive terms is found to be $+13$, since $(+3) + (+6) + (+4) = (+13)$.

When no sign is given before a quantity, the $+$ sign must always be understood. The sum of the coefficients of the negative terms is found to be -17, since $(-9) + (-5) + (-3) = (-17)$. Subtracting the *lesser* sum from the *greater* and prefixing the sign of the greater sum $(-)$ (Art. **41,** rule II), $(+13) + (-17) = -4$. Since the terms are all alike, annex the common symbols xyz to -4, thereby obtaining $-4xyz$ for the result, or sum.

(b)

$\begin{aligned}&3a^2 + 2ab + 4b^2\\&5a^2 - 8ab + b^2\\&-a^2 + 5ab - b^2\\&18a^2 - 20ab - 19b^2\\&14a^2 - 3ab + 20b^2\\\hline&39a^2 - 24ab + 5b^2\quad\text{Ans.}\end{aligned}$

When adding polynomials, always place like terms under each other. (Art. **42.**)

The coefficient of a^2 in the result will be 39, since $(+14) + (+18) + (-1) + (+5) + (+3) = 39$. When the coefficient of a term is not written, 1 is always understood to be its coefficient. (Art. **10.**) The coefficient of ab will be -24, since $(-3) + (-20) + (+5) + (-8) + (+2) = -24$. The coefficient of b^2 will be $(+20) + (-19) + (-1) + (+1) + (+4) = +5$. Hence, the result, or sum, is $39a^2 - 24ab + 5b^2$.

(c)

$\begin{aligned}&4mn + 3ab - 4c\\&+2mn - 4ab \qquad + 3x + 3m^2 - 4p\\\hline&6mn - ab - 4c + 3x + 3m^2 - 4p\quad\text{Ans.}\end{aligned}$

(11)   (a) See Art. **13.**

(b) In multiplication, coefficients are multiplied, and exponents are added. In division, the coefficients of the dividend are divided by those of the divisor, and the exponents of the divisor are subtracted from those of the dividend. See rules of multiplication and division.

(c) See Art. **57.**

(12) (a) a square x square, plus 2 a cube b fifth, minus the parenthesis a plus b.

(b) The cube root of x, plus y times the two-thirds power of the parenthesis a minus n square.

(c) The parenthesis m plus n, times the square of the parenthesis m minus n, times the parenthesis m minus the fraction n over two.

(13) (a) $16a^2b^3$; $a^4 + 4ab$; $4a^2 - 16a^3b + 5a^6 + 7ax$.

(b) Since the terms are not alike, we can only indicate the sum, connecting the terms by their proper signs. (Art. **40.**)

(c) Multiplication: $4ac^2d$ means $4 \times a \times c^2 \times d$. (Art. **9.**)

(14) (a) Removing the vinculum,

$2a - \{3b + [4c - 4a - (2a + 2b)] + [3a - b - c]\}$ (Art. **49.**)

Removing the parenthesis,

$$2a - \{3b + [4c - 4a - 2a - 2b] + [3a - b - c]\}$$

Removing the brackets,

$$2a - \{3b + 4c - 4a - 2a - 2b + 3a - b - c\}$$

Removing the brace,

$$2a - 3b - 4c + 4a + 2a + 2b - 3a + b + c$$

Combining like terms, the result is $5a - 3c$. Ans.

(b) Removing the parenthesis,

$$7a - \{3a - [2a - 5a + 4a]\}$$

Removing the brackets,

$$7a - \{3a - 2a + 5a - 4a\}$$

Removing the brace,

$$7a - 3a + 2a - 5a + 4a$$

Combining terms, the result is $5a$. Ans.

114—31

(c)   Removing the parentheses,

$$a - \{2b + [3c - 3a - a - b] + [2a - b - c]\}$$

Removing the brackets,

$$a - \{2b + 3c - 3a - a - b + 2a - b - c\}$$

Removing the brace,

$$a - 2b - 3c + 3a + a + b - 2a + b + c$$

Combining like terms, the result is $3a - 2c$.   Ans.

(15)   (a) $6a^4b^4 + a^3b^2 - 7a^2b^3 + 2abc + 3$.

(b) $3 + 2abc + a^3b^2 - 7a^2b^3 + 6a^4b^4$.

(c) $1 + ax + a^2 + 2a^3$.   Written like this, the a in the second term is understood as having 1 for an exponent; hence, if the first term be represented by a^0, its value will be 1, since $a^0 = 1$.   Therefore, 1 should be written as the first term when arranged according to the increasing powers of a.

(16)   (a) $2x^3 + 2x^2 + 2x - 2$

$$\underline{x - 1}$$
$$2x^4 + 2x^3 + 2x^2 - 2x$$
$$\underline{\quad - 2x^3 - 2x^2 - 2x + 2}$$
$$2x^4 \qquad\qquad\qquad - 4x + 2 \quad \text{Ans.}$$

(b) $\quad x^2 - 4ax + c$

$$\underline{2x + a}$$
$$2x^3 - 8ax^2 + 2cx$$
$$\underline{\qquad ax^2 \qquad\quad - 4a^2x + ac}$$
$$2x^3 - 7ax^2 + 2cx - 4a^2x + ac \quad \text{Ans.}$$

(c) $\quad - a^3 + 3a^2b - 2b^3$

$$\underline{5a^2 + 9ab}$$
$$- 5a^5 + 15a^4b - 10a^2b^3$$
$$\underline{\qquad - 9a^4b \qquad\qquad + 27a^3b^2 - 18ab^4}$$
$$- 5a^5 + 6a^4b - 10a^2b^3 + 27a^3b^2 - 18ab^4$$

Arranging the terms according to the decreasing powers of a.

$$- 5a^5 + 6a^4b + 27a^3b^2 - 10a^2b^3 - 18ab^4 \quad \text{Ans.}$$

(17) (*a*) Arrange the dividend according to the decreasing powers of x and divide.   Thus,

$$9x^3 + 3x^2 + x - 1 (3x - 1$$
$$\underline{9x^3 - 3x^2} \qquad\qquad (3x^2 + 2x + 1 \quad \text{Ans.}$$
$$6x^2 + \ x$$
$$\underline{6x^2 - 2x}$$
$$3x - 1$$
$$3x - 1$$

(*b*)

$$a^3 - 2ab^2 + b^3 (a - b$$
$$\underline{a^3 - a^2 b} \qquad\quad (a^2 + ab - b^2 \ \text{Ans.}$$
$$a^2 b - 2ab^2$$
$$\underline{a^2 b - \ ab^2}$$
$$-\ ab^2 + b^3$$
$$-\ ab^2 + b^3$$

(*c*) Arranging the terms of the dividend according to the decreasing powers of x,

$$7x^3 - 24x^2 + 58x - 21 (7x - 3$$
$$\underline{7x^3 - \ 3x^2} \qquad\qquad (x^2 - 3x + 7 \quad \text{Ans.}$$
$$-21x^2 + 58x$$
$$\underline{-21x^2 + \ 9x}$$
$$49x - 21$$
$$49x - 21$$

(18) See Arts. **1** and **2.**

ELEMENTS OF ALGEBRA

(PART 2)

(1) See Art. **36.**

(2) (*a*) Writing the work as follows and canceling common factors in both numerator and denominator (Arts. **46** and **47**),

$$\frac{9m^2n^2}{8p^3q^3} \times \frac{5p^2q}{2xy} \times \frac{24x^2y^2}{90mn}$$

$$= \frac{9 \times 5 \times 24 \times m^2 \times n^2 \times p^2 \times q \times x^2 \times y^2}{8 \times 2 \times 90 \times m \times n \times p^3 \times q^3 \times x \times y} = \frac{3mnxy}{4pq^2} \quad \text{Ans.}$$

(*b*) This problem may be written as follows, according to Art. **35,**

$$\frac{3ax + 4}{1} \times \frac{a^2}{a(3ax + 4)(3ax + 4)}$$

Canceling a and $(3ax + 4)$, the result is $\dfrac{a}{3ax + 4}$. **Ans.**

(3) $\dfrac{c(a + b) + cd}{(a + b)c} = \dfrac{ac + bc + cd}{ac + bc}$. Canceling c, which is common to each term, $\dfrac{a + b + d}{a + b} = 1 + \dfrac{d}{a + b}$. **Ans.**

(4) $\dfrac{3 + 2x}{2 - x} - \dfrac{2 - 3x}{2 + x} + \dfrac{16x - x^2}{x^2 - 4}$. If the denominator of the third fraction were written $4 - x^2$, instead of $x^2 - 4$, the common denominator would then be $4 - x^2$.

By Art. **36,** $\dfrac{16x - x^2}{x^2 - 4}$ becomes $-\dfrac{16x - x^2}{-x^2 + 4} = -\dfrac{16x - x^2}{4 - x^2}$.

§ 4

Hence, $\dfrac{3+2x}{2-x} - \dfrac{2-3x}{2+x} - \dfrac{16x-x^2}{4-x^2}$, when reduced to a common denominator, becomes

$$\frac{(3+2x)(2+x) - (2-3x)(2-x) - (16x - x^2)}{4 - x^2}$$

$$= \frac{(6+7x+2x^2) - (4-8x+3x^2) - (16x - x^2)}{4 - x^2}$$

Removing the parentheses,

$$= \frac{6+7x+2x^2 - 4 + 8x - 3x^2 - 16x + x^2}{4 - x^2}$$

Combining like terms in the numerator,

$$= \frac{2-x}{4-x^2}$$

Factoring the denominator (Art. **26**),

$$= \frac{2-x}{(2+x)(2-x)}$$

Canceling the common factor $(2-x)$,

$$= \frac{1}{2+x}, \text{ or } \frac{1}{x+2} \quad \text{Ans.}$$

(5) $\dfrac{a^2+c^2+ac}{a^2+b^2-c^2-2ab} \times \dfrac{a^2+c^2-b^2-2ac}{a^3c+a^2c^2+ac^3}$

Arranging the terms,

$$= \frac{a^2+ac+c^2}{a^2-2ab+b^2-c^2} \times \frac{a^2-2ac+c^2-b^2}{a^3c+a^2c^2+ac^3}$$

which by the use of parentheses, becomes

$$\frac{a^2+ac+c^2}{(a^2-2ab+b^2)-c^2} \times \frac{(a^2-2ac+c^2)-b^2}{a^3c+a^2c^2+ac^3}$$

By Art. **21**, $a^2-2ab+b^2$ and $a^2-2ac+c^2$ are perfect squares, and may be written $(a-b)^2$ and $(a-c)^2$.

Factoring $a^3c+a^2c^2+ac^3$ by Case I, Art. **15**,

$$\frac{a^2+ac+c^2}{(a-b)^2-c^2} \times \frac{(a-c)^2-b^2}{ac(a^2+ac+c^2)}$$

$$= \frac{a^2 + ac + c^2}{(a-b-c)(a-b+c)} \times \frac{(a-c-b)(a-c+b)}{ac(a^2+ac+c^2)}$$

(Art. **26.**)

Canceling common factors and multiplying,

$$= \frac{a-c+b}{(a-b+c)ac}, \text{ or } \frac{a+b-c}{ac(a-b+c)} \quad \text{Ans.}$$

(6) $-\dfrac{c-(a-b)}{c+(a+b)} = \dfrac{(a-b)-c}{c+(a+b)}.$ Ans. (Art. **36.**)

(7) (a) $45x^7y^{10} - 90x^5y^7 - 360x^4y^8$
$$= 45x^4y^7(x^3y^3 - 2x - 8y). \quad \text{Ans.} \quad \text{(Art. 15.)}$$

(b) $a^2b^2 + 2abcd + c^2d^2 = (ab+cd)^2.$ Ans. (Art. **21.**)

(c) $(a+b)^2 - (c-d)^2 = (a+b+c-d)(a+b-c+d).$
Ans. (Art. **26.**)

(8) (a) $\dfrac{x}{x-y} + \dfrac{x-y}{y-x}.$ If the denominator of the second fraction were written $x-y$, instead of $y-x$, then $x-y$ would be the common denominator.

By Art. **36,** the signs of the denominator and the sign before the fraction $\dfrac{x-y}{y-x}$ may be changed, giving $-\dfrac{x-y}{x-y}$; hence,

$$\frac{x}{x-y} - \frac{x-y}{x-y} = \frac{x-x+y}{x-y} = \frac{y}{x-y} \quad \text{Ans.}$$

(b) $\dfrac{x^2}{x^2-1} + \dfrac{x}{x+1} - \dfrac{x}{1-x}.$ If the denominator of the third fraction be written $x-1$ instead of $1-x$, x^2-1 will then be the common denominator.

By Art. **36,** the signs of the denominator and the sign before the fraction may be changed, thereby giving $\dfrac{x}{x-1}$; hence,

$$\frac{x^2}{x^2-1} + \frac{x}{x+1} + \frac{x}{x-1} = \frac{x^2 + x(x-1) + x(x+1)}{x^2-1}$$

$$= \frac{x^2 + x^2 - x + x^2 + x}{x^2-1} = \frac{3x^2}{x^2-1} \quad \text{Ans.}$$

(c) $\dfrac{3a - 4b}{7} - \dfrac{2a - b + c}{3} + \dfrac{13a - 4c}{12}$ when reduced to a

common denominator, becomes

$$\frac{12(3a - 4b) - 28(2a - b + c) + 7\,(13a - 4c)}{84}$$

Expanding the terms and removing the parentheses, the result is

$$\frac{36a - 48b - 56a + 28b - 28c + 91a - 28c}{84}$$

Combining like terms in the numerator,

$$= \frac{71a - 20b - 56c}{84} \quad \text{Ans.}$$

(9) (a) Factoring each expression (Art. **21**),
$$9x^4 + 12x^2y^2 + 4y^4 = (3x^2 + 2y^2)\,(3x^2 + 2y^2) = (3x^2 + 2y^2)^2.$$
$$\text{Ans.}$$

(b) $$49a^4 - 154a^2b^2 + 121b^4$$
$$= (7a^2 - 11b^2)\,(7a^2 - 11b^2) = (7a^2 - 11b^2)^2 \quad \text{Ans.}$$

(c) $64x^2y^2 + 64xy + 16 = 16(2xy + 1)^2.$ Ans.

(10) (a)
$$1 + 2x - \frac{4x - 4}{5x} = \frac{5x + 10x^2 - 4x + 4}{5x} = \frac{10x^2 + x + 4}{5x}.$$
$$\text{Ans.} \quad \text{(Art. \textbf{54}.)}$$

(b) $\dfrac{3x^2 + 2x + 1}{x + 4} = 3x - 10 + \dfrac{41}{x + 4}.$ Ans. (Art. **53**.)

$$x + 4)\,3x^2 +\ \ 2x + 1\,(3x - 10 + \frac{41}{x + 4}$$
$$\underline{3x^2 + 12x}$$
$$-\,10x +\ \ 1$$
$$\underline{-\,10x - 40}$$
$$41$$

(11) (a) $x^3 + 8 = (x + 2)\,(x^2 - 2x + 4).$ Ans.

(b) $x^3 - 27y^3 = (x - 3y)\,(x^2 + 3xy + 9y^2).$ Ans.

(c) $xm - nm + xy - ny = m\,(x - n) + y\,(x - n),$
$$\text{or } (x - n)\,(m + y). \quad \text{Ans.}$$
$$\text{(Arts. \textbf{29} and \textbf{30}.)}$$

(12)   (*a*) Factoring according to Art. **15**, $x^8y^2 - 64x^2y^2$ $= x^2y^2(x^6 - 64)$. Factoring $(x^6 - 64)$, according to Art. **26**,

$$x^6 - 64 = (x^3 + 8)(x^3 - 8)$$

Art. **29**, rule. $x^3 + 8 = (x + 2)(x^2 - 2x + 4)$

Art. **29**, rule. $x^3 - 8 = (x - 2)(x^2 + 2x + 4)$

Therefore, $x^8y^2 - 64x^2y^2 = x^2y^2 (x + 2)(x^2 - 2x + 4)$ $(x - 2)(x^2 + 2x + 4)$, or $x^2y^2 (x + 2)(x - 2)(x^2 + 2x + 4)$ $(x^2 - 2x + 4)$.   Ans.

(*b*) $a^2 - b^2 - c^2 + 1 - 2a + 2bc$.   Arrange as follows:

$$(a^2 - 2a + 1) - (b^2 - 2bc + c^2) = (a - 1)^2 - (b - c)^2.$$
$$\text{(Art. \textbf{21}.)}$$

By Art. **26**,

$$= [a - 1 + b - c][a - 1 - (b - c)]$$
$$= (a - 1 + b - c)(a - 1 - b + c) \quad \text{Ans.}$$

(*c*) $1 - 16a^2 + 8ac - c^2$.   Placing the last three terms in parentheses, $1 - (16a^2 - 8ac + c^2)$.

$16a^2 - 8ac + c^2 = (4a - c)^2$.   (Art. **21**.)

$1 - (16a^2 - 8ac + c^2) = 1 - (4a - c)^2$.

$1 - (4a - c)^2 = [1 + (4a - c)][1 - (4a - c)]$.   (Art. **26**.)

Removing parentheses, and writing parentheses in place of the brackets,

$$1 - (4a - c)^2 = (1 + 4a - c)(1 - 4a + c) \quad \text{Ans.}$$

(13) $(2a^2bc^3)^4 = 16a^8b^4c^{12}$ Ans.

$(- 3a^2b^2c)^5 = - 243a^{10}b^{10}c^5$ Ans.

$(- 7m^3nx^2y^4)^2 = 49m^6n^2x^4y^8$ Ans.

(14) $(c^{-\frac{2}{5}})^{-\frac{1}{3}} = c^{\frac{2}{15}}$ Ans.   (Art. **63**.)

$$(m\sqrt{n^3})^{-\frac{1}{2}} = m^{-\frac{1}{2}}(n^{\frac{3}{2}})^{-\frac{1}{2}} = m^{-\frac{1}{2}}n^{-\frac{3}{4}} = \frac{1}{m^{\frac{1}{2}}n^{\frac{3}{4}}} \quad \text{Ans.}$$

$$(cd^{-2})^{\frac{1}{a}} = c^{\frac{1}{a}}d^{-\frac{2}{a}}, \text{ or } \sqrt[a]{cd^{-2}}, \text{ or } \sqrt[a]{\frac{c}{d^2}} \quad \text{Ans.}$$

$$\text{(Arts. \textbf{60} and \textbf{62}.)}$$

(15)   (a)   According to Art. **62,** $x^{\frac{3}{4}}$ expressed radically is $\sqrt[4]{x^3}$;

$$3x^{\frac{1}{2}}y^{-\frac{3}{2}} \text{ expressed radically is } 3\sqrt{xy^{-3}}$$

$$3x^{\frac{1}{2}}y^{-\frac{5}{6}}z^{\frac{1}{3}} = 3\sqrt[6]{xy^{-5}z^2}, \text{ since } z^{\frac{1}{3}} = z^{\frac{2}{6}} \quad \text{Ans.}$$

(b) $a^{-1}b^{\frac{1}{2}} + \dfrac{c^{-2}}{a+b} + (m-n)^{-1} - \dfrac{a^2b^{-2}c}{c^{-3}}$

$$= \frac{b^{\frac{1}{2}}}{a} + \frac{1}{c^2(a+b)} + \frac{1}{m-n} - \frac{a^2c^4}{b^2} \quad \text{Ans.}$$

(c) $\sqrt[7]{x^6} = x^{\frac{6}{7}}$.   Ans. $\sqrt[3]{x^{-4}} = x^{-\frac{4}{3}}$ Ans.

$$(\sqrt[4]{b^5x^2})^3 = (b^{\frac{5}{4}}x^{\frac{1}{2}})^3 = b^{\frac{15}{4}}x^{\frac{3}{2}} \quad \text{Ans.}$$

ELEMENTS OF ALGEBRA

(PART 3)

———

(1)   Let x = number of miles he traveled per hour.

Then, $\dfrac{48}{x}$ = time it took him.

$\dfrac{48}{x+4}$ = time it would take him if he traveled 4 miles more per hour.

In the latter case the time would have been 6 hours *less;* whence, the equation

$$\frac{48}{x+4} = \frac{48}{x} - 6$$

Clearing of fractions,

$$48x = 48x + 192 - 6x^2 - 24x$$

Combining like terms and transposing,

$$6x^2 + 24x = 192$$

Dividing by 6, $x^2 + 4x = 32$

Solving by inspection,

$$x^2 + 4x - 32 = 0$$
$$(x+8)(x-4) = 0$$
$$x = 4$$

or the number of miles he traveled per hour.   Ans.

§ 5

(2)   (*a*) $\sqrt{3x - 2} = 2(x - 4)$

Squaring, $3x - 2 = 4(x - 4)^2$

or $3x - 2 = 4x^2 - 32x + 64$

Transposing, $-4x^2 + 32x + 3x = 64 + 2$

Combining terms, $-4x^2 + 35x = 66$

Dividing by -4, $x^2 - \dfrac{35x}{4} = -\dfrac{66}{4}$

From the formula, Art. **32,**

$$
\begin{aligned}
x &= \mp \tfrac{1}{2}(p \pm \sqrt{p^2 \pm 4q}) \\
&= \tfrac{1}{2}\left(\tfrac{35}{4} \pm \sqrt{\left(\tfrac{35}{4}\right)^2 - 4 \times \tfrac{66}{4}}\right) \\
&= \tfrac{1}{2}\left(\tfrac{35}{4} \pm \sqrt{\tfrac{169}{16}}\right) \\
&= \tfrac{1}{2}\left(\tfrac{35}{4} \pm \tfrac{13}{4}\right)
\end{aligned}
$$

whence, $x = 6$ or $2\tfrac{3}{4}$ Ans.

By inspection, $x^2 - \dfrac{35x}{4} + \dfrac{66}{4} = 0$

$$(x - \tfrac{11}{4})(x - 6) = 0$$

whence, $x = 6$ or $2\tfrac{3}{4}$ Ans.

(*b*) $\sqrt{x - 4ab} = \dfrac{(a + b)(a - b)}{\sqrt{x}}$

Expanding and clearing of fractions,

$$\sqrt{x^2 - 4abx} = a^2 - b^2$$

Squaring both members,

$$x^2 - 4abx = a^4 - 2a^2b^2 + b^4$$

From the formula, Art. **32,**

$$
\begin{aligned}
x &= \tfrac{1}{2}[4ab \pm \sqrt{(4ab)^2 + 4(a^4 - 2a^2b^2 + b^4)}] \\
&= \tfrac{1}{2}[4ab \pm \sqrt{4a^4 + 8a^2b^2 + 4b^4}] \\
&= \tfrac{1}{2}[4ab \pm \sqrt{4(a^2 + b^2)^2}] \\
&= \tfrac{1}{2}[4ab \pm (2a^2 + 2b^2)] \\
&= 2ab \pm (a^2 + b^2) \\
&= (a + b)^2, \text{ or } -(a - b)^2 \quad \text{Ans.}
\end{aligned}
$$

(3)   (*a*) $\sqrt{3x - 5} = \dfrac{\sqrt{7x^2 + 36x}}{x}$

Clearing of fractions,

$$x\sqrt{3x - 5} = \sqrt{7x^2 + 36x}$$

Removing radicals by squaring,

$$x^2(3x - 5) = 7x^2 + 36x$$
$$3x^3 - 5x^2 = 7x^2 + 36x$$

Dividing by x, $3x^2 - 5x = 7x + 36$

Transposing and uniting,

$$3x^2 - 12x = 36$$

Dividing by 3, $x^2 - 4x = 12$

By inspection, $x^2 - 4x - 12 = 0$
$$(x - 6)(x + 2) = 0$$

Hence, $x = 6$, or -2 Ans.

(*b*) $(x - 2)(x - 4) - 2(x - 1)(x - 3) = 0$, becomes
$x^2 - 6x + 8 - 2x^2 + 8x - 6 = 0$, when expanded.

Transposing and uniting terms,

$$-x^2 + 2x = -2$$

Changing signs, $x^2 - 2x = 2$

From the formula,

$$x = \tfrac{1}{2}(2 \pm \sqrt{(2)^2 + 4 \times 2})$$
$$= \tfrac{1}{2}(2 \pm \sqrt{12})$$
$$= \tfrac{1}{2}(2 \pm \sqrt{4 \times 3})$$
$$= \tfrac{1}{2}(2 \pm 2\sqrt{3})$$
$$= 1 \pm \sqrt{3} \quad \text{Ans.}$$

If it is desired to reduce the root to a single term extract the square root of 3 to six significant figures so that the fifth figure may be correct, obtaining 1.732051 + or 1.7321 to five figures. Then, $x = 1 \pm 1.7321 = 2.7321$ or $-.7321$.

If it is desired to prove that the result is correct by multiplying the factors, use $x - (1 + \sqrt{3})$ and $x - (1 - \sqrt{3})$ for the factors, the product being $x^2 - (1 + \sqrt{3})x - (1 - \sqrt{3})x + (1 - 3) = x^2 - 2x - 2$. If $x - 2.7321$ and $x + .7321$ are multiplied together, the product is $x^2 - 2x - 2.00017041$, a result giving the absolute term a value slightly in excess.

(4)
$$5x - 2y = 51 \qquad (1)$$
$$19x - 3y = 180 \qquad (2)$$

First find the value of x by transposing $- 2y$ to the second member of equation (1), whence $5x = 51 + 2y$,

and
$$x = \frac{51 + 2y}{5} \qquad (3)$$

This gives the value of x in terms of y. Substituting the value of x for the x in (2), (Art. **44**),

$$\frac{19(51 + 2y)}{5} - 3y = 180$$

Expanding,
$$\frac{969 + 38y}{5} - 3y = 180$$

Clearing of fractions,
$$969 + 38y - 15y = 900$$

Transposing and uniting,
$$23y = - 69$$
$$y = - 3 \quad \text{Ans.}$$

Substituting this value in equation (3),

$$x = \frac{51 - 6}{5} = 9 \quad \text{Ans.}$$

(5) (*a*)
$$2x^2 - 27x = 14$$
$$x^2 - \frac{27x}{2} = 7$$

From the formula,
$$x = \tfrac{1}{2}\left(\tfrac{27}{2} \pm \sqrt{(\tfrac{27}{2})^2 + 4 \times 7}\right)$$
$$= \tfrac{1}{2}\left(\tfrac{27}{2} \pm \sqrt{\tfrac{841}{4}}\right)$$
$$= \tfrac{1}{2}\left(\tfrac{27}{2} \pm \tfrac{29}{2}\right)$$
$$= 14 \text{ or } - \tfrac{1}{2} \quad \text{Ans.}$$

By inspection, $\quad x^2 - \frac{27}{2}x - 7 = 0$

$$(x - 14)(x + \tfrac{1}{2}) = 0$$

Hence, $\qquad x = 14, \text{ or } -\tfrac{1}{2}$ Ans.

(b) $$\dot{x}^2 - \frac{2x}{3} + \frac{1}{12} = 0$$

$$x^2 - \tfrac{2}{3}x = -\tfrac{1}{12}$$

From the formula,

$$x = \tfrac{1}{2}\left(\tfrac{2}{3} \pm \sqrt{(\tfrac{2}{3})^2 - 4 \times \tfrac{1}{12}}\right)$$
$$= \tfrac{1}{2}(\tfrac{2}{3} \pm \sqrt{\tfrac{1}{9}})$$
$$= \tfrac{1}{2}(\tfrac{2}{3} \pm \tfrac{1}{3})$$
$$= \tfrac{1}{2} \text{ or } \tfrac{1}{6} \quad \text{Ans.}$$

By inspection, $\quad (x - \tfrac{1}{2})(x - \tfrac{1}{6}) = 0$

Therefore, $\qquad x = \tfrac{1}{2} \text{ or } \tfrac{1}{6}$ Ans.

(c) $$x^2 + ax = bx + ab$$

Transposing and factoring,

$$x^2 + (a - b)x = ab$$

By inspection, $\quad x^2 + (a - b)x - ab = 0$

$$(x + a)(x - b) = 0$$

$$x = b, \text{ or } -a \quad \text{Ans.}$$

(6) $\qquad$ Let x = rate of current
$$y = \text{rate of rowing}$$

Down stream, the rowers are aided by the current, so $x + y = 12$.

Since it takes them twice as long to row a given distance up stream as it does down stream, they will go only $\frac{1}{2}$ as far in 1 hour, or $\frac{1}{2}$ of 12 = 6 miles per hour up stream.

$$
\begin{aligned}
x + y &= 12 \qquad (1)\\
-x + y &= 6 \qquad\ (2)
\end{aligned}
$$

Subtracting, $\qquad 2x \quad = \ 6$, and $x = 3$ miles per hour.
$$\text{Ans.}$$

(7) $11x + 3y = 100$ (1)

                  $4x - 7y = 4$ (2)

Since the signs of the terms containing x in each equation are alike, x may be eliminated by subtraction. If the first equation be multiplied by 4, and the second by 11, the coefficients in each case will become equal. Hence,

Multiplying (1) by 4, $44x + 12y = 400$ (3)

Multiplying (2) by 11, $44x - 77y = 44$ (4)

Subtracting (4) from (3), $89y = 356$

                              $y = 4$ Ans.

Substituting this value for y in (2),

$$4x - 28 = 4$$
$$4x = 32$$
$$x = 8 \quad \text{Ans.}$$

(8) $x + y = 13$ (1)

                      $xy = 36$ (2)

Squaring (1),

$$x^2 + 2xy + y^2 = 169 \quad (3)$$

Multiplying (2) by 4, $4xy = 144$ (4)

Subtracting (4) from (3),

$$x^2 - 2xy + y^2 = 25 \quad (5)$$
$$(x - y)^2 = 25 \quad (6)$$
$$x - y = \pm 5 \quad (7)$$

Adding (7) and (1), $2x = 18$ or 8

                 $x = 9$ or 4   Ans.

Substituting the value of x in (1),

                 $9 + y = 13$

or $4 + y = 13$

whence, $y = 4$ ⎫

or $y = 9$ ⎬ Ans.

(9) (*a*) Transposing,

$$5x^2 - 2x^2 = 24 + 9$$

Uniting terms, $3x^2 = 33$

$$x^2 = 11$$

Extracting the square root of both members,

$$x = \pm \sqrt{11} \quad \text{Ans.}$$

(*b*) $$\frac{3}{4x^2} - \frac{1}{6x^2} = \frac{7}{3}$$

Clearing of fractions, $9 - 2 = 28x^2$

Transposing terms, $28x^2 = 7$

$$x^2 = \tfrac{1}{4}$$

Extracting the square root of both members,

$$x = \pm \tfrac{1}{2} \quad \text{Ans.}$$

(*c*) $$\frac{x^2}{5} - \frac{x^2 - 10}{15} = 7 - \frac{50 + x^2}{25}.$$

Clearing of fractions by multiplying each term of both members by 75, the least common denominator, and expanding,

$$15x^2 - 5x^2 + 50 = 525 - 150 - 3x^2$$

Transposing and uniting terms,

$$13x^2 = 325$$

Dividing by 13, $$x^2 = \frac{325}{13} = 25$$

or $$x = \pm 5 \quad \text{Ans.}$$

(10) $4x + 3y = 48$ (1)

$-3x + 5y = 22$ (2)

From (1), $$y = \frac{48 - 4x}{3}$$ (3)

From (2), $$y = \frac{22 + 3x}{5}$$ (4)

Placing (3) and (4) equal to each other,

$$\frac{48 - 4x}{3} = \frac{22 + 3x}{5}$$

Clearing of fractions,

$$240 - 20x = 66 + 9x$$

Transposing and uniting terms,

$$-29x = -174$$

or

$$x = 6 \quad \text{Ans.}$$

Substituting this value in (4),

$$y = \frac{22 + 18}{5} = 8 \quad \text{Ans.}$$

(11) $\left. \begin{array}{l} 2x - \dfrac{y-3}{5} - 4 = 0 \\[2mm] 3y + \dfrac{x-2}{3} - 9 = 0 \end{array} \right\}$ cleared of fractions, becomes

$$10x - y + 3 - 20 = 0 \qquad (1)$$
$$9y + x - 2 - 27 = 0 \qquad (2)$$

Transposing and uniting,

$$10x - y = 17 \qquad (3)$$
$$x + 9y = 29 \qquad (4)$$

Multiplying (4) by 10 and subtracting (3) from the result

$$10x + 90y = 290$$
$$\underline{10x - y = 17}$$
$$91y = 273$$
$$y = 3 \quad \text{Ans.}$$

Substituting value of y in (4),

$$x + 27 = 29$$
$$x = 2 \quad \text{Ans.}$$

(12)   Let x = value of first horse;
          y = value of second horse.

If the saddle be put on the first horse, its value will be $x + 10$. This value is double that of the second horse, or $2y$, whence the equation, $x + 10 = 2y$.

If the saddle be put on the second horse, its value is $y + 10$. This value is \$13 less than the first, or $x - 13$, whence the equation, $y + 10 = x - 13$.

$$x + 10 = 2y \qquad (1)$$
$$y + 10 = x - 13 \qquad (2)$$

Transposing, $\quad x - 2y = -10 \qquad (3)$

$$-x + y = -23 \qquad (4)$$

Adding (3) and (4), $-y = -33$

$\quad y = \$33$, or value of second horse.   Ans.

Substituting in (1), $x + 10 = 66$;

or $\quad x = \$56$, or value of first horse.   Ans.

(13) $\qquad\qquad$ Let $x = $ A's money
$$y = \text{B's money.}$$

If A should give B \$5, A would have $x - 5$, and B, $y + 5$. B would then have \$6 more than A, whence the equation

$$y + 5 - (x - 5) = 6 \qquad (1)$$

But if A received \$5 from B, A would have $x + 5$, and B, $y - 5$, and 3 times his money, or $3(x + 5)$, would be \$20 more than 4 times B's, or $4(y - 5)$, whence the equation

$$3(x + 5) - 4(y - 5) = 20 \qquad (2)$$

Expanding equations (1) and (2),

$$y + 5 - x + 5 = 6 \qquad (3)$$
$$3x + 15 - 4y + 20 = 20 \qquad (4)$$

Transposing and combining,

$$y - x = -4 \qquad (5)$$
$$-4y + 3x = -15 \qquad (6)$$

Multiplying (5) by 4, and adding to (6),

$$4y - 4x = -16$$
$$\underline{-4y + 3x = -15}$$
$$-x = -31$$
$$x = 31$$

Substituting value of x in (5),

$$y - 31 = -4$$
$$y = 27$$

Hence, $\quad x = \$31,$ A's money. $\Big\}$ Ans.
$\qquad\quad y = \$27,$ B's money.

(14) (a) $\qquad\qquad x^2 - 6x = 16$

By inspection, $\quad x^2 - 6x - 16 = 0$
$$(x - 8)(x + 2) = 0$$

whence, $\qquad\qquad x = 8 \text{ or } -2 \quad$ Ans

(b) $\qquad\qquad\qquad x^2 - 7x = 8$

By inspection, $\quad x^2 - 7x - 8 = 0$
$$(x - 8)(x + 1) = 0$$

whence, $\qquad\qquad x = 8 \text{ or } -1 \quad$ Ans.

(c) $\qquad\qquad\qquad 9x^2 - 12x = 21$

Dividing by 9, $\qquad x^2 - \dfrac{12x}{9} = \dfrac{21}{9}$

From the formula,

$$x = \tfrac{1}{2}\left(\tfrac{12}{9} \pm \sqrt{\left(\tfrac{12}{9}\right)^2 + 4 \times \tfrac{21}{9}}\right)$$
$$= \tfrac{1}{2}\left(\tfrac{12}{9} \pm \tfrac{30}{9}\right)$$
$$= 2\tfrac{1}{3} \text{ or } -1 \quad \text{Ans.}$$

By inspection, $\quad x^2 - \tfrac{12}{9}x - \tfrac{21}{9} = 0$
$$\left(x - \tfrac{21}{9}\right)(x + 1) = 0$$

$$x = 2\tfrac{1}{3}, \text{ or } -1 \quad \text{Ans.}$$

(15) Let $x =$ number of quarts of 90-cent wine in the mixture;

$\qquad y =$ number of quarts of 50-cent wine in the mixture.

Then, $\qquad\qquad x + y = 60 \qquad\qquad$ (1)

and $\qquad 90x + 50y = 4{,}500 = 75 \times 60 \qquad$ (2)

Multiplying (1) by 50,

$$50x + 50y = 3{,}000 \qquad\qquad \text{(3)}$$

Subtracting (3) from (2),

$$40x = 1,500$$

whence, $\qquad x = 37\frac{1}{2}$ qt.   Ans.

Multiplying (1) by 90,

$$90x + 90y = 5,400 \qquad (4)$$

Subtracting (2), $\quad 90x + 50y = 4,500 \qquad (2)$

$$\overline{ \; 40y = 900}$$

whence, $\qquad y = 22\frac{1}{2}$ qt.   Ans.

(16)   Let $x =$ the numerator of the fraction;
$\qquad\quad y =$ the denominator of the fraction.

Then, $\qquad\qquad \dfrac{x}{y} =$ the fraction

From the conditions, $\dfrac{2x}{y+7} = \dfrac{2}{3} \qquad (1)$

and $\qquad\qquad\quad \dfrac{x+2}{2y} = \dfrac{3}{5} \qquad (2)$

Clearing (1) and (2) of fractions, and transposing,

$$6x = 2y + 14 \qquad (3)$$

and $\qquad\qquad 5x = 6y - 10 \qquad (4)$

Solving for x, $x = \dfrac{2y+14}{6} = \dfrac{y+7}{3} \qquad (5)$

$$x = \dfrac{6y-10}{5} \qquad (6)$$

Equating (5) and (6),

$$\dfrac{y+7}{3} = \dfrac{6y-10}{5}$$

Clearing of fractions,

$$5y + 35 = 18y - 30$$

whence, $\qquad\qquad 13y = 65$

or $\qquad\qquad\qquad y = 5$

Substituting this value of y in (3),

$$6x = 10 + 14 = 24$$

whence, $\qquad\qquad x = 4$

Therefore, the fraction is $\frac{4}{5}$.   Ans.

(17)   Let $x = $ greater number;

$\qquad\qquad\qquad y = $ less number.

Then, $\qquad\qquad x + 4 = 3\frac{1}{4}y \qquad\qquad$ (1)

and $\qquad\qquad\qquad y + 8 = \dfrac{x}{2} \qquad\qquad$ (2)

Clearing of fractions,

$$4x + 16 = 13y$$

and $\qquad\qquad 2y + 16 = x$

whence, $\qquad\quad 13y - 4x = 16 \qquad\qquad$ (3)

$\qquad\qquad\qquad 2y - x = -16 \qquad\qquad$ (4)

Multiplying (4) by 4, and subtracting from (3),

$$5y = 80$$

or $\qquad\qquad\qquad y = 16 \quad$ Ans.

Substituting in (4),

$$32 - x = -16$$

whence, $\qquad\qquad x = 48 \quad$ Ans.

LOGARITHMS

(1) First raise $\frac{200}{100}$ to the .29078 power. Since $\frac{200}{100} = \mathbf{2}$, $\left(\frac{200}{100}\right)^{.29078} = 2^{.29078}$, and $\log 2^{.29078} = .29078 \times \log 2 = .29078 \times$ .30103 = .08753. Number corresponding = 1.2233. Then,

$$1 - \left(\frac{200}{100}\right)^{.29078} = 1 - 1.2233 = -.2233.$$

We now find the product required by adding the logarithms of 351.36, 100, 24, and .2233, paying no attention to the negative sign of .2233 until the product is found. See Art. **30.**

$$\begin{array}{rl}
\text{Log } 351.36 & = 2.54575 \\
\log \quad 100 & = 2 \\
\log \quad\;\; 24 & = 1.38021 \\
\log \quad .2233 & = \overline{1}.34889 \\
\hline
sum & = 5.27485 = \\
\end{array}$$

$$\log 351.36 \times 100 \times 24\left[1 - \left(\frac{200}{100}\right)^{.29078}\right]$$

Number corresponding = 188,300.

The number is negative, since multiplying positive and negative signs gives negative; and the sign of .2233 is minus. Hence, $x = -188,300$. Ans.

(2) (*a*) Log 2,376 = 3.37585. Ans. See Arts. **8** and **10.**
    (*b*) Log .6413 = $\overline{1}$.80706. Ans.
    (*c*) Log .0002507 = $\overline{4}$.39915. Ans.

(3) (*a*) Apply rule, Art. **35,**

$$\begin{array}{rl}
\log \quad 755.4 & = 2.87818 \\
\log \; .00324 & = \overline{3}.51055 \\
\hline
difference & = 5.36763 = \text{logarithm of quotient.}
\end{array}$$

The mantissa is not found in the table. The next less mantissa is 36754. The difference between this and the next greater mantissa is $773 - 754 = 19$, and the P. P. is $763 - 754 = 9$. Looking in the P. P. section for the column headed 19, we find opposite 9.5, 5, the fifth figure of the number. The fourth figure is 1, and the first three figures 233; hence, the figures of the number are 23315. Since the characteristic is 5, $755.4 \div .00324 = 233,150$. Ans.

(b)   Apply rule, Art. **35,**

$$\text{log} \quad .05555 = \overline{2}.74468$$
$$\text{log} \ .0008601 = \overline{4}.93455$$

$$\textit{difference} = 1.81013 = \text{logarithm of quotient.}$$

The number whose logarithm is 1.81013 equals 64.584.

Hence, $.05555 \div .0008601 = 64.584.$ Ans.

(c)   Apply rule, Art. **35,**

$$\text{log} \quad 4.62 = \quad .66464$$
$$\text{log} \ .6448 = \overline{1}.80943$$

$$\textit{difference} = \quad .85521 = \text{logarithm of quotient.}$$

Number whose logarithm $= .85521 = 7.1648.$

Hence, $4.62 \div .6448 = 7.1648.$ Ans.

(4) $$x^{.74} = \frac{238 \times 1,000}{.0042^{.6602}}.$$

$$\text{Log} \quad 238 = 2.37658$$
$$\text{log} \ 1,000 = 3.$$

$$\textit{sum} = 5.37658 = \text{log} \ (238 \times 1,000).$$

$$\text{Log} \ .0042 = \overline{3}.6\,2\,3\,2\,5$$
$$.6\,6\,0\,2$$

$$1\,2\,4\,6\,5\,0$$
$$3\,7\,3\,9\,5\,0$$
$$3\,7\,3\,9\,5\,0$$

$$.4\,1\,1\,4\,6\,9\,6\,5\,0 \text{ or } .41147.$$

$$.6\ 6\ 0\ 2$$
$$-\ 3$$
$$\overline{-\ 1.9\ 8\ 0\ 6} = \text{characteristic.}$$

Adding, $.4\ 1\ 1\ 4\ 7$
$$-\ 1.9\ 8\ 0\ 6$$
$$\overline{\overline{2}.4\ 3\ 0\ 8\ 7} \quad \text{(See Art. } \mathbf{42.}\text{)}$$

Then, $\log \left(\dfrac{238 \times 1,000}{.0042^{.6602}} \right) = 5.37658 - \overline{2}.43087 = 6.94571 =$

$.74 \log x$; whence, $\log x = \dfrac{6.94571}{.74} = 9.38609.$ Number whose logarithm $= 9.38609$ is $2,432,700,000 = x.$ Ans.

(5)   Log $.00743 = \overline{3}.87099.$

               Log $.006 = \overline{3}.77815.$

$\sqrt[5]{.00743} = \log .00743 \div 5$ (Art. **45**), and $\sqrt[.6]{.006} = \log .006$ $\div .6.$ Since these numbers are wholly decimal, we apply Art. **46.**

$$5)\overline{3}.8\ 7\ 0\ 9\ 9$$
$$\overline{\overline{1}.5\ 7\ 4\ 1\ 9} = \log \sqrt[5]{.00743}.$$

The characteristic $\overline{3}$ will not contain 5. We then add $\overline{2}$ to it, making $\overline{5}.$ 5 is contained in $\overline{5}$, $\overline{1}$ times. Hence, the characteristic is $\overline{1}.$ Adding the same number, 2, to the mantissa, we have 2.87099. $2.87099 \div 5 = .57419.$ Hence, $\log \sqrt[5]{.00743} = \overline{1}.57419.$

    $.6)\overline{3}.7\ 7\ 8\ 1\ 5$ $.6$ is contained in $\overline{3}$, -5 times.
      $\overline{5}.$ $.6$ is contained in $.77815$, 1.29691 times.
     $1.2\ 9\ 6\ 9\ 1$

$sum = -\ \overline{4.2\ 9\ 6\ 9\ 1} = \sqrt[.6]{.006}.$

          Log $\sqrt[5]{.00743} = \overline{1}.57419$

        log $\sqrt[.6]{.006} = \overline{4}.29691$

             $difference = 3.27728 = \log \text{ of quotient.}$

Number corresponding $= 1,893.6.$

Hence, $\sqrt[5]{.00743} \div \sqrt[.6]{.006} = 1,893.6.$ Ans.

(6) Apply rule, Art. **30,**

$$\log \quad 1{,}728 = 3.23754$$
$$\log .00024 = \bar{4}.38021$$
$$\log \ .7462 = \bar{1}.87286$$
$$\log \ 302.1 = 2.48015$$
$$\log 7.6094 = \ \ .88135$$

$$sum = 2.85211 =$$

$\log \ (1{,}728 \times .00024 \times .7462 \times 302.1 \times 7.6094)$. Number whose logarithm is $2.85211 = 711.40$, the product. Ans.

(7) $\text{Log } \sqrt{5.954} = \ .77481 \div 2 = .38741$

$\quad\quad \log \ \sqrt[3]{61.19} = 1.78668 \div 3 = .59556$

$$sum = \ .98297$$

$\quad\quad \log \ \sqrt[5]{298.54} = 2.47500 \div 5 = .49500.$

Then, $\dfrac{\sqrt{5.954} \times \sqrt[3]{61.19}}{\sqrt[5]{298.54}} = \log \ (\sqrt{5.954} \times \ \sqrt[3]{61.19}) - \log$

$\sqrt[5]{298.54} = .98297 - .49500 = .48797 = $ logarithm of the required result.

Number corresponding $= 3.0759.$ Ans.

(8) $\sqrt[7]{.0532864} = \log .0532864 \div 7.$

Log $.0532864 = \bar{2}.72661.$

Adding $\bar{5}$ to characteristic $\bar{2} = \bar{7}.$

Adding 5 to mantissa $= 5.72662.$

$\bar{7} \div 7 = \bar{1}.$

$5.72661 \div 7 = .81809$, nearly.

Hence, $\log \ \sqrt[7]{.0532864} = \bar{1}.81809.$

Number corresponding to $\log \bar{1}.81809 = .65780.$ Ans.

(9) (a) $32^{4.8}$.

Log $32 = 1.50515.$

$$
\begin{array}{r}
1.5\,0\,5\,1\,5 \\
4.8 \\
\hline
1\,2\,0\,4\,1\,2\,0 \\
6\,0\,2\,0\,6\,0 \\
\hline
7.2\,2\,4\,7\,2\,0
\end{array}
$$

7.22472 is the logarithm of the required power. **See Art. 40.**

Number whose logarithm $= 7.22472$ is $16,777,000$.

Hence, $32^{4.8} = 16,777,000$.   Ans.

(b) $.76^{3.62}$.

Log $.76 = \bar{1}.88081$.

(See Arts. **41** and **42**.)

$$\begin{array}{r} \bar{1} + .8\,8\,0\,8\,1 \\ 3.6\,2 \\ \hline 1\,7\,6\,1\,6\,2 \\ 5\,2\,8\,4\,8\,6 \\ 2\,6\,4\,2\,4\,3 \\ \hline 3.1\,8\,8\,5\,3\,2\,2 \\ -3.6\,2 \\ \hline \bar{1}.5\,6\,8\,5\,3 = \log .37028. \end{array}$$

Hence, $.76^{3.62} = .37028$.   Ans.

(c) $.84^{.38}$.

Log $.84 = \bar{1}.92428$.

$$\begin{array}{r} \bar{1} + .9\,2\,4\,2\,8 \\ .3\,8 \\ \hline 7\,3\,9\,4\,2\,4 \\ 2\,7\,7\,2\,8\,4 \\ \hline .3\,5\,1\,2\,2\,6\,4 \\ -.3\,8 \\ \hline \bar{1}.9\,7\,1\,2\,3 = \log .93590. \end{array}$$

Hence, $.84^{.38} = .93590$.   Ans.

(10)   Log $\sqrt[6]{\dfrac{1}{249}} - \log \sqrt[5]{\dfrac{23}{71}}$ = logarithm of answer.

Log $\sqrt[6]{\dfrac{1}{249}} = \dfrac{1}{6}(\log 1 - \log 249) = \dfrac{1}{6}(0 - 2.39620) = -.39937$

$= $ (adding $+1$ and -1) $\bar{1}.60063$.

Log $\sqrt[5]{\dfrac{23}{71}} = \dfrac{1}{5}(\log 23 - \log 71) = \dfrac{1}{5}(1.36173 - 1.85126) =$

$\dfrac{1}{5}(-.48953) = -.097906 = $ (adding $+1$ and -1) $\bar{1}.902094$, or

$\bar{1}.90209$ when using 5-place logarithms.

Hence, $\bar{1}.60063 - \bar{1}.90209 = \bar{1}.69854 = \log .49950$. There·

fore, $\sqrt[6]{\dfrac{1}{249}} \div \sqrt[5]{\dfrac{23}{71}} = .49950$.   Ans.

(11) The mantissa is not found in the table. The next less mantissa is .81291; the difference between this and the next greater mantissa is $298 - 291 = 7$, and the P. P. is $.81293 - .81291 = 2$. Looking in the P. P. section for the column headed 7, we find opposite 2.1, 3, the fifth figure of the number; the fourth figure is 0, and the first three figures, 650. Hence, the number whose logarithm is .81293 is 65003. Ans.

$2.52460 =$ logarithm of 334.65. Ans. See Art. **23.**

$\bar{1}.27631 =$ logarithm of .18893. Ans. We choose 3 for the fifth figure because, in the proportional parts column headed 23, 6.9 is nearer 8 than 9.2.

(12) The most expeditious way of solving this example is the following:

$$p\,v^{1.41} = p_1 v_1^{1.41}, \text{ or } v_1 = \sqrt[1.41]{\frac{p\,v^{1.41}}{p_1}} = v\sqrt[1.41]{\frac{p}{p_1}}.$$

Substituting values given, $v_1 = 1.495\sqrt[1.41]{\frac{134.7}{16.421}}.$

Log $v_1 = $ log $1.495 + \dfrac{\text{log } 134.7 - \text{log } 16.421}{1.41} = .17464 +$

$\dfrac{2.12937 - 1.21540}{1.41} = .17464 + .64821 = .82285 = $ log 6.6504;

whence, $v_1 = 6.6504$.   Ans.

(13)   Log $\sqrt[5]{\dfrac{7.1895 \times 4,764.2^2 \times 0.00326^5}{.00049 \times 457^3 \times .576^2}} = \dfrac{1}{5}$ [log 7.1895 $+ 2$ log $4,764.2 + 5$ log $.00326 - ($log $.00049 + 3$ log $457 + 2$ log $.576)] = \dfrac{\bar{5}.77878 - 4.18991}{5} = \bar{2}.31777 = $ log $.020786$. Ans.

$$\begin{aligned}
\text{Log } 7.1895 = &\quad .85670 \\
2 \text{ log } 4,764.2 = 2 \times 3.67799 = &\quad 7.35598 \\
5 \text{ log } .00326 = 5 \times \bar{3}.51322 = &\quad \bar{13}.56610 \\
\hline
sum = &\quad \bar{5}.77878
\end{aligned}$$

$$\begin{aligned}
\text{Log } .00049 = &\quad \bar{4}.68931 \\
3 \text{ log } 457 = 3 \times 2.65992 = &\quad 7.97976 \\
2 \text{ log } .576 = 2 \times \bar{1}.76042 = &\quad \bar{1}.52084 \\
\hline
sum = &\quad 4.18991.
\end{aligned}$$

(14)   Substituting the values given,

$$p = \frac{\dfrac{8,000}{960,000} \times \left(\dfrac{3}{16}\right)^{2.18}}{120 \times 2.25} = \frac{8,000 \left(\dfrac{3}{16}\right)^{2.18}}{2.25}.$$

Log $p = \log\ 8,000 + 2.18\ \log\dfrac{3}{16} - \log\ 2.25 = 3.90309 +$
218 $(\log 3 - \log 16) - .35218 = 4.55091 + 2.18 \times (.47712 -$
$1.20412) = 1.96605 = \log 92.480.$ Ans.

(15)   Solving for t, $t = \sqrt[2.18]{\dfrac{p\,l\,d}{960,000}}.$

Substituting values given,

$$t = \sqrt[2.18]{\frac{44}{\dfrac{160 \times 132 \times 2}{960,000}}} = \sqrt[2.18]{.044}.$$
$$\begin{array}{r} 6,000 \\ 3,000 \\ 1,000 \end{array}$$

$$\text{Log } t = \frac{\log .044}{2.18} = \frac{\overline{2}.64345}{2.18} = \frac{-2.18 + .82345}{2.18} =$$
$$1.\overline{3}7773 = \log .23863. \quad \text{Ans.}$$

GEOMETRY AND TRIGONOMETRY

(1) When one straight line meets another straight line at a point between the ends, the sum of the two adjacent angles equals two right angles. Therefore, since one of the angles equals $\frac{4}{5}$ of a right angle, the other angle equals two right angles (or $\frac{10}{5}$) minus $\frac{4}{5}$. We have, then, $\frac{10}{5} - \frac{4}{5} = \frac{6}{5}$, or $1\frac{1}{5}$ right angles. Ans.

(2) It is an isosceles triangle, since the sides opposite the equal angles are equal.

(3) A regular decagon has 10 equal sides; therefore, the length of one side is $40 \div 10 = 4$ in. Ans.

(4) The sum of all the interior angles of any polygon equals two right angles, multiplied by the number of sides in the polygon less two. As a regular dodecagon has 12 equal sides, the sum of the interior angles equals two right angles $\times$ 10 ($= 12 - 2$), or 20 right angles. Since there are 12 equal angles, the size of any one of them equals $20 \div 12$, or $1\frac{2}{3}$ right angles. Ans.

(5) Equilateral triangle.

(6) Since the two angles A and C, Fig. I, are equal, the triangle is isosceles, and a line drawn from the vertex B will bisect the line $A\,C$, the length of which is 7 inches; therefore,

FIG. I

$$A D = D C = 7 \div 2 = 3\tfrac{1}{2} \text{ in.} \quad \text{Ans.}$$

(7) The length of the line $= \sqrt{12^2 - 9^2} + \sqrt{15^2 - 9^2}$, or 19.94 in. Ans.

§ 6

40—33

(8) One of the angles of an equiangular octagon is equal to $\frac{1}{8}$ of 12 right angles, or $1\frac{1}{2}$ right angles, since the sum of the interior angles of the equiangular octagon equals 12 right angles.

(9) See Art. **71.**

(10) In Fig. II, $AB = 4$ inches, and $OA = 6$ inches. We first find the length of OD. $OD = \sqrt{\overline{OA}^2 - \overline{DA}^2}$; but

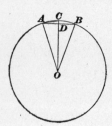

FIG. II

$\overline{OA}^2 = 6^2$, or 36, and $\overline{DA}^2 = \left(\dfrac{4}{2}\right)^2$, or 4;

therefore, $OD = \sqrt{36 - 4}$, or 5.657.

$DC = OC - OD$, or $DC = 6 - 5.657$, or .343 inch. In the right triangle ADC, we have AC, which is the chord of half the arc ACB, equals $\sqrt{2^2 + .343^2}$, or 2.03 in. **Ans.**

(11) Given, $OC = 5\frac{3}{4}$ inches and $OA = 17 \div 2 = 8\frac{1}{2}$ inches, to find AB (see Fig. III). AC, which is one-half the chord AB, equals $\sqrt{\overline{OA}^2 - \overline{OC}^2}$; therefore,

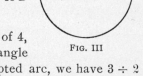

FIG. III

$AC = \sqrt{(8\frac{1}{2})^2 - (5\frac{3}{4})^2}$, or 6.26 inches.

Now, $AB = 2 \times AC$; therefore, $AB = 2 \times 6.26$, or 12.52 in. **Ans.**

(12) The arc intercepted equals $\frac{3}{4}$ of 4, or 3 quadrants. As the inscribed angle is measured by one-half the intercepted arc, we have $3 \div 2 = 1\frac{1}{2}$ quadrants as the size of the angle.

(13) Four right angles $\div \frac{2}{7} = 4 \times \frac{7}{2}$, or 14 equal sectors.

(14) Since 24 inches equals the perimeter, we have $24 \div 8 = 3$ inches, as the length of each side or chord.

Then, $\sqrt{\left(\dfrac{3}{2}\right)^2 + 3.62^2} = 3.92$ in., radius.

$3.92 \times 2 = 7.84$ in., diameter. **Ans.**

(15) In $19°\ 19'\ 19''$ there are 69,559 seconds, and in $360°$, or a circle, there are 1,296,000 seconds. Therefore,

69,559 seconds equal $\dfrac{69,559}{1,296,000}$, or .053672 part of a circle.

Ans.

(16) Referring to Fig. 75 of the text and using the values given in the example, we have $A B = 26$ feet 7 inches, or 26.583 feet; $A C = 40$ feet; and the included angle $A = 36° 20' 43''$. Then in the right triangle $A D B$, $A B$ is known, and also the angle A.

Hence, by rule 1, Art. **98,** $B D = 26.583 \times \sin 36° 20' 43''$ $= 26.583 \times .59265 = 15.754$ feet. By rule 3, Art. **98,** $A D = 26.583 \times \cos 36° 20' 43'' = 26.583 \times .80546 = 21.411$. $A C - A D = 40 - 21.411 = 18.589$ feet $= D C$. In the right triangle $C D B$, the two sides $B D$ and $D C$ are known; hence, $\tan C = \dfrac{B D}{D C} = \dfrac{15.754}{18.589} = .84749$, and angle $C = 40° 16' 52''$. Ans.

Applying rule 2, Art. **98,** $B C = \dfrac{B D}{\sin C} = \dfrac{15.754}{\sin 40° 16' 52''}$ $= \dfrac{15.754}{.64654} = 24.37$, or 24 ft. 4.4 in. Ans.

Angle $B = 180° - (36° 20' 43'' + 40° 16' 52'') = 180° - 76° 37' 36'' = 103° 22' 25''$. Ans.

(17) See Fig. 76 of the text. Solving the triangle $A B C$, we first find $B D$. By rule 1, Art. **98,** $B D = A B \times \sin A = 16\tfrac{5}{12} \times \sin 54° 54' 54'' = 16\tfrac{5}{12} \times .81830 = 13.434$ feet. $\operatorname{Sin} B C D = \dfrac{B D}{B C} = \dfrac{13.434}{13.542} = .99202$; whence, angle $B C D = 82° 45' 30''$. Ans.

By rule 3, $C D = B C \times \cos C = 13\tfrac{13}{24} \times \cos 82° 45' 30'' = 13\tfrac{13}{24} \times .12605 = 1.7069$ feet.

By rule 3, $A D = A B \times \cos A = 16\tfrac{5}{12} \times \cos 54° 54' 54'' = 16\tfrac{5}{12} \times .57479 = 9.4361$ feet.

In the triangle $A B C$, the angle $A C B$ is the supplement (see Art. **27**) of the angle $B C D$ and equals $180° -$ angle $B C D$, or $A C B = 180° - 82° 45' 30'' = 97° 14' 30''$. Ans.

Angle $A B C = 180° - $ (angle $B A C + $ angle $A C B) = 180° - (54° 54' 54'' + 97° 14' 30'') = 180° - 152° 9' 24'' = 27° 50' 36''$. Ans.

Side $AC = AD - CD$, or $AC = 9.4361 - 1.7069 = 7.7292$ $= 7$ ft. $8\frac{3}{4}$ in. Ans.

For the triangle ABC', angle $C' = BCD$ (isosceles triangle), or $C' = 82°\ 45'\ 30''$.

Angle $ABC' = 180° -$ (angle $A +$ angle C') $= 180°$ $-\ (54°\ 54'\ 54'' + 82°\ 45'\ 30'') = \cdot180° - 137°\ 40'\ 24''$ $= 42°\ 19'\ 36''$. Ans.

$AC' = AD + C'D = 9.4361 + 1.7069 = 11.143 = 11$ ft. $1\frac{3}{4}$ in. Ans.

(18) If one-third of a certain angle equals $14°\ 47'\ 10''$, then the angle must be $3 \times 14°\ 47'\ 10''$, or $44°\ 21'\ 30''$. $2\frac{1}{2} \times 44°\ 21'\ 30''$, or $110°\ 53'\ 45''$, equals one of the other two angles. The third angle equals $180° - (110°\ 53'\ 45'' + 44°\ 21'\ 30'')$, or $24°\ 44'\ 45''$.

(19) Referring to Fig. 70 of the text, let $BC = 437$ feet and $AC = 792$ feet, to find the hypotenuse AB and the angles A and B.

$AB = \sqrt{\overline{AC}^2 + \overline{BC}^2} = \sqrt{\overline{792}^2 + \overline{437}^2} = \sqrt{818,233} = 904$ ft. $6\frac{3}{4}$ in. Ans.

By rule 4, Art. **98**, $\tan A = \dfrac{\text{side opposite}}{\text{side adjacent}}$, or $\tan A = \dfrac{437}{792}$ $= .55177$; therefore, $A = 28°\ 53'\ 19''$. Ans.

Angle $B = 90° - 28°\ 53'\ 19''$, or $61°\ 6'\ 41''$. Ans.

(20) See Fig. IV. Angle $B = 180° - (29°\ 21' + 76°\ 44'\ 18'')$ $= 180° - 106°\ 5'\ 18'' = 73°\ 54'\ 42''$.

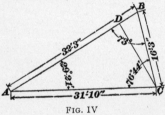

From C, draw CD perpendicular to AB.

$AD = AC \cos A = 31.833 \times \cos 29°\ 21' = 31.833 \times .87164 = 27.747$ feet. $CD = AC \sin A = 31.833 \times \sin 29°\ 21' = 31.833 \times .49014 = 15.603$.

FIG. IV

$BC = \dfrac{CD}{\sin B} = \dfrac{15.603}{\sin 73°\ 54'\ 42''} = 16.24$ feet $= 16$ ft. 3 in.

$DB = \dfrac{CD}{\tan B} = \dfrac{15.603}{\tan 73°\ 54'\ 42''} = 4.5$ feet.

$A B = A D + D B = 27.747 + 4.5 = 32.247 = 32$ feet, 3 inches.

$$\text{Ans.} \begin{cases} B C = 16 \text{ ft. } 3 \text{ in.} \\ A B = 32 \text{ ft. } 3 \text{ in.} \\ B = 73° \ 54' \ 42''. \end{cases}$$

(21)   By rule, Art. **135,**

$$d = \sqrt{\frac{A}{.7854}} = \sqrt{\frac{89.42}{.7854}} = \sqrt{113.8528}, \text{ or } 10.67 \text{ in.} \quad \text{Ans.}$$

Circumference equals 10.67×3.1416, or 33.52 in.   Ans.

In a regular hexagon inscribed in a circle, each side is equal to the radius of the circle; therefore, $\dfrac{10.67}{2} = 5.335$ in. is the length of a side.   Ans.

(22)   Angle $m O B = \frac{1}{16}$ of $360°$, or $22\frac{1}{2}°$. $m O = \frac{1}{2}$ of $m n = \frac{1}{2}$ of 2, or 1 inch.   See Fig. V.

Side $m B = O m \times \tan 22\frac{1}{2}°$, or $m B = 1 \times .41421 = .41421$.

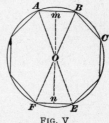

FIG. V

$A B = 2 m B$; therefore, $A B = .82842$ inch.

Area of $A O B = \frac{1}{2} \times .82842 \times 1 = .41421$ square inch, which, multiplied by 8, the number of equal triangles, equals 3.31368 square inches.

Volume of bar $= 3.31368 \times 10 \times 12 = 397.6416$ cu. in.

Weight of bar equals $397.6416 \times .282 = 112.1349$, or 112 lb. 2 oz.   Ans.

(23) $.5236 \times 16^3 = 2,144.66$ cubic inches equals the volume of a sphere 16 inches in diameter.

$.5236 \times 12^3 = 904.78$ cubic inches equals the volume of a sphere 12 inches in diameter.

The difference of the two volumes equals the volume of the spherical shell, and this multiplied by the weight per cubic inch equals the weight of the shell.   Hence, we have $(2,144.66 - 904.78) \times .261 = 323.61$ lb.   Ans.

(24)   The circumference of the circle equals $\dfrac{5\frac{13}{32} \times 360}{27}$, or 72.0833 inches.   The diameter, therefore, is $\dfrac{72.0833}{3.1416}$, or 22.95 in., nearly.   Ans.

(25)   (*a*) $17\frac{1}{64}$ inches = 17.016 inches.
Area of circle = $.7854d^2$ = $.7854 \times 17.016^2$ = 227.41 sq. in.
                                                        Ans.

(*b*)   16° 7′ 21″ = 16.1225°.   By rule, Art. **132,**

$$l = \frac{\pi\, d\, n}{360} = \frac{3.1416 \times 17.016 \times 16.1225}{360} = 2.394 \text{ in.} \textbf{Ans.}$$

(26)   (*a*) By rule, Art. **144,** area = $12 \times 8 \times .7854$
= 75.4 sq. in.   Ans.

(*b*)   Applying the formula, Art. **143,** $a = 6,\ b = 4,\ D$
$$= \frac{6-4}{6+4} = \frac{2}{10} = \frac{1}{5}.$$

Perimeter = $3.1416\,(6+4)\,\dfrac{64 - 3(\frac{1}{5})^4}{64 - 16(\frac{1}{5})^2} = 31.731$ in.   Ans.

(27)   Area of base = $.7854 \times 7^2$ = 38.484 square inches.
Slant height of cone = $\sqrt{11^2 + 3\frac{1}{2}^2}$, or 11.5434 inches.
Circumference of base = 7×3.1416 = 21.9912 inches.

Convex area of cone = $21.9912 \times \dfrac{11.5434}{2} = 126.927$ square
inches.
Total area = $126.927 + 38.484 = 165.41$ sq. in.   Ans.

(28)   Volume of sphere equals $.5236 \times 10^3$ = 523.6 cubic
inches.
Area of base of cone = $.7854 \times 10^2$ = 78.54 square inches.
$\dfrac{3 \times 523.6}{78.54} = 20$ in., altitude of cone.   Ans.

(29)   Volume of sphere = $.5236 \times 12^3$ = 904.7808 cubic
inches.
Area of base of cylinder = $.7854 \times 12^2$ = 113.0976 square
inches.
Height of cylinder = $\dfrac{904.7808}{113.0976} = 8$ in.   Ans.

(30)   (*a*) Area of the triangle equals $\dfrac{AC \times BD}{2}$, or
$\dfrac{9\frac{1}{2} \times 12}{2} = 57$ sq. in.   Ans.

(*b*) See Fig. VI. Angle $BAD = 79°\,22'$; angle ABD
$= 90° - 79°\,22' = 10°\,38'$.   Side AB
$= BD \div \sin\ 79°\,22' = 12 \div .98283 =$
12.209 inches.

Side $AD = BD \times \tan\ 10°\,38' = 12$
$\times .18775 = 2.253$ inches.

Side $DC = AC - AD = 9.5 - 2.253$
$= 7.247$ inches.

FIG. VI

Side $BC = \sqrt{\overline{DB}^2 + \overline{DC}^2} = \sqrt{12^2 + 7.247^2} = \sqrt{196.519}$
$= 14.018$ inches.

Perimeter of triangle equals $AB + BC + AC = 12.209$
$+ 14.018 + 9.5 = 35.73$ in.   Ans.

(31) The diagonal divides the trapezium into two triangles; the sum of the areas of these two triangles equals
the area of the trapezium, which is, therefore,

$$\frac{11 \times 7}{2} + \frac{11 \times 4\frac{1}{4}}{2} = 61\frac{7}{8} \text{ sq. in.} \text{Ans.}$$

(32) Referring to Fig. III, example 11, we have OA or
$OB = 10 \div 2 = 5$ inches, and $AB = 6\frac{3}{4}$ inches.

Sin $COB = \dfrac{CB}{OB} = \dfrac{6\frac{3}{4} \div 2}{5} = .67500$; therefore, angle COB
$= 42°\,27'\,14.3''$.

Angle $AOB = (42°\,27'\,14.3'') \times 2 = 84°\,54'\,28.6''$.   Ans.
$OC = OB \times \cos COB = 5 \times .73782 = 3.6891$.

Area of sector $= 10^2 \times .7854 \times \dfrac{84°\,54'\,28.6''}{360°} = 18.524$ square
inches.

Area of triangle $= \dfrac{6.75 \times 3.6891}{2} = 12.450$ square inches.

$18.524 - 12.450 = 6.074$ sq. in., the area of the segment. Ans.

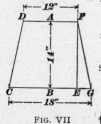

FIG. VII

(33) See Fig. VII. Area of lower base
$= 18^2 \times .7854 = 254.4696$ square inches.

Area of upper base$= 12^2 \times .7854 = 113.0976$
square inches.

$EG = BG - AF = 9 - 6$, or 3 inches.

Slant height $FG = \sqrt{\overline{EG}^2 + \overline{EF}^2} =$
$\sqrt{3^2 + 14^2} = 14.32$ inches.

By formula, Art. **169**,

$$C = \frac{(p + p')s}{2} = \frac{37.6992 + 56.5488}{2} \times 14.32 = 674.8156 \text{ sq. in.}$$

Total area $= 674.8157 + 254.4696 + 113.0976 = 1,042.38$ sq. in.   Ans.

By formula, Art. **170**, $V = (A + a + \sqrt{A \times a})\frac{h}{3} = (113.0976$

$+ 254.4696 + \sqrt{113.0976 \times 254.4696}) \frac{14}{3} = 2,506.997$ cu. in.
Ans.

(34)   Area of surface of sphere 27 inches in diameter
$= \pi d^2 = 3.1416 \times 27^2 = 2,290.2$ sq. in.   Ans.

(35)   Area of end $= 19^2 \times .7854 = 283.5294$ square inches.
Volume $= 283.5294 \times 24 = 6,804.7056$ cu. in. $= 3.938$ cu. ft.
Ans.

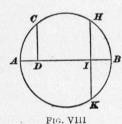

FIG. VIII

(36)   Given, $IB = 2$ inches and $HI = IK = \frac{14}{2} = 7$ inches to find the radius. See Fig. VIII.
$IB : HI = HI : AI$, or $2 : 7 = 7 : AI$.
Therefore, $AI = \frac{49}{2} = 24\frac{1}{2}$ inches.
$AB = AI + IB = 24\frac{1}{2} + 2 = 26\frac{1}{2}$ inches.
Radius $= \frac{AB}{2} = \frac{26\frac{1}{2}}{2} = 13\frac{1}{4}$ in.   Ans.

(37)   (a)   In Fig. IX, given $OB = \frac{16}{2}$ or 8 inches, and $OA = 13 \div 2 = 6\frac{1}{2}$ inches, to find the volume, area, and weight.

Radius of center circle equals $\frac{8 + 6.5}{2}$,

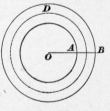

FIG. IX

or $7\frac{1}{4}$ inches.   Length of center line $= 3.1416 \times 2 \times 7\frac{1}{4} = 45.5532$ inches. The radius of the inner circle is $6\frac{1}{2}$ inches, and of the outer circle 8 inches; therefore, the diameter of the cross-section on the line AB is $1\frac{1}{2}$ inches.   Then, the area of the imaginary cross-section is $(1\frac{1}{2})^2 \times .7854 = 1.76715$ sq. in.

Volume of ring $= 1.76715 \times 45.5532 = 80.499$ cu. in.   Ans.

(b)   Weight of ring $= 80.4993 \times .261 = 21$ lb.   Ans.

(38)   The convex area $= 4 \times 5\frac{1}{4} \times 18 = 378$ sq. in.   Ans.
Area of the bases $= 5\frac{1}{4} \times 5\frac{1}{4} \times 2 = 55.125$ square inches.
Total area $= 378 + 55.125 = 433.125$ sq. in.   Ans.
Volume $= (5\frac{1}{4})^2 \times 18 = 496.125$ cu. in.   Ans.

(39)   In Fig. X, $O C = \dfrac{A C}{\tan 30°}.$ ($\frac{1}{6}$ of $360° = 60°$, and
since $A O C = \frac{1}{2}$ of $A O B$, $A O C = 30°$.)

$$O C = \frac{6}{.57735} = 10.392.$$

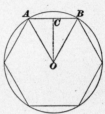

$$\text{Area of } A O B = \frac{12 \times 10.392}{2}$$

$$= 62.352 \text{ square feet.}$$

Since there are 6 equal triangles in a
hexagon, then the area of the base
$= 6 \times 62.352$, or 374.112 square feet.

FIG. X

Perimeter $= 6 \times 12$, or 72 feet.

Convex area $= \dfrac{72 \times 37}{2} = 1,332$ sq. ft.   Ans.

Total area $= 1,332 + 374.112 = 1,706.112$ sq. ft.   Ans.

(40)   Area of the base $= 374.112$ square feet, and altitude $= 37$ feet.   Since the volume equals the area of the
base multiplied by $\frac{1}{3}$ of the altitude, we have

$$\text{volume} = 374.112 \times \frac{37}{3} = 4,614 \text{ cu. ft.}   \text{Ans.}$$

(41)   Given, $A B = 6\frac{7}{8}$ inches, and $O B = O A = 10 \div 2$
$= 5$ inches (see Fig. XI), to find the area of the sector.
Area of circle $= 10^2 \times .7854 = 78.54$ square inches.

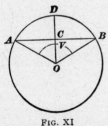

FIG. XI

Sin $A O C = \dfrac{A C}{O A} = \dfrac{6\frac{7}{8} \div 2}{5} = .68750;$

therefore, $A O C = 43° 25' 57''$.
   $A O B = 2 \times A O C = 2 \times 43° 25' 57''$
$= 86° 51' 54'' = 86.865°$.
By rule, Art. **137**,
$$\frac{86.865}{360} \times 78.54 = 18.95 \text{ sq. in.}   \text{Ans.}$$

(42) By rule, Art. **129**, $A = b\,h = 7 \times 10\frac{3}{4}$ (129 inches $= 10\frac{3}{4}$ feet) $= 75\frac{1}{4}$ sq. ft. Ans.

(43) See Art. **130.**

Area of trapezoid $= \left(\dfrac{a+b}{2}\right)h = \dfrac{15\frac{7}{12} + 21\frac{11}{12}}{2} \times 7\frac{2}{3} = 143.75$

sq. ft. Ans.

(44) (*a*) Side of square having an equivalent area $= \sqrt{143.75} = 11.99$ ft. Ans.

(*b*) Diameter of circle having an equivalent area $= \sqrt{\dfrac{143.75}{.7854}} = \sqrt{183.0277} = 13\frac{1}{2}$ ft. Ans.

(*c*) Perimeter of square $= 4 \times 11.99 = 47.96$ ft.
Circumference of circle $= 13\frac{1}{2} \times 3.1416 = 42.41$ ft.

Difference of perimeter $= \overline{5.55\,\text{ft.}} = 5$ ft. 6.6 in.
Ans.

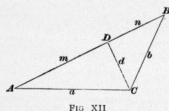

FIG XII

(45) In the triangle $A\,B\,C$, Fig. XII, $A\,B = 24$ feet, $B\,C = 11.25$ feet, and $A\,C = 18$ feet. $m + n : a + b = a - b : m - n,$ or $24 : 29.25 = 6.75 : m - n.$

$$m - n = \frac{29.25 \times 6.75}{24} = 8.226562.$$

Adding $m + n$ and $m - n$, we have

$$m + n = 24$$
$$m - n = \ \ 8.226562$$
$$2\,m = 32.226562$$
$$m = 16.113281.$$

Subtracting $m - n$ from $m + n$, we have

$$2\,n = 15.773438$$
$$n = \ \ 7.886719.$$

In the triangle ADC, side $AC = 18$ feet, side $AD = 16.113281$; hence, according to rule **2**, Art. **98**, $\cos A = \dfrac{16.113281}{18} = .89518$, or angle $A = 26°\ 28'\ 5''$. In the triangle BDC, side $BD = 7.886719$, and side $BC = 11.25$ feet. Hence, $\cos B = \dfrac{7.886719}{11.25} = .70104$, or angle $B = 45°\ 29'\ 23''$. Angle $C = 180° - (45°\ 29'\ 23'' + 26°\ 28'\ 5'') = 108°\ 2'\ 32''$.

Ans. $\begin{cases} A = 26°\ 28'\ 5''. \\ B = 45°\ 29'\ 23''. \\ C = 108°\ 2'\ 32'' \end{cases}$

n	n^2	n^3	n^4	n^5	n	n^2	n^3	n^4	n^5
1.00	1.0000	1.00000	1.00000	1.00000	1.50	2.2500	3.37500	5.06250	7.59375
1.01	1.0201	1.03030	1.04060	1.05101	1.51	2.2801	3.44295	5.19886	7.85027
1.02	1.0404	1.06121	1.08243	1.10408	1.52	2.3104	3.51181	5.33795	8.11368
1.03	1.0609	1.09273	1.12551	1.15927	1.53	2.3409	3.58158	5.47981	8.38411
1.04	1.0816	1.12486	1.16986	1.21665	1.54	2.3716	3.65226	5.62449	8.66171
1.05	1.1025	1.15763	1.21551	1.27628	1.55	2.4025	3.72388	5.77201	8.94661
1.06	1.1236	1.19102	1.26248	1.33823	1.56	2.4336	3.79642	5.92241	9.23896
1.07	1.1449	1.22504	1.31080	1.40255	1.57	2.4649	3.86989	6.07573	9.53890
1.08	1.1664	1.25971	1.36049	1.46933	1.58	2.4964	3.94431	6.23201	9.84658
1.09	1.1881	1.29503	1.41158	1.53862	1.59	2.5281	4.01968	6.39129	10.1622
1.10	1.2100	1.33100	1.46410	1.61051	1.60	2.5600	4.09600	6.55360	10.4858
1.11	1.2321	1.36763	1.51807	1.68506	1.61	2.5921	4.17328	6.71898	10.8176
1.12	1.2544	1.40493	1.57352	1.76234	1.62	2.6244	4.25153	6.88748	11.1577
1.13	1.2769	1.44290	1.63047	1.84244	1.63	2.6569	4.33075	7.05912	11.5064
1.14	1.2996	1.48154	1.68896	1.92541	1.64	2.6896	4.41094	7.23395	11.8637
1.15	1.3225	1.52088	1.74901	2.01136	1.65	2.7225	4.49213	7.41201	12.2298
1.16	1.3456	1.56090	1.81064	2.10034	1.66	2.7556	4.57430	7.59333	12.6049
1.17	1.3689	1.60161	1.87389	2.19245	1.67	2.7889	4.65746	7.77796	12.9892
1.18	1.3924	1.64303	1.93878	2.28776	1.68	2.8224	4.74163	7.96594	13.3828
1.19	1.4161	1.68516	2.00534	2.38635	1.69	2.8561	4.82681	8.15731	13.7858
1.20	1.4400	1.72800	2.07360	2.48832	1.70	2.8900	4.91300	8.35210	14.1986
1.21	1.4641	1.77156	2.14359	2.59374	1.71	2.9241	5.00021	8.55036	14.6211
1.22	1.4884	1.81585	2.21533	2.70271	1.72	2.9584	5.08845	8.75213	15.0537
1.23	1.5129	1.86087	2.28887	2.81531	1.73	2.9929	5.17772	8.95745	15.4964
1.24	1.5376	1.90662	2.36421	2.93163	1.74	3.0276	5.26802	9.16636	15.9495
1.25	1.5625	1.95313	2.44141	3.05176	1.75	3.0625	5.35938	9.37891	16.4131
1.26	1.5876	2.00038	2.52047	3.17580	1.76	3.0976	5.45178	9.59513	16.8874
1.27	1.6129	2.04838	2.60145	3.30384	1.77	3.1329	5.54523	9.81506	17.3727
1.28	1.6384	2.09715	2.68435	3.43597	1.78	3.1684	5.63975	10.0388	17.8690
1.29	1.6641	2.14669	2.76923	3.57231	1.79	3.2041	5.73534	10.2663	18.3766
1.30	1.6900	2.19700	2.85610	3.71293	1.80	3.2400	5.83200	10.4976	18.8957
1.31	1.7161	2.24809	2.94500	3.85795	1.81	3.2761	5.92974	10.7328	19.4264
1.32	1.7424	2.29997	3.03596	4.00746	1.82	3.3124	6.02857	10.9720	19.9690
1.33	1.7689	2.35264	3.12901	4.16158	1.83	3.3489	6.12849	11.2151	20.5237
1.34	1.7956	2.40610	3.22418	4.32040	1.84	3.3856	6.22950	11.4623	21.0906
1.35	1.8225	2.46038	3.32151	4.48403	1.85	3.4225	6.33163	11.7135	21.6700
1.36	1.8496	2.51546	3.42102	4.65259	1.86	3.4596	6.43486	11.9688	22.2620
1.37	1.8769	2.57135	3.52275	4.82617	1.87	3.4969	6.53920	12.2283	22.8669
1.38	1.9044	2.62807	3.62674	5.00490	1.88	3.5344	6.64467	12.4920	23.4849
1.39	1.9321	2.68562	3.73301	5.18888	1.89	3.5721	6.75127	12.7599	24.1162
1.40	1.9600	2.74400	3.84160	5.37824	1.90	3.6100	6.85900	13.0321	24.7610
1.41	1.9881	2.80322	3.95254	5.57308	1.91	3.6481	6.96787	13.3086	25.4195
1.42	2.0164	2.86329	4.06587	5.77353	1.92	3.6864	7.07789	13.5895	26.0919
1.43	2.0449	2.92421	4.18162	5.97971	1.93	3.7249	7.18906	13.8749	26.7785
1.44	2.0736	2.98598	4.29982	6.19174	1.94	3.7636	7.30138	14.1647	27.4795
1.45	2.1025	3.04863	4.42051	6.40973	1.95	3.8025	7.41488	14.4590	28.1951
1.46	2.1316	3.11214	4.54372	6.63383	1.96	3.8416	7.52954	14.7579	28.9255
1.47	2.1609	3.17652	4.66949	6.86415	1.97	3.8809	7.64537	15.0614	29.6709
1.48	2.1904	3.24179	4.79785	7.10082	1.98	3.9204	7.76239	15.3695	30.4317
1.49	2.2201	3.30795	4.92884	7.34398	1.99	3.9601	7.88060	15.6824	31.2080
1.50	2.2500	3.37500	5.06250	7.59375	2.00	4.0000	8.00000	16.0000	32.0000

n	n^2	n^3	n^4	n^5	n	n^2	n^3	n^4	n^5
2.00	4.0000	8.00000	16.0000	32.0000	**2.50**	6.2500	15.6250	39.0625	97.6563
2.01	4.0401	8.12060	16.3224	32.8080	**2.51**	6.3001	15.8133	39.6913	99.6251
2.02	4.0804	8.24241	16.6497	33.6323	**2.52**	6.3504	16.0030	40.3276	101.626
2.03	4.1209	8.36543	16.9818	34.4731	**2.53**	6.4009	16.1943	40.9715	103.658
2.04	4.1616	8.48966	17.3189	35.3306	**2.54**	6.4516	16.3871	41.6231	105.723
2.05	4.2025	8.61513	17.6610	36.2051	**2.55**	6.5025	16.5814	42.2825	107.820
2.06	4.2436	8.74182	18.0081	37.0968	**2.56**	6.5536	16.7772	42.9497	109.951
2.07	4.2849	8.86974	18.3604	38.0060	**2.57**	6.6049	16.9746	43.6247	112.115
2.08	4.3264	8.99891	18.7177	38.9329	**2.58**	6.6564	17.1735	44.3077	114.314
2.09	4.3681	9.12933	19.0803	39.8778	**2.59**	6.7081	17.3740	44.9986	116.546
2.10	4.4100	9.26100	19.4481	40.8410	**2.60**	6.7600	17.5760	45.6976	118.814
2.11	4.4521	9.39393	19.8212	41.8227	**2.61**	6.8121	17.7796	46.4047	121.116
2.12	4.4944	9.52813	20.1996	42.8232	**2.62**	6.8644	17.9847	47.1200	123.454
2.13	4.5369	9.66360	20.5835	43.8428	**2.63**	6.9169	18.1914	47.8435	125.828
2.14	4.5796	9.80034	20.9727	44.8817	**2.64**	6.9696	18.3997	48.5753	128.239
2.15	4.6225	9.93838	21.3675	45.9401	**2.65**	7.0225	18.6096	49.3155	130.686
2.16	4.6656	10.0777	21.7678	47.0185	**2.66**	7.0756	18.8211	50.0641	133.171
2.17	4.7089	10.2183	22.1737	48.1170	**2.67**	7.1289	19.0342	50.8212	135.693
2.18	4.7524	10.3602	22.5853	49.2360	**2.68**	7.1824	19.2488	51.5869	138.253
2.19	4.7961	10.5035	23.0026	50.3756	**2.69**	7.2361	19.4651	52.3611	140.851
2.20	4.8400	10.6480	23.4256	51.5363	**2.70**	7.2900	19.6830	53.1441	143.489
2.21	4.8841	10.7939	23.8544	52.7183	**2.71**	7.3441	19.9025	53.9358	146.166
2.22	4.9284	10.9410	24.2891	53.9219	**2.72**	7.3984	20.1236	54.7363	148.883
2.23	4.9729	11.0896	24.7297	55.1473	**2.73**	7.4529	20.3464	55.5457	151.640
2.24	5.0176	11.2394	25.1763	56.3949	**2.74**	7.5076	20.5708	56.3641	154.438
2.25	5.0625	11.3906	25.6289	57.6650	**2.75**	7.5625	20.7969	57.1914	157.276
2.26	5.1076	11.5432	26.0876	58.9579	**2.76**	7.6176	21.0246	58.0278	160.157
2.27	5.1529	11.6971	26.5524	60.2739	**2.77**	7.6729	21.2539	58.8734	163.079
2.28	5.1984	11.8524	27.0234	61.6133	**2.78**	7.7284	21.4850	59.7282	166.044
2.29	5.2441	12.0090	27.5006	62.9763	**2.79**	7.7841	21.7176	60.5922	169.052
2.30	5.2900	12.1670	27.9841	64.3634	**2.80**	7.8400	21.9520	61.4656	172.104
2.31	5.3361	12.3264	28.4740	65.7749	**2.81**	7.8961	22.1880	62.3484	175.199
2.32	5.3824	12.4872	28.9702	67.2109	**2.82**	7.9524	22.4258	63.2407	178.339
2.33	5.4289	12.6493	29.4730	68.6720	**2.83**	8.0089	22.6652	64.1425	181.523
2.34	5.4756	12.8129	29.9822	70.1583	**2.84**	8.0656	22.9063	65.0539	184.753
2.35	5.5225	12.9779	30.4980	71.6703	**2.85**	8.1225	23.1491	65.9750	188.029
2.36	5.5696	13.1443	31.0204	73.2082	**2.86**	8.1796	23.3937	66.9059	191.351
2.37	5.6169	13.3121	31.5496	74.7725	**2.87**	8.2369	23.6399	67.8465	194.720
2.38	5.6644	13.4813	32.0854	76.3633	**2.88**	8.2944	23.8879	68.7971	198.136
2.39	5.7121	13.6519	32.6281	77.9811	**2.89**	8.3521	24.1376	69.7576	201.599
2.40	5.7600	13.8240	33.1776	79.6262	**2.90**	8.4100	24.3890	70.7281	205.111
2.41	5.8081	13.9975	33.7340	81.2990	**2.91**	8.4681	24.6422	71.7087	208.672
2.42	5.8564	14.1725	34.2974	82.9998	**2.92**	8.5264	24.8971	72.6995	212.283
2.43	5.9049	14.3489	34.8678	84.7289	**2.93**	8.5849	25.1538	73.7005	215.942
2.44	5.9536	14.5268	35.4454	86.4867	**2.94**	8.6436	25.4122	74.7118	219.653
2.45	6.0025	14.7061	36.0300	88.2735	**2.95**	8.7025	25.6724	75.7335	223.414
2.46	6.0516	14.8869	36.6219	90.0898	**2.96**	8.7616	25.9343	76.7656	227.226
2.47	6.1009	15.0692	37.2210	91.9358	**2.97**	8.8209	26.1981	77.8083	231.091
2.48	6.1504	15.2530	37.8274	93.8120	**2.98**	8.8804	26.4636	78.8615	235.007
2.49	6.2001	15.4382	38.4412	95.7187	**2.99**	8.9401	26.7309	79.9254	238.977
2.50	6.2500	15.6250	39.0625	97.6563	**3.00**	9.0000	27.0000	81.0000	243.000

n	n^2	n^3	n^4	n^5	n	n^2	n^3	n^4	n^5
3.00	9.0000	27.0000	81.0000	243.000	3.50	12.2500	42.8750	150.063	525.219
3.01	9.0601	27.2709	82.0854	247.077	3.51	12.3201	43.2436	151.785	532.765
3.02	9.1204	27.5436	83.1817	251.209	3.52	12.3904	43.6142	153.522	540.397
3.03	9.1809	27.8181	84.2889	255.395	3.53	12.4609	43.9870	155.274	548.117
3.04	9.2416	28.0945	85.4072	259.638	3.54	12.5316	44.3619	157.041	555.925
3.05	9.3025	28.3726	86.5365	263.936	3.55	12.6025	44.7389	158.823	563.822
3.06	9.3636	28.6526	87.6770	268.292	3.56	12.6736	45.1180	160.620	571.808
3.07	9.4249	28.9344	88.8287	272.704	3.57	12.7449	45.4993	162.432	579.884
3.08	9.4864	29.2181	89.9918	277.175	3.58	12.8164	45.8827	164.260	588.051
3.09	9.5481	29.5036	91.1662	281.704	3.59	12.8881	46.2683	166.103	596.310
3.10	9.6100	29.7910	92.3521	286.292	3.60	12.9600	46.6560	167.962	604.662
3.11	9.6721	30.0802	93.5495	290.939	3.61	13.0321	47.0459	169.836	613.107
3.12	9.7344	30.3713	94.7585	295.647	3.62	13.1044	47.4379	171.725	621.646
3.13	9.7969	30.6643	95.9792	300.415	3.63	13.1769	47.8321	173.631	630.279
3.14	9.8596	30.9591	97.2117	305.245	3.64	13.2496	48.2285	175.552	639.009
3.15	9.9225	31.2559	98.4560	310.136	3.65	13.3225	48.6271	177.489	647.835
3.16	9.9856	31.5545	99.7122	315.091	3.66	13.3956	49.0279	179.442	656.758
3.17	10.0489	31.8550	100.980	320.108	3.67	13.4689	49.4309	181.411	665.779
3.18	10.1124	32.1574	102.261	325.189	3.68	13.5424	49.8360	183.397	674.899
3.19	10.1761	32.4618	103.553	330.334	3.69	13.6161	50.2434	185.398	684.119
3.20	10.2400	32.7680	104.858	335.544	3.70	13.6900	50.6530	187.416	693.440
3.21	10.3041	33.0762	106.174	340.820	3.71	13.7641	51.0648	189.450	702.861
3.22	10.3684	33.3862	107.504	346.162	3.72	13.8384	51.4788	191.501	712.385
3.23	10.4329	33.6983	108.845	351.571	3.73	13.9129	51.8951	193.569	722.012
3.24	10.4976	34.0122	110.200	357.047	3.74	13.9876	52.3136	195.653	731.742
3.25	10.5625	34.3281	111.566	362.591	3.75	14.0625	52.7344	197.754	741.577
3.26	10.6276	34.6460	112.946	368.204	3.76	14.1376	53.1574	199.872	751.518
3.27	10.6929	34.9658	114.338	373.886	3.77	14.2129	53.5826	202.007	761.565
3.28	10.7584	35.2876	115.743	379.638	3.78	14.2884	54.0102	204.158	771.719
3.29	10.8241	35.6129	117.161	385.460	3.79	14.3641	54.4399	206.327	781.981
3.30	10.8900	35.9370	118.592	391.354	3.80	14.4400	54.8720	208.514	792.352
3.31	10.9561	36.2647	120.036	397.320	3.81	14.5161	55.3063	210.717	802.832
3.32	11.0224	36.5944	121.493	403.358	3.82	14.5924	55.7430	212.938	813.424
3.33	11.0889	36.9260	122.964	409.469	3.83	14.6689	56.1819	215.177	824.126
3.34	11.1556	37.2597	124.447	415.654	3.84	14.7456	56.6231	217.433	834.942
3.35	11.2225	37.5954	125.945	421.914	3.85	14.8225	57.0666	219.707	845.870
3.36	11.2896	37.9331	127.455	428.249	3.86	14.8996	57.5125	221.998	856.913
3.37	11.3569	38.2728	128.979	434.660	3.87	14.9769	57.9606	224.308	868.070
3.38	11.4244	38.6145	130.517	441.147	3.88	15.0544	58.4111	226.635	879.344
3.39	11.4921	38.9582	132.068	447.712	3.89	15.1321	58.8639	228.980	890.734
3.40	11.5600	39.3040	133.634	454.354	3.90	15.2100	59.3190	231.344	902.242
3.41	11.6281	39.6518	135.213	461.075	3.91	15.2881	59.7765	233.726	913.869
3.42	11.6964	40.0017	136.806	467.876	3.92	15.3664	60.2363	236.126	925.615
3.43	11.7649	40.3536	138.413	474.756	3.93	15.4449	60.6985	238.545	937.482
3.44	11.8336	40.7076	140.034	481.717	3.94	15.5236	61.1630	240.982	949.470
3.45	11.9025	41.0636	141.670	488.760	3.95	15.6025	61.6299	243.438	961.580
3.46	11.9716	41.4217	143.319	495.884	3.96	15.6816	62.0991	245.913	973.814
3.47	12.0409	41.7819	144.983	503.092	3.97	15.7609	62.5708	248.406	986.172
3.48	12.1104	42.1442	146.662	510.383	3.98	15.8404	63.0448	250.918	998.655
3.49	12.1801	42.5085	148.355	517.758	3.99	15.9201	63.5212	253.450	1011.26
3.50	12.2500	42.8750	150.063	525.219	4.00	16.0000	64.0000	256.000	1024.00

n	n^2	n^3	n^4	n^5	n	n^2	n^3	n^4	n^5
4.00	16.0000	64.0000	256.000	1024.00	4.50	20.2500	91.1250	410.063	1845.28
4.01	16.0801	64.4812	258.570	1036.86	4.51	20.3401	91.7339	413.720	1865.88
4.02	16.1604	64.9648	261.159	1049.86	4.52	20.4304	92.3454	417.401	1886.65
4.03	16.2409	65.4508	263.767	1062.98	4.53	20.5209	92.9597	421.107	1907.62
4.04	16.3216	65.9393	266.395	1076.23	4.54	20.6116	93.5767	424.838	1928.76
4.05	16.4025	66.4301	269.042	1089.62	4.55	20.7025	94.1964	428.594	1950.10
4.06	16.4836	66.9234	271.709	1103.14	4.56	20.7936	94.8188	432.374	1971.62
4.07	16.5649	67.4191	274.396	1116.79	4.57	20.8849	95.4440	436.179	1993.34
4.08	16.6464	67.9173	277.103	1130.58	4.58	20.9764	96.0719	440.009	2015.24
4.09	16.7281	68.4179	279.829	1144.50	4.59	21.0681	96.7026	443.865	2037.34
4.10	16.8100	68.9210	282.576	1158.56	4.60	21.1600	97.3360	447.746	2059.63
4.11	16.8921	69.4265	285.343	1172.76	4.61	21.2521	97.9722	451.652	2082.11
4.12	16.9744	69.9345	288.130	1187.10	4.62	21.3444	98.6111	455.583	2104.80
4.13	17.0569	70.4450	290.938	1201.57	4.63	21.4369	99.2528	459.541	2127.67
4.14	17.1396	70.9579	293.766	1216.19	4.64	21.5296	99.8973	463.524	2150.75
4.15	17.2225	71.4734	296.615	1230.95	4.65	21.6225	100.545	467.533	2174.03
4.16	17.3056	71.9913	299.484	1245.85	4.66	21.7156	101.195	471.567	2197.50
4.17	17.3889	72.5117	302.374	1260.90	4.67	21.8089	101.848	475.628	2201.18
4.18	17.4724	73.0346	305.285	1276.09	4.68	21.9024	102.503	479.715	2245.07
4.19	17.5561	73.5601	308.217	1291.43	4.69	21.9961	103.162	483.828	2269.16
4.20	17.6400	74.0880	311.170	1306.91	4.70	22.0900	103.823	487.968	2293.45
4.21	17.7241	74.6185	314.144	1322.55	4.71	22.1841	104.487	492.134	2317.95
4.22	17.8084	75.1514	317.139	1338.33	4.72	22.2784	105.154	496.327	2342.66
4.23	17.8929	75.6870	320.156	1354.26	4.73	22.3729	105.824	500.547	2367.59
4.24	17.9776	76.2250	323.194	1370.34	4.74	22.4676	106.496	504.793	2392.72
4.25	18.0625	76.7656	326.254	1386.58	4.75	22.5625	107.172	509.066	2418.07
4.26	18.1476	77.3088	329.335	1402.97	4.76	22.6576	107.850	513.367	2443.63
4.27	18.2329	77.8545	332.439	1419.51	4.77	22.7529	108.531	517.694	2469.40
4.28	18.3184	78.4028	335.564	1436.21	4.78	22.8484	109.215	522.049	2495.40
4.29	18.4041	78.9536	338.711	1453.07	4.79	22.9441	109.902	526.432	2521.61
4.30	18.4900	79.5070	341.880	1470.08	4.80	23.0400	110.592	530.842	2548.04
4.31	18.5761	80.0630	345.071	1487.26	4.81	23.1361	111.285	535.279	2574.69
4.32	18.6624	80.6216	348.285	1504.59	4.82	23.2324	111.980	539.744	2601.57
4.33	18.7489	81.1827	351.521	1522.09	4.83	23.3289	112.679	544.238	2628.67
4.34	18.8356	81.7465	354.780	1539.74	4.84	23.4256	113.380	548.759	2655.99
4.35	18.9225	82.3129	358.061	1557.57	4.85	23.5225	114.084	553.308	2683.54
4.36	19.0096	82.8819	361.365	1575.55	4.86	23.6196	114.791	557.886	2711.32
4.37	19.0969	83.4535	364.692	1593.70	4.87	23.7169	115.501	562.491	2739.33
4.38	19.1844	84.0277	368.041	1612.02	4.88	23.8144	116.214	567.126	2767.57
4.39	19.2721	84.6045	371.414	1630.51	4.89	23.9121	116.930	571.789	2796.05
4.40	19.3600	85.1840	374.810	1649.16	4.90	24.0100	117.649	576.480	2824.75
4.41	19.4481	85.7661	378.229	1667.99	4.91	24.1081	118.371	581.200	2853.69
4.42	19.5364	86.3509	381.671	1686.99	4.92	24.2064	119.095	585.950	2882.87
4.43	19.6249	86.9383	385.137	1706.16	4.93	24.3049	119.823	590.728	2912.29
4.44	19.7136	87.5284	388.626	1725.50	4.94	24.4036	120.554	595.536	2941.95
4.45	19.8025	88.1211	392.139	1745.02	4.95	24.5025	121.287	600.373	2971.84
4.46	19.8916	88.7165	395.676	1764.71	4.96	24.6016	122.024	605.239	3001.98
4.47	19.9809	89.3146	399.236	1784.59	4.97	24.7009	122.763	610.134	3032.37
4.48	20.0704	89.9154	402.821	1804.64	4.98	24.8004	123.506	615.060	3063.00
4.49	20.1601	90.5188	406.430	1824.87	4.99	24.9001	124.251	620.015	3093.87
4.50	20.2500	91.1250	410.063	1845.28	5.00	25.0000	125.000	625.000	3125.00

4

n	n^2	n^3	n^4	n^5	n	n^2	n^3	n^4	n^5
5.00	25.0000	125.000	625.000	3125.00	5.50	30.2500	166.375	915.063	5032.84
5.01	25.1001	125.752	630.015	3156.38	5.51	30.3601	167.284	921.736	5078.76
5.02	25.2004	126.506	635.060	3188.00	5.52	30.4704	168.197	928.445	5125.02
5.03	25.3009	127.264	640.136	3219.88	5.53	30.5809	169.112	935.191	5171.61
5.04	25.4016	128.024	645.241	3252.02	5.54	30.6916	170.031	941.974	5218.54
5.05	25.5025	128.788	650.378	3284.41	5.55	30.8025	170.954	948.794	5265.81
5.06	25.6036	129.554	655.544	3317.05	5.56	30.9136	171.880	955.651	5313.42
5.07	25.7049	130.324	660.742	3349.96	5.57	31.0249	172.809	962.544	5361.37
5.08	25.8064	131.097	665.970	3383.13	5.58	31.1364	173.741	969.475	5409.67
5.09	25.9081	131.872	671.230	3416.56	5.59	31.2481	174.677	976.444	5458.32
5.10	26.0100	132.651	676.520	3450.25	5.60	31.3600	175.616	983.450	5507.32
5.11	26.1121	133.433	681.842	3484.21	5.61	31.4721	176.558	990.493	5556.67
5.12	26.2144	134.218	687.195	3518.44	5.62	31.5844	177.504	997.574	5606.37
5.13	26.3169	135.006	692.579	3552.93	5.63	31.6969	178.454	1004.69	5656.42
5.14	26.4196	135.797	697.995	3587.70	5.64	31.8096	179.466	1011.85	5706.84
5.15	26.5225	136.591	703.443	3622.73	5.65	31.9225	180.362	1019.05	5757.61
5.16	26.6256	137.388	708.923	3658.04	5.66	32.0356	181.321	1026.28	5808.74
5.17	26.7289	138.188	714.434	3693.62	5.67	32.1489	182.284	1033.55	5860.24
5.18	26.8324	138.992	719.978	3729.48	5.68	32.2624	183.250	1040.86	5912.10
5.19	26.9361	139.798	725.553	3765.62	5.69	32.3761	184.220	1048.21	5964.33
5.20	27.0400	140.608	731.162	3802.04	5.70	32.4900	185.193	1055.60	6016.92
5.21	27.1441	141.421	736.802	3838.74	5.71	32.6041	186.169	1063.03	6069.89
5.22	27.2484	142.237	742.475	3875.72	5.72	32.7184	187.149	1070.49	6123.22
5.23	27.3529	143.056	748.181	3912.99	5.73	32.8329	188.133	1078.00	6176.94
5.24	27.4576	143.878	753.920	3950.54	5.74	32.9476	189.119	1085.54	6231.02
5.25	27.5625	144.703	759.691	3988.38	5.75	33.0625	190.109	1093.13	6285.49
5.26	27.6676	145.532	765.496	4026.51	5.76	33.1776	191.103	1100.75	6340.34
5.27	27.7729	146.363	771.334	4064.93	5.77	33.2929	192.100	1108.42	6395.57
5.28	27.8784	147.198	777.205	4103.64	5.78	33.4084	193.101	1116.12	6451.18
5.29	27.9841	148.036	783.110	4142.65	5.79	33.5241	194.105	1123.87	6507.18
5.30	28.0900	148.877	789.048	4181.95	5.80	33.6400	195.112	1131.65	6563.57
5.31	28.1961	149.721	795.020	4221.56	5.81	33.7561	196.123	1139.47	6620.35
5.32	28.3024	150.569	801.026	4261.46	5.82	33.8724	197.137	1147.34	6677.52
5.33	28.4089	151.419	807.066	4301.66	5.83	33.9889	198.155	1155.25	6735.08
5.34	28.5156	152.273	813.139	4342.16	5.84	34.1056	199.177	1163.19	6793.04
5.35	28.6225	153.130	819.248	4382.97	5.85	34.2225	200.202	1171.18	6851.40
5.36	28.7296	153.991	825.390	4424.09	5.86	34.3396	201.230	1179.21	6910.16
5.37	28.8369	154.854	831.567	4465.51	5.87	34.4569	202.262	1187.28	6969.32
5.38	28.9444	155.721	837.778	4507.25	5.88	34.5744	203.297	1195.39	7028.89
5.39	29.0521	156.591	844.025	4549.29	5.89	34.6921	204.336	1203.54	7088.86
5.40	29.1600	157.464	850.306	4591.65	5.90	34.8100	205.379	1211.74	7149.24
5.41	29.2681	158.340	856.622	4634.32	5.91	34.9281	206.425	1219.97	7210.04
5.42	29.3764	159.220	862.973	4677.31	5.92	35.0464	207.475	1228.25	7271.24
5.43	29.4849	160.103	869.359	4720.62	5.93	35.1649	208.528	1236.57	7332.86
5.44	29.5936	160.989	875.781	4764.25	5.94	35.2836	209.585	1244.93	7394.90
5.45	29.7025	161.879	882.239	4808.20	5.95	35.4025	210.645	1253.34	7457.36
5.46	29.8116	162.771	888.731	4852.47	5.96	35.5216	211.709	1261.78	7520.23
5.47	29.9209	163.667	895.260	4897.07	5.97	35.6409	212.776	1270.27	7583.53
5.48	30.0304	164.567	901.825	4942.00	5.98	35.7604	213.847	1278.81	7647.26
5.49	30.1401	165.469	908.426	4987.26	5.99	35.8801	214.922	1287.38	7711.42
5.50	30.2500	166.375	915.063	5032.84	6.00	36.0000	216.000	1296.00	7776.00

5

n	n^2	n^3	n^4	n^5	n	n^2	n^3	n^4	n^5
6.00	36.0000	216.000	1296.00	7776.00	6.50	42.2500	274.625	1785.06	11602.9
6.01	36.1201	217.082	1304.66	7841.02	6.51	42.3801	275.894	1796.07	11692.4
6.02	36.2404	218.167	1313.37	7906.47	6.52	42.5104	277.168	1807.13	11782.5
6.03	36.3609	219.256	1322.12	7972.35	6.53	42.6409	278.445	1818.25	11873.1
6.04	36.4816	220.349	1330.91	8038.68	6.54	42.7716	279.726	1829.41	11964.3
6.05	36.6025	221.445	1339.74	8105.45	6.55	42.9025	281.011	1840.62	12056.1
6.06	36.7236	222.545	1348.62	8172.65	6.56	43.0336	282.300	1851.89	12148.4
6.07	36.8449	223.649	1357.55	8240.31	6.57	43.1649	283.593	1863.21	12241.3
6.08	36.9664	224.756	1366.51	8308.41	6.58	43.2964	284.890	1874.58	12334.7
6.09	37.0881	225.867	1375.53	8376.96	6.59	43.4281	286.191	1886.00	12428.7
6.10	37.2100	226.981	1384.58	8445.96	6.60	43.5600	287.496	1897.47	12523.3
6.11	37.3321	228.099	1393.69	8515.42	6.61	43.6921	288.805	1909.00	12618.5
6.12	37.4544	229.221	1402.83	8585.33	6.62	43.8244	290.118	1920.58	12714.2
6.13	37.5769	230.346	1412.02	8655.70	6.63	43.9569	291.434	1932.21	12810.5
6.14	37.6996	231.476	1421.26	8726.54	6.64	44.0896	292.755	1943.89	12907.4
6.15	37.8225	232.608	1430.54	8797.83	6.65	44.2225	294.080	1955.63	13004.9
6.16	37.9456	233.745	1439.87	8869.59	6.66	44.3556	295.408	1967.42	13103.0
6.17	38.0689	234.885	1449.24	8941.82	6.67	44.4889	296.741	1979.26	13201.7
6.18	38.1924	236.029	1458.66	9014.52	6.68	44.6224	298.078	1991.16	13300.9
6.19	38.3161	237.177	1468.12	9087.68	6.69	44.7561	299.418	2003.11	13400.8
6.20	38.4400	238.328	1477.63	9161.33	6.70	44.8900	300.763	2015.11	13501.3
6.21	38.5641	239.483	1487.19	9235.45	6.71	45.0241	302.112	2027.17	13602.3
6.22	38.6884	240.642	1496.79	9310.05	6.72	45.1584	303.464	2039.28	13704.0
6.23	38.8129	241.804	1506.44	9385.13	6.73	45.2929	304.821	2051.45	13806.2
6.24	38.9376	242.971	1516.14	9460.69	6.74	45.4276	306.182	2063.67	13909.1
6.25	39.0625	244.141	1525.88	9536.74	6.75	45.5625	307.547	2075.94	14012.6
6.26	39.1876	245.314	1535.67	9613.28	6.76	45.6976	308.916	2088.27	14116.7
6.27	39.3129	246.492	1545.50	9690.31	6.77	45.8329	310.289	2100.65	14221.4
6.28	39.4384	247.673	1555.39	9767.83	6.78	45.9684	311.666	2113.09	14326.8
6.29	39.5641	248.858	1565.32	9845.85	6.79	46.1041	313.047	2125.59	14432.7
6.30	39.6900	250.047	1575.30	9924.37	6.80	46.2400	314.432	2138.14	14539.3
6.31	39.8161	251.240	1585.32	10003.4	6.81	46.3761	315.821	2150.74	14646.6
6.32	39.9424	252.436	1595.40	10082.9	6.82	46.5124	317.215	2163.40	14754.4
6.33	40.0689	253.636	1605.52	10162.9	6.83	46.6489	318.612	2176.12	14862.9
6.34	40.1956	254.840	1615.69	10243.5	6.84	46.7856	320.014	2188.89	14972.0
6.35	40.3225	256.048	1625.90	10324.5	6.85	46.9225	321.419	2201.72	15081.8
6.36	40.4496	257.259	1636.17	10406.0	6.86	47.0596	322.829	2214.61	15192.2
6.37	40.5769	258.475	1646.48	10488.1	6.87	47.1969	324.243	2227.55	15303.3
6.38	40.7044	259.694	1656.85	10570.7	6.88	47.3344	325.661	2240.55	15415.0
6.39	40.8321	260.917	1667.26	10653.8	6.89	47.4721	327.083	2253.60	15527.3
6.40	40.9600	262.144	1677.72	10737.4	6.90	47.6100	328.509	2266.71	15640.3
6.41	41.0881	263.375	1688.23	10821.6	6.91	47.7481	329.939	2279.88	15754.0
6.42	41.2164	264.609	1698.79	10906.2	6.92	47.8864	331.374	2293.11	15868.3
6.43	41.3449	265.848	1709.40	10991.4	6.93	48.0249	332.813	2306.39	15983.3
6.44	41.4736	267.090	1720.06	11077.2	6.94	48.1636	334.255	2319.73	16098.9
6.45	41.6025	268.336	1730.77	11163.5	6.95	48.3025	335.702	2333.13	16215.3
6.46	41.7316	269.586	1741.53	11250.3	6.96	48.4416	337.154	2346.59	16332.3
6.47	41.8609	270.840	1752.33	11337.6	6.97	48.5809	338.609	2360.10	16449.9
6.48	41.9904	272.098	1763.19	11425.5	6.98	48.7204	340.068	2373.68	16568.3
6.49	42.1201	273.359	1774.10	11513.9	6.99	48.8601	341.532	2387.31	16687.3
6.50	42.2500	274.625	1785.06	11602.9	7.00	49.0000	343.000	2401.00	16807.0

n	n^2	n^3	n^4	n^5	n	n^2	n^3	n^4	n^5
7.00	49.0000	343.000	2401.00	16807.0	**7.50**	56.2500	421.875	3164.06	23730.5
7.01	49.1401	344.472	2414.75	16927.4	**7.51**	56.4001	423.565	3180.97	23889.1
7.02	49.2804	345.948	2428.56	17048.5	**7.52**	56.5504	425.259	3197.95	24048.6
7.03	49.4209	347.429	2442.43	17170.3	**7.53**	56.7009	426.958	3214.99	24208.9
7.04	49.5616	348.914	2456.35	17292.7	**7.54**	56.8516	428.661	3232.10	24370.1
7.05	49.7025	350.403	2470.34	17415.9	**7.55**	57.0025	430.369	3249.29	24532.1
7.06	49.8436	351.896	2484.38	17539.8	**7.56**	57.1536	432.081	3266.53	24695.0
7.07	49.9849	353.393	2498.49	17664.3	**7.57**	57.3049	433.798	3283.85	24858.8
7.08	50.1264	354.895	2512.66	17789.6	**7.58**	57.4564	435.520	3301.24	25023.4
7.09	50.2681	356.401	2526.88	17915.6	**7.59**	57.6081	437.245	3318.69	25188.9
7.10	50.4100	357.911	2541.17	18042.3	**7.60**	57.7600	438.976	3336.22	25355.3
7.11	50.5521	359.425	2555.51	18169.7	**7.61**	57.9121	440.711	3353.81	25522.5
7.12	50.6944	360.944	2569.92	18297.8	**7.62**	58.0644	442.451	3371.47	25690.6
7.13	50.8369	362.467	2584.39	18426.7	**7.63**	58.2169	444.195	3389.21	25859.7
7.14	50.9796	363.994	2598.92	18556.3	**7.64**	58.3696	445.994	3407.01	26029.6
7.15	51.1225	365.526	2613.51	18686.6	**7.65**	58.5225	447.697	3424.88	26200.4
7.16	51.2656	367.062	2628.16	18817.6	**7.66**	58.6756	449.455	3442.83	26372.0
7.17	51.4089	368.602	2642.88	18949.4	**7.67**	58.8289	451.218	3460.84	26544.6
7.18	51.5524	370.146	2657.65	19081.9	**7.68**	58.9824	452.985	3478.92	26718.1
7.19	51.6961	371.695	2672.49	19215.2	**7.69**	59.1361	454.757	3497.08	26892.5
7.20	51.8400	373.248	2687.39	19349.2	**7.70**	59.2900	456.533	3515.30	27067.8
7.21	51.9841	374.805	2702.35	19483.9	**7.71**	59.4441	458.314	3533.60	27244.1
7.22	52.1284	376.367	2717.37	19619.4	**7.72**	59.5984	460.100	3551.97	27421.2
7.23	52.2729	377.933	2732.46	19755.7	**7.73**	59.7529	461.890	3570.41	27599.3
7.24	52.4176	379.503	2747.60	19892.7	**7.74**	59.9076	463.685	3588.92	27778.2
7.25	52.5625	381.078	2762.82	20030.4	**7.75**	60.0625	465.484	3607.50	27958.2
7.26	52.7076	382.657	2778.09	20168.9	**7.76**	60.2176	467.289	3626.16	28139.0
7.27	52.8529	384.241	2793.43	20308.2	**7.77**	60.3729	469.097	3644.89	28320.8
7.28	52.9984	385.828	2808.83	20448.3	**7.78**	60.5284	470.911	3663.69	28503.5
7.29	53.1441	387.420	2824.30	20589.1	**7.79**	60.6841	472.729	3682.56	28687.1
7.30	53.2900	389.017	2839.82	20730.7	**7.80**	60.8400	474.552	3701.51	28871.7
7.31	53.4361	390.618	2855.42	20873.1	**7.81**	60.9961	476.380	3720.52	29057.3
7.32	53.5824	392.223	2871.07	21016.3	**7.82**	61.1524	478.212	3739.62	29243.8
7.33	53.7289	393.833	2886.80	21160.2	**7.83**	61.3089	480.049	3758.78	29431.3
7.34	53.8756	395.447	2902.58	21304.9	**7.84**	61.4656	481.890	3778.02	29619.7
7.35	54.0225	397.065	2918.43	21450.5	**7.85**	61.6225	483.737	3797.33	29809.1
7.36	54.1696	398.688	2934.35	21596.8	**7.86**	61.7796	485.588	3816.72	29999.4
7.37	54.3169	400.316	2950.33	21743.9	**7.87**	61.9369	487.443	3836.18	30190.7
7.38	54.4644	401.947	2966.37	21891.8	**7.88**	62.0944	489.304	3855.71	30383.0
7.39	54.6121	403.583	2982.48	22040.5	**7.89**	62.2521	491.169	3875.32	30576.3
7.40	54.7600	405.224	2998.66	22190.1	**7.90**	62.4100	493.039	3895.01	30770.6
7.41	54.9081	406.869	3014.90	22340.4	**7.91**	62.5681	494.914	3914.77	30965.8
7.42	55.0564	408.518	3031.21	22491.6	**7.92**	62.7264	496.793	3934.60	31162.0
7.43	55.2049	410.172	3047.58	22643.5	**7.93**	62.8849	498.677	3954.51	31359.3
7.44	55.3536	411.831	3064.02	22796.3	**7.94**	63.0436	500.566	3974.50	31557.5
7.45	55.5025	413.494	3080.52	22949.9	**7.95**	63.2025	502.460	3994.56	31756.7
7.46	55.6516	415.161	3097.10	23104.4	**7.96**	63.3616	504.358	4014.69	31957.0
7.47	55.8009	416.833	3113.74	23259.6	**7.97**	63.5209	506.262	4034.90	32158.2
7.48	55.9504	418.509	3130.45	23415.7	**7.98**	63.6804	508.170	4055.19	32360.4
7.49	56.1001	420.190	3147.22	23572.7	**7.99**	63.8401	510.082	4075.56	32563.7
7.50	56.2500	421.875	3164.06	23730.5	**8.00**	64.0000	512.000	4096.00	32768.0

n	n^2	n^3	n^4	n^5	n	n^2	n^3	n^4	n^5
8.00	64.0000	512.000	4096.00	32768.0	8.50	72.2500	614.125	5220.06	44370.5
8.01	64.1601	513.922	4116.52	32973.3	8.51	72.4201	616.295	5244.67	44632.1
8.02	64.3204	515.850	4137.11	33179.7	8.52	72.5904	618.470	5269.37	44895.0
8.03	64.4809	517.782	4157.79	33387.0	8.53	72.7609	620.650	5294.15	45159.1
8.04	64.6416	519.718	4178.54	33595.4	8.54	72.9316	622.836	5319.02	45424.4
8.05	64.8025	521.660	4199.36	33804.9	8.55	73.1025	625.026	5343.98	45691.0
8.06	64.9636	523.607	4220.27	34015.4	8.56	73.2736	627.222	5369.02	45958.8
8.07	65.1249	525.558	4241.25	34226.9	8.57	73.4449	629.423	5394.15	46227.9
8.08	65.2864	527.514	4262.31	34439.5	8.58	73.6164	631.629	5419.37	46498.2
8.09	65.4481	529.475	4283.45	34653.1	8.59	73.7881	633.840	5444.68	46769.8
8.10	65.6100	531.441	4304.67	34867.8	8.60	73.9600	636.056	5470.08	47042.7
8.11	65.7721	533.412	4325.97	35083.6	8.61	74.1321	638.277	5495.57	47316.8
8.12	65.9344	535.387	4347.35	35300.4	8.62	74.3044	640.504	5521.14	47592.3
8.13	66.0969	537.368	4368.80	35518.3	8.63	74.4769	642.736	5546.81	47869.0
8.14	66.2596	539.353	4390.33	35737.3	8.64	74.6496	644.973	5572.56	48146.9
8.15	66.4225	541.343	4411.95	35957.4	8.65	74.8225	647.215	5598.41	48426.2
8.16	66.5856	543.338	4433.64	36178.5	8.66	74.9956	649.462	5624.34	48706.8
8.17	66.7489	545.339	4455.42	36400.7	8.67	75.1689	651.714	5650.36	48988.7
8.18	66.9124	547.343	4477.27	36624.1	8.68	75.3424	653.972	5676.48	49271.8
8.19	67.0761	549.353	4499.20	36848.5	8.69	75.5161	656.235	5702.68	49556.3
8.20	67.2400	551.368	4521.22	37074.0	8.70	75.6900	658.503	5728.98	49842.1
8.21	67.4041	553.388	4543.31	37300.6	8.71	75.8641	660.776	5755.36	50129.2
8.22	67.5684	555.412	4565.49	37528.3	8.72	76.0384	663.055	5781.84	50417.6
8.23	67.7329	557.442	4587.75	37757.1	8.73	76.2129	665.339	5808.41	50707.4
8.24	67.8976	559.476	4610.08	37987.1	8.74	76.3876	667.628	5835.07	50998.5
8.25	68.0625	561.516	4632.50	38218.2	8.75	76.5625	669.922	5861.82	51290.9
8.26	68.2276	563.560	4655.01	38450.3	8.76	76.7376	672.221	5888.66	51584.7
8.27	68.3929	565.609	4677.59	38683.7	8.77	76.9129	674.526	5915.59	51879.8
8.28	68.5584	567.664	4700.25	38918.1	8.78	77.0884	676.836	5942.62	52176.2
8.29	68.7241	569.723	4723.00	39153.7	8.79	77.2641	679.151	5969.74	52474.0
8.30	68.8900	571.787	4745.83	39390.4	8.80	77.4400	681.472	5996.95	52773.2
8.31	69.0561	573.856	4768.74	39628.3	8.81	77.6161	683.798	6024.26	53073.7
8.32	69.2224	575.930	4791.74	39867.3	8.82	77.7924	686.129	6051.66	53375.6
8.33	69.3889	578.010	4814.82	40107.4	8.83	77.9689	688.465	6079.15	53678.9
8.34	69.5556	580.094	4837.98	40348.8	8.84	78.1456	690.807	6106.73	53983.5
8.35	69.7225	582.183	4861.23	40591.2	8.85	78.3225	693.154	6134.41	54289.6
8.36	69.8896	584.277	4884.56	40834.9	8.86	78.4996	695.506	6162.19	54597.0
8.37	70.0569	586.376	4907.97	41079.7	8.87	78.6769	697.864	6190.05	54905.8
8.38	70.2244	588.480	4931.47	41325.7	8.88	78.8544	700.227	6218.02	55216.0
8.39	70.3921	590.590	4955.05	41572.9	8.89	79.0321	702.595	6246.07	55527.6
8.40	70.5600	592.704	4978.71	41821.2	8.90	79.2100	704.969	6274.22	55840.6
8.41	70.7281	594.823	5002.46	42070.7	8.91	79.3881	707.348	6302.47	56155.0
8.42	70.8964	596.948	5026.30	42321.4	8.92	79.5664	709.732	6330.81	56470.8
8.43	71.0649	599.077	5050.22	42573.4	8.93	79.7449	712.122	6359.25	56788.1
8.44	71.2336	601.212	5074.23	42826.5	8.94	79.9236	714.517	6387.78	57106.8
8.45	71.4025	603.351	5098.32	43080.8	8.95	80.1025	716.917	6416.41	57426.9
8.46	71.5716	605.496	5122.49	43336.3	8.96	80.2816	719.323	6445.14	57748.4
8.47	71.7409	607.645	5146.76	43593.0	8.97	80.4609	721.734	6473.96	58071.4
8.48	71.9104	609.800	5171.11	43851.0	8.98	80.6404	724.151	6502.87	58395.8
8.49	72.0801	611.960	5195.54	44110.1	8.99	80.8201	726.573	6531.89	58721.7
8.50	72.2500	614.125	5220.06	44370.5	9.00	81.0000	729.000	6561.00	59049.0

n	n^2	n^3	n^4	n^5	n	n^2	n^3	n^4	n^5
9.00	81.0000	729.000	6561.00	59049.0	9.50	90.2500	857.375	8145.06	77378.1
9.01	81.1801	731.433	6590.21	59377.8	9.51	90.4401	860.085	8179.41	77786.2
9.02	81.3604	733.871	6619.51	59708.0	9.52	90.6304	862.801	8213.87	78196.0
9.03	81.5409	736.314	6648.92	60039.7	9.53	90.8209	865.523	8248.44	78607.6
9.04	81.7216	738.763	6678.42	60372.9	9.54	91.0116	868.251	8283.11	79020.9
9.05	81.9025	741.218	6708.02	60707.6	9.55	91.2025	870.984	8317.90	79435.9
9.06	82.0836	743.677	6737.72	61043.7	9.56	91.3936	873.723	8352.79	79852.7
9.07	82.2649	746.143	6767.51	61381.3	9.57	91.5849	876.467	8387.79	80271.2
9.08	82.4464	748.613	6797.41	61720.5	9.58	91.7764	879.218	8422.91	80691.5
9.09	82.6281	751.089	6827.40	62061.1	9.59	91.9681	881.974	8458.13	81113.5
9.10	82.8100	753.571	6857.50	62403.2	9.60	92.1600	884.736	8493.47	81537.3
9.11	82.9921	756.058	6887.69	62746.8	9.61	92.3521	887.504	8528.91	81962.8
9.12	83.1744	758.551	6917.98	63092.0	9.62	92.5444	890.277	8564.47	82390.2
9.13	83.3569	761.048	6948.37	63438.6	9.63	92.7369	893.056	8600.13	82819.3
9.14	83.5396	763.552	6978.86	63786.8	9.64	92.9296	895.841	8635.91	83250.2
9.15	83.7225	766.061	7009.46	64136.5	9.65	93.1225	898.632	8671.80	83682.9
9.16	83.9056	768.575	7040.15	64487.8	9.66	93.3156	901.429	8707.80	84117.4
9.17	84.0889	771.095	7070.94	64840.5	9.67	93.5089	904.231	8743.91	84553.7
9.18	84.2724	773.621	7101.84	65194.9	9.68	93.7024	907.039	8780.14	84991.8
9.19	84.4561	776.152	7132.83	65550.7	9.69	93.8961	909.853	8816.48	85431.7
9.20	84.6400	778.688	7163.93	65908.2	9.70	94.0900	912.673	8852.93	85873.4
9.21	84.8241	781.230	7195.13	66267.1	9.71	94.2841	915.499	8889.49	86317.0
9.22	85.0084	783.777	7226.43	66627.7	9.72	94.4784	918.330	8926.17	86762.4
9.23	85.1929	786.330	7257.83	66989.8	9.73	94.6729	921.167	8962.96	87209.6
9.24	85.3776	788.889	7289.33	67353.5	9.74	94.8676	924.010	8999.86	87658.7
9.25	85.5625	791.453	7320.94	67718.7	9.75	95.0625	926.859	9036.88	88109.6
9.26	85.7476	794.023	7352.65	68085.5	9.76	95.2576	929.714	9074.01	88562.3
9.27	85.9329	796.598	7384.46	68454.0	9.77	95.4529	932.575	9111.26	89017.0
9.28	86.1184	799.179	7416.38	68824.0	9.78	95.6484	935.441	9148.62	89473.5
9.29	86.3041	801.765	7448.40	69195.6	9.79	95.8441	938.314	9186.09	89931.8
9.30	86.4900	804.357	7480.52	69568.8	9.80	96.0400	941.192	9223.68	90392.1
9.31	86.6761	806.954	7512.75	69943.7	9.81	96.2361	944.076	9261.39	90854.2
9.32	86.8624	809.558	7545.08	70320.1	9.82	96.4324	946.966	9299.21	91318.2
9.33	87.0489	812.166	7577.51	70698.2	9.83	96.6289	949.862	9337.14	91784.1
9.34	87.2356	814.781	7610.05	71077.9	9.84	96.8256	952.764	9375.20	92251.9
9.35	87.4225	817.400	7642.69	71459.2	9.85	97.0225	955.672	9413.37	92721.7
9.36	87.6096	820.026	7675.44	71842.1	9.86	97.2196	958.585	9451.65	93193.3
9.37	87.7969	822.657	7708.30	72226.7	9.87	97.4169	961.505	9490.05	93666.8
9.38	87.9844	825.294	7741.25	72613.0	9.88	97.6144	964.430	9528.57	94142.3
9.39	88.1721	827.936	7774.32	73000.9	9.89	97.8121	967.362	9567.21	94619.7
9.40	88.3600	830.584	7807.49	73390.4	9.90	98.0100	970.299	9605.96	95099.0
9.41	88.5481	833.238	7840.77	73781.6	9.91	98.2081	973.242	9644.83	95580.3
9.42	88.7364	835.897	7874.15	74174.5	9.92	98.4064	976.191	9683.82	96063.5
9.43	88.9249	838.562	7907.64	74569.0	9.93	98.6049	979.147	9722.93	96548.7
9.44	89.1136	841.232	7941.23	74965.2	9.94	98.8036	982.108	9762.15	97035.8
9.45	89.3025	843.909	7974.94	75363.1	9.95	99.0025	985.075	9801.50	97524.9
9.46	89.4916	846.591	8008.75	75762.7	9.96	99.2016	988.048	9840.96	98015.9
9.47	89.6809	849.278	8042.66	76164.0	9.97	99.4009	991.027	9880.54	98509.0
9.48	89.8704	851.971	8076.69	76567.0	9.98	99.6004	994.012	9920.24	99004.0
9.49	90.0601	854.670	8110.82	76971.7	9.99	99.8001	997.003	9960.06	99501.0
9.50	90.2500	857.375	8145.06	77378.1	10.00	100.000	1000.00	10000.0	100000

n	n^2	n^3	n^4	n^5
1	1	1	1	1
2	4	8	16	32
3	9	27	81	243
4	16	64	256	1024
5	25	125	625	3125
6	36	216	1296	7776
7	49	343	2401	16807
8	64	512	4096	32768
9	81	729	6561	59049

TABLE

OF

COMMON LOGARITHMS ·

OF NUMBERS

From 1 to 10,000.

N.	Log.	N.	Log.	N.	Log.	N.	Log.	N.	Log.
0	— ∞	**20**	30 103	**40**	60 206	**60**	77 815	**80**	90 309
1	00 000	21	32 222	41	61 278	61	78 533	81	90 849
2	30 103	22	34 242	42	62 325	62	79 239	82	91 381
3	47 712	23	36 173	43	63 347	63	79 934	83	91 908
4	60 206	24	38 021	44	64 345	64	80 618	84	92 428
5	69 897	25	39 794	45	65 321	65	81 291	85	92 942
6	77 815	26	41 497	46	66 276	66	81 954	86	93 450
7	84 510	27	43 136	47	67 210	67	82 607	87	93 952
8	90 309	28	44 716	48	68 124	68	83 251	88	94 448
9	95 424	29	46 240	49	69 020	69	83 885	89	94 939
10	00 000	**30**	47 712	**50**	69 897	**70**	84 510	**90**	95 424
11	04 139	31	49 136	51	70 757	71	85 126	91	95 904
12	07 918	32	50 515	52	71 600	72	85 733	92	96 379
13	11 394	33	51 851	53	72 428	73	86 332	93	96 848
14	14 613	34	53 148	54	73 239	74	86 923	94	97 313
15	17 609	35	54 407	55	74 036	75	87 506	95	97 772
16	20 412	36	55 630	56	74 819	76	88 081	96	98 227
17	23 045	37	56 820	57	75 587	77	88 649	97	98 677
18	25 527	38	57 978	58	76 343	78	89 209	98	99 123
19	27 875	39	59 106	59	77 085	79	89 763	99	99 564
20	30 103	**40**	60 206	**60**	77 815	**80**	90 309	**100**	00 000

N.	L. 0	1	2	3	4	5	6	7	8	9
100	00 000	043	087	130	173	217	260	303	346	389
101	432	475	518	561	604	647	689	732	775	817
102	860	903	945	988	*030	*072	*115	*157	*199	*242
103	01 284	326	368	410	452	494	536	578	620	662
104	703	745	787	828	870	912	953	995	*036	*078
105	02 119	160	202	243	284	325	366	407	449	490
106	531	572	612	653	694	735	776	816	857	898
107	938	979	*019	*060	*100	*141	*181	*222	*262	*302
108	03 342	383	423	463	503	543	583	623	663	703
109	743	782	822	862	902	941	981	*021	*060	*100
110	04 139	179	218	258	297	336	376	415	454	493
111	532	571	610	650	689	727	766	805	844	883
112	922	961	999	*038	*077	*115	*154	*192	*231	*269
113	05 308	346	385	423	461	500	538	576	614	652
114	690	729	767	805	843	881	918	956	994	*032
115	06 070	108	145	183	221	258	296	333	371	408
116	446	483	521	558	595	633	670	707	744	781
117	819	856	893	930	967	*004	*041	*078	*115	*151
118	07 188	225	262	298	335	372	408	445	482	518
119	555	591	628	664	700	737	773	809	846	882
120	918	954	990	*027	*063	*099	*135	*171	*207	*243
121	08 279	314	350	386	422	458	493	529	565	600
122	636	672	707	743	778	814	849	884	920	955
123	991	*026	*061	*096	*132	*167	*202	*237	*272	*307
124	09 342	377	412	447	482	517	552	587	621	656
125	691	726	760	795	830	864	899	934	968	*003
126	10 037	072	106	140	175	209	243	278	312	346
127	380	415	449	483	517	551	585	619	653	687
128	721	755	789	823	857	890	924	958	992	*025
129	11 059	093	126	160	193	227	261	294	327	361
130	394	428	461	494	528	561	594	628	661	694
131	727	760	793	826	860	893	926	959	992	*024
132	12 057	090	123	156	189	222	254	287	320	352
133	385	418	450	483	516	548	581	613	646	678
134	710	743	775	808	840	872	905	937	969	*001
135	13 033	066	098	130	162	194	226	258	290	322
136	354	386	418	450	481	513	545	577	609	640
137	672	704	735	767	799	830	862	893	925	956
138	988	*019	*051	*082	*114	*145	*176	*207	*239	*270
139	14 301	333	364	395	426	457	489	520	551	582
140	613	644	675	706	737	768	799	829	860	891
141	922	953	983	*014	*045	*076	*106	*137	*168	*198
142	15 229	259	290	320	351	381	412	442	473	503
143	534	564	594	625	655	685	715	746	776	806
144	836	866	897	927	957	987	*017	*047	*077	*107
145	16 137	167	197	227	256	286	316	346	376	406
146	435	465	495	524	554	584	613	643	673	702
147	732	761	791	820	850	879	909	938	967	997
148	17 026	056	085	114	143	173	202	231	260	289
149	319	348	377	406	435	464	493	522	551	580
150	609	638	667	696	725	754	782	811	840	869
N.	L. 0	1	2	3	4	5	6	7	8	9

P. P.

	44	43	42
1	4.4	4.3	4.2
2	8.8	8.6	8.4
3	13.2	12.9	12.6
4	17.6	17.2	16.8
5	22.0	21.5	21.0
6	26.4	25.8	25.2
7	30.8	30.1	29.4
8	35.2	34.4	33.6
9	39.6	38.7	37.8

	41	40	39
1	4.1	4.0	3.9
2	8.2	8.0	7.8
3	12.3	12.0	11.7
4	16.4	16.0	15.6
5	20.5	20.0	19.5
6	24.6	24.0	23.4
7	28.7	28.0	27.3
8	32.8	32.0	31.2
9	36.9	36.0	35.1

	38	37	36
1	3.8	3.7	3.6
2	7.6	7.4	7.2
3	11.4	11.1	10.8
4	15.2	14.8	14.4
5	19.0	18.5	18.0
6	22.8	22.2	21.6
7	26.6	25.9	25.2
8	30.4	29.6	28.8
9	34.2	33.3	32.4

	35	34	33
1	3.5	3.4	3.3
2	7.0	6.8	6.6
3	10.5	10.2	9.9
4	14.0	13.6	13.2
5	17.5	17.0	16.5
6	21.0	20.4	19.8
7	24.5	23.8	23.1
8	28.0	27.2	26.4
9	31.5	30.6	29.7

	32	31	30
1	3.2	3.1	3.0
2	6.4	6.2	6.0
3	9.6	9.3	9.0
4	12.8	12.4	12.0
5	16.0	15.5	15.0
6	19.2	18.6	18.0
7	22.4	21.7	21.0
8	25.6	24.8	24.0
9	28.8	27.9	27.0

N.	L. 0	1	2	3	4	5	6	7	8	9
150	17 609	638	667	696	725	754	782	811	840	869
151	898	926	955	984	*013	*041	*070	*099	*127	*156
152	18 184	213	241	270	298	327	355	384	412	441
153	469	498	526	554	583	611	639	667	696	724
154	752	780	808	837	865	893	921	949	977	*005
155	19 033	061	089	117	145	173	201	229	257	285
156	312	340	368	396	424	451	479	507	535	562
157	590	618	645	673	700	728	756	783	811	838
158	866	893	921	948	976	*003	*030	*058	*085	*112
159	20 140	167	194	222	249	276	303	330	358	385
160	412	439	466	493	520	548	575	602	629	656
161	683	710	737	763	790	817	844	871	898	925
162	952	978	*005	*032	*059	*085	*112	*139	*165	*192
163	21 219	245	272	299	325	352	378	405	431	458
164	484	511	537	564	590	617	643	669	696	722
165	748	775	801	827	854	880	906	932	958	985
166	22 011	037	063	089	115	141	167	194	220	246
167	272	298	324	350	376	401	427	453	479	505
168	531	557	583	608	634	660	686	712	737	763
169	789	814	840	866	891	917	943	968	994	*019
170	23 045	070	096	121	147	172	198	223	249	274
171	300	325	350	376	401	426	452	477	502	528
172	553	578	603	629	654	679	704	729	754	779
173	805	830	855	880	905	930	955	980	*005	*030
174	24 055	080	·105	130	155	180	204	229	254	279
175	304	329	353	378	403	428	452	477	502	527
176	551	576	601	625	650	674	699	724	748	773
177	797	822	846	871	895	920	944	969	993	*018
178	25 042	066	091	115	139	164	188	212	237	261
179	285	310	334	358	382	406	431	455	479	503
180	527	551	575	600	624	648	672	696	720	744
181	768	792	816	840	864	888	912	935	959	983
182	26 007	031	055	079	102	126	150	174	198	221
183	245	269	293	316	340	364	387	411	435	458
184	482	505	529	553	576	600	623	647	670	694
185	717	741	764	788	811	834	858	881	905	928
186	951	975	998	*021	*045	*068	*091	*114	*138	*161
187	27 184	207	231	254	277	300	323	346	370	393
188	416	439	462	485	508	531	554	577	600	623
189	646	669	692	715	738	761	784	807	830	852
190	875	898	921	944	967	989	*012	*035	*058	*081
191	28 103	126	149	171	194	217	240	262	285	307
192	330	353	375	398	421	443	466	488	511	533
193	556	578	601	623	646	668	691	713	735	758
194	780	803	825	847	870	892	914	937	959	981
195	29 003	026	048	070	092	115	137	159	181	203
196	226	248	270	292	314	336	358	380	403	425
197	447	469	491	513	535	557	579	601	623	645
198	667	688	710	732	754	776	798	820	842	863
199	885	907	929	951	973	994	*016	*038	*060	*081
200	30 103	125	146	168	190	211	233	255	276	298
N.	L. 0	1	2	3	4	5	6	7	8	9

P. P.

	29	28
1	2.9	2.8
2	5.8	5.6
3	8.7	8.4
4	11.6	11.2
5	14.5	14.0
6	17.4	16.8
7	20.3	19.6
8	23.2	22.4
9	26.1	25.2

	27	26
1	2.7	2.6
2	5.4	5.2
3	8.1	7.8
4	10.8	10.4
5	13.5	13.0
6	16.2	15.6
7	18.9	18.2
8	21.6	20.8
9	24.3	23.4

	25
1	2.5
2	5.0
3	7.5
4	10.0
5	12.5
6	15.0
7	17.5
8	20.0
9	22.5

	24	23
1	2.4	2.3
2	4.8	4.6
3	7.2	6.9
4	9.6	9.2
5	12.0	11.5
6	14.4	13.8
7	16.8	16.1
8	19.2	18.4
9	21.6	20.7

	22	21
1	2.2	2.1
2	4.4	4.2
3	6.6	6.3
4	8.8	8.4
5	11.0	10.5
6	13.2	12.6
7	15.4	14.7
8	17.6	16.8
9	19.8	18.9

LOGARITHMS.

N.	L. 0	1	2	3	4	5	6	7	8	9
200	30 103	125	146	168	190	211	233	255	276	298
201	320	341	363	384	406	428	449	471	492	514
202	535	557	578	600	621	643	664	685	707	728
203	750	771	792	814	835	856	878	899	920	942
204	963	984	*006	*027	*048	*069	*091	*112	*133	*154
205	31 175	197	218	239	260	281	302	323	345	366
206	387	408	429	450	471	492	513	534	555	576
207	597	618	639	660	681	702	723	744	765	785
208	806	827	848	869	890	911	931	952	973	994
209	32 015	035	056	077	098	118	139	160	181	201
210	222	243	263	284	305	325	346	366	387	408
211	428	449	469	490	510	531	552	572	593	613
212	634	654	675	695	715	736	756	777	797	818
213	838	858	879	899	919	940	960	980	*001	*021
214	33 041	062	082	102	122	143	163	183	203	224
215	244	264	284	304	325	345	365	385	405	425
216	445	465	486	506	526	546	566	586	606	626
217	646	666	686	706	726	746	766	786	806	826
218	846	866	885	905	925	945	965	985	*005	*025
219	34 044	064	084	104	124	143	163	183	203	223
220	242	262	282	301	321	341	361	380	400	420
221	439	459	479	498	518	537	557	577	596	616
222	635	655	674	694	713	733	753	772	792	811
223	830	850	869	889	908	928	947	967	986	*005
224	35 025	044	064	083	102	122	141	160	180	199
225	218	238	257	276	295	315	334	353	372	392
226	411	430	449	468	488	507	526	545	564	583
227	603	622	641	660	679	698	717	736	755	774
228	793	813	832	851	870	889	908	927	946	965
229	984	*003	*021	*040	*059	*078	*097	*116	*135	*154
230	36 173	192	211	229	248	267	286	305	324	342
231	361	380	399	418	436	455	474	493	511	530
232	549	568	586	605	624	642	661	680	698	717
233	736	754	773	791	810	829	847	866	884	903
234	922	940	959	977	996	*014	*033	*051	*070	*088
235	37 107	125	144	162	181	199	218	236	254	273
236	291	310	328	346	365	383	401	420	438	457
237	475	493	511	530	548	566	585	603	621	639
238	658	676	694	712	731	749	767	785	803	822
239	840	858	876	894	912	931	949	967	985	*003
240	38 021	039	057	075	093	112	130	148	166	184
241	202	220	238	256	274	292	310	328	346	364
242	382	399	417	435	453	471	489	507	525	543
243	561	578	596	614	632	650	668	686	703	721
244	739	757	775	792	810	828	846	863	881	899
245	917	934	952	970	987	*005	*023	*041	*058	*076
246	39 094	111	129	146	164	182	199	217	235	252
247	270	287	305	322	340	358	375	393	410	428
248	445	463	480	498	515	533	550	568	585	602
249	620	637	655	672	690	707	724	742	759	777
250	794	811	829	846	863	881	898	915	933	950
N.	L. 0	1	2	3	4	5	6	7	8	9

P. P.

	22	21
1	2.2	2.1
2	4.4	4.2
3	6.6	6.3
4	8.8	8.4
5	11.0	10.5
6	13.2	12.6
7	15.4	14.7
8	17.6	16.8
9	19.8	18.9

	20
1	2.0
2	4.0
3	6.0
4	8.0
5	10.0
6	12.0
7	14.0
8	16.0
9	18.0

	19
1	1.9
2	3.8
3	5.7
4	7.6
5	9.5
6	11.4
7	13.3
8	15.2
9	17.1

	18
1	1.8
2	3.6
3	5.4
4	7.2
5	9.0
6	10.8
7	12.6
8	14.4
9	16.2

	17
1	1.7
2	3.4
3	5.1
4	6.8
5	8.5
6	10.2
7	11.9
8	13.6
9	15.3

N.	L. 0	1	2	3	4	5	6	7	8	9
250	39 794	811	829	846	863	881	898	915	933	950
251	967	985	*002	*019	*037	*054	*071	*088	*106	*123
252	40 140	157	175	192	209	226	243	261	278	295
253	312	329	346	364	381	398	415	432	449	466
254	483	500	518	535	552	569	586	603	620	637
255	654	671	688	705	722	739	756	773	790	807
256	824	841	858	875	892	909	926	943	960	976
257	993	*010	*027	*044	*061	*078	*095	*111	*128	*145
258	41 162	179	196	212	229	246	263	280	296	313
259	330	347	363	380	397	414	430	447	464	481
260	497	514	531	547	564	581	597	614	631	647
261	664	681	697	714	731	747	764	780	797	814
262	830	847	863	880	896	913	929	946	963	979
263	996	*012	*029	*045	*062	*078	*095	*111	*127	*144
264	42 160	177	193	210	226	243	259	275	292	308
265	325	341	357	374	390	406	423	439	455	472
266	488	504	521	537	553	570	586	602	619	635
267	651	667	684	700	716	732	749	765	781	797
268	813	830	846	862	878	894	911	927	943	959
269	975	991	*008	*024	*040	*056	*072	*088	*104	*120
270	43 136	152	169	185	201	217	233	249	265	281
271	297	313	329	345	361	377	393	409	425	441
272	457	473	489	505	521	537	553	569	584	600
273	616	632	648	664	680	696	712	727	743	759
274	775	791	807	823	838	854	870	886	902	917
275	933	949	965	981	996	*012	*028	*044	*059	*075
276	44 091	107	122	138	154	170	185	201	217	232
277	248	264	279	295	311	326	342	358	373	389
278	404	420	436	451	467	483	498	514	529	545
279	560	576	592	607	623	638	654	669	685	700
280	716	731	747	762	778	793	809	824	840	855
281	871	886	902	917	932	948	963	979	994	*010
282	45 025	040	056	071	086	102	117	133	148	163
283	179	194	209	225	240	255	271	286	301	317
284	332	347	362	378	393	408	423	439	454	469
285	484	500	515	530	545	561	576	591	606	621
286	637	652	667	682	697	712	728	743	758	773
287	788	803	818	834	849	864	879	894	909	924
288	939	954	969	984	*000	*015	*030	*045	*060	*075
289	46 090	105	120	135	150	165	180	195	210	225
290	240	255	270	285	300	315	330	345	359	374
291	389	404	419	434	449	464	479	494	509	523
292	538	553	568	583	598	613	627	642	657	672
293	687	702	716	731	746	761	776	790	805	820
294	835	850	864	879	894	909	923	938	953	967
295	982	997	*012	*026	*041	*056	*070	*085	*100	*114
296	47 129	144	159	173	188	202	217	232	246	261
297	276	290	305	319	334	349	363	378	392	407
298	422	436	451	465	480	494	509	524	538	553
299	567	582	596	611	625	640	654	669	683	698
300	712	727	741	756	770	784	799	813	828	842
N.	L. 0	1	2	3	4	5	6	7	8	9

P. P.

	18		17		16		15		14
1	1.8	1	1.7	1	1.6	1	1.5	1	1.4
2	3.6	2	3.4	2	3.2	2	3.0	2	2.8
3	5.4	3	5.1	3	4.8	3	4.5	3	4.2
4	7.2	4	6.8	4	6.4	4	6.0	4	5.6
5	9.0	5	8.5	5	8.0	5	7.5	5	7.0
6	10.8	6	10.2	6	9.6	6	9.0	6	8.4
7	12.6	7	11.9	7	11.2	7	10.5	7	9.8
8	14.4	8	13.6	8	12.8	8	12.0	8	11.2
9	16.2	9	15.3	9	14.4	9	13.5	9	12.6

N.	L. 0	1	2	3	4	5	6	7	8	9
300	47 712	727	741	756	770	784	799	813	828	842
301	857	871	885	900	914	929	943	958	972	986
302	48 001	015	029	044	058	073	087	101	116	130
303	144	159	173	187	202	216	230	244	259	273
304	287	302	316	330	344	359	373	387	401	416
305	430	444	458	473	487	501	515	530	544	558
306	572	586	601	615	629	643	657	671	686	700
307	714	728	742	756	770	785	799	813	827	841
308	855	869	883	897	911	926	940	954	968	982
309	996	*010	*024	*038	*052	*066	*080	*094	*108	*122
310	49 136	150	164	178	192	206	220	234	248	262
311	276	290	304	318	332	346	360	374	388	402
312	415	429	443	457	471	485	499	513	527	541
313	554	568	582	596	610	624	638	651	665	679
314	693	707	721	734	748	762	776	790	803	817
315	831	845	859	872	886	900	914	927	941	955
316	969	982	996	*010	*024	*037	*051	*065	*079	*092
317	50 106	120	133	147	161	174	188	202	215	229
318	243	256	270	284	297	311	325	338	352	365
319	379	393	406	420	433	447	461	474	488	501
320	515	529	542	556	569	583	596	610	623	637
321	651	664	678	691	705	718	732	745	759	772
322	786	799	813	826	840	853	866	880	893	907
323	920	934	947	961	974	987	*001	*014	*028	*041
324	51 055	068	081	095	108	121	135	148	162	175
325	188	202	215	228	242	255	268	282	295	308
326	322	335	348	362	375	388	402	415	428	441
327	455	468	481	495	508	521	534	548	561	574
328	587	601	614	627	640	654	667	680	693	706
329	720	733	746	759	772	786	799	812	825	838
330	851	865	878	891	904	917	930	943	957	970
331	983	996	*009	*022	*035	*048	*061	*075	*088	*101
332	52 114	127	140	153	166	179	192	205	218	231
333	244	257	270	284	297	310	323	336	349	362
334	375	388	401	414	427	440	453	466	479	492
335	504	517	530	543	556	569	582	595	608	621
336	634	647	660	673	686	699	711	724	737	750
337	763	776	789	802	815	827	840	853	866	879
338	892	905	917	930	943	956	969	982	994	*007
339	53 020	033	046	058	071	084	097	110	122	135
340	148	161	173	186	199	212	224	237	250	263
341	275	288	301	314	326	339	352	364	377	390
342	403	415	428	441	453	466	479	491	504	517
343	529	542	555	567	580	593	605	618	631	643
344	656	668	681	694	706	719	732	744	757	769
345	782	794	807	820	832	845	857	870	882	895
346	908	920	933	945	958	970	983	995	*008	*020
347	54 033	045	058	070	083	095	108	120	133	145
348	158	170	183	195	208	220	233	245	258	270
349	283	295	307	320	332	345	357	370	382	394
350	407	419	432	444	456	469	481	494	506	518
N.	L. 0	1	2	3	4	5	6	7	8	9

P. P.

15

1	1.5
2	3.0
3	4.5
4	6.0
5	7.5
6	9.0
7	10.5
8	12.0
9	13.5

14

1	1.4
2	2.8
3	4.2
4	5.6
5	7.0
6	8.4
7	9.8
8	11.2
9	12.6

13

1	1.3
2	2.6
3	3.9
4	5.2
5	6.5
6	7.8
7	9.1
8	10.4
9	11.7

12

1	1.2
2	2.4
3	3.6
4	4.8
5	6.0
6	7.2
7	8.4
8	9.6
9	10.8

N.	L. 0	1	2	3	4	5	6	7	8	9
350	54 407	419	432	444	456	469	481	494	506	518
351	531	543	555	568	580	593	605	617	630	642
352	654	667	679	691	704	716	728	741	753	765
353	777	790	802	814	827	839	851	864	876	888
354	900	913	925	937	949	962	974	986	998	*011
355	55 023	035	047	060	072	084	096	108	121	133
356	145	157	169	182	194	206	218	230	242	255
357	267	279	291	303	315	328	340	352	364	376
358	388	400	413	425	437	449	461	473	485	497
359	509	522	534	546	558	570	582	594	606	618
360	630	642	654	666	678	691	703	715	727	739
361	751	763	775	787	799	811	823	835	847	859
362	871	883	895	907	919	931	943	955	967	979
363	991	*003	*015	*027	*038	*050	*062	*074	*086	*098
364	56 110	122	134	146	158	170	182	194	205	217
365	229	241	253	265	277	289	301	312	324	336
366	348	360	372	384	396	407	419	431	443	455
367	467	478	490	502	514	526	538	549	561	573
368	585	597	608	620	632	644	656	667	679	691
369	703	714	726	738	750	761	773	785	797	808
370	820	832	844	855	867	879	891	902	914	926
371	937	949	961	972	984	996	*008	*019	*031	*043
372	57 054	066	078	089	101	113	124	136	148	159
373	171	183	194	206	217	229	241	252	264	276
374	287	299	310	322	334	345	.357	368	380	392
375	403	415	426	438	449	461	473	484	496	507
376	519	530	542	553	565	576	588	600	611	623
377	634	646	657	669	680	692	703	715	726	738
378	749	761	772	784	795	807	818	830	841	852
379	864	875	887	898	910	921	933	944	955	967
380	978	990	*001	*013	*024	*035	*047	*058	*070	*081
381	58 092	104	115	127	138	149	161	172	184	195
382	206	218	229	240	252	263	274	286	297	309
383	320	331	343	354	365	377	388	399	410	422
384	433	444	456	467	478	490	501	512	524	535
385	546	557	569	580	591	602	614	625	636	647
386	659	670	681	692	704	715	726	737	749	760
387	771	782	794	805	816	827	838	850	861	872
388	883	894	906	917	928	939	950	961	973	984
389	995	*006	*017	*028	*040	*051	*062	*073	*084	*095
390	59 106	118	129	140	151	162	173	184	195	207
391	218	229	240	251	262	273	284	295	306	318
392	329	340	351	362	373	384	395	406	417	428
393	439	450	461	472	483	494	506	517	528	539
394	550	561	572	583	594	605	616	627	638	649
395	660	671	682	693	704	715	726	737	748	759
396	770	780	791	802	813	824	835	846	857	868
397	879	890	901	912	923	934	945	956	966	977
398	988	999	*010	*021	*032	*043	*054	*065	*076	*086
399	60 097	108	119	130	141	152	163	173	184	195
400	206	217	228	239	249	260	271	282	293	304
N.	L. 0	1	2	3	4	5	6	7	8	9

P. P.

13
1 | 1.3
2 | 2.6
3 | 3.9
4 | 5.2
5 | 6.5
6 | 7.8
7 | 9.1
8 | 10.4
9 | 11.7

12
1 | 1.2
2 | 2.4
3 | 3.6
4 |
5 | 6.0
6 | 7.2
7 | 8.4
8 | 9.6
9 | 10.8

11
1 | 1.1
2 | 2.2
3 | 3.3
4 | 4.4
5 | 5.5
6 | 6.6
7 | 7.7
8 | 8.8
9 | 9.9

10
1 | 1.0
2 | 2.0
3 | 3.0
4 | 4.0
5 | 5.0
6 | 6.0
7 | 7.0
8 | 8.0
9 | 9.0

N.	L. 0	1	2	3	4	5	6	7	8	9	P. P.
400	60 206	217	228	239	249	260	271	282	293	304	
401	314	325	336	347	358	369	379	390	401	412	
402	423	433	444	455	466	477	487	498	509	520	
403	531	541	552	563	574	584	595	606	617	627	
404	638	649	660	670	681	692	703	713	724	735	
405	746	756	767	778	788	799	810	821	831	842	
406	853	863	874	885	895	906	917	927	938	949	
407	959	970	981	991	*002	*013	*023	*034	*045	*055	**11**
408	61 066	077	087	098	109	119	130	140	151	162	1 1.1
409	172	183	194	204	215	225	236	247	257	268	2 2.2
410	278	289	300	310	321	331	342	352	363	374	3 3.3 / 4 4.4
411	384	395	405	416	426	437	448	458	469	479	5 5.5 / 6 6.6
412	490	500	511	521	532	542	553	563	574	584	7 7.7
413	595	606	616	627	637	648	658	669	679	690	8 8.8
414	700	711	721	731	742	752	763	773	784	794	9 9.9
415	805	815	826	836	847	857	868	878	888	899	
416	909	920	930	941	951	962	972	982	993	*003	
417	62 014	024	034	045	055	066	076	086	097	107	
418	118	128	138	149	159	170	180	190	201	211	
419	221	232	242	252	263	273	284	294	304	315	
420	325	335	346	356	366	377	387	397	408	418	
421	428	439	449	459	469	480	490	500	511	521	
422	531	542	552	562	572	583	593	603	613	624	**10**
423	634	644	655	665	675	685	696	706	716	726	1 1.0
424	737	747	757	767	778	788	798	808	818	829	2 2.0
425	839	849	859	870	880	890	900	910	921	931	3 3.0
426	941	951	961	972	982	992	*002	*012	*022	*033	4 4.0 / 5 5.0
427	63 043	053	063	073	083	094	104	114	124	134	6 6.0
428	144	155	165	175	185	195	205	215	225	236	7 7.0
429	246	256	266	276	286	296	306	317	327	337	8 8.0
430	347	357	367	377	387	397	407	417	428	438	9 9.0
431	448	458	468	478	488	498	508	518	528	538	
432	548	558	568	579	589	599	609	619	629	639	
433	649	659	669	679	689	699	709	719	729	739	
434	749	759	769	779	789	799	809	819	829	839	
435	849	859	869	879	889	899	909	919	929	939	
436	949	959	969	979	988	998	*008	*018	*028	*038	
437	64 048	058	068	078	088	098	108	118	128	137	**9**
438	147	157	167	177	187	197	207	217	227	237	1 0.9
439	246	256	266	276	286	296	306	316	326	335	2 1.8
440	345	355	365	375	385	395	404	414	424	434	3 2.7 / 4 3.6
441	444	454	464	473	483	493	503	513	523	532	5 4.5
442	542	552	562	572	582	591	601	611	621	631	6 5.4
443	640	650	660	670	680	689	699	709	719	729	7 6.3
444	738	748	758	768	777	787	797	807	816	826	8 7.2
445	836	846	856	865	875	885	895	904	914	924	9 8.1
446	933	943	953	963	972	982	992	*002	*011	*021	
447	65 031	040	050	060	070	079	089	099	108	118	
448	128	137	147	157	167	176	186	196	205	215	
449	225	234	244	254	263	273	283	292	302	312	
450	321	331	341	350	360	369	379	389	398	408	
N.	L. 0	1	2	3	4	5	6	7	8	9	P. P.

N.	L. 0	1	2	3	4	5	6	7	8	9
450	65 321	331	341	350	360	369	379	389	398	408
451	418	427	437	447	456	466	475	485	495	504
452	514	523	533	543	552	562	571	581	591	600
453	610	619	629	639	648	658	667	677	686	696
454	706	715	725	734	744	753	763	772	782	792
455	801	811	820	830	839	849	858	868	877	887
456	896	906	916	925	935	944	954	963	973	982
457	992	*001	*011	*020	*030	*039	*049	*058	*068	*077
458	66 087	096	106	115	124	134	143	153	162	172
459	181	191	200	210	219	229	238	247	257	266
460	276	285	295	304	314	323	332	342	351	361
461	370	380	389	398	408	417	427	436	445	455
462	464	474	483	492	502	511	521	530	539	549
463	558	567	577	586	596	605	614	624	633	642
464	652	661	671	680	689	699	708	717	727	736
465	745	755	764	773	783	792	801	811	820	829
466	839	848	857	867	876	885	894	904	913	922
467	932	941	950	960	969	978	987	997	*006	*015
468	67 025	034	043	052	062	071	080	089	099	108
469	117	127	136	145	154	164	173	182	191	201
470	210	219	228	237	247	256	265	274	284	293
471	302	311	321	330	339	348	357	367	376	385
472	394	403	413	422	431	440	449	459	468	477
473	486	495	504	514	523	532	541	550	560	569
474	578	587	596	605	614	624	633	642	651	660
475	669	679	688	697	706	715	724	733	742	752
476	761	770	779	788	797	806	815	825	834	843
477	852	861	870	879	888	897	906	916	925	934
478	943	952	961	970	979	988	997	*006	*015	*024
479	68 034	043	052	061	070	079	088	097	106	115
480	124	133	142	151	160	169	178	187	196	205
481	215	224	233	242	251	260	269	278	287	296
482	305	314	323	332	341	350	359	368	377	386
483	395	404	413	422	431	440	449	458	467	476
484	485	494	502	511	520	529	538	547	556	565
485	574	583	592	601	610	619	628	637	646	655
486	664	673	681	690	699	708	717	726	735	744
487	753	762	771	780	789	797	806	815	824	833
488	842	851	860	869	878	886	895	904	913	922
489	931	940	949	958	966	975	984	993	*002	*011
490	69 020	028	037	046	055	064	073	082	090	099
491	108	117	126	135	144	152	161	170	179	188
492	197	205	214	223	232	241	249	258	267	276
493	285	294	302	311	320	329	338	346	355	364
494	373	381	390	399	408	417	425	434	443	452
495	461	469	478	487	496	504	513	522	531	539
496	548	557	566	574	583	592	601	609	618	627
497	636	644	653	662	671	679	688	697	705	714
498	723	732	740	749	758	767	775	784	793	801
499	810	819	827	836	845	854	862	871	880	888
500	897	906	914	923	932	940	949	958	966	975
N.	L. 0	1	2	3	4	5	6	7	8	9

P. P.

	10
1	1.0
2	2.0
3	3.0
4	4.0
5	5.0
6	6.0
7	7.0
8	8.0
9	9.0

	9
1	0.9
2	1.8
3	2.7
4	3.6
5	4.5
6	5.4
7	6.3
8	7.2
9	8.1

	8
1	0.8
2	1.6
3	2.4
4	3.2
5	4.0
6	4.8
7	5.6
8	6.4
9	7.2

N.	L. 0	1	2	3	4	5	6	7	8	9
500	69 897	906	914	923	932	940	949	958	966	975
501	984	992	*001	*010	*018	*027	*036	*044	*053	*062
502	70 070	079	088	096	105	114	122	131	140	148
503	157	165	174	183	191	200	209	217	226	234
504	243	252	260	269	278	286	295	303	312	321
505	329	338	346	355	364	372	381	389	398	406
506	415	424	432	441	449	458	467	475	484	492
507	501	509	518	526	535	544	552	561	569	578
508	586	595	603	612	621	629	638	646	655	663
509	672	680	689	697	706	714	723	731	740	749
510	757	766	774	783	791	800	808	817	825	834
511	842	851	859	868	876	885	893	902	910	919
512	927	935	944	952	961	969	978	986	995	*003
513	71 012	020	029	037	046	054	063	071	079	088
514	096	105	113	122	130	139	147	155	164	172
515	181	189	198	206	214	223	231	240	248	257
516	265	273	282	290	299	307	315	324	332	341
517	349	357	366	374	383	391	399	408	416	425
518	433	441	450	458	466	475	483	492	500	508
519	517	525	533	542	550	559	567	575	584	592
520	600	609	617	625	634	642	650	659	667	675
521	684	692	700	709	717	725	734	742	750	759
522	767	775	784	792	800	809	817	825	834	842
523	850	858	867	875	883	892	900	908	917	925
524	933	941	950	958	966	975	983	991	999	*008
525	72 016	024	032	041	049	057	066	074	082	090
526	099	107	115	123	132	140	148	156	165	173
527	181	189	198	206	214	222	230	239	247	255
528	263	272	280	288	296	304	313	321	329	337
529	346	354	362	370	378	387	395	403	411	419
530	428	436	444	452	460	469	477	485	493	501
531	509	518	526	534	542	550	558	567	575	583
532	591	599	607	616	624	632	640	648	656	665
533	673	681	689	697	705	713	722	730	738	746
534	754	762	770	779	787	795	803	811	819	827
535	835	843	852	860	868	876	884	892	900	908
536	916	925	933	941	949	957	965	973	981	989
537	997	*006	*014	*022	*030	*038	*046	*054	*062	*070
538	73 078	086	094	102	111	119	127	135	143	151
539	159	167	175	183	191	199	207	215	223	231
540	239	247	255	263	272	280	288	296	304	312
541	320	328	336	344	352	360	368	376	384	392
542	400	408	416	424	432	440	448	456	464	472
543	480	488	496	504	512	520	528	536	544	552
544	560	568	576	584	592	600	608	616	624	632
545	640	648	656	664	672	679	687	695	703	711
546	719	727	735	743	751	759	767	775	783	791
547	799	807	815	823	830	838	846	854	862	870
548	878	886	894	902	910	918	926	933	941	949
549	957	965	973	981	989	997	*005	*013	*020	*028
550	74 036	044	052	060	068	076	084	092	099	107
N.	L. 0	1	2	3	4	5	6	7	8	9

P. P.

9
1	0.9
2	1.8
3	2.7
4	3.6
5	4.5
6	5.4
7	6.3
8	7.2
9	8.1

8
1	0.8
2	1.6
3	2.4
4	3.2
5	4.0
6	4.8
7	5.6
8	6.4
9	7.2

7
1	0.7
2	1.4
3	2.1
4	2.8
5	3.5
6	4.2
7	4.9
8	5.6
9	6.3

N.	L. 0	1	2	3	4	5	6	7	8	9	P. P.
550	74 036	044	052	060	068	076	084	092	099	107	
551	115	123	131	139	147	155	162	170	178	186	
552	194	202	210	218	225	233	241	249	257	265	
553	273	280	288	296	304	312	320	327	335	343	
554	351	359	367	374	382	390	398	406	414	421	
555	429	437	445	453	461	468	476	484	492	500	
556	507	515	523	531	539	547	554	562	570	578	
557	586	593	601	609	617	624	632	640	648	656	
558	663	671	679	687	695	702	710	718	726	733	
559	741	749	757	764	772	780	788	796	803	811	
560	819	827	834	842	850	858	865	873	881	889	
561	896	904	912	920	927	935	943	950	958	966	**8**
562	974	981	989	997	*005	*012	*020	*028	*035	*043	1 0.8
563	75 051	059	066	074	082	089	097	105	113	120	2 1.6
564	128	136	143	151	159	166	174	182	189	197	3 2.4
565	205	213	220	228	236	243	251	259	266	274	4 3.2
566	282	289	297	305	312	320	328	335	343	351	5 4.0
567	358	366	374	381	389	397	404	412	420	427	6 4.8
568	435	442	450	458	465	473	481	488	496	504	7 5.6
569	511	519	526	534	542	549	557	565	572	580	8 6.4
570	587	595	603	610	618	626	633	641	648	656	9 7.2
571	664	671	679	686	694	702	709	717	724	732	
572	740	747	755	762	770	778	785	793	800	808	
573	815	823	831	838	846	853	861	868	876	884	
574	891	899	906	914	921	929	937	944	952	959	
575	967	974	982	989	997	*005	*012	*020	*027	*035	
576	76 042	050	057	065	072	080	087	095	103	110	
577	118	125	133	140	148	155	163	170	178	185	
578	193	200	208	215	223	230	238	245	253	260	
579	268	275	283	290	298	305	313	320	328	335	
580	343	350	358	365	373	380	388	395	403	410	
581	418	425	433	440	448	455	462	470	477	485	
582	492	500	507	515	522	530	537	545	552	559	
583	567	574	582	589	597	604	612	619	626	634	
584	641	649	656	664	671	678	686	693	701	708	
585	716	723	730	738	745	753	760	768	775	782	**7**
586	790	797	805	812	819	827	834	842	849	856	1 0.7
587	864	871	879	886	893	901	908	916	923	930	2 1.4
588	938	945	953	960	967	975	982	989	997	*004	3 2.1
589	77 012	019	026	034	041	048	056	063	070	078	4 2.8
590	085	093	100	107	115	122	129	137	144	151	5 3.5
591	159	166	173	181	188	195	203	210	217	225	6 4.2
592	232	240	247	254	262	269	276	283	291	298	7 4.9
593	305	313	320	327	335	342	349	357	364	371	8 5.6
594	379	386	393	401	408	415	422	430	437	444	9 6.3
595	452	459	466	474	481	488	495	503	510	517	
596	525	532	539	546	554	561	568	576	583	590	
597	597	605	612	619	627	634	641	648	656	663	
598	670	677	685	692	699	706	714	721	728	735	
599	743	750	757	764	772	779	786	793	801	808	
600	815	822	830	837	844	851	859	866	873	880	
N.	L. 0	1	2	3	4	5	6	7	8	9	P. P.

N.	L. 0	1	2	3	4	5	6	7	8	9
600	77 815	822	830	837	844	851	859	866	873	880
601	887	895	902	909	915	924	931	938	945	952
602	960	967	974	981	988	996	*003	*010	*017	*025
603	78 032	039	046	053	061	068	075	082	089	097
604	104	111	118	125	132	140	147	154	161	168
605	176	183	190	197	204	211	219	226	233	240
606	247	254	262	269	276	283	290	297	305	312
607	319	326	333	340	347	355	362	369	376	383
608	390	398	405	412	419	426	433	440	447	455
609	462	469	476	483	490	497	504	512	519	526
610	533	540	547	554	561	569	576	583	590	597
611	604	611	618	625	633	640	647	654	661	668
612	675	682	689	696	704	711	718	725	732	739
613	746	753	760	767	774	781	789	796	803	810
614	817	824	831	838	845	852	859	866	873	880
615	888	895	902	909	916	923	930	937	944	951
616	958	965	972	979	986	993	*000	*007	*014	*021
617	79 029	036	043	050	057	064	071	078	085	092
618	099	106	113	120	127	134	141	148	155	162
619	169	176	183	190	197	204	211	218	225	232
620	239	246	253	260	267	274	281	288	295	302
621	309	316	323	330	337	344	351	358	365	372
622	379	386	393	400	407	414	421	428	435	442
623	449	456	463	470	477	484	491	498	505	511
624	518	525	532	539	546	553	560	567	574	581
625	588	595	602	609	616	623	630	637	644	650
626	657	664	671	678	685	692	699	706	713	720
627	727	734	741	748	754	761	768	775	782	789
628	796	803	810	817	824	831	837	844	851	858
629	865	872	879	886	893	900	906	913	920	927
630	934	941	948	955	962	969	975	982	989	996
631	80 003	010	017	024	030	037	044	051	058	065
632	072	079	085	092	099	106	113	120	127	134
633	140	147	154	161	168	175	182	188	195	202
634	209	216	223	229	236	243	250	257	264	271
635	277	284	291	298	305	312	318	325	332	339
636	346	353	359	366	373	380	387	393	400	407
637	414	421	428	434	441	448	455	462	468	475
638	482	489	496	502	509	516	523	530	536	543
639	550	557	564	570	577	584	591	598	604	611
640	618	625	632	638	645	652	659	665	672	679
641	686	693	699	706	713	720	726	733	740	747
642	754	760	767	774	781	787	794	801	808	814
643	821	828	835	841	848	855	862	868	875	882
644	889	895	902	909	916	922	929	936	943	949
645	956	963	969	976	983	990	996	*003	*010	*017
646	81 023	030	037	043	050	057	064	070	077	084
647	090	097	104	111	117	124	131	137	144	151
648	158	164	171	178	184	191	198	204	211	218
649	224	231	238	245	251	258	265	271	278	285
650	291	298	305	311	318	325	331	338	345	351
N.	L. 0	1	2	3	4	5	6	7	8	9

P. P.

8

1	0.8
2	1.6
3	2.4
4	3.2
5	4.0
6	4.8
7	5.6
8	6.4
9	7.2

7

1	0.7
2	1.4
3	2.1
4	2.8
5	3.5
6	4.2
7	4.9
8	5.6
9	6.3

6

1	0.6
2	1.2
3	1.8
4	2.4
5	3.0
6	3.6
7	4.2
8	4.8
9	5.4

N.	L. 0	1	2	3	4	5	6	7	8	9	P. P.
650	81 291	298	305	311	318	325	331	338	345	351	
651	358	365	371	378	385	391	398	405	411	418	
652	425	431	438	445	451	458	465	471	478	485	
653	491	498	505	511	518	525	531	538	544	551	
654	558	564	571	578	584	591	598	604	611	617	
655	624	631	637	644	651	657	664	671	677	684	
656	690	697	704	710	717	723	730	737	743	750	
657	757	763	770	776	783	790	796	803	809	816	
658	823	829	836	842	849	856	862	869	875	882	
659	889	895	902	908	915	921	928	935	941	948	
660	954	961	968	974	981	987	994	*000	*007	*014	
661	82 020	027	033	040	046	053	060	066	073	079	**7**
662	086	092	099	105	112	119	125	132	138	145	1 0.7
663	151	158	164	171	178	184	191	197	204	210	2 1.4
664	217	223	230	236	243	249	256	263	269	276	3 2.1
665	282	289	295	302	308	315	321	328	334	341	4 2.8
666	347	354	360	367	373	380	387	393	400	406	5 3.5
667	413	419	426	432	439	445	452	458	465	471	6 4.2
668	478	484	491	497	504	510	517	523	530	536	7 4.9
669	543	549	556	562	569	575	582	588	595	601	8 5.6
670	607	614	620	627	633	640	646	653	659	666	9 6.3
671	672	679	685	692	698	705	711	718	724	730	
672	737	743	750	756	763	769	776	782	789	795	
673	802	808	814	821	827	834	840	847	853	860	
674	866	872	879	885	892	898	905	911	918	924	
675	930	937	943	950	956	963	969	975	982	988	
676	995	*001	*008	*014	*020	*027	*033	*040	*046	*052	
677	83 059	065	072	078	085	091	097	104	110	117	
678	123	129	136	142	149	155	161	168	174	181	
679	187	193	200	206	213	219	225	232	238	245	
680	251	257	264	270	276	283	289	296	302	308	
681	315	321	327	334	340	347	353	359	366	372	
682	378	385	391	398	404	410	417	423	429	436	
683	442	448	455	461	467	474	480	487	493	499	
684	506	512	518	525	531	537	544	550	556	563	**6**
685	569	575	582	588	594	601	607	613	620	626	1 0.6
686	632	639	645	651	658	664	670	677	683	689	2 1.2
687	696	702	708	715	721	727	734	740	746	753	3 1.8
688	759	765	771	778	784	790	797	803	809	816	4 2.4
689	822	828	835	841	847	853	860	866	872	879	5 3.0
690	885	891	897	904	910	916	923	929	935	942	6 3.6
691	948	954	960	967	973	979	985	992	998	*004	7 4.2
692	84 011	017	023	029	036	042	048	055	061	067	8 4.8
693	073	080	086	092	098	105	111	117	123	130	9 5.4
694	136	142	148	155	161	167	173	180	186	192	
695	198	205	211	217	223	230	236	242	248	255	
696	261	267	273	280	286	292	298	305	311	317	
697	323	330	336	342	348	354	361	367	373	379	
698	386	392	398	404	410	417	423	429	435	442	
699	448	454	460	466	473	479	485	491	497	504	
700	510	516	522	528	535	541	547	553	559	566	
N.	L. 0	1	2	3	4	5	6	7	8	9	P. P.

N.	L. 0	1	2	3	4	5	6	7	8	9	P. P.
700	84 510	516	522	528	535	541	547	553	559	566	
701	572	578	584	590	597	603	609	615	621	628	
702	634	640	646	652	658	665	671	677	683	689	
703	696	702	708	714	720	726	733	739	745	751	
704	757	763	770	776	782	788	794	800	807	813	
705	819	825	831	837	844	850	856	862	868	874	
706	880	887	893	899	905	911	917	924	930	936	
707	942	948	954	960	967	973	979	985	991	997	**7**
708	85 003	009	016	022	028	034	040	046	052	058	1 0.7
709	065	071	077	083	089	095	101	107	114	120	2 1.4
710	126	132	138	144	150	156	163	169	175	181	3 2.1 4 2.8 5 3.5
711	187	193	199	205	211	217	224	230	236	242	6 4.2
712	248	254	260	266	272	278	285	291	297	303	7 4.9
713	309	315	321	327	333	339	345	352	358	364	8 5.6
714	370	376	382	388	394	400	406	412	418	425	9 6.3
715	431	437	443	449	455	461	467	473	479	485	
716	491	497	503	509	516	522	528	534	540	546	
717	552	558	564	570	576	582	588	594	600	606	
718	612	618	625	631	637	643	649	655	661	667	
719	673	679	685	691	697	703	709	715	721	727	
720	733	739	745	751	757	763	769	775	781	788	
721	794	800	806	812	818	824	830	836	842	848	
722	854	860	866	872	878	884	890	896	902	908	
723	914	920	926	932	938	944	950	956	962	*968	
724	974	980	986	992	998	*004	*010	*016	*022	*028	**6**
725	86 034	040	046	052	058	064	070	076	082	088	1 0.6
726	094	100	106	112	118	124	130	136	141	147	2 1.2
727	153	159	165	171	177	183	189	195	201	207	3 1.8 4 2.4
728	213	219	225	231	237	243	249	255	261	267	5 3.0
729	273	279	285	291	297	303	308	314	320	326	6 3.6
730	332	338	344	350	356	362	368	374	380	386	7 4.2 8 4.8
731	392	398	404	410	415	421	427	433	439	445	9 5.4
732	451	457	463	469	475	481	487	493	499	504	
733	510	516	522	528	534	540	546	552	558	564	
734	570	576	581	587	593	599	605	611	617	623	
735	629	635	641	646	652	658	664	670	676	682	
736	688	694	700	705	711	717	723	729	735	741	
737	747	753	759	764	770	776	782	788	794	800	
738	806	812	817	823	829	835	841	847	853	859	
739	864	870	876	882	888	894	900	906	911	917	
740	923	929	935	941	947	953	958	964	970	976	**5**
741	982	988	994	999	*005	*011	*017	*023	*029	*035	1 0.5
742	87 040	046	052	058	064	070	075	081	087	093	2 1.0
743	099	105	111	116	122	128	134	140	146	151	3 1.5 4 2.0
744	157	163	169	175	181	186	192	198	204	210	5 2.5
745	216	221	227	233	239	245	251	256	262	268	6 3.0
746	274	280	286	291	297	303	309	315	320	326	7 3.5 8 4.0
747	332	338	344	349	355	361	367	373	379	384	9 4.5
748	390	396	402	408	413	419	425	431	437	442	
749	448	454	460	466	471	477	483	489	495	500	
750	506	512	518	523	529	535	541	547	552	558	
N.	L. 0	1	2	3	4	5	6	7	8	9	P. P.

N.	L. 0	1	2	3	4	5	6	7	8	9	P. P.
750	87 506	512	518	523	529	535	541	547	552	558	
751	564	570	576	581	587	593	599	604	610	616	
752	622	628	633	639	645	651	656	662	668	674	
753	679	685	691	697	703	708	714	720	726	731	
754	737	743	749	754	760	766	772	777	783	789	
755	795	800	806	812	818	823	829	835	841	846	
756	852	858	864	869	875	881	887	892	898	904	
757	910	915	921	927	933	938	944	950	955	961	
758	967	973	978	984	990	996	*001	*007	*013	*018	
759	88 024	030	036	041	047	053	058	064	070	076	
760	081	087	093	098	104	110	116	121	127	133	
761	138	144	150	156	161	167	173	178	184	190	
762	195	201	207	213	218	224	230	235	241	247	**6**
763	252	258	264	270	275	281	287	292	298	304	1 0.6
764	309	315	321	326	332	338	343	349	355	360	2 1.2
765	366	372	377	383	389	395	400	406	412	417	3 1.8
766	423	429	434	440	446	451	457	463	468	474	4 2.4
767	480	485	491	497	502	508	513	519	525	530	5 3.0
768	536	542	547	553	559	564	570	576	581	587	6 3.6
769	593	598	604	610	615	621	627	632	638	643	7 4.2
770	649	655	660	666	672	677	683	689	694	700	8 4.8
771	705	711	717	722	728	734	739	745	750	756	9 5.4
772	762	767	773	779	784	790	795	801	807	812	
773	818	824	829	835	840	846	852	857	863	868	
774	874	880	885	891	897	902	908	913	919	925	
775	930	936	941	947	953	958	964	969	975	981	
776	986	992	997	*003	*009	*014	*020	*025	*031	*037	
777	89 042	048	053	059	064	070	076	081	087	092	
778	098	104	109	115	120	126	131	137	143	148	
779	154	159	165	170	176	182	187	193	198	204	
780	209	215	221	226	232	237	243	248	254	260	
781	265	271	276	282	287	293	298	304	310	315	
782	321	326	332	337	343	348	354	360	365	371	**5**
783	376	382	387	393	398	404	409	415	421	426	1 0.5
784	432	437	443	448	454	459	465	470	476	481	2 1.0
785	487	492	498	504	509	515	520	526	531	537	3 1.5
786	542	548	553	559	564	570	575	581	586	592	4 2.0
787	597	603	609	614	620	625	631	636	642	647	5 2.5
788	653	658	664	669	675	680	686	691	697	702	6 3.0
789	708	713	719	724	730	735	741	746	752	757	7 3.5
790	763	768	774	779	785	790	796	801	807	812	8 4.0
791	818	823	829	834	840	845	851	856	862	867	9 4.5
792	873	878	883	889	894	900	905	911	916	922	
793	927	933	938	944	949	955	960	966	971	977	
794	982	988	993	998	*004	*009	*015	*020	*026	*031	
795	90 037	042	048	053	059	064	069	075	080	086	
796	091	097	102	108	113	119	124	129	135	140	
797	146	151	157	162	168	173	179	184	189	195	
798	200	206	211	217	222	227	233	238	244	249	
799	255	260	266	271	276	282	287	293	298	304	
800	309	314	320	325	331	336	342	347	352	358	
N.	L. 0	1	2	3	4	5	6	7	8	9	P. P.

N.	L. 0	1	2	3	4	5	6	7	8	9
800	90 309	314	320	325	331	336	342	347	352	358
801	363	369	374	380	385	390	396	401	407	412
802	417	423	428	434	439	445	450	455	461	466
803	472	477	482	488	493	499	504	509	515	520
804	526	531	536	542	547	553	558	563	569	574
805	580	585	590	596	601	607	612	617	623	628
806	634	639	644	650	655	660	666	671	677	682
807	687	693	698	703	709	714	720	725	730	736
808	741	747	752	757	763	768	773	779	784	789
809	795	800	806	811	816	822	827	832	838	843
810	849	854	859	865	870	875	881	886	891	897
811	902	907	913	918	924	929	934	940	945	950
812	956	961	966	972	977	982	988	993	998	*004
813	91 009	014	020	025	030	036	041	046	052	057
814	062	068	073	078	084	089	094	100	105	110
815	116	121	126	132	137	142	148	153	158	164
816	169	174	180	185	190	196	201	206	212	217
817	222	228	233	238	243	249	254	259	265	270
818	275	281	286	291	297	302	307	312	318	323
819	328	334	339	344	350	355	360	365	371	376
820	381	387	392	397	403	408	413	418	424	429
821	434	440	445	450	455	461	466	471	477	482
822	487	492	498	503	508	514	519	524	529	535
823	540	545	551	556	561	566	572	577	582	587
824	593	598	603	609	614	619	624	630	635	640
825	645	651	656	661	666	672	677	682	687	693
826	698	703	709	714	719	724	730	735	740	745
827	751	756	761	766	772	777	782	787	793	798
828	803	808	814	819	824	829	834	840	845	850
829	855	861	866	871	876	882	887	892	897	903
830	908	913	918	924	929	934	939	944	950	955
831	960	965	971	976	981	986	991	997	*002	*007
832	92 012	018	023	028	033	038	044	049	054	059
833	065	070	075	080	085	091	096	101	106	111
834	117	122	127	132	137	143	148	153	158	163
835	169	174	179	184	189	195	200	205	210	215
836	221	226	231	236	241	247	252	257	262	267
837	273	278	283	288	293	298	304	309	314	319
838	324	330	335	340	345	350	355	361	366	371
839	376	381	387	392	397	402	407	412	418	423
840	428	433	438	443	449	454	459	464	469	474
841	480	485	490	495	500	505	511	516	521	526
842	531	536	542	547	552	557	562	567	572	578
843	583	588	593	598	603	609	614	619	624	629
844	634	639	645	650	655	660	665	670	675	681
845	686	691	696	701	706	711	716	722	727	732
846	737	742	747	752	758	763	768	773	778	783
847	788	793	799	804	809	814	819	824	829	834
848	840	845	850	855	860	865	870	875	881	886
849	891	896	901	906	911	916	921	927	932	937
850	942	947	952	957	962	967	973	978	983	988
N.	L. 0	1	2	3	4	5	6	7	8	9

P. P.

6

1	0.6
2	1.2
3	1.8
4	2.4
5	3.0
6	3.6
7	4.2
8	4.8
9	5.4

5

1	0.5
2	1.0
3	1.5
4	2.0
5	2.5
6	3.0
7	3.5
8	4.0
9	4.5

N.	L. 0	1	2	3	4	5	6	7	8	9	P. P.
850	92 942	947	952	957	962	967	973	978	983	988	
851	993	998	*003	*008	*013	*018	*024	*029	*034	*039	
852	93 044	049	054	059	064	069	075	080	085	090	
853	095	100	105	110	115	120	125	131	136	141	
854	146	151	156	161	166	171	176	181	186	192	
855	197	202	207	212	217	222	227	232	237	242	
856	247	252	258	263	268	273	278	283	288	293	
857	298	303	308	313	318	323	328	334	339	344	
858	349	354	359	364	369	374	379	384	389	394	
859	399	404	409	414	420	425	430	435	440	445	
860	450	455	460	465	470	475	480	485	490	495	
861	500	505	510	515	520	526	531	536	541	546	
862	551	556	561	566	571	576	581	586	591	596	
863	601	606	611	616	621	626	631	636	641	646	
864	651	656	661	666	671	676	682	687	692	697	
865	702	707	712	717	722	727	732	737	742	747	
866	752	757	762	767	772	777	782	787	792	797	
867	802	807	812	817	822	827	832	837	842	847	
868	852	857	862	867	872	877	882	887	892	897	
869	902	907	912	917	922	927	932	937	942	947	
870	952	957	962	967	972	977	982	987	992	997	
871	94 002	007	012	017	022	027	032	037	042	047	
872	052	057	062	067	072	077	082	086	091	096	
873	101	106	111	116	121	126	131	136	141	146	
874	151	156	161	166	171	176	181	186	191	196	
875	201	206	211	216	221	226	231	236	240	245	
876	250	255	260	265	270	275	280	285	290	295	
877	300	305	310	315	320	325	330	335	340	345	
878	349	354	359	364	369	374	379	384	389	394	
879	399	404	409	414	419	424	429	433	438	443	
880	448	453	458	463	468	473	478	483	488	493	
881	498	503	507	512	517	522	527	532	537	542	
882	547	552	557	562	567	571	576	581	586	591	
883	596	601	606	611	616	621	626	630	635	640	
884	645	650	655	660	665	670	675	680	685	689	
885	694	699	704	709	714	719	724	729	734	738	
886	743	748	753	758	763	768	773	778	783	787	
887	792	797	802	807	812	817	822	827	832	836	
888	841	846	851	856	861	866	871	876	880	885	
889	890	895	900	905	910	915	919	924	929	934	
890	939	944	949	954	959	963	968	973	978	983	
891	988	993	998	*002	*007	*012	*017	*022	*027	*032	
892	95 036	041	046	051	056	061	066	071	075	080	
893	085	090	095	100	105	109	114	119	124	129	
894	134	139	143	148	153	158	163	168	173	177	
895	182	187	192	197	202	207	211	216	221	226	
896	231	236	240	245	250	255	260	265	270	274	
897	279	284	289	294	299	303	308	313	318	323	
898	328	332	337	342	347	352	357	361	366	371	
899	376	381	386	390	395	400	405	410	415	419	
900	424	429	434	439	444	448	453	458	463	468	
N.	L. 0	1	2	3	4	5	6	7	8	9	P. P.

P. P.

6
1 | 0.6
2 | 1.2
3 | 1.8
4 | 2.4
5 | 3.0
6 | 3.6
7 | 4.2
8 | 4.8
9 | 5.4

5
1 | 0.5
2 | 1.0
3 | 1.5
4 | 2.0
5 | 2.5
6 | 3.0
7 | 3.5
8 | 4.0
9 | 4.5

4
1 | 0.4
2 | 0.8
3 | 1.2
4 | 1.6
5 | 2.0
6 | 2.4
7 | 2.8
8 | 3.2
9 | 3.6

N.	L. 0	1	2	3	4	5	6	7	8	9	P. P.
900	95 424	429	434	439	444	448	453	458	463	468	
901	472	477	482	487	492	497	501	506	511	516	
902	521	525	530	535	540	545	550	554	559	564	
903	569	574	578	583	588	593	598	602	607	612	
904	617	622	626	631	636	641	646	650	655	660	
905	665	670	674	679	684	689	694	698	703	708	
906	713	718	722	727	732	737	742	746	751	756	
907	761	766	770	775	780	785	789	794	799	804	
908	809	813	818	823	828	832	837	842	847	852	
909	856	861	866	871	875	880	885	890	895	899	
910	904	909	914	918	923	928	933	938	942	947	
911	952	957	961	966	971	976	980	985	990	995	**5**
912	999	*004	*009	*014	*019	*023	*028	*033	*038	*042	1 0.5
913	96 047	052	057	061	066	071	076	080	085	090	2 1.0
914	095	099	104	109	114	118	123	128	133	137	3 1.5
915	142	147	152	156	161	166	171	175	180	185	4 2.0
916	190	194	199	204	209	213	218	223	227	232	5 2.5
917	237	242	246	251	256	261	265	270	275	280	6 3.0
918	284	289	294	298	303	308	313	317	322	327	7 3.5
919	332	336	341	346	350	355	360	365	369	374	8 4.0
920	379	384	388	393	398	402	407	412	417	421	9 4.5
921	426	431	435	440	445	450	454	459	464	468	
922	473	478	483	487	492	497	501	506	511	515	
923	520	525	530	534	539	544	548	553	558	562	
924	567	572	577	581	586	591	595	600	605	609	
925	614	619	624	628	633	638	642	647	652	656	
926	661	666	670	675	680	685	689	694	699	703	
927	708	713	717	722	727	731	736	741	745	750	
928	755	759	764	769	774	778	783	788	792	797	
929	802	806	811	816	820	825	830	834	839	844	
930	848	853	858	862	867	872	876	881	886	890	
931	895	900	904	909	914	918	923	928	932	937	
932	942	946	951	956	960	965	970	974	979	984	
933	988	993	997	*002	*007	*011	*016	*021	*025	*030	**4**
934	97 035	039	044	049	053	058	063	067	072	077	1 0.4
935	081	086	090	095	100	104	109	114	118	123	2 0.8
936	128	132	137	142	146	151	155	160	165	169	3 1.2
937	174	179	183	188	192	197	202	206	211	216	4 1.6
938	220	225	230	234	239	243	248	253	257	262	5 2.0
939	267	271	276	280	285	290	294	299	304	308	6 2.4
940	313	317	322	327	331	336	340	345	350	354	7 2.8
941	359	364	368	373	377	382	387	391	396	400	8 3.2
942	405	410	414	419	424	428	433	437	442	447	9 3.6
943	451	456	460	465	470	474	479	483	488	493	
944	497	502	506	511	516	520	525	529	534	539	
945	543	548	552	557	562	566	571	575	580	585	
946	589	594	598	603	607	612	617	621	626	630	
947	635	640	644	649	653	658	663	667	672	676	
948	681	685	690	695	699	704	708	713	717	722	
949	727	731	736	740	745	749	754	759	763	768	
950	772	777	782	786	791	795	800	804	809	813	
N.	L. 0	1	2	3	4	5	6	7	8	9	P. P.

N.	L. 0	1	2	3	4	5	6	7	8	9
950	97 772	777	782	786	791	795	800	804	809	813
951	818	823	827	832	836	841	845	850	855	859
952	864	868	873	877	882	886	891	896	900	905
953	909	914	918	923	928	932	937	941	946	950
954	955	959	964	968	973	978	982	987	991	996
955	98 000	005	009	014	019	023	028	032	037	041
956	046	050	055	059	064	068	073	078	082	087
957	091	096	100	105	109	114	118	123	127	132
958	137	141	146	150	155	159	164	168	173	177
959	182	186	191	195	200	204	209	214	218	223
960	227	232	236	241	245	250	254	259	263	268
961	272	277	281	286	290	295	299	304	308	313
962	318	322	327	331	336	340	345	349	354	358
963	363	367	372	376	381	385	390	394	399	403
964	408	412	417	421	426	430	435	439	444	448
965	453	457	462	466	471	475	480	484	489	493
966	498	502	507	511	516	520	525	529	534	538
967	543	547	552	556	561	565	570	574	579	583
968	588	592	597	601	605	610	614	619	623	628
969	632	637	641	646	650	655	659	664	668	673
970	677	682	686	691	695	700	704	709	713	717
971	722	726	731	735	740	744	749	753	758	762
972	767	771	776	780	784	789	793	798	802	807
973	811	816	820	825	829	834	838	843	847	851
974	856	860	865	869	874	878	883	887	892	896
975	900	905	909	914	918	923	927	932	936	941
976	945	949	954	958	963	967	972	976	981	985
977	989	994	998	*003	*007	*012	*016	*021	*025	*029
978	99 034	038	043	047	052	056	061	065	069	074
979	078	083	087	092	096	100	105	109	114	118
980	123	127	131	136	140	145	149	154	158	162
981	167	171	176	180	185	189	193	198	202	207
982	211	216	220	224	229	233	238	242	247	251
983	255	260	264	269	273	277	282	286	291	295
984	300	304	308	313	317	322	326	330	335	339
985	344	348	352	357	361	366	370	374	379	383
986	388	392	396	401	405	410	414	419	423	427
987	432	436	441	445	449	454	458	463	467	471
988	476	480	484	489	493	498	502	506	511	515
989	520	524	528	533	537	542	546	550	555	559
990	564	568	572	577	581	585	590	594	599	603
991	607	612	616	621	625	629	634	638	642	647
992	651	656	660	664	669	673	677	682	686	691
993	695	699	704	708	712	717	721	726	730	734
994	739	743	747	752	756	760	765	769	774	778
995	782	787	791	795	800	804	808	813	817	822
996	826	830	835	839	843	848	852	856	861	865
997	870	874	878	883	887	891	896	900	904	909
998	913	917	922	926	930	935	939	944	948	952
999	957	961	965	970	974	978	983	987	991	996
1000	00 000	004	009	013	017	022	026	030	035	039
N.	L. 0	1	2	3	4	5	6	7	8	9

P. P.

5
1 | 0.5
2 | 1.0
3 | 1.5
4 | 2.0
5 | 2.5
6 | 3.0
7 | 3.5
8 | 4.0
9 | 4.5

4
1 | 0.4
2 | 0.8
3 | 1.2
4 | 1.6
5 | 2.0
6 | 2.4
7 | 2.8
8 | 3.2
9 | 3.6

TABLES

OF

NATURAL SINES, COSINES, TANGENTS, AND COTANGENTS

GIVING THE VALUES OF THE FUNCTIONS FOR
ALL DEGREES AND MINUTES FROM
0° TO 90°

′	0°		1°		2°		3°		4°		′
	Sine	Cosine	Sine	Cosine	Sine	Cosine	Sine	Cosine	Sine	Cosine	
0	.00000	1.	.01745	.99985	.03490	.99939	.05234	.99863	.06976	.99756	60
1	.00029	1.	.01774	.99984	.03519	.99938	.05263	.99861	.07005	.99754	59
2	.00058	1.	.01803	.99984	.03548	.99937	.05292	.99860	.07034	.99752	58
3	.00087	1.	.01832	.99983	.03577	.99936	.05321	.99858	.07063	.99750	57
4	.00116	1.	.01862	.99983	.03606	.99935	.05350	.99857	.07092	.99748	56
5	.00145	1.	.01891	.99982	.03635	.99934	.05379	.99855	.07121	.99746	55
6	.00175	1.	.01920	.99982	.03664	.99933	.05408	.99854	.07150	.99744	54
7	.00204	1.	.01949	.99981	.03693	.99932	.05437	.99852	.07179	.99742	53
8	.00233	1.	.01978	.99980	.03723	.99931	.05466	.99851	.07208	.99740	52
9	.00262	1.	.02007	.99980	.03752	.99930	.05495	.99849	.07237	.99738	51
10	.00291	1.	.02036	.99979	.03781	.99929	.05524	.99847	.07266	.99736	50
11	.00320	.99999	.02065	.99979	.03810	.99927	.05553	.99846	.07295	.99734	49
12	.00349	.99999	.02094	.99978	.03839	.99926	.05582	.99844	.07324	.99731	48
13	.00378	.99999	.02123	.99977	.03868	.99925	.05611	.99842	.07353	.99729	47
14	.00407	.99999	.02152	.99977	.03897	.99924	.05640	.99841	.07382	.99727	46
15	.00436	.99999	.02181	.99976	.03926	.99923	.05669	.99839	.07411	.99725	45
16	.00465	.99999	.02211	.99976	.03955	.99922	.05698	.99838	.07440	.99723	44
17	.00495	.99999	.02240	.99975	.03984	.99921	.05727	.99836	.07469	.99721	43
18	.00524	.99999	.02269	.99974	.04013	.99919	.05756	.99834	.07498	.99719	42
19	.00553	.99998	.02298	.99974	.04042	.99918	.05785	.99833	.07527	.99716	41
20	.00582	.99998	.02327	.99973	.04071	.99917	.05814	.99831	.07556	.99714	40
21	.00611	.99998	.02356	.99972	.04100	.99916	.05844	.99829	.07585	.99712	39
22	.00640	.99998	.02385	.99972	.04129	.99915	.05873	.99827	.07614	.99710	38
23	.00669	.99998	.02414	.99971	.04159	.99913	.05902	.99826	.07643	.99708	37
24	.00698	.99998	.02443	.99970	.04188	.99912	.05931	.99824	.07672	.99705	36
25	.00727	.99997	.02472	.99969	.04217	.99911	.05960	.99822	.07701	.99703	35
26	.00756	.99997	.02501	.99969	.04246	.99910	.05989	.99821	.07730	.99701	34
27	.00785	.99997	.02530	.99968	.04275	.99909	.06018	.99819	.07759	.99699	33
28	.00814	.99997	.02560	.99967	.04304	.99907	.06047	.99817	.07788	.99696	32
29	.00844	.99996	.02589	.99966	.04333	.99906	.06076	.99815	.07817	.99694	31
30	.00873	.99996	.02618	.99966	.04362	.99905	.06105	.99813	.07846	.99692	30
31	.00902	.99996	.02647	.99965	.04391	.99904	.06134	.99812	.07875	.99689	29
32	.00931	.99996	.02676	.99964	.04420	.99902	.06163	.99810	.07904	.99687	28
33	.00960	.99995	.02705	.99963	.04449	.99901	.06192	.99808	.07933	.99685	27
34	.00989	.99995	.02734	.99963	.04478	.99900	.06221	.99806	.07962	.99683	26
35	.01018	.99995	.02763	.99962	.04507	.99898	.06250	.99804	.07991	.99680	25
36	.01047	.99995	.02792	.99961	.04536	.99897	.06279	.99803	.08020	.99678	24
37	.01076	.99994	.02821	.99960	.04565	.99896	.06308	.99801	.08049	.99676	23
38	.01105	.99994	.02850	.99959	.04594	.99894	.06337	.99799	.08078	.99673	22
39	.01134	.99994	.02879	.99959	.04623	.99893	.06366	.99797	.08107	.99671	21
40	.01164	.99993	.02908	.99958	.04653	.99892	.06395	.99795	.08136	.99668	20
41	.01193	.99993	.02938	.99957	.04682	.99890	.06424	.99793	.08165	.99666	19
42	.01222	.99993	.02967	.99956	.04711	.99889	.06453	.99792	.08194	.99664	18
43	.01251	.99992	.02996	.99955	.04740	.99888	.06482	.99790	.08223	.99661	17
44	.01280	.99992	.03025	.99954	.04769	.99886	.06511	.99788	.08252	.99659	16
45	.01309	.99991	.03054	.99953	.04798	.99885	.06540	.99786	.08281	.99657	15
46	.01338	.99991	.03083	.99952	.04827	.99883	.06569	.99784	.08310	.99654	14
47	.01367	.99991	.03112	.99952	.04856	.99882	.06598	.99782	.08339	.99652	13
48	.01396	.99990	.03141	.99951	.04885	.99881	.06627	.99780	.08368	.99649	12
49	.01425	.99990	.03170	.99950	.04914	.99879	.06656	.99778	.08397	.99647	11
50	.01454	.99989	.03199	.99949	.04943	.99878	.06685	.99776	.08426	.99644	10
51	.01483	.99989	.03228	.99948	.04972	.99876	.06714	.99774	.08455	.99642	9
52	.01513	.99989	.03257	.99947	.05001	.99875	.06743	.99772	.08484	.99639	8
53	.01542	.99988	.03286	.99946	.05030	.99873	.06773	.99770	.08513	.99637	7
54	.01571	.99988	.03316	.99945	.05059	.99872	.06802	.99768	.08542	.99635	6
55	.01600	.99987	.03345	.99944	.05088	.99870	.06831	.99766	.08571	.99632	5
56	.01629	.99987	.03374	.99943	.05117	.99869	.06860	.99764	.08600	.99630	4
57	.01658	.99986	.03403	.99942	.05146	.99867	.06889	.99762	.08629	.99627	3
58	.01687	.99986	.03432	.99941	.05175	.99866	.06918	.99760	.08658	.99625	2
59	.01716	.99985	.03461	.99940	.05205	.99864	.06947	.99758	.08687	.99622	1
60	.01745	.99985	.03490	.99939	.05234	.99863	.06976	.99756	.08716	.99619	0
′	Cosine	Sine	Cosine	Sine	Cosine	Sine	Cosine	Sine	Cosine	Sine	′
	89°		88°		87°		86°		85°		

′	5° Sine	5° Cosine	6° Sine	6° Cosine	7° Sine	7° Cosine	8° Sine	8° Cosine	9° Sine	9° Cosine	′
0	.08716	.99619	.10453	.99452	.12187	.99255	.13917	.99027	.15643	.98769	60
1	.08745	.99617	.10482	.99449	.12216	.99251	.13946	.99023	.15672	.98764	59
2	.08774	.99614	.10511	.99446	.12245	.99248	.13975	.99019	.15701	.98760	58
3	.08803	.99612	.10540	.99443	.12274	.99244	.14004	.99015	.15730	.98755	57
4	.08831	.99609	.10569	.99440	.12302	.99240	.14033	.99011	.15758	.98751	56
5	.08860	.99607	.10597	.99437	.12331	.99237	.14061	.99006	.15787	.98746	55
6	.08889	.99604	.10626	.99434	.12360	.99233	.14090	.99002	.15816	.98741	54
7	.08918	.99602	.10655	.99431	.12389	.99230	.14119	.98998	.15845	.98737	53
8	.08947	.99599	.10684	.99428	.12418	.99226	.14148	.98994	.15873	.98732	52
9	.08976	.99596	.10713	.99424	.12447	.99222	.14177	.98990	.15902	.98728	51
10	.09005	.99594	.10742	.99421	.12476	.99219	.14205	.98986	.15931	.98723	50
11	.09034	.99591	.10771	.99418	.12504	.99215	.14234	.98982	.15959	.98718	49
12	.09063	.99588	.10800	.99415	.12533	.99211	.14263	.98978	.15988	.98714	48
13	.09092	.99586	.10829	.99412	.12562	.99208	.14292	.98973	.16017	.98709	47
14	.09121	.99583	.10858	.99409	.12591	.99204	.14320	.98969	.16046	.98704	46
15	.09150	.99580	.10887	.99406	.12620	.99200	.14349	.98965	.16074	.98700	45
16	.09179	.99578	.10916	.99402	.12649	.99197	.14378	.98961	.16103	.98695	44
17	.09208	.99575	.10945	.99399	.12678	.99193	.14407	.98957	.16132	.98690	43
18	.09237	.99572	.10973	.99396	.12706	.99189	.14436	.98953	.16160	.98686	42
19	.09266	.99570	.11002	.99393	.12735	.99186	.14464	.98948	.16189	.98681	41
20	.09295	.99567	.11031	.99390	.12764	.99182	.14493	.98944	.16218	.98676	40
21	.09324	.99564	.11060	.99386	.12793	.99178	.14522	.98940	.16246	.98671	39
22	.09353	.99562	.11089	.99383	.12822	.99175	.14551	.98936	.16275	.98667	38
23	.09382	.99559	.11118	.99380	.12851	.99171	.14580	.98931	.16304	.98662	37
24	.09411	.99556	.11147	.99377	.12880	.99167	.14608	.98927	.16333	.98657	36
25	.09440	.99553	.11176	.99374	.12908	.99163	.14637	.98923	.16361	.98652	35
26	.09469	.99551	.11205	.99370	.12937	.99160	.14666	.98919	.16390	.98648	34
27	.09498	.99548	.11234	.99367	.12966	.99156	.14695	.98914	.16419	.98643	33
28	.09527	.99545	.11263	.99364	.12995	.99152	.14723	.98910	.16447	.98638	32
29	.09556	.99542	.11291	.99360	.13024	.99148	.14752	.98906	.16476	.98633	31
30	.09585	.99540	.11320	.99357	.13053	.99144	.14781	.98902	.16505	.98629	30
31	.09614	.99537	.11349	.99354	.13081	.99141	.14810	.98897	.16533	.98624	29
32	.09642	.99534	.11378	.99351	.13110	.99137	.14838	.98893	.16562	.98619	28
33	.09671	.99531	.11407	.99347	.13139	.99133	.14867	.98889	.16591	.98614	27
34	.09700	.99528	.11436	.99344	.13168	.99129	.14896	.98884	.16620	.98609	26
35	.09729	.99526	.11465	.99341	.13197	.99125	.14925	.98880	.16648	.98604	25
36	.09758	.99523	.11494	.99337	.13226	.99122	.14954	.98876	.16677	.98600	24
37	.09787	.99520	.11523	.99334	.13254	.99118	.14982	.98871	.16706	.98595	23
38	.09816	.99517	.11552	.99331	.13283	.99114	.15011	.98867	.16734	.98590	22
39	.09845	.99514	.11580	.99327	.13312	.99110	.15040	.98863	.16763	.98585	21
40	.09874	.99511	.11609	.99324	.13341	.99106	.15069	.98858	.16792	.98580	20
41	.09903	.99508	.11638	.99320	.13370	.99102	.15097	.98854	.16820	.98575	19
42	.09932	.99506	.11667	.99317	.13399	.99098	.15126	.98849	.16849	.98570	18
43	.09961	.99503	.11696	.99314	.13427	.99094	.15155	.98845	.16878	.98565	17
44	.09990	.99500	.11725	.99310	.13456	.99091	.15184	.98841	.16906	.98561	16
45	.10019	.99497	.11754	.99307	.13485	.99087	.15212	.98836	.16935	.98556	15
46	.10048	.99494	.11783	.99303	.13514	.99083	.15241	.98832	.16964	.98551	14
47	.10077	.99491	.11812	.99300	.13543	.99079	.15270	.98827	.16992	.98546	13
48	.10106	.99488	.11840	.99297	.13572	.99075	.15299	.98823	.17021	.98541	12
49	.10135	.99485	.11869	.99293	.13600	.99071	.15327	.98818	.17050	.98536	11
50	.10164	.99482	.11898	.99290	.13629	.99067	.15356	.98814	.17078	.98531	10
51	.10192	.99479	.11927	.99286	.13658	.99063	.15385	.98809	.17107	.98526	9
52	.10221	.99476	.11956	.99283	.13687	.99059	.15414	.98805	.17136	.98521	8
53	.10250	.99473	.11985	.99279	.13716	.99055	.15442	.98800	.17164	.98516	7
54	.10279	.99470	.12014	.99276	.13744	.99051	.15471	.98796	.17193	.98511	6
55	.10308	.99467	.12043	.99272	.13773	.99047	.15500	.98791	.17222	.98506	5
56	.10337	.99464	.12071	.99269	.13802	.99043	.15529	.98787	.17250	.98501	4
57	.10366	.99461	.12100	.99265	.13831	.99039	.15557	.98782	.17279	.98496	3
58	.10395	.99458	.12129	.99262	.13860	.99035	.15586	.98778	.17308	.98491	2
59	.10424	.99455	.12158	.99258	.13889	.99031	.15615	.98773	.17336	.98486	1
60	.10453	.99452	.12187	.99255	.13917	.99027	.15643	.98769	.17365	.98481	0
′	Cosine	Sine	Cosine	Sine	Cosine	Sine	Cosine	Sine	Cosine	Sine	′
	84°		83°		82°		81°		80°		

′	10°		11°		12°		13°		14°		′
	Sine	Cosine	Sine	Cosine	Sine	Cosine	Sine	Cosine	Sine	Cosine	
0	.17365	.98481	.19081	.98163	.20791	.97815	.22495	.97437	.24192	.97030	60
1	.17393	.98476	.19109	.98157	.20820	.97809	.22523	.97430	.24220	.97023	59
2	.17422	.98471	.19138	.98152	.20848	.97803	.22552	.97424	.24249	.97015	58
3	.17451	.98466	.19167	.98146	.20877	.97797	.22580	.97417	.24277	.97008	57
4	.17479	.98461	.19195	.98140	.20905	.97791	.22608	.97411	.24305	.97001	56
5	.17508	.98455	.19224	.98135	.20933	.97784	.22637	.97404	.24333	.96994	55
6	.17537	.98450	.19252	.98129	.20962	.97778	.22665	.97398	.24362	.96987	54
7	.17565	.98445	.19281	.98124	.20990	.97772	.22693	.97391	.24390	.96980	53
8	.17594	.98440	.19309	.98118	.21019	.97766	.22722	.97384	.24418	.96973	52
9	.17623	.98435	.19338	.98112	.21047	.97760	.22750	.97378	.24446	.96966	51
10	.17651	.98430	.19366	.98107	.21076	.97754	.22778	.97371	.24474	.96959	50
11	.17680	.98425	.19395	.98101	.21104	.97748	.22807	.97365	.24503	.96952	49
12	.17708	.98420	.19423	.98096	.21132	.97742	.22835	.97358	.24531	.96945	48
13	.17737	.98414	.19452	.98090	.21161	.97735	.22863	.97351	.24559	.96937	47
14	.17766	.98409	.19481	.98084	.21189	.97729	.22892	.97345	.24587	.96930	46
15	.17794	.98404	.19509	.98079	.21218	.97723	.22920	.97338	.24615	.96923	45
16	.17823	.98399	.19538	.98073	.21246	.97717	.22948	.97331	.24644	.96916	44
17	.17852	.98394	.19566	.98067	.21275	.97711	.22977	.97325	.24672	.96909	43
18	.17880	.98389	.19595	.98061	.21303	.97705	.23005	.97318	.24700	.96902	42
19	.17909	.98383	.19623	.98056	.21331	.97698	.23033	.97311	.24728	.96894	41
20	.17937	.98378	.19652	.98050	.21360	.97692	.23062	.97304	.24756	.96887	40
21	.17966	.98373	.19680	.98044	.21388	.97686	.23090	.97298	.24784	.96880	39
22	.17995	.98368	.19709	.98039	.21417	.97680	.23118	.97291	.24813	.96873	38
23	.18023	.98362	.19737	.98033	.21445	.97673	.23146	.97284	.24841	.96866	37
24	.18052	.98357	.19766	.98027	.21474	.97667	.23175	.97278	.24869	.96858	36
25	.18081	.98352	.19794	.98021	.21502	.97661	.23203	.97271	.24897	.96851	35
26	.18109	.98347	.19823	.98016	.21530	.97655	.23231	.97264	.24925	.96844	34
27	.18138	.98341	.19851	.98010	.21559	.97648	.23260	.97257	.24954	.96837	33
28	.18166	.98336	.19880	.98004	.21587	.97642	.23288	.97251	.24982	.96829	32
29	.18195	.98331	.19908	.97998	.21616	.97636	.23316	.97244	.25010	.96822	31
30	.18224	.98325	.19937	.97992	.21644	.97630	.23345	.97237	.25038	.96815	30
31	.18252	.98320	.19965	.97987	.21672	.97623	.23373	.97230	.25066	.96807	29
32	.18281	.98315	.19994	.97981	.21701	.97617	.23401	.97223	.25094	.96800	28
33	.18309	.98310	.20022	.97975	.21729	.97611	.23429	.97217	.25122	.96793	27
34	.18338	.98304	.20051	.97969	.21758	.97604	.23458	.97210	.25151	.96786	26
35	.18367	.98299	.20079	.97963	.21786	.97598	.23486	.97203	.25179	.96778	25
36	.18395	.98294	.20108	.97958	.21814	.97592	.23514	.97196	.25207	.96771	24
37	.18424	.98288	.20136	.97952	.21843	.97585	.23542	.97189	.25235	.96764	23
38	.18452	.98283	.20165	.97946	.21871	.97579	.23571	.97182	.25263	.96756	22
39	.18481	.98277	.20193	.97940	.21899	.97573	.23599	.97176	.25291	.96749	21
40	.18509	.98272	.20222	.97934	.21928	.97566	.23627	.97169	.25320	.96742	20
41	.18538	.98267	.20250	.97928	.21956	.97560	.23656	.97162	.25348	.96734	19
42	.18567	.98261	.20279	.97922	.21985	.97553	.23684	.97155	.25376	.96727	18
43	.18595	.98256	.20307	.97916	.22013	.97547	.23712	.97148	.25404	.96719	17
44	.18624	.98250	.20336	.97910	.22041	.97541	.23740	.97141	.25432	.96712	16
45	.18652	.98245	.20364	.97905	.22070	.97534	.23769	.97134	.25460	.96705	15
46	.18681	.98240	.20393	.97899	.22098	.97528	.23797	.97127	.25488	.96697	14
47	.18710	.98234	.20421	.97893	.22126	.97521	.23825	.97120	.25516	.96690	13
48	.18738	.98229	.20450	.97887	.22155	.97515	.23853	.97113	.25545	.96682	12
49	.18767	.98223	.20478	.97881	.22183	.97508	.23882	.97106	.25573	.96675	11
50	.18795	.98218	.20507	.97875	.22212	.97502	.23910	.97100	.25601	.96667	10
51	.18824	.98212	.20535	.97869	.22240	.97496	.23938	.97093	.25629	.96660	9
52	.18852	.98207	.20563	.97863	.22268	.97489	.23966	.97086	.25657	.96653	8
53	.18881	.98201	.20592	.97857	.22297	.97483	.23995	.97079	.25685	.96645	7
54	.18910	.98196	.20620	.97851	.22325	.97476	.24023	.97072	.25713	.96638	6
55	.18938	.98190	.20649	.97845	.22353	.97470	.24051	.97065	.25741	.96630	5
56	.18967	.98185	.20677	.97839	.22382	.97463	.24079	.97058	.25769	.96623	4
57	.18995	.98179	.20706	.97833	.22410	.97457	.24108	.97051	.25798	.96615	3
58	.19024	.98174	.20734	.97827	.22438	.97450	.24136	.97044	.25826	.96608	2
59	.19052	.98168	.20763	.97821	.22467	.97444	.24164	.97037	.25854	.96600	1
60	.19081	.98163	.20791	.97815	.22495	.97437	.24192	.97030	.25882	.96593	0
′	Cosine	Sine	Cosine	Sine	Cosine	Sine	Cosine	Sine	Cosine	Sine	′
	79°		78°		77°		76°		75°		

′	15° Sine	Cosine	16° Sine	Cosine	17° Sine	Cosine	18° Sine	Cosine	19° Sine	Cosine	′
0	.25882	.96593	.27564	.96126	.29237	.95630	.30902	.95106	.32557	.94552	60
1	.25910	.96585	.27592	.96118	.29265	.95622	.30929	.95097	.32584	.94542	59
2	.25938	.96578	.27620	.96110	.29293	.95613	.30957	.95088	.32612	.94533	58
3	.25966	.96570	.27648	.96102	.29321	.95605	.30985	.95079	.32639	.94523	57
4	.25994	.96562	.27676	.96094	.29348	.95596	.31012	.95070	.32667	.94514	56
5	.26022	.96555	.27704	.96086	.29376	.95588	.31040	.95061	.32694	.94504	55
6	.26050	.96547	.27731	.96078	.29404	.95579	.31068	.95052	.32722	.94495	54
7	.26079	.96540	.27759	.96070	.29432	.95571	.31095	.95043	.32749	.94485	53
8	.26107	.96532	.27787	.96062	.29460	.95562	.31123	.95033	.32777	.94476	52
9	.26135	.96524	.27815	.96054	.29487	.95554	.31151	.95024	.32804	.94466	51
10	.26163	.96517	.27843	.96046	.29515	.95545	.31178	.95015	.32832	.94457	50
11	.26191	.96509	.27871	.96037	.29543	.95536	.31206	.95006	.32859	.94447	49
12	.26219	.96502	.27899	.96029	.29571	.95528	.31233	.94997	.32887	.94438	48
13	.26247	.96494	.27927	.96021	.29599	.95519	.31261	.94988	.32914	.94428	47
14	.26275	.96486	.27955	.96013	.29626	.95511	.31289	.94979	.32942	.94418	46
15	.26303	.96479	.27983	.96005	.29654	.95502	.31316	.94970	.32969	.94409	45
16	.26331	.96471	.28011	.95997	.29682	.95493	.31344	.94961	.32997	.94399	44
17	.26359	.96463	.28039	.95989	.29710	.95485	.31372	.94952	.33024	.94390	43
18	.26387	.96456	.28067	.95981	.29737	.95476	.31399	.94943	.33051	.94380	42
19	.26415	.96448	.28095	.95972	.29765	.95467	.31427	.94933	.33079	.94370	41
20	.26443	.96440	.28123	.95964	.29793	.95459	.31454	.94924	.33106	.94361	40
21	.26471	.96433	.28150	.95956	.29821	.95450	.31482	.94915	.33134	.94351	39
22	.26500	.96425	.28178	.95948	.29849	.95441	.31510	.94906	.33161	.94342	38
23	.26528	.96417	.28206	.95940	.29876	.95433	.31537	.94897	.33189	.94332	37
24	.26556	.96410	.28234	.95931	.29904	.95424	.31565	.94888	.33216	.94322	36
25	.26584	.96402	.28262	.95923	.29932	.95415	.31593	.94878	.33244	.94313	35
26	.26612	.96394	.28290	.95915	.29960	.95407	.31620	.94869	.33271	.94303	34
27	.26640	.96386	.28318	.95907	.29987	.95398	.31648	.94860	.33298	.94293	33
28	.26668	.96379	.28346	.95898	.30015	.95389	.31675	.94851	.33326	.94284	32
29	.26696	.96371	.28374	.95890	.30043	.95380	.31703	.94842	.33353	.94274	31
30	.26724	.96363	.28402	.95882	.30071	.95372	.31730	.94832	.33381	.94264	30
31	.26752	.96355	.28429	.95874	.30098	.95363	.31758	.94823	.33408	.94254	29
32	.26780	.96347	.28457	.95865	.30126	.95354	.31786	.94814	.33436	.94245	28
33	.26808	.96340	.28485	.95857	.30154	.95345	.31813	.94805	.33463	.94235	27
34	.26836	.96332	.28513	.95849	.30182	.95337	.31841	.94795	.33490	.94225	26
35	.26864	.96324	.28541	.95841	.30209	.95328	.31868	.94786	.33518	.94215	25
36	.26892	.96316	.28569	.95832	.30237	.95319	.31896	.94777	.33545	.94206	24
37	.26920	.96308	.28597	.95824	.30265	.95310	.31923	.94768	.33573	.94196	23
38	.26948	.96301	.28625	.95816	.30292	.95301	.31951	.94758	.33600	.94186	22
39	.26976	.96293	.28652	.95807	.30320	.95293	.31979	.94749	.33627	.94176	21
40	.27004	.96285	.28680	.95799	.30348	.95284	.32006	.94740	.33655	.94167	20
41	.27032	.96277	.28708	.95791	.30376	.95275	.32034	.94730	.33682	.94157	19
42	.27060	.96269	.28736	.95782	.30403	.95266	.32061	.94721	.33710	.94147	18
43	.27088	.96261	.28764	.95774	.30431	.95257	.32089	.94712	.33737	.94137	17
44	.27116	.96253	.28792	.95766	.30459	.95248	.32116	.94702	.33764	.94127	16
45	.27144	.96246	.28820	.95757	.30486	.95240	.32144	.94693	.33792	.94118	15
46	.27172	.96238	.28847	.95749	.30514	.95231	.32171	.94684	.33819	.94108	14
47	.27200	.96230	.28875	.95740	.30542	.95222	.32199	.94674	.33846	.94098	13
48	.27228	.96222	.28903	.95732	.30570	.95213	.32227	.94665	.33874	.94088	12
49	.27256	.96214	.28931	.95724	.30597	.95204	.32254	.94656	.33901	.94078	11
50	.27284	.96206	.28959	.95715	.30625	.95195	.32282	.94646	.33929	.94068	10
51	.27312	.96198	.28987	.95707	.30653	.95186	.32309	.94637	.33956	.94058	9
52	.27340	.96190	.29015	.95698	.30680	.95177	.32337	.94627	.33983	.94049	8
53	.27368	.96182	.29042	.95690	.30708	.95168	.32364	.94618	.34011	.94039	7
54	.27396	.96174	.29070	.95681	.30736	.95159	.32392	.94609	.34038	.94029	6
55	.27424	.96166	.29098	.95673	.30763	.95150	.32419	.94599	.34065	.94019	5
56	.27452	.96158	.29126	.95664	.30791	.95142	.32447	.94590	.34093	.94009	4
57	.27480	.96150	.29154	.95656	.30819	.95133	.32474	.94580	.34120	.93999	3
58	.27508	.96142	.29182	.95647	.30846	.95124	.32502	.94571	.34147	.93989	2
59	.27536	.96134	.29209	.95639	.30874	.95115	.32529	.94561	.34175	.93979	1
60	.27564	.96126	.29237	.95630	.30902	.95106	.32557	.94552	.34202	.93969	0
′	Cosine	Sine	Cosine	Sine	Cosine	Sine	Cosine	Sine	Cosine	Sine	′
	74°		73°		72°		71°		70°		

′	20° Sine	Cosine	21° Sine	Cosine	22° Sine	Cosine	23° Sine	Cosine	24° Sine	Cosine	′
0	.34202	.93969	.35837	.93358	.37461	.92718	.39073	.92050	.40674	.91355	60
1	.34229	.93959	.35864	.93348	.37488	.92707	.39100	.92039	.40700	.91343	59
2	.34257	.93949	.35891	.93337	.37515	.92697	.39127	.92028	.40727	.91331	58
3	.34284	.93939	.35918	.93327	.37542	.92686	.39153	.92016	.40753	.91319	57
4	.34311	.93929	.35945	.93316	.37569	.92675	.39180	.92005	.40780	.91307	56
5	.34339	.93919	.35973	.93306	.37595	.92664	.39207	.91994	.40806	.91295	55
6	.34366	.93909	.36000	.93295	.37622	.92653	.39234	.91982	.40833	.91283	54
7	.34393	.93899	.36027	.93285	.37649	.92642	.39260	.91971	.40860	.91272	53
8	.34421	.93889	.36054	.93274	.37676	.92631	.39287	.91959	.40886	.91260	52
9	.34448	.93879	.36081	.93264	.37703	.92620	.39314	.91948	.40913	.91248	51
10	.34475	.93869	.36108	.93253	.37730	.92609	.39341	.91936	.40939	.91236	50
11	.34503	.93859	.36135	.93243	.37757	.92598	.39367	.91925	.40966	.91224	49
12	.34530	.93849	.36162	.93232	.37784	.92587	.39394	.91914	.40992	.91212	48
13	.34557	.93839	.36190	.93222	.37811	.92576	.39421	.91902	.41019	.91200	47
14	.34584	.93829	.36217	.93211	.37838	.92565	.39448	.91891	.41045	.91188	46
15	.34612	.93819	.36244	.93201	.37865	.92554	.39474	.91879	.41072	.91176	45
16	.34639	.93809	.36271	.93190	.37892	.92543	.39501	.91868	.41098	.91164	44
17	.34666	.93799	.36298	.93180	.37919	.92532	.39528	.91856	.41125	.91152	43
18	.34694	.93789	.36325	.93169	.37946	.92521	.39555	.91845	.41151	.91140	42
19	.34721	.93779	.36352	.93159	.37973	.92510	.39581	.91833	.41178	.91128	41
20	.34748	.93769	.36379	.93148	.37999	.92499	.39608	.91822	.41204	.91116	40
21	.34775	.93759	.36406	.93137	.38026	.92488	.39635	.91810	.41231	.91104	39
22	.34803	.93748	.36434	.93127	.38053	.92477	.39661	.91799	.41257	.91092	38
23	.34830	.93738	.36461	.93116	.38080	.92466	.39688	.91787	.41284	.91080	37
24	.34857	.93728	.36488	.93106	.38107	.92455	.39715	.91775	.41310	.91068	36
25	.34884	.93718	.36515	.93095	.38134	.92444	.39741	.91764	.41337	.91056	35
26	.34912	.93708	.36542	.93084	.38161	.92432	.39768	.91752	.41363	.91044	34
27	.34939	.93698	.36569	.93074	.38188	.92421	.39795	.91741	.41390	.91032	33
28	.34966	.93688	.36596	.93063	.38215	.92410	.39822	.91729	.41416	.91020	32
29	.34993	.93677	.36623	.93052	.38241	.92399	.39848	.91718	.41443	.91008	31
30	.35021	.93667	.36650	.93042	.38268	.92388	.39875	.91706	.41469	.90996	30
31	.35048	.93657	.36677	.93031	.38295	.92377	.39902	.91694	.41496	.90984	29
32	.35075	.93647	.36704	.93020	.38322	.92366	.39928	.91683	.41522	.90972	28
33	.35102	.93637	.36731	.93010	.38349	.92355	.39955	.91671	.41549	.90960	27
34	.35130	.93626	.36758	.92999	.38376	.92343	.39982	.91660	.41575	.90948	26
35	.35157	.93616	.36785	.92988	.38403	.92332	.40008	.91648	.41602	.90936	25
36	.35184	.93606	.36812	.92978	.38430	.92321	.40035	.91636	.41628	.90924	24
37	.35211	.93596	.36839	.92967	.38456	.92310	.40062	.91625	.41655	.90911	23
38	.35239	.93585	.36867	.92956	.38483	.92299	.40088	.91613	.41681	.90899	22
39	.35266	.93575	.36894	.92945	.38510	.92287	.40115	.91601	.41707	.90887	21
40	.35293	.93565	.36921	.92935	.38537	.92276	.40141	.91590	.41734	.90875	20
41	.35320	.93555	.36948	.92924	.38564	.92265	.40168	.91578	.41760	.90863	19
42	.35347	.93544	.36975	.92913	.38591	.92254	.40195	.91566	.41787	.90851	18
43	.35375	.93534	.37002	.92902	.38617	.92243	.40221	.91555	.41813	.90839	17
44	.35402	.93524	.37029	.92892	.38644	.92231	.40248	.91543	.41840	.90826	16
45	.35429	.93514	.37056	.92881	.38671	.92220	.40275	.91531	.41866	.90814	15
46	.35456	.93503	.37083	.92870	.38698	.92209	.40301	.91519	.41892	.90802	14
47	.35484	.93493	.37110	.92859	.38725	.92198	.40328	.91508	.41919	.90790	13
48	.35511	.93483	.37137	.92849	.38752	.92186	.40355	.91496	.41945	.90778	12
49	.35538	.93472	.37164	.92838	.38778	.92175	.40381	.91484	.41972	.90766	11
50	.35565	.93462	.37191	.92827	.38805	.92164	.40408	.91472	.41998	.90753	10
51	.35592	.93452	.37218	.92816	.38832	.92152	.40434	.91461	.42024	.90741	9
52	.35619	.93441	.37245	.92805	.38859	.92141	.40461	.91449	.42051	.90729	8
53	.35647	.93431	.37272	.92794	.38886	.92130	.40488	.91437	.42077	.90717	7
54	.35674	.93420	.37299	.92784	.38912	.92119	.40514	.91425	.42104	.90704	6
55	.35701	.93410	.37326	.92773	.38939	.92107	.40541	.91414	.42130	.90692	5
56	.35728	.93400	.37353	.92762	.38966	.92096	.40567	.91402	.42156	.90680	4
57	.35755	.93389	.37380	.92751	.38993	.92085	.40594	.91390	.42183	.90668	3
58	.35782	.93379	.37407	.92740	.39020	.92073	.40621	.91378	.42209	.90655	2
59	.35810	.93368	.37434	.92729	.39046	.92062	.40647	.91366	.42235	.90643	1
60	.35837	.93358	.37461	.92718	.39073	.92050	.40674	.91355	.42262	.90631	0
′	Cosine	Sine	Cosine	Sine	Cosine	Sine	Cosine	Sine	Cosine	Sine	′
	69°		68°		67°		66°		65°		

′	25° Sine	25° Cosine	26° Sine	26° Cosine	27° Sine	27° Cosine	28° Sine	28° Cosine	29° Sine	29° Cosine	′
0	.42262	.90631	.43837	.89879	.45399	.89101	.46947	.88295	.48481	.87462	60
1	.42288	.90618	.43863	.89867	.45425	.89087	.46973	.88281	.48506	.87448	59
2	.42315	.90606	.43889	.89854	.45451	.89074	.46999	.88267	.48532	.87434	58
3	.42341	.90594	.43916	.89841	.45477	.89061	.47024	.88254	.48557	.87420	57
4	.42367	.90582	.43942	.89828	.45503	.89049	.47050	.88240	.48583	.87406	56
5	.42394	.90569	.43968	.89816	.45529	.89035	.47076	.88226	.48608	.87391	55
6	.42420	.90557	.43994	.89803	.45554	.89021	.47101	.88213	.48634	.87377	54
7	.42446	.90545	.44020	.89790	.45580	.89008	.47127	.88199	.48659	.87363	53
8	.42473	.90532	.44046	.89777	.45606	.88995	.47153	.88185	.48684	.87349	52
9	.42499	.90520	.44072	.89764	.45632	.88981	.47178	.88172	.48710	.87335	51
10	.42525	.90507	.44098	.89752	.45658	.88968	.47204	.88158	.48735	.87321	50
11	.42552	.90495	.44124	.89739	.45684	.88955	.47229	.88144	.48761	.87306	49
12	.42578	.90483	.44151	.89726	.45710	.88942	.47255	.88130	.48786	.87292	48
13	.42604	.90470	.44177	.89713	.45736	.88928	.47281	.88117	.48811	.87278	47
14	.42631	.90458	.44203	.89700	.45762	.88915	.47306	.88103	.48837	.87264	46
15	.42657	.90446	.44229	.89687	.45787	.88902	.47332	.88089	.48862	.87250	45
16	.42683	.90433	.44255	.89674	.45813	.88888	.47358	.88075	.48888	.87235	44
17	.42709	.90421	.44281	.89662	.45839	.88875	.47383	.88062	.48913	.87221	43
18	.42736	.90408	.44307	.89649	.45865	.88862	.47409	.88048	.48938	.87207	42
19	.42762	.90396	.44333	.89636	.45891	.88848	.47434	.88034	.48964	.87193	41
20	.42788	.90383	.44359	.89623	.45917	.88835	.47460	.88020	.48989	.87178	40
21	.42815	.90371	.44385	.89610	.45942	.88822	.47486	.88006	.49014	.87164	39
22	.42841	.90358	.44411	.89597	.45968	.88808	.47511	.87993	.49040	.87150	38
23	.42867	.90346	.44437	.89584	.45994	.88795	.47537	.87979	.49065	.87136	37
24	.42894	.90334	.44464	.89571	.46020	.88782	.47562	.87965	.49090	.87121	36
25	.42920	.90321	.44490	.89558	.46046	.88768	.47588	.87951	.49116	.87107	35
26	.42946	.90309	.44516	.89545	.46072	.88755	.47614	.87937	.49141	.87093	34
27	.42972	.90296	.44542	.89532	.46097	.88741	.47639	.87923	.49166	.87079	33
28	.42999	.90284	.44568	.89519	.46123	.88728	.47665	.87909	.49192	.87064	32
29	.43025	.90271	.44594	.89506	.46149	.88715	.47690	.87896	.49217	.87050	31
30	.43051	.90259	.44620	.89493	.46175	.88701	.47716	.87882	.49242	.87036	30
31	.43077	.90246	.44646	.89480	.46201	.88688	.47741	.87868	.49268	.87021	29
32	.43104	.90233	.44672	.89467	.46226	.88674	.47767	.87854	.49293	.87007	28
33	.43130	.90221	.44698	.89454	.46252	.88661	.47793	.87840	.49318	.86993	27
34	.43156	.90208	.44724	.89441	.46278	.88647	.47818	.87826	.49344	.86978	26
35	.43182	.90196	.44750	.89428	.46304	.88634	.47844	.87812	.49369	.86964	25
36	.43209	.90183	.44776	.89415	.46330	.88620	.47869	.87798	.49394	.86949	24
37	.43235	.90171	.44802	.89402	.46355	.88607	.47895	.87784	.49419	.86935	23
38	.43261	.90158	.44828	.89389	.46381	.88593	.47920	.87770	.49445	.86921	22
39	.43287	.90146	.44854	.89376	.46407	.88580	.47946	.87756	.49470	.86906	21
40	.43313	.90133	.44880	.89363	.46433	.88566	.47971	.87743	.49495	.86892	20
41	.43340	.90120	.44906	.89350	.46458	.88553	.47997	.87729	.49521	.86878	19
42	.43366	.90108	.44932	.89337	.46484	.88539	.48022	.87715	.49546	.86863	18
43	.43392	.90095	.44958	.89324	.46510	.88526	.48048	.87701	.49571	.86849	17
44	.43418	.90082	.44984	.89311	.46536	.88512	.48073	.87687	.49596	.86834	16
45	.43445	.90070	.45010	.89298	.46561	.88499	.48099	.87673	.49622	.86820	15
46	.43471	.90057	.45036	.89285	.46587	.88485	.48124	.87659	.49647	.86805	14
47	.43497	.90045	.45062	.89272	.46613	.88472	.48150	.87645	.49672	.86791	13
48	.43523	.90032	.45088	.89259	.46639	.88458	.48175	.87631	.49697	.86777	12
49	.43549	.90019	.45114	.89245	.46664	.88445	.48201	.87617	.49723	.86762	11
50	.43575	.90007	.45140	.89232	.46690	.88431	.48226	.87603	.49748	.86748	10
51	.43602	.89994	.45166	.89219	.46716	.88417	.48252	.87589	.49773	.86733	9
52	.43628	.89981	.45192	.89206	.46742	.88404	.48277	.87575	.49798	.86719	8
53	.43654	.89968	.45218	.89193	.46767	.88390	.48303	.87561	.49824	.86704	7
54	.43680	.89956	.45243	.89180	.46793	.88377	.48328	.87546	.49849	.86690	6
55	.43706	.89943	.45269	.89167	.46819	.88363	.48354	.87532	.49874	.86675	5
56	.43733	.89930	.45295	.89153	.46844	.88349	.48379	.87518	.49899	.86661	4
57	.43759	.89918	.45321	.89140	.46869	.88336	.48405	.87504	.49924	.86646	3
58	.43785	.89905	.45347	.89127	.46896	.88322	.48430	.87490	.49950	.86632	2
59	.43811	.89892	.45373	.89114	.46921	.88308	.48456	.87476	.49975	.86617	1
60	.43837	.89879	.45399	.89101	.46947	.88295	.48481	.87462	.50000	.86603	0
′	Cosine	Sine	Cosine	Sine	Cosine	Sine	Cosine	Sine	Cosine	Sine	′
	64°		63°		62°		61°		60°		

,	30° Sine	Cosine	31° Sine	Cosine	32° Sine	Cosine	33° Sine	Cosine	34° Sine	Cosine	,
0	.50000	.86603	.51504	.85717	.52992	.84805	.54464	.83867	.55919	.82904	60
1	.50025	.86588	.51529	.85702	.53017	.84789	.54488	.83851	.55943	.82887	59
2	.50050	.86573	.51554	.85687	.53041	.84774	.54513	.83835	.55968	.82871	58
3	.50076	.86559	.51579	.85672	.53066	.84759	.54537	.83819	.55992	.82855	57
4	.50101	.86544	.51604	.85657	.53091	.84743	.54561	.83804	.56016	.82839	56
5	.50126	.86530	.51628	.85642	.53115	.84728	.54586	.83788	.56040	.82822	55
6	.50151	.86515	.51653	.85627	.53140	.84712	.54610	.83772	.56064	.82806	54
7	.50176	.86501	.51678	.85612	.53164	.84697	.54635	.83756	.56088	.82790	53
8	.50201	.86486	.51703	.85597	.53189	.84681	.54659	.83740	.56112	.82773	52
9	.50227	.86471	.51728	.85582	.53214	.84666	.54683	.83724	.56136	.82757	51
10	.50252	.86457	.51753	.85567	.53238	.84650	.54708	.83708	.56160	.82741	50
11	.50277	.86442	.51778	.85551	.53263	.84635	.54732	.83692	.56184	.82724	49
12	.50302	.86427	.51803	.85536	.53288	.84619	.54756	.83676	.56208	.82708	48
13	.50327	.86413	.51828	.85521	.53312	.84604	.54781	.83660	.56232	.82692	47
14	.50352	.86398	.51852	.85506	.53337	.84588	.54805	.83645	.56256	.82675	46
15	.50377	.86384	.51877	.85491	.53361	.84573	.54829	.83629	.56280	.82659	45
16	.50403	.86369	.51902	.85476	.53386	.84557	.54854	.83613	.56305	.82643	44
17	.50428	.86354	.51927	.85461	.53411	.84542	.54878	.83597	.56329	.82626	43
18	.50453	.86340	.51952	.85446	.53435	.84526	.54902	.83581	.56353	.82610	42
19	.50478	.86325	.51977	.85431	.53460	.84511	.54927	.83565	.56377	.82593	41
20	.50503	.86310	.52002	.85416	.53484	.84495	.54951	.83549	.56401	.82577	40
21	.50528	.86295	.52026	.85401	.53509	.84480	.54975	.83533	.56425	.82561	39
22	.50553	.86281	.52051	.85385	.53534	.84464	.54999	.83517	.56449	.82544	38
23	.50578	.86266	.52076	.85370	.53558	.84448	.55024	.83501	.56473	.82528	37
24	.50603	.86251	.52101	.85355	.53583	.84433	.55048	.83485	.56497	.82511	36
25	.50628	.86237	.52126	.85340	.53607	.84417	.55072	.83469	.56521	.82495	35
26	.50654	.86222	.52151	.85325	.53632	.84402	.55097	.83453	.56545	.82478	34
27	.50679	.86207	.52175	.85310	.53656	.84386	.55121	.83437	.56569	.82462	33
28	.50704	.86192	.52200	.85294	.53681	.84370	.55145	.83421	.56593	.82446	32
29	.50729	.86178	.52225	.85279	.53705	.84355	.55169	.83405	.56617	.82429	31
30	.50754	.86163	.52250	.85264	.53730	.84339	.55194	.83389	.56641	.82413	30
31	.50779	.86148	.52275	.85249	.53754	.84324	.55218	.83373	.56665	.82396	29
32	.50804	.86133	.52299	.85234	.53779	.84308	.55242	.83356	.56689	.82380	28
33	.50829	.86119	.52324	.85218	.53804	.84292	.55266	.83340	.56713	.82363	27
34	.50854	.86104	.52349	.85203	.53828	.84277	.55291	.83324	.56736	.82347	26
35	.50879	.86089	.52374	.85188	.53853	.84261	.55315	.83308	.56760	.82330	25
36	.50904	.86074	.52399	.85173	.53877	.84245	.55339	.83292	.56784	.82314	24
37	.50929	.86059	.52423	.85157	.53902	.84230	.55363	.83276	.56808	.82297	23
38	.50954	.86045	.52448	.85142	.53926	.84214	.55388	.83260	.56832	.82281	22
39	.50979	.86030	.52473	.85127	.53951	.84198	.55412	.83244	.56856	.82264	21
40	.51004	.86015	.52498	.85112	.53975	.84182	.55436	.83228	.56880	.82248	20
41	.51029	.86000	.52522	.85096	.54000	.84167	.55460	.83212	.56904	.82231	19
42	.51054	.85985	.52547	.85081	.54024	.84151	.55484	.83195	.56928	.82214	18
43	.51079	.85970	.52572	.85066	.54049	.84135	.55509	.83179	.56952	.82198	17
44	.51104	.85956	.52597	.85051	.54073	.84120	.55533	.83163	.56976	.82181	16
45	.51129	.85941	.52621	.85035	.54097	.84104	.55557	.83147	.57000	.82165	15
46	.51154	.85926	.52646	.85020	.54122	.84088	.55581	.83131	.57024	.82148	14
47	.51179	.85911	.52671	.85005	.54146	.84072	.55605	.83115	.57047	.82132	13
48	.51204	.85896	.52696	.84989	.54171	.84057	.55630	.83098	.57071	.82115	12
49	.51229	.85881	.52720	.84974	.54195	.84041	.55654	.83082	.57095	.82098	11
50	.51254	.85866	.52745	.84959	.54220	.84025	.55678	.83066	.57119	.82082	10
51	.51279	.85851	.52770	.84943	.54244	.84009	.55702	.83050	.57143	.82065	9
52	.51304	.85836	.52794	.84928	.54269	.83994	.55726	.83034	.57167	.82048	8
53	.51329	.85821	.52819	.84913	.54293	.83978	.55750	.83017	.57191	.82032	7
54	.51354	.85806	.52844	.84897	.54317	.83962	.55775	.83001	.57215	.82015	6
55	.51379	.85792	.52869	.84882	.54342	.83946	.55799	.82985	.57238	.81999	5
56	.51404	.85777	.52893	.84866	.54366	.83930	.55823	.82969	.57262	.81982	4
57	.51429	.85762	.52918	.84851	.54391	.83915	.55847	.82953	.57286	.81965	3
58	.51454	.85747	.52943	.84836	.54415	.83899	.55871	.82936	.57310	.81949	2
59	.51479	.85732	.52967	.84820	.54440	.83883	.55895	.82920	.57334	.81932	1
60	.51504	.85717	.52992	.84805	.54464	.83867	.55919	.82904	.57358	.81915	0
,	Cosine	Sine	Cosine	Sine	Cosine	Sine	Cosine	Sine	Cosine	Sine	,
	59°		58°		57°		56°		55°		

,	35° Sine	35° Cosine	36° Sine	36° Cosine	37° Sine	37° Cosine	38° Sine	38° Cosine	39° Sine	39° Cosine	,
0	.57358	.81915	.58779	.80902	.60182	.79864	.61566	.78801	.62932	.77715	60
1	.57381	.81899	.58802	.80885	.60205	.79846	.61589	.78783	.62955	.77696	59
2	.57405	.81882	.58826	.80867	.60228	.79829	.61612	.78765	.62977	.77678	58
3	.57429	.81865	.58849	.80850	.60251	.79811	.61635	.78747	.63000	.77660	57
4	.57453	.81848	.58873	.80833	.60274	.79793	.61658	.78729	.63022	.77641	56
5	.57477	.81832	.58896	.80816	.60298	.79776	.61681	.78711	.63045	.77623	55
6	.57501	.81815	.58920	.80799	.60321	.79758	.61704	.78694	.63068	.77605	54
7	.57524	.81798	.58943	.80782	.60344	.79741	.61726	.78676	.63090	.77586	53
8	.57548	.81782	.58967	.80765	.60367	.79723	.61749	.78658	.63113	.77568	52
9	.57572	.81765	.58990	.80748	.6c390	.79706	.61772	.78640	.63135	.77550	51
10	.57596	.81748	.59014	.80730	.60414	.79688	.61795	.78622	.63158	.77531	50
11	.57619	.81731	.59037	.80713	.60437	.79671	.61818	.78604	.63180	.77513	49
12	.57643	.81714	.59061	.80696	.60460	.79653	.61841	.78586	.63203	.77494	48
13	.57667	.81698	.59084	.80679	.60483	.79635	.61864	.78568	.63225	.77476	47
14	.57691	.81681	.59108	.80662	.60506	.79618	.61887	.78550	.63248	.77458	46
15	.57715	.81664	.59131	.80644	.60529	.79600	.61909	.78532	.63271	.77439	45
16	.57738	.81647	.59154	.80627	.60553	.79583	.61932	.78514	.63293	.77421	44
17	.57762	.81631	.59178	.80610	.60576	.79565	.61955	.78496	.63316	.77402	43
18	.57786	.81614	.59201	.80593	.60599	.79547	.61978	.78478	.63338	.77384	42
19	.57810	.81597	.59225	.80576	.60622	.79530	.62001	.78460	.63361	.77366	41
20	.57833	.81580	.59248	.80558	.60645	.79512	.62024	.78442	.63383	.77347	40
21	.57857	.81563	.59272	.80541	.60668	.79494	.62046	.78424	.63406	.77329	39
22	.57881	.81546	.59295	.80524	.60691	.79477	.62069	.78405	.63428	.77310	38
23	.57904	.81530	.59318	.80507	.60714	.79459	.62092	.78387	.63451	.77292	37
24	.57928	.81513	.59342	.80489	.60738	.79441	.62115	.78369	.63473	.77273	36
25	.57952	.81496	.59365	.80472	.60761	.79424	.62138	.78351	.63496	.77255	35
26	.57976	.81479	.59389	.80455	.60784	.79406	.62160	.78333	.63518	.77236	34
27	.57999	.81462	.59412	.80438	.60807	.79388	.62183	.78315	.63540	.77218	33
28	.58023	.81445	.59436	.80420	.60830	.79371	.62206	.78297	.63563	.77199	32
29	.58047	.81428	.59459	.80403	.60853	.79353	.62229	.78279	.63585	.77181	31
30	.58070	.81412	.59482	.80386	.60876	.79335	.62251	.78261	.63608	.77162	30
31	.58094	.81395	.59506	.80368	.60899	.79318	.62274	.78243	.63630	.77144	29
32	.58118	.81378	.59529	.80351	.60922	.79300	.62297	.78225	.63653	.77125	28
33	.58141	.81361	.59552	.80334	.60945	.79282	.62320	.78206	.63675	.77107	27
34	.58165	.81344	.59576	.80316	.60968	.79264	.62342	.78188	.63698	.77088	26
35	.58189	.81327	.59599	.80299	.60991	.79247	.62365	.78170	.63720	.77070	25
36	.58212	.81310	.59622	.80282	.61015	.79229	.62388	.78152	.63742	.77051	24
37	.58236	.81293	.59646	.80264	.61038	.79211	.62411	.78134	.63765	.77033	23
38	.58260	.81276	.59669	.80247	.61061	.79193	.62433	.78116	.63787	.77014	22
39	.58283	.81259	.59693	.80230	.61084	.79176	.62456	.78098	.63810	.76996	21
40	.58307	.81242	.59716	.80212	.61107	.79158	.62479	.78079	.63832	.76977	20
41	.58330	.81225	.59739	.80195	.61130	.79140	.62502	.78061	.63854	.76959	19
42	.58354	.81208	.59763	.80178	.61153	.79122	.62524	.78043	.63877	.76940	18
43	.58378	.81191	.59786	.80160	.61176	.79105	.62547	.78025	.63899	.76921	17
44	.58401	.81174	.59809	.80143	.61199	.79087	.62570	.78007	.63922	.76903	16
45	.58425	.81157	.59832	.80125	.61222	.79069	.62592	.77988	.63944	.76884	15
46	.58449	.81140	.59856	.80108	.61245	.79051	.62615	.77970	.63966	.76866	14
47	.58472	.81123	.59879	.80091	.61268	.79033	.62638	.77952	.63989	.76847	13
48	.58496	.81106	.59902	.80073	.61291	.79016	.62660	.77934	.64011	.76828	12
49	.58519	.81089	.59926	.80056	.61314	.78998	.62683	.77916	.64033	.76810	11
50	.58543	.81072	.59949	.80038	.61337	.78980	.62706	.77897	.64056	.76791	10
51	.58567	.81055	.59972	.80021	.61360	.78962	.62728	.77879	.64078	.76772	9
52	.58590	.81038	.59995	.80003	.61383	.78944	.62751	.77861	.64100	.76754	8
53	.58614	.81021	.60019	.79986	.61406	.78926	.62774	.77843	.64123	.76735	7
54	.58637	.81004	.60042	.79968	.61429	.78908	.62796	.77824	.64145	.76717	6
55	.58661	.80987	.60065	.79951	.61451	.78891	.62819	.77806	.64167	.76698	5
56	.58684	.80970	.60089	.79934	.61474	.78873	.62842	.77788	.64190	.76679	4
57	.58708	.80953	.60112	.79916	.61497	.78855	.62864	.77769	.64212	.76661	3
58	.58731	.80936	.60135	.79899	.61520	.78837	.62887	.77751	.64234	.76642	2
59	.58755	.80919	.60158	.79881	.61543	.78819	.62909	.77733	.64256	.76623	1
60	.58779	.80902	.60182	.79864	.61566	.78801	.62932	.77715	.64279	.76604	0
,	Cosine	Sine	Cosine	Sine	Cosine	Sine	Cosine	Sine	Cosine	Sine	,
	54°		53°		52°		51°		50°		

′	40° Sine	40° Cosine	41° Sine	41° Cosine	42° Sine	42° Cosine	43° Sine	43° Cosine	44° Sine	44° Cosine	′
0	.64279	.76604	.65606	.75471	.66913	.74314	.68200	.73135	.69466	.71934	60
1	.64301	.76586	.65628	.75452	.66935	.74295	.68221	.73116	.69487	.71914	59
2	.64323	.76567	.65650	.75433	.66956	.74276	.68242	.73096	.69508	.71894	58
3	.64346	.76548	.65672	.75414	.66978	.74256	.68264	.73076	.69529	.71873	57
4	.64368	.76530	.65694	.75395	.66999	.74237	.68285	.73056	.69549	.71853	56
5	.64390	.76511	.65716	.75375	.67021	.74217	.68306	.73036	.69570	.71833	55
6	.64412	.76492	.65738	.75356	.67043	.74198	.68327	.73016	.69591	.71813	54
7	.64435	.76473	.65759	.75337	.67064	.74178	.68349	.72996	.69612	.71792	53
8	.64457	.76455	.65781	.75318	.67086	.74159	.68370	.72976	.69633	.71772	52
9	.64479	.76436	.65803	.75299	.67107	.74139	.68391	.72957	.69654	.71752	51
10	.64501	.76417	.65825	.75280	.67129	.74120	.68412	.72937	.69675	.71732	50
11	.64524	.76398	.65847	.75261	.67151	.74100	.68434	.72917	.69696	.71711	49
12	.64546	.76380	.65869	.75241	.67172	.74080	.68455	.72897	.69717	.71691	48
13	.64568	.76361	.65891	.75222	.67194	.74061	.68476	.72877	.69737	.71671	47
14	.64590	.76342	.65913	.75203	.67215	.74041	.68497	.72857	.69758	.71650	46
15	.64612	.76323	.65935	.75184	.67237	.74022	.68518	.72837	.69779	.71630	45
16	.64635	.76304	.65956	.75165	.67258	.74002	.68539	.72817	.69800	.71610	44
17	.64657	.76286	.65978	75146	.67280	.73983	.68561	.72797	.69821	.71590	43
18	.64679	.76267	.66000	.75126	.67301	.73963	.68582	.72777	.69842	.71569	42
19	.64701	.76248	.66022	.75107	.67323	.73944	.68603	.72757	.69862	.71549	41
20	.64723	.76229	.66044	.75088	.67344	.73924	.68624	.72737	.69883	.71529	40
21	.64746	.76210	.66066	.75069	.67366	.73904	.68645	.72717	.69904	.71508	39
22	.64768	.76192	.66088	.75050	.67387	.73885	.68666	.72697	.69925	.71488	38
23	.64790	.76173	.66109	.75030	.67409	.73865	.68688	.72677	.69946	.71468	37
24	.64812	.76154	.66131	.75011	.67430	.73846	.68709	.72657	.69966	.71447	36
25	.64834	.76135	.66153	.74992	.67452	.73826	.68730	.72637	.69987	.71427	35
26	.64856	.76116	.66175	.74973	.67473	.73806	.68751	.72617	.70008	.71407	34
27	.64878	.76097	.66197	.74953	.67495	.73787	.68772	.72597	.70029	.71386	33
28	.64901	.76078	.66218	.74934	.67516	.73767	.68793	.72577	.70049	.71366	32
29	.64923	.76059	.66240	.74915	.67538	.73747	.68814	.72557	.70070	.71345	31
30	.64945	.76041	.66262	.74896	.67559	.73728	.68835	.72537	.70091	.71325	30
31	.64967	.76022	.66284	.74876	.67580	.73708	.68857	.72517	.70112	.71305	29
32	.64989	.76003	.66306	.74857	.67602	.73688	.68878	.72497	.70132	.71284	28
33	.65011	.75984	.66327	.74838	.67623	.73669	.68899	.72477	.70153	.71264	27
34	.65033	.75965	.66349	.74818	.67645	.73649	.68920	.72457	.70174	.71243	26
35	.65055	.75946	.66371	.74799	.67666	.73629	.68941	.72437	.70195	.71223	25
36	.65077	.75927	.66393	.74780	.67688	.73610	.68962	.72417	.70215	.71203	24
37	.65100	.75908	.66414	.74760	.67709	.73590	.68983	.72397	.70236	.71182	23
38	.65122	.75889	.66436	.74741	.67730	.73570	.69004	.72377	.70257	.71162	22
39	.65144	.75870	.66458	.74722	.67752	.73551	.69025	.72357	.70277	.71141	21
40	.65166	.75851	.66480	.74703	.67773	.73531	.69046	.72337	.70298	.71121	20
41	.65188	.75832	.66501	.74683	.67795	.73511	.69067	.72317	.70319	.71100	19
42	.65210	.75813	.66523	.74664	.67816	.73491	.69088	.72297	.70339	.71080	18
43	.65232	.75794	.66545	.74644	.67837	.73472	.69109	.72277	.70360	.71059	17
44	.65254	.75775	.66566	.74625	.67859	.73452	.69130	.72257	.70381	.71039	16
45	.65276	.75756	.66588	.74606	.67880	.73432	.69151	.72236	.70401	.71019	15
46	.65298	.75738	.66610	.74586	.67901	.73413	.69172	.72216	.70422	.70998	14
47	.65320	.75719	.66632	.74567	.67923	.73393	.69193	.72196	.70443	.70978	13
48	.65342	.75700	.66653	.74548	.67944	.73373	.69214	.72176	.70463	.70957	12
49	.65364	.75680	.66675	.74528	.67965	.73353	.69235	.72156	.70484	.70937	11
50	.65386	.75661	.66697	.74509	.67987	.73333	.69256	.72136	.70505	.70916	10
51	.65408	.75642	.66718	.74489	.68008	.73314	.69277	.72116	.70525	.70896	9
52	.65430	.75623	.66740	.74470	.68029	.73294	.69298	.72095	.70546	.70875	8
53	.65452	.75604	.66762	.74451	.68051	.73274	.69319	.72075	.70567	.70855	7
54	.65474	.75585	.66783	.74431	.68072	.73254	.69340	.72055	.70587	.70834	6
55	.65496	.75566	.66805	.74412	.68093	.73234	.69361	.72035	.70608	.70813	5
56	.65518	.75547	.66827	.74392	.68115	.73215	.69382	.72015	.70628	.70793	4
57	.65540	.75528	.66848	.74373	.68136	.73195	.69403	.71995	.70649	.70772	3
58	.65562	.75509	.66870	.74353	.68157	.73175	.69424	.71974	.70670	.70752	2
59	.65584	.75490	.66891	.74334	.68179	.73155	.69445	.71954	.70690	.70731	1
60	.65606	.75471	.66913	.74314	.68200	.73135	.69466	.71934	.70711	.70711	0
′	Cosine	Sine	Cosine	Sine	Cosine	Sine	Cosine	Sine	Cosine	Sine	′
	49°		48°		47°		46°		45°		

′	0° Tang	0° Cotang	1° Tang	1° Cotang	2° Tang	2° Cotang	3° Tang	3° Cotang	4° Tang	4° Cotang	′
0	.00000	Infin.	.01746	57.2900	.03492	28.6363	.05241	19.0811	.06993	14.3007	60
1	.00029	3437.75	.01775	56.3506	.03521	28.3994	.05270	18.9755	.07022	14.2411	59
2	.00058	1718.87	.01804	55.4415	.03550	28.1664	.05299	18.8711	.07051	14.1821	58
3	.00087	1145.92	.01833	54.5613	.03579	27.9372	.05328	18.7678	.07080	14.1235	57
4	.00116	859.436	.01862	53.7086	.03609	27.7117	.05357	18.6656	.07110	14.0655	56
5	.00145	687.549	.01891	52.8821	.03638	27.4899	.05387	18.5645	.07139	14.0079	55
6	.00175	572.957	.01920	52.0807	.03667	27.2715	.05416	18.4645	.07168	13.9507	54
7	.00204	491.106	.01949	51.3032	.03696	27.0566	.05445	18.3655	.07197	13.8940	53
8	.00233	429.718	.01978	50.5485	.03725	26.8450	.05474	18.2677	.07227	13.8378	52
9	.00262	381.971	.02007	49.8157	.03754	26.6367	.05503	18.1708	.07256	13.7821	51
10	.00291	343.774	.02036	49.1039	.03783	26.4316	.05533	18.0750	.07285	13.7267	50
11	.00320	312.521	.02066	48.4121	.03812	26.2296	.05562	17.9802	.07314	13.6719	49
12	.00349	286.478	.02095	47.7395	.03842	26.0307	.05591	17.8863	.07344	13.6174	48
13	.00378	264.441	.02124	47.0853	.03871	25.8348	.05620	17.7934	.07373	13.5634	47
14	.00407	245.552	.02153	46.4489	.03900	25.6418	.05649	17.7015	.07402	13.5098	46
15	.00436	229.182	.02182	45.8294	.03929	25.4517	.05678	17.6106	.07431	13.4566	45
16	.00465	214.858	.02211	45.2261	.03958	25.2644	.05708	17.5205	.07461	13.4039	44
17	.00495	202.219	.02240	44.6386	.03987	25.0798	.05737	17.4314	.07490	13.3515	43
18	.00524	190.984	.02269	44.0661	.04016	24.8978	.05766	17.3432	.07519	13.2996	42
19	.00553	180.932	.02298	43.5081	.04046	24.7185	.05795	17.2558	.07548	13.2480	41
20	.00582	171.885	.02328	42.9641	.04075	24.5418	.05824	17.1693	.07578	13.1969	40
21	.00611	163.700	.02357	42.4335	.04104	24.3675	.05854	17.0837	.07607	13.1461	39
22	.00640	156.259	.02386	41.9158	.04133	24.1957	.05883	16.9990	.07636	13.0958	38
23	.00669	149.465	.02415	41.4106	.04162	24.0263	.05912	16.9150	.07665	13.0458	37
24	.00698	143.237	.02444	40.9174	.04191	23.8593	.05941	16.8319	.07695	12.9962	36
25	.00727	137.507	.02473	40.4358	.04220	23.6945	.05970	16.7496	.07724	12.9469	35
26	.00756	132.219	.02502	39.9655	.04250	23.5321	.05999	16.6681	.07753	12.8981	34
27	.00785	127.321	.02531	39.5059	.04279	23.3718	.06029	16.5874	.07782	12.8496	33
28	.00815	122.774	.02560	39.0568	.04308	23.2137	.06058	16.5075	.07812	12.8014	32
29	.00844	118.540	.02589	38.6177	.04337	23.0577	.06087	16.4283	.07841	12.7536	31
30	.00873	114.589	.02619	38.1885	.04366	22.9038	.06116	16.3499	.07870	12.7062	30
31	.00902	110.892	.02648	37.7686	.04395	22.7519	.06145	16.2722	.07899	12.6591	29
32	.00931	107.426	.02677	37.3579	.04424	22.6020	.06175	16.1952	.07929	12.6124	28
33	.00960	104.171	.02706	36.9560	.04454	22.4541	.06204	16.1190	.07958	12.5660	27
34	.00989	101.107	.02735	36.5627	.04483	22.3081	.06233	16.0435	.07987	12.5199	26
35	.01018	98.2179	.02764	36.1776	.04512	22.1640	.06262	15.9687	.08017	12.4742	25
36	.01047	95.4895	.02793	35.8006	.04541	22.0217	.06291	15.8945	.08046	12.4288	24
37	.01076	92.9085	.02822	35.4313	.04570	21.8813	.06321	15.8211	.08075	12.3838	23
38	.01105	90.4633	.02851	35.0695	.04599	21.7426	.06350	15.7483	.08104	12.3390	22
39	.01135	88.1436	.02881	34.7151	.04628	21.6056	.06379	15.6762	.08134	12.2946	21
40	.01164	85.9398	.02910	34.3678	.04658	21.4704	.06408	15.6048	.08163	12.2505	20
41	.01193	83.8435	.02939	34.0273	.04687	21.3369	.06437	15.5340	.08192	12.2067	19
42	.01222	81.8470	.02968	33.6935	.04716	21.2049	.06467	15.4638	.08221	12.1632	18
43	.01251	79.9434	.02997	33.3662	.04745	21.0747	.06496	15.3943	.08251	12.1201	17
44	.01280	78.1263	.03026	33.0452	.04774	20.9460	.06525	15.3254	.08280	12.0772	16
45	.01309	76.3900	.03055	32.7303	.04803	20.8188	.06554	15.2571	.08309	12.0346	15
46	.01338	74.7292	.03084	32.4213	.04833	20.6932	.06584	15.1893	.08339	11.9923	14
47	.01367	73.1390	.03114	32.1181	.04862	20.5691	.06613	15.1222	.08368	11.9504	13
48	.01396	71.6151	.03143	31.8205	.04891	20.4465	.06642	15.0557	.08397	11.9087	12
49	.01425	70.1533	.03172	31.5284	.04920	20.3253	.06671	14.9898	.08427	11.8673	11
50	.01455	68.7501	.03201	31.2416	.04949	20.2056	.06700	14.9244	.08456	11.8262	10
51	.01484	67.4019	.03230	30.9599	.04978	20.0872	.06730	14.8596	.08485	11.7853	9
52	.01513	66.1055	.03259	30.6833	.05007	19.9702	.06759	14.7954	.08514	11.7448	8
53	.01542	64.8580	.03288	30.4116	.05037	19.8546	.06788	14.7317	.08544	11.7045	7
54	.01571	63.6567	.03317	30.1446	.05066	19.7403	.06817	14.6685	.08573	11.6645	6
55	.01600	62.4992	.03346	29.8823	.05095	19.6273	.06847	14.6059	.08602	11.6248	5
56	.01629	61.3829	.03376	29.6245	.05124	19.5156	.06876	14.5438	.08632	11.5853	4
57	.01658	60.3058	.03405	29.3711	.05153	19.4051	.06905	14.4823	.08661	11.5461	3
58	.01687	59.2659	.03434	29.1220	.05182	19.2959	.06934	14.4212	.08690	11.5072	2
59	.01716	58.2612	.03463	28.8771	.05212	19.1879	.06963	14.3607	.08720	11.4685	1
60	.01746	57.2900	.03492	28.6363	.05241	19.0811	.06993	14.3007	.08749	11.4301	0
′	Cotang	Tang	Cotang	Tang	Cotang	Tang	Cotang	Tang	Cotang	Tang	′
	89°		88°		87°		86°		85°		

′	5° Tang	Cotang	6° Tang	Cotang	7° Tang	Cotang	8° Tang	Cotang	9° Tang	Cotang	′
0	.08749	11.4301	.10510	9.51436	.12278	8.14435	.14054	7.11537	.15838	6.31375	60
1	.08778	11.3919	.10540	9.48781	.12308	8.12481	.14084	7.10038	.15868	6.30189	59
2	.08807	11.3540	.10569	9.46141	.12338	8.10536	.14113	7.08546	.15898	6.29007	58
3	.08837	11.3163	.10599	9.43515	.12367	8.08600	.14143	7.07059	.15928	6.27829	57
4	.08866	11.2789	.10628	9.40904	.12397	8.06674	14173	7.05579	.15958	6.26655	56
5	.08895	11.2417	.10657	9.38307	.12426	8.04756	.14202	7.04105	.15988	6.25486	55
6	.08925	11.2048	.10687	9.35724	.12456	8.02848	.14232	7.02637	.16017	6.24321	54
7	.08954	11.1681	.10716	9.33155	.12485	8.00948	.14262	7.01174	.16047	6.23160	53
8	.08983	11.1316	.10746	9.30599	.12515	7.99058	.14291	6.99718	.16077	6.22003	52
9	.09013	11.0954	.10775	9.28058	.12544	7.97176	.14321	6.98268	.16107	6.20851	51
10	.09042	11.0594	.10805	9.25530	.12574	7.95302	.14351	6.96823	.16137	6.19703	50
11	.09071	11.0237	.10834	9.23016	.12603	7.93438	.14381	6.95385	.16167	6.18559	49
12	.09101	10.9882	.10863	9.20516	.12633	7.91582	.14410	6.93952	.16196	6.17419	48
13	.09130	10.9529	.10893	9.18028	.12662	7.89734	.14440	6.92525	.16226	6.16283	47
14	.09159	10.9178	.10922	9.15554	.12692	7.87895	.14470	6.91104	.16256	6.15151	46
15	.09189	10.8829	.10952	9.13093	.12722	7.86064	.14499	6.89688	.16286	6.14023	45
16	.09218	10.8483	.10981	9.10646	.12751	7.84242	.14529	6.88278	.16316	6.12899	44
17	.09247	10.8139	.11011	9.08211	.12781	7.82428	.14559	6.86874	.16346	6.11779	43
18	.09277	10.7797	.11040	9.05789	.12810	7.80622	.14588	6.85475	.16376	6.10664	42
19	.09306	10.7457	.11070	9.03379	.12840	7.78825	.14618	6.84082	.16405	6.09552	41
20	.09335	10.7119	.11099	9.00983	.12869	7.77035	.14648	6.82694	.16435	6.08444	40
21	.09365	10.6783	.11128	8.98598	.12899	7.75254	.14678	6.81812	.16465	6.07340	39
22	.09394	10.6450	.11158	8.96227	.12929	7.73480	.14707	6.79936	.16495	6.06240	38
23	.09423	10.6118	.11187	8.93867	.12958	7.71715	.14737	6.78564	.16525	6.05143	37
24	.09453	10.5789	.11217	8.91520	.12988	7.69957	.14767	6.77199	.16555	6.04051	36
25	.09482	10.5462	.11246	8.89185	.13017	7.68208	.14796	6.75838	.16585	6.02962	35
26	.09511	10.5136	.11276	8.86862	.13047	7.66466	.14826	6.74483	.16615	6.01878	34
27	.09541	10.4813	.11305	8.84551	.13076	7.64732	.14856	6.73133	.16645	6.00797	33
28	.09570	10.4491	.11335	8.82252	.13106	7.63005	.14886	6.71789	.16674	5.99720	32
29	.09600	10.4172	.11364	8.79964	.13136	7.61287	.14915	6.70450	.16704	5.98646	31
30	.09629	10.3854	.11394	8.77689	.13165	7.59575	.14945	6.69116	.16734	5.97576	30
31	.09658	10.3538	.11423	8.75425	.13195	7.57872	.14975	6.67787	.16764	5.96510	29
32	.09688	10.3224	.11452	8.73172	.13224	7.56176	.15005	6.66463	.16794	5.95448	28
33	.09717	10.2913	.11482	8.70931	.13254	7.54487	.15034	6.65144	.16824	5.94390	27
34	.09746	10.2602	.11511	8.68701	.13284	7.52806	.15064	6.63831	.16854	5.93335	26
35	.09776	10.2294	.11541	8.66482	.13313	7.51132	.15094	6.62523	.16884	5.92283	25
36	.09805	10.1988	.11570	8.64275	.13343	7.49465	.15124	6.61219	.16914	5.91236	24
37	.09834	10.1683	.11600	8.62078	.13372	7.47806	.15153	6.59921	.16944	5.90191	23
38	.09864	10.1381	.11629	8.59893	.13402	7.46154	.15183	6.58627	.16974	5.89151	22
39	.09893	10.1080	.11659	8.57718	.13432	7.44509	.15213	6.57339	.17004	5.88114	21
40	.09923	10.0780	.11688	8.55555	.13461	7.42871	.15243	6.56055	.17033	5.87080	20
41	.09952	10.0483	.11718	8.53402	.13491	7.41240	.15272	6.54777	.17063	5.86051	19
42	.09981	10.0187	.11747	8.51259	.13521	7.39616	.15302	6.53503	.17093	5.85024	18
43	.10011	9.98931	.11777	8.49128	.13550	7.37999	.15332	6.52234	.17123	5.84001	17
44	.10040	9.96007	.11806	8.47007	.13580	7.36389	.15362	6.50970	.17153	5.82982	16
45	.10069	9.93101	.11836	8.44896	.13609	7.34786	.15391	6.49710	.17183	5.81966	15
46	.10099	9.90211	.11865	8.42795	.13639	7.33190	.15421	6.48456	.17213	5.80953	14
47	.10128	9.87338	.11895	8.40705	.13669	7.31600	.15451	6.47206	.17243	5.79944	13
48	.10158	9.84482	.11924	8.38625	.13698	7.30018	.15481	6.45961	.17273	5.78938	12
49	.10187	9.81641	.11954	8.36555	.13728	7.28442	.15511	6.44720	.17303	5.77936	11
50	.10216	9.78817	.11983	8.34496	.13758	7.26873	.15540	6.43484	.17333	5.76937	10
51	.10246	9.76009	.12013	8.32446	.13787	7.25310	.15570	6.42253	.17363	5.75941	9
52	.10275	9.73217	.12042	8.30406	.13817	7.23754	.15600	6.41026	.17393	5.74949	8
53	.10305	9.70441	.12072	8.28376	.13846	7.22204	.15630	6.39804	.17423	5.73960	7
54	.10334	9.67680	.12101	8.26355	.13876	7.20661	.15660	6.38587	.17453	5.72974	6
55	.10363	9.64935	.12131	8.24345	.13906	7.19125	.15689	6.37374	.17483	5.71992	5
56	.10393	9.62205	.12160	8.22344	.13935	7.17594	.15719	6.36165	.17513	5.71013	4
57	.10422	9.59490	.12190	8.20352	.13965	7.16071	.15749	6.34961	.17543	5.70037	3
58	.10452	9.56791	.12219	8.18370	.13995	7.14553	.15779	6.33761	.17573	5.69064	2
59	.10481	9.54106	.12249	8.16398	.14024	7.13042	.15809	6.32566	.17603	5.68094	1
60	.10510	9.51436	.12278	8.14435	.14054	7.11537	.15838	6.31375	.17633	5.67128	0
′	Cotang	Tang	Cotang	Tang	Cotang	Tang	Cotang	Tang	Cotang	Tang	′
	84°		83°		82°		81°		80°		

′	10° Tang	Cotang	11° Tang	Cotang	12° Tang	Cotang	13° Tang	Cotang	14° Tang	Cotang	′
0	.17633	5.67128	.19438	5.14455	.21256	4.70463	.23087	4.33148	.24933	4.01078	60
1	.17663	5.66165	.19468	5.13658	.21286	4.69791	.23117	4.32573	.24964	4.00582	59
2	.17693	5.65205	.19498	5.12862	.21316	4.69121	.23148	4.32001	.24995	4.00086	58
3	.17723	5.64248	.19529	5.12069	.21347	4.68452	.23179	4.31430	.25026	3.99592	57
4	.17753	5.63295	.19559	5.11279	.21377	4.67786	.23209	4.30860	.25056	3.99099	56
5	.17783	5.62344	.19589	5.10490	.21408	4.67121	.23240	4.30291	.25087	3.98607	55
6	.17813	5.61397	.19619	5.09704	.21438	4.66458	.23271	4.29724	.25118	3.98117	54
7	.17843	5.60452	.19649	5.08921	.21469	4.65797	.23301	4.29159	.25149	3.97627	53
8	.17873	5.59511	.19680	5.08139	.21499	4.65138	.23332	4.28595	.25180	3.97139	52
9	.17903	5.58573	.19710	5.07360	.21529	4.64480	.23363	4.28032	.25211	3.96651	51
10	.17933	5.57638	.19740	5.06584	.21560	4.63825	.23393	4.27471	.25242	3.96165	50
11	.17963	5.56706	.19770	5.05809	.21590	4.63171	.23424	4.26911	.25273	3.95680	49
12	.17993	5.55777	.19801	5.05037	.21621	4.62518	.23455	4.26352	.25304	3.95196	48
13	.18023	5.54851	.19831	5.04267	.21651	4.61868	.23485	4.25795	.25335	3.94713	47
14	.18053	5.53927	.19861	5.03499	.21682	4.61219	.23516	4.25239	.25366	3.94232	46
15	.18083	5.53007	.19891	5.02734	.21712	4.60572	.23547	4.24685	.25397	3.93751	45
16	.18113	5.52090	.19921	5.01971	.21743	4.59927	.23578	4.24132	.25428	3.93271	44
17	.18143	5.51176	.19952	5.01210	.21773	4.59283	.23608	4.23580	.25459	3.92793	43
18	.18173	5.50264	.19982	5.00451	.21804	4.58641	.23639	4.23030	.25490	3.92316	42
19	.18203	5.49356	.20012	4.99695	.21834	4.58001	.23670	4.22481	.25521	3.91839	41
20	.18233	5.48451	.20042	4.98940	.21864	4.57363	.23700	4.21933	.25552	3.91364	40
21	.18263	5.47548	.20073	4.98188	.21895	4.56726	.23731	4.21387	.25583	3.90890	39
22	.18293	5.46648	.20103	4.97438	.21925	4.56091	.23762	4.20842	.25614	3.90417	38
23	.18323	5.45751	.20133	4.96690	.21956	4.55458	.23793	4.20298	.25645	3.89945	37
24	.18353	5.44857	.20164	4.95945	.21986	4.54826	.23823	4.19756	.25676	3.89474	36
25	.18384	5.43966	.20194	4.95201	.22017	4.54196	.23854	4.19215	.25707	3.89004	35
26	.18414	5.43077	.20224	4.94460	.22047	4.53568	.23885	4.18675	.25738	3.88536	34
27	.18444	5.42192	.20254	4.93721	.22078	4.52941	.23916	4.18137	.25769	3.88068	33
28	.18474	5.41309	.20285	4.92984	.22108	4.52316	.23946	4.17600	.25800	3.87601	32
29	.18504	5.40429	.20315	4.92249	.22139	4.51693	.23977	4.17064	.25831	3.87136	31
30	.18534	5.39552	.20345	4.91516	.22169	4.51071	.24008	4.16530	.25862	3.86671	30
31	.18564	5.38677	.20376	4.90785	.22200	4.50451	.24039	4.15997	.25893	3.86208	29
32	.18594	5.37805	.20406	4.90056	.22231	4.49832	.24069	4.15465	.25924	3.85745	28
33	.18624	5.36936	.20436	4.89330	.22261	4.49215	.24100	4.14934	.25955	3.85284	27
34	.18654	5.36070	.20466	4.88605	.22292	4.48600	.24131	4.14405	.25986	3.84824	26
35	.18684	5.35206	.20497	4.87882	.22322	4.47986	.24162	4.13877	.26017	3.84364	25
36	.18714	5.34345	.20527	4.87162	.22353	4.47374	.24193	4.13350	.26048	3.83906	24
37	.18745	5.33487	.20557	4.86444	.22383	4.46764	.24223	4.12825	.26079	3.83449	23
38	.18775	5.32631	.20588	4.85727	.22414	4.46155	.24254	4.12301	.26110	3.82992	22
39	.18805	5.31778	.20618	4.85013	.22444	4.45548	.24285	4.11778	.26141	3.82537	21
40	.18835	5.30928	.20648	4.84300	.22475	4.44942	.24316	4.11256	.26172	3.82083	20
41	.18865	5.30080	.20679	4.83590	.22505	4.44338	.24347	4.10736	.26203	3.81630	19
42	.18895	5.29235	.20709	4.82882	.22536	4.43735	.24377	4.10216	.26235	3.81177	18
43	.18925	5.28393	.20739	4.82175	.22567	4.43134	.24408	4.09699	.26266	3.80726	17
44	.18955	5.27553	.20770	4.81471	.22597	4.42534	.24439	4.09182	.26297	3.80276	16
45	.18986	5.26715	.20800	4.80769	.22628	4.41936	.24470	4.08666	.26328	3.79827	15
46	.19016	5.25880	.20830	4.80068	.22658	4.41340	.24501	4.08152	.26359	3.79378	14
47	.19046	5.25048	.20861	4.79370	.22689	4.40745	.24532	4.07639	.26390	3.78931	13
48	.19076	5.24218	.20891	4.78673	.22719	4.40152	.24562	4.07127	.26421	3.78485	12
49	.19106	5.23391	.20921	4.77978	.22750	4.39560	.24593	4.06616	.26452	3.78040	11
50	.19136	5.22566	.20952	4.77286	.22781	4.38969	.24624	4.06107	.26483	3.77595	10
51	.19166	5.21744	.20982	4.76595	.22811	4.38381	.24655	4.05599	.26515	3.77152	9
52	.19197	5.20925	.21013	4.75906	.22842	4.37793	.24686	4.05092	.26546	3.76709	8
53	.19227	5.20107	.21043	4.75219	.22872	4.37207	.24717	4.04586	.26577	3.76268	7
54	.19257	5.19293	.21073	4.74534	.22903	4.36623	.24747	4.04081	.26608	3.75828	6
55	.19287	5.18480	.21104	4.73851	.22934	4.36040	.24778	4.03578	.26639	3.75388	5
56	.19317	5.17671	.21134	4.73170	.22964	4.35459	.24809	4.03076	.26670	3.74950	4
57	.19347	5.16863	.21164	4.72490	.22995	4.34879	.24840	4.02574	.26701	3.74512	3
58	.19378	5.16058	.21195	4.71813	.23026	4.34300	.24871	4.02074	.26733	3.74075	2
59	.19408	5.15256	.21225	4.71137	.23056	4.33723	.24902	4.01576	.26764	3.73640	1
60	.19438	5.14455	.21256	4.70463	.23087	4.33148	.24933	4.01078	.26795	3.73205	0
′	Cotang	Tang	Cotang	Tang	Cotang	Tang	Cotang	Tang	Cotang	Tang	′
	79°		78°		77°		76°		75°		

′	15° Tang	Cotang	16° Tang	Cotang	17° Tang	Cotang	18° Tang	Cotang	19° Tang	Cotang	′
0	.26795	3.73205	.28675	3.48741	.30573	3.27085	.32492	3.07768	.34433	2.90421	60
1	.26826	3.72771	.28706	3.48359	.30605	3.26745	.32524	3.07464	.34465	2.90147	59
2	.26857	3.72338	.28738	3.47977	.30637	3.26406	.32556	3.07160	.34498	2.89873	58
3	.26888	3.71907	.28769	3.47596	.30669	3.26067	.32588	3.06857	.34530	2.89600	57
4	.26920	3.71476	.28800	3.47216	.30700	3.25729	.32621	3.06554	.34563	2.89327	56
5	.26951	3.71046	.28832	3.46837	.30732	3.25392	.32653	3.06252	.34596	2.89055	55
6	.26982	3.70616	.28864	3.46458	.30764	3.25055	.32685	3.05950	.34628	2.88783	54
7	.27013	3.70188	.28895	3.46080	.30796	3.24719	.32717	3.05649	.34661	2.88511	53
8	.27044	3.69761	.28927	3.45703	.30828	3.24383	.32749	3.05349	.34693	2.88240	52
9	.27076	3.69335	.28958	3.45327	.30860	3.24049	.32782	3.05049	.34726	2.87970	51
10	.27107	3.68909	.28990	3.44951	.30891	3.23714	.32814	3.04749	.34758	2.87700	50
11	.27138	3.68485	.29021	3.44576	.30923	3.23381	.32846	3.04450	.34791	2.87430	49
12	.27169	3.68061	.29053	3.44202	.30955	3.23048	.32878	3.04152	.34824	2.87161	48
13	.27201	3.67638	.29084	3.43829	.30987	3.22715	.32911	3.03854	.34856	2.86892	47
14	.27232	3.67217	.29116	3.43456	.31019	3.22384	.32943	3.03556	.34889	2.86624	46
15	.27263	3.66796	.29147	3.43084	.31051	3.22053	.32975	3.03260	.34922	2.86356	45
16	.27294	3.66376	.29179	3.42713	.31083	3.21722	.33007	3.02963	.34954	2.86089	44
17	.27326	3.65957	.29210	3.42343	.31115	3.21392	.33040	3.02667	.34987	2.85822	43
18	.27357	3.65538	.29242	3.41973	.31147	3.21063	.33072	3.02372	.35020	2.85555	42
19	.27388	3.65121	.29274	3.41604	.31178	3.20734	.33104	3.02077	.35052	2.85289	41
20	.27419	3.64705	.29305	3.41236	.31210	3.20406	.33136	3.01783	.35085	2.85023	40
21	.27451	3.64289	.29337	3.40869	.31242	3.20079	.33169	3.01489	.35118	2.84758	39
22	.27482	3.63874	.29368	3.40502	.31274	3.19752	.33201	3.01196	.35150	2.84494	38
23	.27513	3.63461	.29400	3.40136	.31306	3.19426	.33233	3.00903	.35183	2.84229	37
24	.27545	3.63048	.29432	3.39771	.31338	3.19100	.33266	3.00611	.35216	2.83965	36
25	.27576	3.62636	.29463	3.39406	.31370	3.18775	.33298	3.00319	.35248	2.83702	35
26	.27607	3.62224	.29495	3.39042	.31402	3.18451	.33330	3.00028	.35281	2.83439	34
27	.27638	3.61814	.29526	3.38679	.31434	3.18127	.33363	2.99738	.35314	2.83176	33
28	.27670	3.61405	.29558	3.38317	.31466	3.17804	.33395	2.99447	.35346	2.82914	32
29	.27701	3.60996	.29590	3.37955	.31498	3.17481	.33427	2.99158	.35379	2.82653	31
30	.27732	3.60588	.29621	3.37594	.31530	3.17159	.33460	2.98868	.35412	2.82391	30
31	.27764	3.60181	.29653	3.37234	.31562	3.16838	.33492	2.98580	.35445	2.82130	29
32	.27795	3.59775	.29685	3.36875	.31594	3.16517	.33524	2.98292	.35477	2.81870	28
33	.27826	3.59370	.29716	3.36516	.31626	3.16197	.33557	2.98004	.35510	2.81610	27
34	.27858	3.58966	.29748	3.36158	.31658	3.15877	.33589	2.97717	.35543	2.81350	26
35	.27889	3.58562	.29780	3.35800	.31690	3.15558	.33621	2.97430	.35576	2.81091	25
36	.27921	3.58160	.29811	3.35443	.31722	3.15240	.33654	2.97144	.35608	2.80833	24
37	.27952	3.57758	.29843	3.35087	.31754	3.14922	.33686	2.96858	.35641	2.80574	23
38	.27983	3.57357	.29875	3.34732	.31786	3.14605	.33718	2.96573	.35674	2.80316	22
39	.28015	3.56957	.29906	3.34377	.31818	3.14288	.33751	2.96288	.35707	2.80059	21
40	.28046	3.56557	.29938	3.34023	.31850	3.13972	.33783	2.96004	.35740	2.79802	20
41	.28077	3.56159	.29970	3.33670	.31882	3.13656	.33816	2.95721	.35772	2.79545	19
42	.28109	3.55761	.30001	3.33317	.31914	3.13341	.33848	2.95437	.35805	2.79289	18
43	.28140	3.55364	.30033	3.32965	.31946	3.13027	.33881	2.95155	.35838	2.79033	17
44	.28172	3.54968	.30065	3.32614	.31978	3.12713	.33913	2.94872	.35871	2.78778	16
45	.28203	3.54573	.30097	3.32264	.32010	3.12400	.33945	2.94591	.35904	2.78523	15
46	.28234	3.54179	.30128	3.31914	.32042	3.12087	.33978	2.94309	.35937	2.78269	14
47	.28266	3.53785	.30160	3.31565	.32074	3.11775	.34010	2.94028	.35969	2.78014	13
48	.28297	3.53393	.30192	3.31216	.32106	3.11464	.34043	2.93748	.36002	2.77761	12
49	.28329	3.53001	.30224	3.30868	.32139	3.11153	.34075	2.93468	.36035	2.77507	11
50	.28360	3.52609	.30255	3.30521	.32171	3.10842	.34108	2.93189	.36068	2.77254	10
51	.28391	3.52219	.30287	3.30174	.32203	3.10532	.34140	2.92910	.36101	2.77002	9
52	.28423	3.51829	.30319	3.29829	.32235	3.10223	.34173	2.92632	.36134	2.76750	8
53	.28454	3.51441	.30351	3.29483	.32267	3.09914	.34205	2.92354	.36167	2.76498	7
54	.28486	3.51053	.30382	3.29139	.32299	3.09606	.34238	2.92076	.36199	2.76247	6
55	.28517	3.50666	.30414	3.28795	.32331	3.09298	.34270	2.91799	.36232	2.75996	5
56	.28549	3.50279	.30446	3.28452	.32363	3.08991	.34303	2.91523	.36265	2.75746	4
57	.28580	3.49894	.30478	3.28109	.32396	3.08685	.34335	2.91246	.36298	2.75496	3
58	.28612	3.49509	.30509	3.27767	.32428	3.08379	.34368	2.90971	.36331	2.75246	2
59	.28643	3.49125	.30541	3.27426	.32460	3.08073	.34400	2.90696	.36364	2.74997	1
60	.28675	3.48741	.30573	3.27085	.32492	3.07768	.34433	2.90421	.36397	2.74748	0
′	Cotang	Tang	Cotang	Tang	Cotang	Tang	Cotang	Tang	Cotang	Tang	′
	74°		73°		72°		71°		70°		

′	20° Tang	20° Cotang	21° Tang	21° Cotang	22° Tang	22° Cotang	23° Tang	23° Cotang	24° Tang	24° Cotang	′
0	.36397	2.74748	.38386	2.60509	.40403	2.47509	.42447	2.35585	.44523	2.24604	60
1	.36430	2.74499	.38420	2.60283	.40436	2.47302	.42482	2.35395	.44558	2.24428	59
2	.36463	2.74251	.38453	2.60057	.40470	2.47095	.42516	2.35205	.44593	2.24252	58
3	.36496	2.74004	.38487	2.59831	.40504	2.46888	.42551	2.35015	.44627	2.24077	57
4	.36529	2.73756	.38520	2.59606	.40538	2.46682	.42585	2.34825	.44662	2.23902	56
5	.36562	2.73509	.38553	2.59381	.40572	2.46476	.42619	2.34636	.44697	2.23727	55
6	.36595	2.73263	.38587	2.59156	.40606	2.46270	.42654	2.34447	.44732	2.23553	54
7	.36628	2.73017	.38620	2.58932	.40640	2.46065	.42688	2.34258	.44767	2.23378	53
8	.36661	2.72771	.38654	2.58708	.40674	2.45860	.42722	2.34069	.44802	2.23204	52
9	.36694	2.72526	.38687	2.58484	.40707	2.45655	.42757	2.33881	.44837	2.23030	51
10	.36727	2.72281	.38721	2.58261	.40741	2.45451	.42791	2.33693	.44872	2.22857	50
11	.36760	2.72036	.38754	2.58038	.40775	2.45246	.42826	2.33505	.44907	2.22683	49
12	.36793	2.71792	.38787	2.57815	.40809	2.45043	.42860	2.33317	.44942	2.22510	48
13	.36826	2.71548	.38821	2.57593	.40843	2.44839	.42894	2.33130	.44977	2.22337	47
14	.36859	2.71305	.38854	2.57371	.40877	2.44636	.42929	2.32943	.45012	2.22164	46
15	.36892	2.71062	.38888	2.57150	.40911	2.44433	.42963	2.32756	.45047	2.21992	45
16	.36925	2.70819	.38921	2.56928	.40945	2.44230	.42998	2.32570	.45082	2.21819	44
17	.36958	2.70577	.38955	2.56707	.40979	2.44027	.43032	2.32383	.45117	2.21647	43
18	.36991	2.70335	.38988	2.56487	.41013	2.43825	.43067	2.32197	.45152	2.21475	42
19	.37024	2.70094	.39022	2.56266	.41047	2.43623	.43101	2.32012	.45187	2.21304	41
20	.37057	2.69853	.39055	2.56046	.41081	2.43422	.43136	2.31826	.45222	2.21132	40
21	.37090	2.69612	.39089	2.55827	.41115	2.43220	.43170	2.31641	.45257	2.20961	39
22	.37123	2.69371	.39122	2.55608	.41149	2.43019	.43205	2.31456	.45292	2.20790	38
23	.37157	2.69131	.39156	2.55389	.41183	2.42819	.43230	2.31271	.45327	2.20619	37
24	.37190	2.68892	.39190	2.55170	.41217	2.42618	.43274	2.31086	.45362	2.20449	36
25	.37223	2.68653	.39223	2.54952	.41251	2.42418	.43308	2.30902	.45397	2.20278	35
26	.37256	2.68414	.39257	2.54734	.41285	2.42218	.43343	2.30718	.45432	2.20108	34
27	.37289	2.68175	.39290	2.54516	.41319	2.42019	.43378	2.30534	.45467	2.19938	33
28	.37322	2.67937	.39324	2.54299	.41353	2.41819	.43412	2.30351	.45502	2.19769	32
29	.37355	2.67700	.39357	2.54082	.41387	2.41620	.43447	2.30167	.45538	2.19599	31
30	.37388	2.67462	.39391	2.53865	.41421	2.41421	.43481	2.29984	.45573	2.19430	30
31	.37422	2.67225	.39425	2.53648	.41455	2.41223	.43516	2.29801	.45608	2.19261	29
32	.37455	2.66989	.39458	2.53432	.41490	2.41025	.43550	2.29619	.45643	2.19092	28
33	.37488	2.66752	.39492	2.53217	.41524	2.40827	.43585	2.29437	.45678	2.18923	27
34	.37521	2.66516	.39526	2.53001	.41558	2.40629	.43620	2.29254	.45713	2.18755	26
35	.37554	2.66281	.39559	2.52786	.41592	2.40432	.43654	2.29073	.45748	2.18587	25
36	.37588	2.66046	.39593	2.52571	.41626	2.40235	.43689	2.28891	.45784	2.18419	24
37	.37621	2.65811	.39626	2.52357	.41660	2.40038	.43724	2.28710	.45819	2.18251	23
38	.37654	2.65576	.39660	2.52142	.41694	2.39841	.43758	2.28528	.45854	2.18084	22
39	.37687	2.65342	.39694	2.51929	.41728	2.39645	.43793	2.28348	.45889	2.17916	21
40	.37720	2.65109	.39727	2.51715	.41763	2.39449	.43828	2.28167	.45924	2.17749	20
41	.37754	2.64875	.39761	2.51502	.41797	2.39253	.43862	2.27987	.45960	2.17582	19
42	.37787	2.64642	.39795	2.51289	.41831	2.39058	.43897	2.27806	.45995	2.17416	18
43	.37820	2.64410	.39829	2.51076	.41865	2.38863	.43932	2.27626	.46030	2.17249	17
44	.37853	2.64177	.39862	2.50864	.41899	2.38668	.43966	2.27447	.46065	2.17083	16
45	.37887	2.63945	.39896	2.50652	.41933	2.38473	.44001	2.27267	.46101	2.16917	15
46	.37920	2.63714	.39930	2.50440	.41968	2.38279	.44036	2.27088	.46136	2.16751	14
47	.37953	2.63483	.39963	2.50229	.42002	2.38084	.44071	2.26909	.46171	2.16585	13
48	.37986	2.63252	.39997	2.50018	.42036	2.37891	.44105	2.26730	.46206	2.16420	12
49	.38020	2.63021	.40031	2.49807	.42070	2.37697	.44140	2.26552	.46242	2.16255	11
50	.38053	2.62791	.40065	2.49597	.42105	2.37504	.44175	2.26374	.46277	2.16090	10
51	.38086	2.62561	.40098	2.49386	.42139	2.37311	.44210	2.26196	.46312	2.15925	9
52	.38120	2.62332	.40132	2.49177	.42173	2.37118	.44244	2.26018	.46348	2.15760	8
53	.38153	2.62103	.40166	2.48967	.42207	2.36925	.44279	2.25840	.46383	2.15596	7
54	.38186	2.61874	.40200	2.48758	.42242	2.36733	.44314	2.25663	.46418	2.15432	6
55	.38220	2.61646	.40234	2.48549	.42276	2.36541	.44349	2.25486	.46454	2.15268	5
56	.38253	2.61418	.40267	2.48340	.42310	2.36349	.44384	2.25309	.46489	2.15104	4
57	.38286	2.61190	.40301	2.48132	.42345	2.36158	.44418	2.25132	.46525	2.14940	3
58	.38320	2.60963	.40335	2.47924	.42379	2.35967	.44453	2.24956	.46560	2.14777	2
59	.38353	2.60736	.40369	2.47716	.42413	2.35776	.44488	2.24780	.46595	2.14614	1
60	.38386	2.60509	.40403	2.47509	.42447	2.35585	.44523	2.24604	.46631	2.14451	0
′	Cotang	Tang	Cotang	Tang	Cotang	Tang	Cotang	Tang	Cotang	Tang	′
	69°		68°		67°		66°		65°		

′	25° Tang	25° Cotang	26° Tang	26° Cotang	27° Tang	27° Cotang	28° Tang	28° Cotang	29° Tang	29° Cotang	′
0	.46631	2.14451	.48773	2.05030	.50953	1.96261	.53171	1.88073	.55431	1.80405	60
1	.46666	2.14288	.48809	2.04879	.50989	1.96120	.53208	1.87941	.55469	1.80281	59
2	.46702	2.14125	.48845	2.04728	.51026	1.95979	.53246	1.87809	.55507	1.80158	58
3	.46737	2.13963	.48881	2.04577	.51063	1.95838	.53283	1.87677	.55545	1.80034	57
4	.46772	2.13801	.48917	2.04426	.51099	1.95698	.53320	1.87546	.55583	1.79911	56
5	.46808	2.13639	.48953	2.04276	.51136	1.95557	.53358	1.87415	.55621	1.79788	55
6	.46843	2.13477	.48989	2.04125	.51173	1.95417	.53395	1.87283	.55659	1.79665	54
7	.46879	2.13316	.49026	2.03975	.51209	1.95277	.53432	1.87152	.55697	1.79542	53
8	.46914	2.13154	.49062	2.03825	.51246	1.95137	.53470	1.87021	.55736	1.79419	52
9	.46950	2.12993	.49098	2.03675	.51283	1.94997	.53507	1.86891	.55774	1.79296	51
10	.46985	2.12832	.49134	2.03526	.51319	1.94858	.53545	1.86760	.55812	1.79174	50
11	.47021	2.12671	.49170	2.03376	.51356	1.94718	.53582	1.86630	.55850	1.79051	49
12	.47056	2.12511	.49206	2.03227	.51393	1.94579	.53620	1.86499	.55888	1.78929	48
13	.47092	2.12350	.49242	2.03078	.51430	1.94440	.53657	1.86369	.55926	1.78807	47
14	.47128	2.12190	.49278	2.02929	.51467	1.94301	.53694	1.86239	.55964	1.78685	46
15	.47163	2.12030	.49315	2.02780	.51503	1.94162	.53732	1.86109	.56003	1.78563	45
16	.47199	2.11871	.49351	2.02631	.51540	1.94023	.53769	1.85979	.56041	1.78441	44
17	.47234	2.11711	.49387	2.02483	.51577	1.93885	.53807	1.85850	.56079	1.78319	43
18	.47270	2.11552	.49423	2.02335	.51614	1.93746	.53844	1.85720	.56117	1.78198	42
19	.47305	2.11392	.49459	2.02187	.51651	1.93608	.53882	1.85591	.56156	1.78077	41
20	.47341	2.11233	.49495	2.02039	.51688	1.93470	.53920	1.85462	.56194	1.77955	40
21	.47377	2.11075	.49532	2.01891	.51724	1.93332	.53957	1.85333	.56232	1.77834	39
22	.47412	2.10916	.49568	2.01743	.51761	1.93195	.53995	1.85204	.56270	1.77713	38
23	.47448	2.10758	.49604	2.01596	.51798	1.93057	.54032	1.85075	.56309	1.77592	37
24	.47483	2.10600	.49640	2.01449	.51835	1.92920	.54070	1.84946	.56347	1.77471	36
25	.47519	2.10442	.49677	2.01302	.51872	1.92782	.54107	1.84818	.56385	1.77351	35
26	.47555	2.10284	.49713	2.01155	.51909	1.92645	.54145	1.84689	.56424	1.77230	34
27	.47590	2.10126	.49749	2.01008	.51946	1.92508	.54183	1.84561	.56462	1.77110	33
28	.47626	2.09969	.49786	2.00862	.51983	1.92371	.54220	1.84433	.56501	1.76990	32
29	.47662	2.09811	.49822	2.00715	.52020	1.92235	.54258	1.84305	.56539	1.76869	31
30	.47698	2.09654	.49858	2.00569	.52057	1.92098	.54296	1.84177	.56577	1.76749	30
31	.47733	2.09498	.49894	2.00423	.52094	1.91962	.54333	1.84049	.56616	1.76629	29
32	.47769	2.09341	.49931	2.00277	.52131	1.91826	.54371	1.83922	.56654	1.76510	28
33	.47805	2.09184	.49967	2.00131	.52168	1.91690	.54409	1.83794	.56693	1.76390	27
34	.47840	2.09028	.50004	1.99986	.52205	1.91554	.54446	1.83667	.56731	1.76271	26
35	.47876	2.08872	.50040	1.99841	.52242	1.91418	.54484	1.83540	.56769	1.76151	25
36	.47912	2.08716	.50076	1.99695	.52279	1.91282	.54522	1.83413	.56808	1.76032	24
37	.47948	2.08560	.50113	1.99550	.52316	1.91147	.54560	1.83286	.56846	1.75913	23
38	.47984	2.08405	.50149	1.99406	.52353	1.91012	.54597	1.83159	.56885	1.75794	22
39	.48019	2.08250	.50185	1.99261	.52390	1.90876	.54635	1.83033	.56923	1.75675	21
40	.48055	2.08094	.50222	1.99116	.52427	1.90741	.54673	1.82906	.56962	1.75556	20
41	.48091	2.07939	.50258	1.98972	.52464	1.90607	.54711	1.82780	.57000	1.75437	19
42	.48127	2.07785	.50295	1.98828	.52501	1.90472	.54748	1.82654	.57039	1.75319	18
43	.48163	2.07630	.50331	1.98684	.52538	1.90337	.54786	1.82528	.57078	1.75200	17
44	.48198	2.07476	.50368	1.98540	.52575	1.90203	.54824	1.82402	.57116	1.75082	16
45	.48234	2.07321	.50404	1.98396	.52613	1.90069	.54862	1.82276	.57155	1.74964	15
46	.48270	2.07167	.50441	1.98253	.52650	1.89935	.54900	1.82150	.57193	1.74846	14
47	.48306	2.07014	.50477	1.98110	.52687	1.89801	.54938	1.82025	.57232	1.74728	13
48	.48342	2.06860	.50514	1.97966	.52724	1.89667	.54975	1.81899	.57271	1.74610	12
49	.48378	2.06706	.50550	1.97823	.52761	1.89533	.55013	1.81774	.57309	1.74492	11
50	.48414	2.06553	.50587	1.97681	.52798	1.89400	.55051	1.81649	.57348	1.74375	10
51	.48450	2.06400	.50623	1.97538	.52836	1.89266	.55089	1.81524	.57386	1.74257	9
52	.48486	2.06247	.50660	1.97395	.52873	1.89133	.55127	1.81399	.57425	1.74140	8
53	.48521	2.06094	.50696	1.97253	.52910	1.89000	.55165	1.81274	.57464	1.74022	7
54	.48557	2.05942	.50733	1.97111	.52947	1.88867	.55203	1.81150	.57503	1.73905	6
55	.48593	2.05790	.50769	1.96969	.52985	1.88734	.55241	1.81025	.57541	1.73788	5
56	.48629	2.05637	.50806	1.96827	.53022	1.88602	.55279	1.80901	.57580	1.73671	4
57	.48665	2.05485	.50843	1.96685	.53059	1.88469	.55317	1.80777	.57619	1.73555	3
58	.48701	2.05333	.50879	1.96544	.53096	1.88337	.55355	1.80653	.57657	1.73438	2
59	.48737	2.05182	.50916	1.96402	.53134	1.88205	.55393	1.80529	.57696	1.73321	1
60	.48773	2.05030	.50953	1.96261	.53171	1.88073	.55431	1.80405	.57735	1.73205	0
′	Cotang	Tang	Cotang	Tang	Cotang	Tang	Cotang	Tang	Cotang	Tang	′
	64°		63°		62°		61°		60°		

,	30° Tang	30° Cotang	31° Tang	31° Cotang	32° Tang	32° Cotang	33° Tang	33° Cotang	34° Tang	34° Cotang	,
0	.57735	1.73205	.60086	1.66428	.62487	1.60033	.64941	1.53986	.67451	1.48256	60
1	.57774	1.73089	.60126	1.66318	.62527	1.59930	.64982	1.53888	.67493	1.48163	59
2	.57813	1.72973	.60165	1.66209	.62568	1.59826	.65024	1.53791	.67536	1.48070	58
3	.57851	1.72857	.60205	1.66099	.62608	1.59723	.65065	1.53693	.67578	1.47977	57
4	.57890	1.72741	.60245	1.65990	.62649	1.59620	.65106	1.53595	.67620	1.47885	56
5	.57929	1.72625	.60284	1.65881	.62689	1.59517	.65148	1.53497	.67663	1.47792	55
6	.57968	1.72509	.60324	1.65772	.62730	1.59414	.65189	1.53400	.67705	1.47699	54
7	.58007	1.72393	.60364	1.65663	.62770	1.59311	.65231	1.53302	.67748	1.47607	53
8	.58046	1.72278	.60403	1.65554	.62811	1.59208	.65272	1.53205	.67790	1.47514	52
9	.58085	1.72163	.60443	1.65445	.62852	1.59105	.65314	1.53107	.67832	1.47422	51
10	.58124	1.72047	.60483	1.65337	.62892	1.59002	.65355	1.53010	.67875	1.47330	50
11	.58162	1.71932	.60522	1.65228	.62933	1.58900	.65397	1.52913	.67917	1.47238	49
12	.58201	1.71817	.60562	1.65120	.62973	1.58797	.65438	1.52816	.67960	1.47146	48
13	.58240	1.71702	.60602	1.65011	.63014	1.58695	.65480	1.52719	.68002	1.47053	47
14	.58279	1.71588	.60642	1.64903	.63055	1.58593	.65521	1.52622	.68045	1.46962	46
15	.58318	1.71473	.60681	1.64795	.63095	1.58490	.65563	1.52525	.68088	1.46870	45
16	.58357	1.71358	.60721	1.64687	.63136	1.58388	.65604	1.52429	.68130	1.46778	44
17	.58396	1.71244	.60761	1.64579	.63177	1.58286	.65646	1.52332	.68173	1.46686	43
18	.58435	1.71129	.60801	1.64471	.63217	1.58184	.65688	1.52235	.68215	1.46595	42
19	.58474	1.71015	.60841	1.64363	.63258	1.58083	.65729	1.52139	.68258	1.46503	41
20	.58513	1.70901	.60881	1.64256	.63299	1.57981	.65771	1.52043	.68301	1.46411	40
21	.58552	1.70787	.60921	1.64148	.63340	1.57879	.65813	1.51946	.68343	1.46320	39
22	.58591	1.70673	.60960	1.64041	.63380	1.57778	.65854	1.51850	.68386	1.46229	38
23	.58631	1.70560	.61000	1.63934	.63421	1.57676	.65896	1.51754	.68429	1.46137	37
24	.58670	1.70446	.61040	1.63826	.63462	1.57575	.65938	1.51658	.68471	1.46046	36
25	.58709	1.70332	.61080	1.63719	.63503	1.57474	.65980	1.51562	.68514	1.45955	35
26	.58748	1.70219	.61120	1.63612	.63544	1.57372	.66021	1.51466	.68557	1.45864	34
27	.58787	1.70106	.61160	1.63505	.63584	1.57271	.66063	1.51370	.68600	1.45773	33
28	.58826	1.69992	.61200	1.63398	.63625	1.57170	.66105	1.51275	.68642	1.45682	32
29	.58865	1.69879	.61240	1.63292	.63666	1.57069	.66147	1.51179	.68685	1.45592	31
30	.58905	1.69766	.61280	1.63185	.63707	1.56969	.66189	1.51084	.68728	1.45501	30
31	.58944	1.69653	.61320	1.63079	.63748	1.56868	.66230	1.50988	.68771	1.45410	29
32	.58983	1.69541	.61360	1.62972	.63789	1.56767	.66272	1.50893	.68814	1.45320	28
33	.59022	1.69428	.61400	1.62866	.63830	1.56667	.66314	1.50797	.68857	1.45229	27
34	.59061	1.69316	.61440	1.62760	.63871	1.56566	.66356	1.50702	.68900	1.45139	26
35	.59101	1.69203	.61480	1.62654	.63912	1.56466	.66398	1.50607	.68942	1.45049	25
36	.59149	1.69091	.61520	1.62548	.63953	1.56366	.66440	1.50512	.68985	1.44958	24
37	.59179	1.68979	.61561	1.62442	.63994	1.56265	.66482	1.50417	.69028	1.44868	23
38	.59218	1.68866	.61601	1.62336	.64035	1.56165	.66524	1.50322	.69071	1.44778	22
39	.59258	1.68754	.61641	1.62230	.64076	1.56065	.66566	1.50228	.69114	1.44688	21
40	.59297	1.68643	.61681	1.62125	.64117	1.55966	.66608	1.50133	.69157	1.44598	20
41	.59336	1.68531	.61721	1.62019	.64158	1.55866	.66650	1.50038	.69200	1.44508	19
42	.59376	1.68419	.61761	1.61914	.64199	1.55766	.66692	1.49944	.69243	1.44418	18
43	.59415	1.68308	.61801	1.61808	.64240	1.55666	.66734	1.49849	.69286	1.44329	17
44	.59454	1.68196	.61842	1.61703	.64281	1.55567	.66776	1.49755	.69329	1.44239	16
45	.59494	1.68085	.61882	1.61598	.64322	1.55467	.66818	1.49661	.69372	1.44149	15
46	.59533	1.67974	.61922	1.61493	.64363	1.55368	.66860	1.49566	.69416	1.44060	14
47	.59573	1.67863	.61962	1.61388	.64404	1.55269	.66902	1.49472	.69459	1.43970	13
48	.59612	1.67752	.62003	1.61283	.64446	1.55170	.66944	1.49378	.69502	1.43881	12
49	.59651	1.67641	.62043	1.61179	.64487	1.55071	.66986	1.49284	.69545	1.43792	11
50	.59691	1.67530	.62083	1.61074	.64528	1.54972	.67028	1.49190	.69588	1.43703	10
51	.59730	1.67419	.62124	1.60970	.64569	1.54873	.67071	1.49097	.69631	1.43614	9
52	.59770	1.67309	.62164	1.60865	.64610	1.54774	.67113	1.49003	.69675	1.43525	8
53	.59809	1.67198	.62204	1.60761	.64652	1.54675	.67155	1.48909	.69718	1.43436	7
54	.59849	1.67088	.62245	1.60657	.64693	1.54576	.67197	1.48816	.69761	1.43347	6
55	.59888	1.66978	.62285	1.60553	.64734	1.54478	.67239	1.48722	.69804	1.43258	5
56	.59928	1.66867	.62325	1.60449	.64775	1.54379	.67282	1.48629	.69847	1.43169	4
57	.59967	1.66757	.62366	1.60345	.64817	1.54281	.67324	1.48536	.69891	1.43080	3
58	.60007	1.66647	.62406	1.60241	.64858	1.54183	.67366	1.48442	.69934	1.42992	2
59	.60046	1.66538	.62446	1.60137	.64899	1.54085	.67409	1.48349	.69977	1.42903	1
60	.60086	1.66428	.62487	1.60033	.64941	1.53986	.67451	1.48256	.70021	1.42815	0
,	Cotang	Tang	Cotang	Tang	Cotang	Tang	Cotang	Tang	Cotang	Tang	,
	59°		58°		57°		56°		55°		

′	35° Tang	Cotang	36° Tang	Cotang	37° Tang	Cotang	38° Tang	Cotang	39° Tang	Cotang	′
0	.70021	1.42815	.72654	1.37638	.75355	1.32704	.78129	1.27994	.80978	1.23490	60
1	.70064	1.42726	.72699	1.37554	.75401	1.32624	.78175	1.27917	.81027	1.23416	59
2	.70107	1.42638	.72743	1.37470	.75447	1.32544	.78222	1.27841	.81075	1.23343	58
3	.70151	1.42550	.72788	1.37386	.75492	1.32464	.78269	1.27764	.81123	1.23270	57
4	.70194	1.42462	.72832	1.37302	.75538	1.32384	.78316	1.27688	.81171	1.23196	56
5	.70238	1.42374	.72877	1.37218	.75584	1.32304	.78363	1.27611	.81220	1.23123	55
6	.70281	1.42286	.72921	1.37134	.75629	1.32224	.78410	1.27535	.81268	1.23050	54
7	.70325	1.42198	.72966	1.37050	.75675	1.32144	.78457	1.27458	.81316	1.22977	53
8	.70368	1.42110	.73010	1.36967	.75721	1.32064	.78504	1.27382	.81364	1.22904	52
9	.70412	1.42022	.73055	1.36883	.75767	1.31984	.78551	1.27306	.81413	1.22831	51
10	.70455	1.41934	.73100	1.36800	.75812	1.31904	.78598	1.27230	.81461	1.22758	50
11	.70499	1.41847	.73144	1.36716	.75858	1.31825	.78645	1.27153	.81510	1.22685	49
12	.70542	1.41759	.73189	1.36633	.75904	1.31745	.78692	1.27077	.81558	1.22612	48
13	.70586	1.41672	.73234	1.36549	.75950	1.31666	.78739	1.27001	.81606	1.22539	47
14	.70629	1.41584	.73278	1.36466	.75996	1.31586	.78786	1.26925	.81655	1.22467	46
15	.70673	1.41497	.73323	1.36383	.76042	1.31507	.78834	1.26849	.81703	1.22394	45
16	.70717	1.41409	.73368	1.36300	.76088	1.31427	.78881	1.26774	.81752	1.22321	44
17	.70760	1.41322	.73413	1.36217	.76134	1.31348	.78928	1.26698	.81800	1.22249	43
18	.70804	1.41235	.73457	1.36134	.76180	1.31269	.78975	1.26622	.81849	1.22176	42
19	.70848	1.41148	.73502	1.36051	.76226	1.31190	.79022	1.26546	.81898	1.22104	41
20	.70891	1.41061	.73547	1.35968	.76272	1.31110	.79070	1.26471	.81946	1.22031	40
21	.70935	1.40974	.73592	1.35885	.76318	1.31031	.79117	1.26395	.81995	1.21959	39
22	.70979	1.40887	.73637	1.35802	.76364	1.30952	.79164	1.26319	.82044	1.21886	38
23	.71023	1.40800	.73681	1.35719	.76410	1.30873	.79212	1.26244	.82092	1.21814	37
24	.71066	1.40714	.73726	1.35637	.76456	1.30795	.79259	1.26169	.82141	1.21742	36
25	.71110	1.40627	.73771	1.35554	.76502	1.30716	.79306	1.26093	.82190	1.21670	35
26	.71154	1.40540	.73816	1.35472	.76548	1.30637	.79354	1.26018	.82238	1.21598	34
27	.71198	1.40454	.73861	1.35389	.76594	1.30558	.79401	1.25943	.82287	1.21526	33
28	.71242	1.40367	.73906	1.35307	.76640	1.30480	.79449	1.25867	.82336	1.21454	32
29	.71285	1.40281	.73951	1.35224	.76686	1.30401	.79496	1.25792	.82385	1.21382	31
30	.71329	1.40195	.73996	1.35142	.76733	1.30323	.79544	1.25717	.82434	1.21310	30
31	.71373	1.40109	.74041	1.35060	.76779	1.30244	.79591	1.25642	.82483	1.21238	29
32	.71417	1.40022	.74086	1.34978	.76825	1.30166	.79639	1.25567	.82531	1.21166	28
33	.71461	1.39936	.74131	1.34896	.76871	1.30087	.79686	1.25492	.82580	1.21094	27
34	.71505	1.39850	.74176	1.34814	.76918	1.30009	.79734	1.25417	.82629	1.21023	26
35	.71549	1.39764	.74221	1.34732	.76964	1.29931	.79781	1.25343	.82678	1.20951	25
36	.71593	1.39679	.74267	1.34650	.77010	1.29853	.79829	1.25268	.82727	1.20879	24
37	.71637	1.39593	.74312	1.34568	.77057	1.29775	.79877	1.25193	.82776	1.20808	23
38	.71681	1.39507	.74357	1.34487	.77103	1.29696	.79924	1.25118	.82825	1.20736	22
39	.71725	1.39421	.74402	1.34405	.77149	1.29618	.79972	1.25044	.82874	1.20665	21
40	.71769	1.39336	.74447	1.34323	.77196	1.29541	.80020	1.24969	.82923	1.20593	20
41	.71813	1.39250	.74492	1.34242	.77242	1.29463	.80067	1.24895	.82972	1.20522	19
42	.71857	1.39165	.74538	1.34160	.77289	1.29385	.80115	1.24820	.83022	1.20451	18
43	.71901	1.39079	.74583	1.34079	.77335	1.29307	.80163	1.24746	.83071	1.20379	17
44	.71946	1.38994	.74628	1.33998	.77382	1.29229	.80211	1.24672	.83120	1.20308	16
45	.71990	1.38909	.74674	1.33916	.77428	1.29152	.80258	1.24597	.83169	1.20237	15
46	.72034	1.38824	.74719	1.33835	.77475	1.29074	.80306	1.24523	.83218	1.20166	14
47	.72078	1.38738	.74764	1.33754	.77521	1.28997	.80354	1.24449	.83268	1.20095	13
48	.72122	1.38653	.74810	1.33673	.77568	1.28919	.80402	1.24375	.83317	1.20024	12
49	.72167	1.38568	.74855	1.33592	.77615	1.28842	.80450	1.24301	.83366	1.19953	11
50	.72211	1.38484	.74900	1.33511	.77661	1.28764	.80498	1.24227	.83415	1.19882	10
51	.72255	1.38399	.74946	1.33430	.77708	1.28687	.80546	1.24153	.83465	1.19811	9
52	.72299	1.38314	.74991	1.33349	.77754	1.28610	.80594	1.24079	.83514	1.19740	8
53	.72344	1.38229	.75037	1.33268	.77801	1.28533	.80642	1.24005	.83564	1.19669	7
54	.72388	1.38145	.75082	1.33187	.77848	1.28456	.80690	1.23931	.83613	1.19599	6
55	.72432	1.38060	.75128	1.33107	.77895	1.28379	.80738	1.23858	.83662	1.19528	5
56	.72477	1.37976	.75173	1.33026	.77941	1.28302	.80786	1.23784	.83712	1.19457	4
57	.72521	1.37891	.75219	1.32946	.77988	1.28225	.80834	1.23710	.83761	1.19387	3
58	.72565	1.37807	.75264	1.32865	.78035	1.28148	.80882	1.23637	.83811	1.19316	2
59	.72610	1.37722	.75310	1.32785	.78082	1.28071	.80930	1.23563	.83860	1.19246	1
60	.72654	1.37638	.75355	1.32704	.78129	1.27994	.80978	1.23490	.83910	1.19175	0
′	Cotang	Tang	Cotang	Tang	Cotang	Tang	Cotang	Tang	Cotang	Tang	′
	54°		53°		52°		51°		50°		

′	40° Tang	40° Cotang	41° Tang	41° Cotang	42° Tang	42° Cotang	43° Tang	43° Cotang	44° Tang	44° Cotang	′
0	.83910	1.19175	.86929	1.15037	.90040	1.11061	.93252	1.07237	.96569	1.03553	60
1	.83960	1.19105	.86980	1.14969	.90093	1.10996	.93306	1.07174	.96625	1.03493	59
2	.84009	1.19035	.87031	1.14902	.90146	1.10931	.93360	1.07112	.96681	1.03433	58
3	.84059	1.18964	.87082	1.14834	.90199	1.10867	.93415	1.07049	.96738	1.03372	57
4	.84108	1.18894	.87133	1.14767	.90251	1.10802	.93469	1.06987	.96794	1.03312	56
5	.84158	1.18824	.87184	1.14699	.90304	1.10737	.93524	1.06925	.96850	1.03252	55
6	.84208	1.18754	.87236	1.14632	.90357	1.10672	.93578	1.06862	.96907	1.03192	54
7	.84258	1.18684	.87287	1.14565	.90410	1.10607	.93633	1.06800	.96963	1.03132	53
8	.84307	1.18614	.87338	1.14498	.90463	1.10543	.93688	1.06738	.97020	1.03072	52
9	.84357	1.18544	.87389	1.14430	.90516	1.10478	.93742	1.06676	.97076	1.03012	51
10	.84407	1.18474	.87441	1.14363	.90569	1.10414	.93797	1.06613	.97133	1.02952	50
11	.84157	1.18404	.87492	1.14296	.90621	1.10349	.93852	1.06551	.97189	1.02892	49
12	.84507	1.18334	.87543	1.14229	.90674	1.10285	.93906	1.06489	.97246	1.02832	48
13	.84556	1.18264	.87595	1.14162	.90727	1.10220	.93961	1.06427	.97302	1.02772	47
14	.84606	1.18194	.87646	1.14095	.90781	1.10156	.94016	1.06365	.97359	1.02713	46
15	.84656	1.18125	.87698	1.14028	.90834	1.10091	.94071	1.06303	.97416	1.02653	45
16	.84706	1.18055	.87749	1.13961	.90887	1.10027	.94125	1.06241	.97472	1.02593	44
17	.84756	1.17986	.87801	1.13894	.90940	1.09963	.94180	1.06179	.97529	1.02533	43
18	.84806	1.17916	.87852	1.13828	.90993	1.09899	.94235	1.06117	.97586	1.02474	42
19	.84856	1.17846	.87904	1.13761	.91046	1.09834	.94290	1.06056	.97643	1.02414	41
20	.84906	1.17777	.87955	1.13694	.91099	1.09770	.94345	1.05994	.97700	1.02355	40
21	.84956	1.17708	.88007	1.13627	.91153	1.09706	.94400	1.05932	.97756	1.02295	39
22	.85006	1.17638	.88059	1.13561	.91206	1.09642	.94455	1.05870	.97813	1.02236	38
23	.85057	1.17569	.88110	1.13494	.91259	1.09578	.94510	1.05809	.97870	1.02176	37
24	.85107	1.17500	.88162	1.13428	.91313	1.09514	.94565	1.05747	.97927	1.02117	36
25	.85157	1.17430	.88214	1.13361	.91366	1.09450	.94620	1.05685	.97984	1.02057	35
26	.85207	1.17361	.88265	1.13295	.91419	1.09386	.94676	1.05624	.98041	1.01998	34
27	.85257	1.17292	.88317	1.13228	.91473	1.09322	.94731	1.05562	.98098	1.01939	33
28	.85308	1.17223	.88369	1.13162	.91526	1.09258	.94786	1.05501	.98155	1.01879	32
29	.85358	1.17154	.88421	1.13096	.91580	1.09195	.94841	1.05439	.98213	1.01820	31
30	.85408	1.17085	.88473	1.13029	.91633	1.09131	.94896	1.05378	.98270	1.01761	30
31	.85458	1.17016	.88524	1.12963	.91687	1.09067	.94952	1.05317	.98327	1.01702	29
32	.85509	1.16947	.88576	1.12897	.91740	1.09003	.95007	1.05255	.98384	1.01642	28
33	.85559	1.16878	.88628	1.12831	.91794	1.08940	.95062	1.05194	.98441	1.01583	27
34	.85609	1.16809	.88680	1.12765	.91847	1.08876	.95118	1.05133	.98499	1.01524	26
35	.85660	1.16741	.88732	1.12699	.91901	1.08813	.95173	1.05072	.98556	1.01465	25
36	.85710	1.16672	.88784	1.12633	.91955	1.08749	.95229	1.05010	.98613	1.01406	24
37	.85761	1.16603	.88836	1.12567	.92008	1.08686	.95284	1.04949	.98671	1.01347	23
38	.85811	1.16535	.88888	1.12501	.92062	1.08622	.95340	1.04888	.98728	1.01288	22
39	.85862	1.16466	.88940	1.12435	.92116	1.08559	.95395	1.04827	.98786	1.01229	21
40	.85912	1.16398	.88992	1.12369	.92170	1.08496	.95451	1.04766	.98843	1.01170	20
41	.85963	1.16329	.89045	1.12303	.92224	1.08432	.95506	1.04705	.98901	1.01112	19
42	.86014	1.16261	.89097	1.12238	.92277	1.08369	.95562	1.04644	.98958	1.01053	18
43	.86064	1.16192	.89149	1.12172	.92331	1.08306	.95618	1.04583	.99016	1.00994	17
44	.86115	1.16124	.89201	1.12106	.92385	1.08243	.95673	1.04522	.99073	1.00935	16
45	.86166	1.16056	.89253	1.12041	.92439	1.08179	.95729	1.04461	.99131	1.00876	15
46	.86216	1.15987	.89306	1.11975	.92493	1.08116	.95785	1.04401	.99189	1.00818	14
47	.86267	1.15919	.89358	1.11909	.92547	1.08053	.95841	1.04340	.99247	1.00759	13
48	.86318	1.15851	.89410	1.11844	.92601	1.07990	.95897	1.04279	.99304	1.00701	12
49	.86368	1.15783	.89463	1.11778	.92655	1.07927	.95952	1.04218	.99362	1.00642	11
50	.86419	1.15715	.89515	1.11713	.92709	1.07864	.96008	1.04158	.99420	1.00583	10
51	.86470	1.15647	.89567	1.11648	.92763	1.07801	.96064	1.04097	.99478	1.00525	9
52	.86521	1.15579	.89620	1.11582	.92817	1.07738	.96120	1.04036	.99536	1.00467	8
53	.86572	1.15511	.89672	1.11517	.92872	1.07676	.96176	1.03976	.99594	1.00408	7
54	.86623	1.15443	.89725	1.11452	.92926	1.07613	.96232	1.03915	.99652	1.00350	6
55	.86674	1.15375	.89777	1.11387	.92980	1.07550	.96288	1.03855	.99710	1.00291	5
56	.86725	1.15308	.89830	1.11321	.93034	1.07487	.96344	1.03794	.99768	1.00233	4
57	.86776	1.15240	.89883	1.11256	.93088	1.07425	.96400	1.03734	.99826	1.00175	3
58	.86827	1.15172	.89935	1.11191	.93143	1.07362	.96457	1.03674	.99884	1.00116	2
59	.86878	1.15104	.89988	1.11126	.93197	1.07299	.96513	1.03613	.99942	1.00058	1
60	.86929	1.15037	.90040	1.11061	.93252	1.07237	.96569	1.03553	1.00000	1.00000	0
′	Cotang	Tang	Cotang	Tang	Cotang	Tang	Cotang	Tang	Cotang	Tang	′
	49°		48°		47°		46°		45°		

INDEX

Integral expression, §4, pp4, 27.
part of a number, §2, p29.
part of expression, §4, p27.
places, §5, p43.
Intersection, Point of, §6, p2.
Inverse proportion, §2, pp59, 62.
ratio, §2, p55.
Involution, §2, p23.
by logarithms, §5, p55.
Irrational factors, §2, p32.
Isosceles triangle, §6, p9.

K

Known quantities, §5, p1.

L

Least common denominator, §1, p26.
Letters, Use of, in algebra, §3, p1.
Like numbers, §1, p1.
terms, §3, p7.
Line, Broken, §6, p1.
Curved, §6, p1.
Horizontal, §6, p2.
Perpendicular, §6, p2.
Straight, §6, p1.
Vertical, §6, p2.
Linear measure, Surveyor's, §2, p8.
measures, §2, p8.
Lines, Parallel, §6, p1.
Liquid measure, §2, p10.
Literal equation, §5, pp5, 9.
exponent, §4, p31.
Location of decimal point, §2, p34.
Logarithmic functions, §2, p64.
Logarithms, §5, p41.
Briggs' or common, §5, p41.
Division by, §5, p52.
Evolution by, §5, p57.
Hyperbolic or natural, §5, p41.
Involution by, §5, p55.
Multiplication by, §5, p51.
Napierian, §5, p41.
Long ton table, §2, p10.
Loss or gain per cent., §2, p6.

M

Major axis of ellipse, §6, p56.
Means (Proportion), §2, p59.
Measure, Definition of, §2, p8.
Dry, §2, p10.
Linear, §2, p8.
of angles of arcs, §2, p11.
of money, §2, p11.
of time, §2, p11.
Square, §2, p9.
Surveyors' linear, §2, p8.
Surveyors' square, §2, p9.
Measures, Classification of, §2, p8.
Measures—Continued
Cubic, §2, p9.
Liquid, §2, p10.
Miscellaneous, §2, p11.
of capacity, §2, p10.
of extension, §2, p8.
of stonework, §8, p68.
of weight, §2, p9.
Standard units of, §2, p8.
Members of an equation, §5, p1.
Mensuration, §6, p46.
of plane surfaces, §6, p46.
of solids, §6, p60.
Meter, §2, p11.
Method of extracting cube root, §2, p50.
of extracting fifth root, §2, p52*f*.
of extracting fourth root, §2, p52*f*.
of extracting square root, §2, p43.
Minor axis of ellipse, §6, p56.
Minuend, §1, p9.
Minus, §1, p9.
Minutes of a degree, §6, p20.
Miscellaneous tables, §2, p11.
Mixed number, §1, p23.
number, To reduce to improper fraction, §1, p25.
quantity, §4, p27.
Money, Measure of U. S., §2, p11.
Monomial, §3, p7.
To extract any root of, §4, p32.
To raise to any power, §4, p32.
Monomials, Addition of, §3, p12.
Division of, §3, p32.
Factors of, §4, p5.
Multiplication of, §3, p25.
Subtraction of, §3, p18.
Multiple of a quantity, §4, p2.
Multiplicand, §1, p11.
Multiplication, §1, p11.
by logarithms, §5, p51.
of decimals, §1, p40.
of denominate numbers, §2, p19.
of fractions, §1, p31; §4, p25.
of monomials, §3, p25.
of polynomials, §3, p29.
Proof of, §1, p15.
Rule for, §1, p14.
Sign of, §1, p11.
table, §1, p12.
Multiplier, §1, p11.

N

Natural functions, §6, p22.
logarithms, §5, p41.
Naught, §1, p2.
Nonagon, §6, p55.
Notation, §1, p1.
Arabic, §1, p2.